D0002386

Environmental Chemistry: Essentials of Chemistry for Engineering Practice

Volume 4A

ISBN 0-13-285420-1

90000

9 780132 854207

PRENTICE HALL PTR ENVIRONMENTAL MANAGEMENT AND ENGINEERING SERIES

ENVIRONMENTAL CHEMISTRY: ESSENTIALS OF CHEMISTRY FOR ENGINEERING PRACTICE

VOLUME 4A

Teh Fu Yen

Department of Environmental Engineering & Civil Engineering
University of Southern California

Prentice Hall PTR, Upper Saddle River, New Jersey 07458
http://www.phptr.com

Library of Congress Catalog-in-Publication Data

Yen, Teh Fu
    Environmental chemistry : essentials of chemistry for engineering
practice / Teh Fu Yen.
        p.   cm. -- (Environmental chemistry : A) (Prentice Hall PTR
environmental management and engineering series : v. 4A)
    Includes bibliographical references and index.
    ISBN 0-13-285420-1
    1. Environmental chemistry.   I. Title.   II. Series.   III. Series:
TD193.Y46 1999 vol. 4
540--DC21   98-10891
                                                      CIP

Editorial/production supervision: *Vanessa Moore*
Cover design director: *Jerry Votta*
Cover design: *Anthony Gemmellaro*
Manufacturing manager: *Alan Fischer*
Acquisitions editor: *Bernard M. Goodwin*
Marketing manager: *Kaylie Smith*

© 1999 Prentice Hall PTR
Prentice-Hall, Inc.
A Simon & Schuster Company
Upper Saddle River, NJ 07458

Prentice Hall books are widely used by corporations and government
agencies for training, marketing, and resale.

The publisher offers discounts on this book when ordered in bulk
quantities. For more information, contact Corporate Sales Department,
Phone: 800-382-3419, Fax: 201-236-7141, Email: corpsales@prenhall.com

or write: Prentice Hall PTR
              Corporate Sales Department
              One Lake Street
              Upper Saddle River, NJ 07458

Printed in the United States of America

10   9   8   7   6   5   4   3   2   1

ISBN 0-13-285420-1

Prentice-Hall International (UK) Limited, *London*
Prentice-Hall of Australia Pty. Limited, *Sydney*
Prentice-Hall of Canada, Inc., *Toronto*
Prentice-Hall Hispanoamericana S.A., *Mexico*
Prentice-Hall of India Private Limited, *New Delhi*
Prentice-Hall of Japan, Inc., *Tokyo*
Simon & Schuster Asia Pte. Ltd., *Singapore*
Editora Prentice-Hall do Brasil, Ltda., *Rio de Janeiro*

Dedicated to My Wife

Shiao Ping Siao, Ph. D.

at Jet Propulsion Laboratory

California Institute of Technology

for Her Encouragement,

Understanding, and Sacrifice

ACKNOWLEDGMENTS

Usually, an instructional text is the accumulated knowledge of previously published works. I owe my debts to a number of pioneers who not only contributed to basic science, but have also analyzed these sciences and summarized them into books and reviews. This list includes W. Stumm, J.J. Morgan, R. Mitchell, H.M. Clark, W.J. Weber, Jr., H.T. Odum, P.L. McCarty, J.H. Seinfeld, M.R. Hoffman, S.K. Friedlander, D.M. Imboden, R.D. Schwarzenbach, R.A. Horne, J.L. Schnoor, J.W. Moore, G. Sposito, N.J. Bunce, T.G. Spiro, G.M. Masters, and so on. Some of them are the prodigious Tyler awardees by USC and many of them are my life-long mentors. This present volume could not have been completed without their help.

I would like to express my sincere thanks to the administrators of USC, particularly to L.M. Silverman, Dean of Engineering, L.C. Welford, chairman of the department, and to my colleagues in the environmental field, for allowing me to have the opportunity to write this. Most of all, I owe my deep gratitude to all of my former graduate students and undergraduate students. I thank Jeff Kuo, Rebecca Chou, Yu Wang, and Karen Kodama for their valuable help. I am obliged to the students who helped with clerical work. This list includes Linda Raftree, Nancy Yan, Michael Lee, Brian Whitten, and Rochelle Wong.

Lastly, but not the least, I would like to acknowledge the entire staff at Prentice Hall: to Bernard Goodwin for his patience, to Vanessa Moore for her excellent editorial and production work, and to Robert Chang for his tedious and careful electronic setting of the entire manuscript.

CONTENTS

Environmental Chemistry:
Chemical Principles for Environmental Processes, Volume 4B

PREFACE

*S*everal books have recently been written on the topic of environmental chemistry. Most of these texts, however, are intended for environmental sciences or environmental studies pursued by nonengineering students. Included in this group are environmental chemistry books written for chemistry majors to take along with elective courses in their undergraduate curriculum. Among all these books, there is only one that introduces the basic concepts of chemistry and analytical measurements. Although it could be used as an environmental engineering undergraduate textbook, this book lacks the linkages and connections between chemistry and its applications to environmental practices. No environmental chemistry books are available for the advanced graduate level of environmental engineering. And no text has been written wherein the close relationship between chemistry and environmental engineering is explained in the topics that are familiar to the environmental engineering discipline.

This lack of information initiatived the present text, because most of the education in environmental engineering is conducted at the graduate level and the majority of entering students have undergraduate degrees in civil engineering, mechanical engineering, biology, microbiology, or geology, with an insufficient background in chemistry. This book will fulfill this need in a more comprehensive manner. Also, it will be useful for professionals currently working in the field of environmental engineering, who are trained in science and other disciplines of engineering, and who might use the book as a self-study guide toward a deeper knowledge of environmental engineering.

Environmental Chemistry is divided into two volumes: *Volume 4A: Essentials of Chemistry for Engineering Practice*, and *Volume 4B: Chemical Principles for Environmental Processes*. Volume 4A includes two sections: a review of basic chemistry and chemistry of major spheres. In the first section, we will review general chemistry topics that are relevant to environmental engineering. These topics include physical chemistry, organic chemistry, analytical chemistry (including instrumental methods), and colloid and surface chemistry. The discussions on biochemistry and geochemistry are in Chapter 15.

The second section deals with natural or global cycles (lithosphere, atmosphere, hydrosphere, pedosphere, biosphere) and their interactions, and the life cycle, or biosphere, in particular, which involves human activity and its detrimental effects on the environment.

For the major spheres (cycles), we adopted energy resources in lithosphere, fossil, alternative (solar, wind, geothermal, and so on), and nuclear energies. No one will deny the importance of oil pollution and nuclear waste disposal and treatment technology. Basic atmospheric chemistry and upper atmospheric chemistry are presented in the atmosphere chapters. The essential components of aquatic chemistry are placed with hydrosphere chapters. These components include the chemistry of natural waters, groundwater, and wastewater. The pedosphere embodies soil chemistry, chemistry pertaining to hazardous waste, and its remediations. For the last spheres, the biosphere will consist of environmental geochemistry and biochemistry. Also, topics such as chemical toxicology and noise pollution will be addressed. In this manner, we can see the interactions and results among the five cycles—which comprise the objective of environmental engineering practice.

Each chapter begins with a short introduction and then proceeds to thoroughly explain the principles designated in the title of that chapter. Each chapter contains pertinent equations, figures and tables, several examples, a list of references, and a problem set at the end to give students practice at solving environmentally related problems.

Teh Fu Yen
University of Southern California

FOREWORD

As the human race marches toward the dawn of the next millennium, environmental problems are no longer regional or national issues, but rather intercontinental, international, and global concerns. Any isolated incident will generate impacts on every living creature on this Earth, often to an extent of and beyond the necessities of such human needs as food, clothing, dwelling, and transportation. In the coming millennium, we will witness much closer networks and cooperations among different political units on the problems existing in all environmental media—air, water, and soil.

Environmental incidences such as the 50,000 kg of kepone dumped into the canal in Virginia, the infamous Love Canal Case, the Bhopal toxic episode, and the ozone hole, all led to significant ecological and economic damages. Even more disastrous events that claimed thousands of lives include the Chernobyl accident, the Exxon Valdez oil spill, as well as the Kuwait oilfield fire followed by an associated cyclone in Bangladesh. International cooperations toward alleviating environmental problems can be illustrated by the control of ozone-hole depletion, seen in the significant reduction of CFC usage as indicated by the Montreal Protocol established in 1987, which was followed by the London Amendment in 1990 and the Copenhagen Agreement in 1992. Consequently, the oil industry, represented by 24 companies, agreed to ban petroleum exploration in the Antarctic for 50 years. The United Nations, composed of 150 countries, also sponsored a conference on Environment and Development in Rio de Janeiro in 1992 to issue a world statement on climate changes. Recently, multinational agreements have supported all ISO 14000s dealing with environmental management. These facts illustrate the importance of the concerted effort of all nations, including third world countries. Indirectly, this trend in globalization also reflects the need for a more comprehensive text on environmental science and engineering, particularly in the field of environmental chemistry with its interdisciplinary topics.

What exactly is environmental chemistry? It is difficult to precisely define the scope of environmental chemistry, but it is basically a science that studies the effects of chemicals in the environment and indentifies the sources, reactions, transports, and fates of chemical species. If the chemical species show adverse effects on health, technology should be developed to reduce, minimize, and eliminate them. Again, what type of chemicals? The following constitutes a tentative list:

Xenobiotics	Synthetic, anthropogenic (man-made) compounds.
Pollutants	Substances present in an amount greater than natural abundance and having a net detrimental effect.
Contaminants	Substances deviating from normal distribution (concentration) in the environment.
Naturally occcuring substances	Mineral deposits, humic matter, lignin, tanning, etc.
Receptors	Those affected by pollutants.
Sinks	Long-time depositions of pollutants; e.g., limestone is a sink in the case of acid rain deposition: $H_2SO_4 + CaCO_3 \longrightarrow CaSO_4 + H_2O + CO_2$

How do we define the environment? Historically, human beings have been aware of environmental problems for centuries. For example, the ancient Chinese defined our environment in terms of five major elements and discussed their inter-relationships in a book published more than 24 centuries ago. The Chinese labeled the five elements as:

水 meaning water (hydrosphere)

火 meaning air (atmosphere)

金 meaning energy (lithosphere)

木 meaning life (biosphere)

土 meaning soil (pedosphere)

For example, Chi Tze, (*Hung Fan*, 400 B.C.) recognized five cycles:

> "There exist five cycles. The first is water; the second, fire; the third, wood, the fourth, metal; the fifth, earth. The nature of water is to moisten and descend; of fire, to stagnate and ascend; of wood, to be round and attached; of metal, to yield and to transformed; of earth, to provide sowing and reaping. That which moistens and descends produces salt; that which stagnates and ascends becomes bitter; that which is round and attached becomes sour; that which yields and is tranformed becomes acrid; sowing and reaping produces sweetness."

Today's discipline of environmental chemistry is not much different from that practiced more than two thousand years ago. In a number of standard environmental chemistry texts, the content is divided into energy, air, water, soil, and life. Hence, this volume will discuss the five global cycles in detail.

This treatise places primary emphasis on chemistry. For instance, physical chemistry, organic chemistry, analytical chemistry, and colloid chemistry are reviewed at the beginning of the chapters associated with these topics. Subsequently, topics such as nuclear chemistry, atmospheric chemistry, cosmochemistry, photochemistry, aquatic chemistry, soil chemistry, combustion chemistry, solid waste chemistry, electrochemistry, biochemistry, geochemistry, marine chemistry, sonochemistry, and so on are introduced in appropriate chapters. Many other relevant subjects, such as thermodynamics, kinetics, equilibria, and reaction mechanism are also discussed extensively. An obvious example would be on the subject of photochemistry, which appears in three different chapters (Chapter 8 in Volume 4A, and Chapters 23 and 24 in Volume 4B) in light of its various applications.

A list of general references in environmental chemistry is listed below. These books benefited me and I recommend them to the reader.

A.M. Buswell, *The Chemistry of Water and Sewage Treatment*, Chemical Catalog Co., New York, 1928.

J. Holluta, *Die Chemie and Chemisiu Technologie des Wassers*, 1937.

C.N. Sawyer, *Chemistry for Sanitary Engineers*, McGraw-Hill, New York, 1960.

R. Bremond and R. Vuichard, *Parametres de la qualité des eaux*, 1973.

R.A. Horne, *The Chemistry of Our Environment*, Wiley-Interscience, New York, 1978.

T.G. Spiro and W.M. Stigliani, *Environmental Issues in Chemical Perspective*, SUNY Press, 1980.

S.E. Manahan, *Environmental Chemistry,* 1st ed. to 6th ed., Lewis Publishers, Boca Raton, Florida, 1973 to 1994.

J.W. Moore and E.A. Moore, *Environmental Chemistry*, Academic Press, New York, 1976.

C.N. Sawer; P.L. McCarty; and G.F. Parkin, *Chemistry for Environmental Engineering*, 1st ed. to 4th ed., McGraw-Hill, New York, 1960–1994.

R.A. Bailey; H.M. Clark; J.P. Ferris; S. Krause; and R.L. Strong, *Chemistry of the Environment*, Academic Press, New York, 1978.

V.L. Snoeyink and D. Jenkins, *Water Chemistry*, Wiley, New York 1980.

P.A. Vesilind and J.J. Pierce, *Environmental Engineering*, Butterworth, Kent, England 1982.

J.H. Seinfield, *Air Pollution, Physical and Chemical Fundamentals*, McGraw-Hill, New York, 1975.

R.P. Wayne, *Chemistry of Atmospheres*, Oxford University Press, Oxford, 1st and 2nd ed., 1985, 1991.

T.G. Spiro and W.M. Stigliani, *Chemistry of the Environment*, Prentice-Hall, 1996.

REVIEW ON BASIC CHEMISTRY

The burning of the oil fields in Kuwait towards the end of the Gulf War, 1991. This man-made gigantic disaster for the environment will directly impact human beings. The Aitken particulates released from the black smoke will circulate the atmosphere for years. (Courtesy of the Kuwait Embassy)

CHAPTER 1

PHYSICAL CHEMISTRY

Physical chemistry is concerned with the study of the physical properties and structure of matter using the laws of chemical interaction. Generally, the purpose of physical chemistry is threefold:

- to collect the appropriate data required to define the properties of matter
- to establish the energy relations in physical and chemical transformations
- to predict the extent and rate of the transformation taking place and identify its controlling factors

For our concern as environmental engineers, the principles of physical chemistry could lead to an understanding of such concepts as the identification of compositions in aqueous solutions, the effects of additives on water purification, the extent and prevention of corrosion in piping, and so on. There are two common approaches to understanding physical chemistry. The first is the **synthetic approach**, which begins with the study of the structure and behavior of matter from subatomic particles, electrons, and nuclei, to atoms and molecules, and then proceeds to their states of aggregation and subsequent chemical reactions. The other is the **analytical approach**, which begins with the investigation of large objects, such as biosystems and bodies of water, and works its way back to atoms and particles. The analytical approach will be used in this book. In this chapter, we will discuss the subjects of gas-liquid-solid phase behavior, thermodynamics, and kinetics. At the end we will discuss some of the commonly used units and conventions.

1.1 GAS-LIQUID-SOLID

All matter exists in one of three states of aggregation: **gaseous**, **liquid**, or **solid**. The particular state of a substance is determined by the pressure and temperature under which it exists. Because the gaseous phase is the most random form of the three states, we can easily understand liquid and solid state behavior by fully comprehending the gaseous state. Thus, our attention will be focused here on the gaseous phase.

There are several basic laws or generalizations that are important to the study of gases. The first one is **Boyle's Law**: The volume of any definite quantity of gas at constant temperature varies inversely with the pressure on the gas. Expressed mathematically

$$V = \frac{K_1}{P} \quad (T = \text{constant}) \qquad [1\text{-}1]$$

If V is plotted versus P at a constant temperature, it will exhibit a hyperbolic characteristic curve, as shown in Figure 1-1.

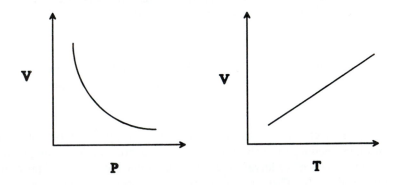

Figure 1-1.   Illustration of Boyle's Law and Charles's Law.

Charles's or **Gay-Lussac's Law** states that the volume of a definite quantity of gas at constant pressure is directly proportional to the absolute temperature (Fig. 1-1), or

$$V = K_2 T \quad (P = \text{constant}) \tag{1-2}$$

To obtain a simultaneous variation of the volume with pressure and temperature, we proceed as follows:

$$V = f(P, T)$$

$$dV = \left(\frac{\partial V}{\partial P}\right)_T dP + \left(\frac{\partial V}{\partial T}\right)_P dT \tag{1-3}$$

From Equation [1-1] by differentiation, we get

$$\left(\frac{\partial V}{\partial P}\right)_T = -\frac{K_1}{P^2} = -\frac{PV}{P^2} = -\frac{V}{P} \tag{1-4}$$

Similarly, from Equation [1-2] we get

$$\left(\frac{\partial V}{\partial T}\right)_P = K_2 = \frac{V}{T} \tag{1-5}$$

Combining Equations [1-4] and [1-5] into Equation [1-3]

$$dV = -V/P \, dP + V/T \, dT$$

or

$$dV/V + dP/P = dT/T$$

$$\ln V + \ln P = \ln T + \ln C$$

$$PV = \text{constant} \times T$$

$$PV = RT \quad \text{or} \quad PV = nRT \tag{1-6}$$

Equation [1-6] is the **ideal gas equation**, where R is a universal constant for all ideal gases. In general, $R = Nk$ where N is Avogadro's number and k is Boltzmann's constant in terms of individual molecules. The value of R can be found from the fact that 1 mole of any ideal gas at **standard conditions** — that is, at 0°C and 1 atmosphere of pressure — occupies a volume of 22.414 liters. Therefore,

$$R = \frac{PV}{nT} = \frac{(1\,\text{atm})(22.414\,\text{L})}{(1\,\text{mole})(273.16\,\text{degree})}$$

$$= 0.082 \text{ liter-atm/degree/mole}$$

R can be expressed in any set of units representing work or energy. As an exercise, the following can be derived:

$$R = 8.314 \text{ joule/degree/mole} = 1.987 \text{ cal/degree/mole}$$

As stated above, k is Boltmann's constant in terms of individual molecules. In this instance, k can be easily computed out as

$$k = 1.38 \times 10^{-23} \text{ J/°K}$$

if the Avogadro's number is used

$$N = 6.02 \times 10^{23}/\text{mole}$$

As shown in Equation [1-3], V is considered a function of T and P. The partial derivatives in the equation have definite physical meanings and are measurable quantities. There are three commonly tabulated properties:

- **compressibility coefficient**

$$\kappa = -\frac{1}{V}\left(\frac{\partial V}{\partial P}\right)_T$$

- **expansion coefficient**

$$\alpha = \frac{1}{V}\left(\frac{\partial V}{\partial T}\right)_P$$

- **pressure coefficient**

$$\beta = \frac{1}{P}\left(\frac{\partial P}{\partial T}\right)_V$$

If a gas obeys the ideal gas law, it can be easily found that

$$\alpha = \kappa \beta P$$

[Example 1-1]   Thermometers are frequently broken in the laboratory by overheating. If a thermometer is exactly filled with mercury at 50°C, what pressure will be developed within the thermometer if it is heated to 52°C? (For mercury, the expansion coefficient is 1.8×10^{-4} per degree and the compressibility coefficient is 3.9×10^{-6} per atm.)

$$V = f(P,T)$$

$$dV = \left(\frac{\partial V}{\partial T}\right)_P dT + \left(\frac{\partial V}{\partial P}\right)_T dP$$

$V = \text{constant}, \quad dV = 0$

$$\left(\frac{\partial P}{\partial T}\right)_V = \frac{-\left(\dfrac{\partial V}{\partial T}\right)_P}{\left(\dfrac{\partial V}{\partial P}\right)_T} = \frac{\alpha}{\kappa}$$

For Hg, $\alpha = 1.8 \times 10^{-4}$ degree^{-1}, $\kappa = 3.9 \times 10^{-6}$ degree^{-1}. Thus,

$$\left(\frac{\partial P}{\partial T}\right)_V = 46 \text{ atm/degree}$$

1.2 THERMODYNAMICS

Thermodynamics is the study of the energy accompanying physical and chemical processes and the transformation of energy from one form to another. The two most important words in thermodynamics are **heat** and **work**, which are related forms of energy. Heat energy can do work, and work energy can generate heat. In dealing with thermodynamic problems, the term **"system"** is frequently employed. A system is defined as any parts of the world selected for study. In turn, the portion of the universe excluded from the system is called the surroundings or environment. A **boundary** (real or imaginary) separates the system from the surroundings. An **open system** can exchange both matter and energy with its surroundings, while an **isolated system** cannot. **A closed system** can exchange energy, but it cannot change matter. As an example, Figure 1-2 gives a general representation of a natural water system treated as an open system.

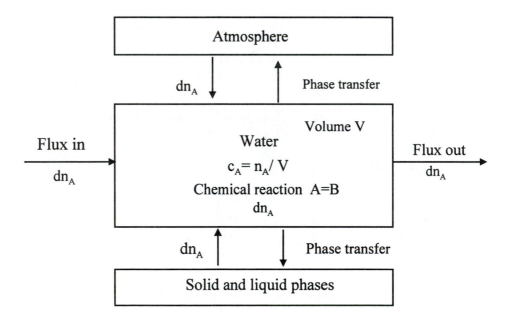

Figure 1-2.   General representation of natural water systems is treated as an open system. The system receives fluxes of matter from the surroundings and undergoes chemical changes symbolized by the reaction A=B. The time invariant condition is represented by $dC_A/dt=0$. (Stumm and Morgan) [Ref. 1-15]

1.2.1 Temperature, Heat, and Work

The **zeroth law of thermodynamics** can be stated as: systems in thermal equilibrium have the same temperature. If two systems are in thermal equilibrium with a third system, then they all are in equilibrium with each other, and they all have the same temperature. Heat is a form of energy that passes from one body to another solely as a result of temperature difference. If the temperature of a system is kept constant, $dT = 0$, it is said to be under **isothermal conditions**. An **adiabatic process** is one for which there is no heat transfer between it and its surroundings, $dq = 0$. The basic unit of heat is the **calorie**, defined as the heat required to raise the temperature of one gram of water one Celsius degree. In engineering practices, it is common to measure heat in **Btu**, which is the heat required to raise one pound of water one Fahrenheit degree. The unit Btu equals 252 calories.

It is possible to have a system of methods to transfer energy to a system as work. **Mechanical, or pressure-volume work,** is the most familiar. For a closed system, it is equivalent to the pressure times the change in volume:

$$dw = P\ dV \tag{1-7}$$

Since heat and work are both forms of energy, they can be equated.

1.2.2 The First Law of Thermodynamics

The **first law of thermodynamics**, or the **law of conservation of energy**, states that energy can be neither created nor destroyed. The mathematical statement of the first law could be written as

$$\Delta E = q - w \tag{1-8}$$

where
ΔE = change in internal energy of the system

q = heat flowing into the system

w = work done by the system

By convention, q has a positive value if heat is absorbed by the system, and a negative value otherwise. If the system does work on the surroundings, w has a positive value, as shown in Figure 1-3 on the next page.

In chemical systems, **expansion work** is usually the work performed. For a special case, if the volume of the system remains constant, then no expansion work can be done (i.e., $w = 0$). For this case

$$\Delta E = q_v \quad (V = \text{constant}) \tag{1-9}$$

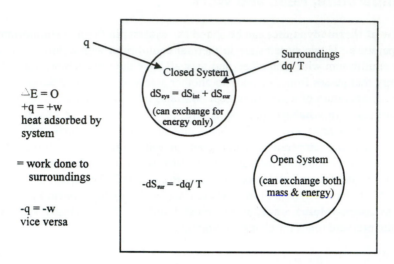

$\Delta E = O$
$+q = +w$
heat adsorbed by
system

$= $ work done to
surroundings

$-q = -w$
vice versa

q

Closed System

$dS_{sys} = dS_{int} + dS_{sur}$

(can exchange for
energy only)

Surroundings
dq/T

$-dS_{sur} = -dq/T$

Open System

(can exchange both
mass & energy)

Isolated System (can't exchange energy for mass)
$$dS_{sys} = dS_{int} + dS_{sur}$$

Figure 1-3.   Illustration of a closed system, surroundings, and an isolated system or "universe" of a system plus surroundings. Heat transferred to the system, q, is positive, and that lost from the surroundings is –q. The entropy change of the system, dS_{sys}, is the sum of an internal change dS_{int} and a flow from the surroundings dS_{sur}.

Most chemical systems that environmental engineers encounter, however, are open to the atmosphere and consequently operate under constant pressure rather than constant volume. For such systems, another property, **enthalpy**, is handier to use. The enthalpy, H, of a system is defined as follows:

$$H = E + PV \qquad\qquad [1\text{-}10]$$

Assuming that a chemical reaction takes place at a constant pressure and temperature, the change in the internal energy of the system would be

$$\Delta E = E_2 - E_1 = q_p - w = q_p - PdV = q_p - P(V_2 - V_1)$$

where q_p is the heat absorbed at constant pressure. By rearranging the terms; then

$$(E_2 + PV_2) - (E_1 + PV_1) = q_p = H_2 - H_1$$

or

$$\Delta H = q_p \quad \text{(Constant } T, P\text{)} \qquad\qquad [1\text{-}11]$$

It is a universal practice to designate ΔH as **heat of reaction**. Chemical changes that are accompanied by the absorption of heat, which makes ΔH positive, are called **endothermic reactions**. **Exothermic reactions** are those with a negative ΔH value. The heat of reaction for a chemical reaction can be easily calculated from standard enthalpies, usually available in handbooks, of the species involved. Calculation of the heat of combustion of methane gas is illustrated in the following example:

$$CH_4(g) + 2O_2(g) \rightarrow CO_2(g) + 2H_2O(l)$$

$$\Delta H^{\circ}_{298} \qquad -17.89 \qquad 0 \qquad -94.05 \qquad 2(-68.32)$$

$$H^{\circ}_{298} \text{ for combustion } = (-94.05) + 2(-68.32) - (-17.89) - 0$$

$$= -212.80 \text{ Kcal/mole of methane}$$

1.2.3   The Second Law of Thermodynamics and Entropy Pollution

The first law, stating that energy must be conserved in all ordinary processes, imposes no direction on energy transformations. However, certain restrictions do exist. For example, heat always flows from a higher temperature level to a lower one and never in the reverse direction. Also, the efficiency of transformation from one form of work to another, such as from mechanical to electrical in an electrical generator, can be made to approach 100%. The transformation of heat (thermal energy) into work is especially inefficient, the highest efficiency being 45% for a modern turbine, as shown in Table 1-1 on the next page. This inefficiency indicates that various forms of energy have different qualities. In this sense, work can be termed as energy of a higher quality than heat.

The concept of **entropy** was developed to serve as a general criterion of spontaneity for physical and chemical changes, or for direction of energy transformation. For the given state of a system, entropy, S, can be defined quantitatively as

$$S = k \ln \Omega \qquad\qquad [1\text{-}12]$$

where

k = Boltzmann's constant

$\Omega=$ the thermodynamic probability, defined as the number of ways that the particles of the system can be arranged among the energy levels accessible to them.

Table 1-1.   Efficiency of Energy Converters

Type	Efficiency	Type of Conversion
Electric generator-Electric motor	99	M→E
Low	62	E→M
High	92	E→M
Dry cell battery	90	C→E
Large steam boiler	88	C→T
Home furnace - Gas	85	C→T
Home furnace - Oil	65	C→T
Storage battery (lead acid)	72	E→C→E
Fuel cell	60	C→E
Man on bicycle	50	C→M
Liquid fuel Rocket (H_2)	47	C→T
Turbine – Steam	45	T→M
Turbine - Gas (aircraft or industrial)	35	C→T
Electric power plant - Fossil fueled	40	C→T
Nuclear fueled	32	N→T→M→E
Internal combustion engine - Diesel	37	C→T
Otto cycle (automobile)	25	T→M
Lasers	30-10	E→R
Lamps - High intensity	32	E→R
Lamps - Fluorescent	20	E→R
Lamps - Incandescent	4	E→R
Unaided walking man	12	C→M
Solar cell	10-15	R→E
Steam locomotive	8	C→T→M
Thermocouple	6	T→E

M, mechanical; E, electrical; T, thermal; C, chemical; R, radiant; N, nuclear

Source: Much of the data of this table was obtained from C.M. Summers, *Sci. Amer.*, 224(3), 155 (Sept. 1971).

In most textbooks, entropy is defined by the following differential equation:

$$dS = dq_{rev} / T \qquad\qquad [1\text{-}13]$$

where the quantity q_{rev} is the amount of heat that the system absorbs if a chemical change is brought about in a reversible manner. If a spontaneous change occurs in a system, it will always be found that the total entropy change, including everything involved, is a positive value. A calculation of entropy change can help us determine whether a chemical or physical transformation could occur. If $S > 0$, the change will occur spontaneously; if $S < 0$, the change usually occurs in the reverse direction; and if $S = 0$, the system is at equilibrium. In general, the **second law of thermodynamics** states that all processes in nature tend to occur only with an increase in entropy and that the direction of change is always such as to lead to the entropy increase.

Table 1-2. Quality of Various Forms of Energy

Form of Energy	Entropy Per Unit Energy
Gravitational	0
Nuclear	10^{-4}
Thermal	
Stars (10^6 K)	10^{-3}
Earth (10^2 K)	10^2
Chemical	1-10
Radiant	
Sunlight (visible)	1-10
Cosmic microwave	10^4

Source: Data adapted from F.J. Dyson, *Sci.Amer.*, 224(3), 50-59 (Sept. 1971).

The first law tells us that the energy of the universe is constant, while the second law indicates that energy has different qualities and the entropy of the universe tends toward a maximum. Table 1-2 lists the quality of various forms of energy in terms of entropy — the higher the entropy per unit energy, the lower the quality of the energy. Those forms, having small amounts of entropy per unit energy, tend to transform into others with higher values, thereby producing greater quantities of entropy. Therefore, any energy crisis is not the result of a lack of energy, because energy cannot be created or destroyed. Instead, it has resulted from the production of entropy associated with the conversion of high-grade energy sources into lower-grade ones. The production of entropy has been referred to as **entropy pollution,** because it is a kind of measure of the extent to which the universe has been irreversibly degraded. Table 1-3 gives the major energy resources available at the surface of the earth; each resource will be discussed further in later chapters.

Table 1-3.   Estimated Energy Resources

Type	Total World Supply [a]	Economically Available (at No More Than Double Current Costs)	
		World	U.S.
	Depletable supplies		$(10^{21}$ J)
Fossil (chemical)			
Tar sands	2.1	-----	-----
Natural gas	3.8	2.2 - 3.8	0.6 - 1.1
Petroleum	6.0	3.2 - 6.0	0.6 - 1.1
Oil shale	13.3	-----	-----
Coal and lignite	185.0	21.1 - 31.5	5.0 - 7.2
Total Fossil	210.2	26.5 - 41.3	6.2 - 9.4
Nuclear			
Ordinary fission	$2 \times 10^{4\,b}$	14.0	1.4
Breeder fission	$6 \times 10^{6\,b}$	4000.0	400.0
Fusion (D-T)	215	-----	-----
Fusion (D-D)	1×10^{10}	-----	-----
	Continuous supplies		$(10^{21}$ J/ year)
Solar	899	-----	50.0^{c}
Tidal	0.094	-----	0.009
Geothermal	0.010	-----	0.001

a Total supply including amount consumed to date.

b Estimated from total quantity of uranium and thorium within 1 mile of land surface. Assume 1% to be able for mining (*Int. At. Energy Ag. Bull.*, 14(4), 11, 1972).

c Total supply is listed because no cost figures are available.

Source: Data adapted from C. Starr, *Sci. Amer.*, 224(3), 43, (Sept. 1971).

1.2.4   Free Energy

To use entropy change as a criterion of spontaneous change requires taking both the system and all its surroundings into consideration. Usually, it is more convenient to limit our attention to the system only. This concentration can be accomplished in the following way:

$$\Delta S_{universe} = \Delta S_{system} + \Delta S_{surrounding}$$

$$= \Delta S_{system} + \frac{q_{surrounding}}{T} \geq 0 \qquad \text{[1-14]}$$

Because,

$$\Delta H = q_{system} = -q_{surroundings}$$

$$\Delta S_{universe} = \Delta S_{system} - \frac{\Delta H_{system}}{T} \geq 0 \qquad \text{[1-15]}$$

Multiplying both sides by -T

$$-T\Delta S_{universe} = \Delta H_{system} - T\Delta S_{system} = \Delta G_{system} \leq 0 \qquad \text{[1-16]}$$

ΔG_{system} is defined by Equation [1-16] and is known as the change in **Gibbs free energy** of the system. So, if $\Delta G < 0$, the reaction will go spontaneously; if $\Delta G = 0$, the system is in equilibrium. ΔG is also defined as

$$G = H - TS \qquad \text{[1-17]}$$

At constant T and P

$$\Delta G = \Delta H - T\Delta S$$

$$= \Delta E + P\Delta V - T\Delta S$$

$$= q - w + P\Delta V - T\Delta S \qquad \text{[1-18]}$$

If the system change is brought about reversibly, then q becomes q_{rev} and w becomes w_{max}, and the maximum quality of work that can be obtained is

$$\Delta G = q_{rev} - w_{max} + P\Delta V - q_{rev}$$

and

$$- \Delta G = w_{max} - P \Delta V$$

$P \Delta V$ gives the portion of the work that must be wasted; therefore, the $- \Delta G$ indicates the useful work available for the system change.

$$- \Delta G = w_{useful} \quad \text{(constant } T, P)$$

[1-19]

In principle, any spontaneous process can be made to do useful work as shown in Equation [1-19]. To find the relationship between the free energy and equilibrium constant, we proceed as follows:

$$dG = -SdT + VdP$$

[1-20]

At constant temperature

$$dG = VdP = RT(dP/P) = RT \, d \, (\ln P)$$

[1-21]

To give a reference point for the free energy as G° at 25°C and 1 atmosphere,

$$G - G^{\circ} = RT \ln(P/P^{\circ}) = RT \ln \alpha, \text{ where } \alpha \propto P \propto \text{concentration}$$

[1-22]

where α is the activity. Consider the following reaction:

$$aA + bB \rightarrow cC + dD$$

$$\Delta G = \Sigma G_{products} - \Sigma G_{reactants}$$

[1-23]

The free energy of this reaction is given by the following equation by substituting Equation [1-22] into Equation [1-23]:

$$\Delta G = \Delta G^{\circ} + RT \ln \left(\frac{\{C\}^c \{D\}^d}{\{A\}^a \{B\}^b} \right)$$

As the reaction proceeds to a state of equilibrium, ΔG will be zero, and thus

$$\Delta G^{\circ} = - RT \ln \left(\frac{\{C\}^c \{D\}^d}{\{A\}^a \{B\}^b} \right)_{equilibrium} = -RT \ln K$$

[1-24]

where K is the equilibrium constant. Values for the standard free energies of various substances can be found from engineering or chemistry handbooks. By calculating the standard free energy change for the reaction, K is easily determined from the preceding equation.

1.2.5 Thermodynamic Properties

Thermodynamic systems may consist of one or more parts called **phases**, in which they are physically and chemically homogeneous. Thermodynamic systems are characterized by a small number of properties. The properties may be divided into two types: extensive and intensive. **Extensive properties** are additive; that is, they depend on the amount of substances present. Examples of such properties are total mass, volume, and energy. On the other hand, **intensive properties** are those whose values are independent of the total amount, but which depend on the concentration of the substance(s) in a system. Examples of intensive properties are pressure, temperature, molar volume, and chemical potential. Figure 1-4 on the next page illustrates a simplified model for the thermodynamic description of natural water systems. P and T are intensive variables, and the mole numbers, n_i, in each phase are extensive variables that together determine the volume, mass, composition, and other properties of the system.

Various forms of thermodynamic work are available. Basically, they can all be expressed as an intensive property times an extensive variation, as shown in Table 1-4 on the next page.

Many thermodynamic properties and their relationships have been derived, making it a difficult task to memorize them all. To solve the problem, a handy scheme has been devised for memorizing important thermodynamic relations. A detailed description of the scheme based on Yen is given in Figure 1-5 on page 19.

There are many thermodynamic functions that can be derived from the code sentence, "The Gibbs Potential Has Shown Endless Valuable Applications," for the functions of T, G, P, H, S, E, V, and A. This is actually based on the principle of symmetry of thermodynamic potentials; for example, Jacobian. In order to obtain dE as a function of appropriate independent variables, look at the two diagonal lines toward the base E, taking the signs

$$dE = -PdV + TdS$$

Similarly

$$dG = VdP - SdT$$

$$dH = VdP + TdS$$

$$dA = -PdV - SdT \qquad \text{[1-24a]}$$

P, T

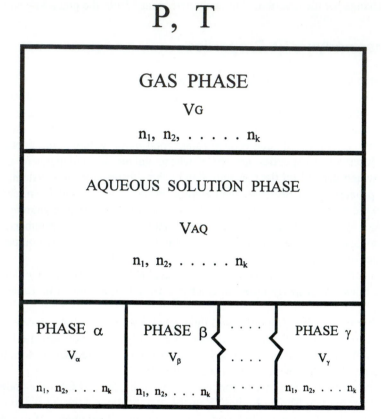

Figure 1-4. Simplified model for the thermodynamic description of natural water systems.

Table 1-4.   Expressions for the Thermodynamic Work dw Done on a System

Type	Intensive Property	Extensive Variation	Expression
Expansion	Pressure, P	Volume, dV	$-PdV$
Electrical	Potential, E	Charge, de	$-Ede$
Gravitational	Force, mg	Height, dh	mg dh
Chemical	Chemical potential, μ	Moles, dn	μdn
Surface	Interfacial tension, γ	Area, dA	γdA

Source: Stumm and Morgan, Ref. 1-15

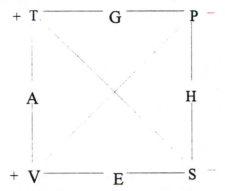

Figure 1-5. Thermodynamic functions based on group theory [from T.F. Yen, *J. Chem Edu.* 31, 610 (1954)] Code sentence "**T**he **G**ibbs **P**otential **H**as **S**hown **E**ndless **V**aluable **A**pplications".

Again for triangular relationship, for example, ΔSVT

$$\left(\frac{\partial E}{\partial S}\right)_V = T$$

the variable V is situated at the right angle while the independent variable and answer are at the other apexes.

$$\left(\frac{\partial E}{\partial V}\right)_S = -P$$

$$\left(\frac{\partial G}{\partial P}\right)_T = V$$

$$\left(\frac{\partial G}{\partial T}\right)_P = -S$$

$$\left(\frac{\partial H}{\partial S}\right)_P = T \qquad\qquad\qquad\qquad \text{[1-24b]}$$

$$\left(\frac{\partial H}{\partial P}\right)_S = V$$

$$\left(\frac{\partial A}{\partial V}\right)_T = -P$$

$$\left(\frac{\partial A}{\partial T}\right)_V = -S$$

The Maxwell relationship can be obtained by considering the right triangle with the same base; for example, ΔTVS, ΔPSV, and so on.

$$\left(\frac{\partial T}{\partial V}\right)_S = -\left(\frac{\partial P}{\partial S}\right)_V$$

$$-\left(\frac{\partial P}{\partial T}\right)_V = -\left(\frac{\partial S}{\partial V}\right)_T$$

$$-\left(\frac{\partial S}{\partial P}\right)_T = \left(\frac{\partial V}{\partial T}\right)_P$$

$$\left(\frac{\partial V}{\partial S}\right)_P = \left(\frac{\partial T}{\partial P}\right)_S$$

[1-24c]

from the corners of the diagram

$$\left(\frac{\partial V}{\partial S}\right)_E = \frac{T}{P}$$

$$\left(\frac{\partial T}{\partial V}\right)_A = \frac{-P}{S}$$

$$-\left(\frac{\partial P}{\partial T}\right)_G = \frac{-S}{V}$$

$$-\left(\frac{\partial S}{\partial P}\right)_H = \frac{V}{T}$$

[1-24d]

from the trapezoid $EATS$, $AGPV$, and so on

$$E - A = TS$$
$$A - G = -PV$$
$$G - H = -ST$$
$$H - E = VP$$

[1-24e]

and chemical potentials such as

$$\mu = \left(\frac{\partial E}{\partial n}\right)_{S,V} = \left(\frac{\partial A}{\partial n}\right)_{V,T} = \left(\frac{\partial G}{\partial n}\right)_{T,P} = \left(\frac{\partial H}{\partial n}\right)_{P,S}$$

[1-25]

The symmetry is based on group theory.

A definite quantity of heat is required to raise the temperature of a given mass of any material by one Celsius degree. This quantity is called the heat capacity of the system, C. Thus,

$$C = \frac{dq}{dT} \qquad\qquad [1\text{-}26]$$

If a unit mass is taken as the basis for heat capacity, the equation becomes $dq = m\,C\,dT$, where m represents mass and C is now called **specific heat capacity**. The specific heat capacity of water is approximately $1(\text{cal})/(\text{g})(°\text{C})$. When the volume is held constant, by combining the preceding equation and $\Delta E = q - w$ — that is, Equations [1-8] and [1-26] — C_v at a constant volume can be obtained:

$$C_V = \left(\frac{\partial E}{\partial T} \right)_V \qquad\qquad [1\text{-}27]$$

Similarly, by some simple manipulation, we can get C_p at constant pressure:

$$C_P = \left(\frac{\partial H}{\partial T} \right)_P \qquad\qquad [1\text{-}28]$$

The general equation to describe the C_p and C_v is

$$C_P - C_V = \left[\left(\frac{\partial E}{\partial V} \right)_T + P \right] \left(\frac{\partial V}{\partial T} \right)_P \qquad\qquad [1\text{-}29]$$

The actual value of the difference for an ideal gas could easily be found to equal R. Table 1-5 lists the molar heat capacities for various gases.

1.2.6 Applications to Solid Systems

The following is a discussion leading to the understanding of some properties of metals, ceramic materials, and rubbers. From Figure 1-5, we can easily obtain the **Helmholtz free energy** equation, as shown here

$$A = E - TS$$

or

$$dA = dE - TdS - SdT \qquad\qquad [1\text{-}24e]$$

Table 1-5.   Molar Heat Capacities of Gases

Gas	C_p	C_v	$C_p/C_v = \gamma$
Argon, A	4.97	2.98	1.67
Helium, He	4.97	2.98	1.67
Mercury, Hg	4.97	2.98	1.67
Hydrogen, H_2	6.90	4.91	1.41
Oxygen, O_2	7.05	5.05	1.40
Nitrogen, N_2	6.94	4.95	1.40
Chlorine, Cl_2	3.25	6.14	1.34
Nitric oxide, NO	7.11	5.11	1.39
Carbon monoxide, CO	6.97	4.97	1.40
Hydrogen chloride, HCl	7.05	5.01	1.41
Carbon dioxide, CO_2	8.96	6.92	1.29
Nitrous oxide, N_2O	9.33	7.29	1.28
Sulfur dioxide, SO_2	9.40	7.30	1.29
Ammonia, NH_3	8.63	6.57	1.31
Methane, CH_3	8.60	6.59	1.31
Ethane, C_2H_4	12.71	10.65	1.19
Dimethyl ether, C_2H_4O	15.89	13.73	1.16

* in cal deg^{-1} mole^{-1} at 25°C

Also from Figure 1-5

$$E = H - VP$$

$$dE = dH - VdP - PdV \qquad \text{[1-24f]}$$

and from Figure 1-5

$$dH = VdP + TdS$$

Thus, combining this relation with Equation [1-24f]

$$dE = TdS - PdV$$

Then, substituting into Equation [1-24e], it follows that

$$dA = -PdV - SdT \qquad\qquad [1\text{-}24\text{g}]$$

For an elastomer, chain extension will take place isothermally with a change of ΔL from the length of polymeric chains, and $dW = -PdV$ from Equation [1-24g], as shown here

$$\therefore dA_T = dW = FdL \qquad\qquad [1\text{-}24\text{h}]$$

where F is the force required to extend or to compress the chain segment. Thus, one can rewrite the Helmholtz free energy equation as

$$F = \left(\frac{\partial A}{\partial L}\right)_{T,V} = \left(\frac{\partial E}{\partial L}\right)_{T,V} - T\left(\frac{\partial S}{\partial L}\right)_{T,V} \qquad\qquad [1\text{-}30]$$

because deformation takes place with no volume change. For the preceding equation, the first term becomes important in the case of metals and ceramics

$$F = \left(\frac{\partial E}{\partial L}\right)_{T,V} \qquad\qquad [1\text{-}30\text{a}]$$

However, internal energy causes heatup and fracture with extension for rubber. The opposite conditions apply to elasticity as entropy decreases with extension and a large change of chain segment conformations

$$F = -T\left(\frac{\partial S}{\partial L}\right)_{T,V} \qquad\qquad [1\text{-}30\text{b}]$$

which indicates that the second term becomes important for rubber.

Under deformation, the chain segment can be analyzed with an end-to-end distance of the polymer chain. The end-to-end distance can be related to a probability function $P(r)$, and the entropy of this chain segment is as follows (here distance r is proportional to L):

$$S = S_0 + k \ln P(r)$$

$$P(r) = \frac{\exp\left[-\left(\dfrac{r}{\rho}\right)^2\right]}{\left(\rho\pi^{\frac{1}{2}}\right)^3}$$

which has a Gaussian distribution, and where ρ is density. Hence,

$$S = S_0 - k\left[3\ln(\pi^{\frac{1}{2}}\rho) + \left(\frac{r}{\rho}\right)^2\right]$$

Thus,

$$\left(\frac{\partial S}{\partial r}\right) = \frac{-2kr}{\rho^2}$$

or,

$$F = \frac{2kTr}{\rho^2} = kr \qquad\qquad\qquad [1\text{-}31]$$

after substituting with

$$F = -T\left(\frac{\partial S}{\partial L}\right)_{T,V} \qquad\qquad\qquad [1\text{-}30b]$$

which means the force to extend or compress the chain segment is proportional to distance r and is directly proportional to temperature. The chain acts like a spring.

1.3 KINETICS

Thermodynamics is able to tell us what can happen, and to what extent, but it is unable to tell us how a change will actually occur. **Chemical kinetics** searches for the factors that influence the rate of reaction and brings a time factor into consideration. The rate of reactions depends on the nature of the reacting substances, the temperature, and the concentration of the reactants. The **rate of a chemical reaction** is the rate at which the concentrations of reacting species vary with time; that is, $-dC/dt$, where C is the concentration of the reactant. The sum of all the exponents to which the concentrations in the rate equation are raised is the **order** of the chemical reaction. Thus, a rate equation is expressed as

$$-\frac{dC}{dt} = kC_1^{n_1}\,C_2^{n_2}\,C_3^{n_3}\,.... \qquad\qquad\qquad [1\text{-}32]$$

where

k = rate constant

n = order of the reaction $(n_1 + n_2 + ...)$

1.3.1 First-Order Reactions

A **first order reaction** is one in which the rate of reaction is proportional to the concentration of the reactant. For example, the following reaction is a first-order reaction:

$$N_2O_5 \rightarrow 2\,NO_2 + 1/2\,O_2$$

Therefore

$$-\frac{dC}{dt} = kC \qquad\qquad [1\text{-}33]$$

If the initial concentration, at $t = 0$, is C_o, the concentration (C) at some later time (t) can be found by integrating the preceding equation, which gives

$$-\int_{C_0}^{C} \frac{dC}{C} = k \int_{0}^{t} dt$$

and

$$-\ln \frac{C}{C_o} = \ln \frac{C_o}{C} = kt$$

or

$$C = C_o \exp(-kt) \qquad\qquad [1\text{-}34]$$

The **half-life** of the reaction can be determined by inserting the requirements that at $t = t_{1/2}$ and the concentration $C = \frac{1}{2} C_o$ into Equation [1-34], that gives

$$t_{1/2} = \frac{\ln 2}{k} = \frac{0.693}{k} \qquad\qquad [1\text{-}35]$$

1.3.2 Second-Order Reactions

For a **second-order reaction**, for example A + B $\rightarrow$ products, the rate equation can be expressed as follows:

$$-\frac{dC_A}{dt} = -\frac{dC_B}{dt} = kC_A C_B$$

or

$$\frac{dX}{dt} = k\,(a-x)\,(b-x)$$

where

x = amount of the reactants consumed

a = initial concentration of A

b = initial concentration of B

If $a \neq b$, the following equation can be obtained through simple mathematical manipulation:

$$k = \frac{2.303}{t(a-b)} \log \frac{b(a-x)}{a(b-x)}$$
[1-36]

1.3.3   Consecutive Reactions

Chemical reactions such as

$$A \xrightarrow{\ k_1\ } B \xrightarrow{\ k_2\ } C$$

which proceed from reactants to products through one or more intermediate stages are called **consecutive reactions**. The rate equations are as follows:

$$-\frac{dC_A}{dt} = k_1\,C_A$$

$$\frac{dC_B}{dt} = k_1\,C_A - k_2\,C_B$$

$$\frac{dC_C}{dt} = k_2\,C_B$$

If at $t = 0$ we have $C_A = C_{A0}$, $C_B = C_C = 0$, then a solution for the concentration of each component at time t is as follows (it is a good exercise to solve the following equations):

$$C_A = C_{A0}e^{-k_1t}$$ [1-37]

$$C_B = \frac{k_1 C_{A0}}{k_2 - k_1}\left\{e^{-k_1t} - e^{-k_2t}\right\}$$ [1-38]

$$C_c = C_{A0}\left\{1 + \frac{k_1 e^{-k_2t}}{k_2 - k_1} - \frac{k_2 e^{-k_1t}}{k_2 - k_1}\right\}$$ [1-39]

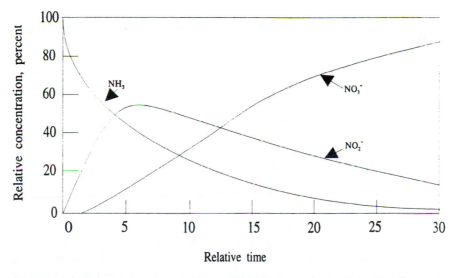

Figure 1-6. Nitrogen changes during nitrification, assuming consecutive first-order reactions.

Consecutive reactions are of great importance in environmental engineering. Bacterial nitrification of ammonia can be described by a consecutive reaction. Ammonia is oxidized by *Nitrosomonas* bacteria to nitrite, which is then oxidized by *Nitrobacter* bacteria to nitrate as indicated here

$$NH_3 \xrightarrow[\textit{Nitrosomonas}]{} NO_2^- \xrightarrow[\textit{Nitrobacter}]{} NO_3$$

The changes in nitrogen forms are shown in Figure 1-6, where the concentrations of nitrite and nitrate were set equal to zero when $t = 0$, and k_1 was assumed to be equal to $2k_2$.

There are some other types of complex reactions, such as **parallel types**, in which two reacting species compete with each other to react with a third reacting species. We will discuss these topics later in the book. For example a general solution of the kinetics is in Section 15.4.2, solution of more complex kinetics is in Section 27.2.1, Volume 4B.

1.3.4 Temperature Dependence of Reaction Rates

Chemical and biological reaction rates generally increase with increasing temperature. Most of the reactions follow the **Arrhenius-type of temperature dependence**

$$\frac{d \ln k}{dT} = \frac{E_a}{RT^2} \qquad\qquad [1\text{-}40]$$

where E_a is a constant termed the **activation energy**. By integrating the preceding equation, we get

$$\ln k = \frac{-E_a}{RT} + \ln k \qquad\qquad [1\text{-}41]$$

or

$$k = A \exp\left(-\frac{E_a}{RT}\right)$$

where T is expressed in Kelvin and A is called the frequency factor. A semilog plot of rate constant versus the reciprocal of temperature should be a straight line. Some of the common suggestions such as "the rate of reaction will double if temperature increases by $10°$ and half if temperature decreases by $10°$ " are based on the Arrhenius form. The frequency or preexponential factor, A is selected to the opportunity of molecular collision frequency.

1.4 UNITS AND CONVENTIONS

Environmental engineers may have to measure or estimate large or small quantities, such as the annual solar energy input to the earth, or the concentration of a pollutant in parts per billion (ppb). Therefore, it is advisable to be familiar with decimal multipliers that are commonly used, as listed in Table 1-6 on page 30. When the name of a unit is preceded by one of these prefixes, the size of the basic unit is modified by that decimal multiplier. For example, 1 Tg stands for 10^{12} grams and 1 Pg is for 10^{15} grams. In the field of energy, there are special notations for large energy values, where 1 **Quad** = 10^{15} Btu (British thermal unit) and 1 **Quin** = 10^{18} Btu. Accordingly, 1 PBtu = 1 Quad, or 1 EBtu = 1 Quin and 1 Quin = k Quad.

One important conversion factor for air pollution study is that for the conversion of ppm to $\mu g/m^3$ or mg/cm^3, or vice versa. One **ppm** means 1 volume in 1 million volumes. For instance, to convert 1 ppm of SO_2 at 1 atmosphere and 0°C, we would proceed as follows:

$$1 \text{ ppm} = (1/10^6)(1 \text{ mole}/22.4 \text{ liter})(64 \text{ gram/mole})(10^6 \ \mu g/g)(10^3 \text{ liter/m}^3)$$

$$= 2857 \ \mu g/m^3$$

or

$$= 2612 \ \mu g/m^3 \text{ at } 25 \ °C$$

Conversion factors for several air pollutants are given in Table 1-7.
Conversely, 1000 $\mu g/m^3$ of CO can be calculated as

$$(1000 \mu g/m^3)(1g/10^6 \mu g)(1 \text{mole}/28g)(22.4 \text{L/mole})(1m^3/10^6 cm^3)(1 \ cm^3/10^3 \ L)(10^6 \ L/L)$$

$$= 0.8 \text{ ppm}$$

A table of common unit conversions is included in Table 1-8. Throughout the book both English and metric system are used separately. In many cases, special units have been designated for the convenient usages. Many names of elements and constants are based on the International Union of Pure and Applied Chemistry (IUPAC) recommendation. Some useful constants are listed in Table 1-9.

TABLE 1-6.   Decimal Multipliers that Serve as SI Unit Prefixes

Prefix	Origin	Symbol	Multiplying Factor
yotta	Greek or Latin *octo*, "eight"	Y	10^{24}
zetta	Latin *septem*, "seven"	Z	10^{21}
exa	Greek *hex*, "six"	E	10^{18}
peta	Greek *pente*, "five"	P	10^{15}
tera	Greek *teras*, "monster"	T	10^{12}
giga	Greek *gigas*, "giant"	G	10^{9}
mega	Greek *megas*, "large"	M	10^{6}
kilo	Greek *chilioi*, "thousand"	k	10^{3}
hecto	Greek *hekaton*, "hundred"	h	10^{2}
deka	Greek *deka*, "ten"	da	10^{1}
deci	Latin *decimus*, "tenth"	d	10^{-1}
centi	Latin *centum*, "hundred"	c	10^{-2}
milli	Latin *mille*, "thousand"	m	10^{-3}
micro	Latin *micro* (Greek *mikros*), "small"	μ	10^{-6}
nano	Latin *nanus* (Greek *nanos*), "dwarf"	n	10^{-9}
pico	Spanish *pico*, "a bit," Italian *piccolo*, "small"	p	10^{-12}
femto	Danish-Norwegian *femten*, "fifteen"	f	10^{-15}
atto	Danish-Norwegian *atten*, "eighteen"	a	10^{-18}
zepto	Latin *septem*, "seven"	z	10^{-21}
yocto	Greek or Latin *octo*, "eight"	y	10^{-24}

Table 1-7. Conversion Factors for Air Pollutants

	Temperature (°C)	Pressure (mm)	1 ppm equivalence in $\mu g/m^3$
Carbon monoxide (CO)	0	760	1,250
	25	760	1,145
Nitric oxide (NO)	25	760	1,230
Nitrogen dioxide (NO$_2$)	25	760	1,880
Oxone (O$_2$)	0	760	2,141
	25	760	1,962
PAN {CH$_3$(CO)O$_2$NO$_2$}	0	760	5,398
	25	760	4,945
Sulfur dioxide (SO$_2$)	0	760	2,860
	25	760	2,620

Modified after H.C. Perkins, *Air Pollution*, McGraw Hill, 1974, p.385.

Table 1-8. Common Unit Conversions

Gas Constant (R)	Volume	Density
0.082 atm^{-1}/g-mole °K	1 ft^3 = 28.316 liter	1g/cm^3 = 1000 kg/m^3
62.36 mmHg^{-1}/g-mole °K	= 7.481 gal	= 62.428 lb/ft^3
8.314 Joule/g-mole °K	1 in^3 = 16.39 cc	= 8.345 lb/gal
1.314 atm-ft^3/lb-mole °K	= 5.787 x 10^{-4} ft^3	= 0.03613 lb/in^3
1.987 cal/g-mole °K	1 gal = 3.785 liter	
1.987 Btu/lb-mole °R	= 8.34 lb H$_2$O	
0.73 atm-ft^3/lb-mole °R	1 m^3 = 35.32 ft^3	
10.73 psi-ft^3/lb-mole °R	= 264.2 gal	
1545 ft-lbf/lb-mole °R		
Length	**Viscosity**	**Conversion Factor**
1 mile = 1609 m = 5280 ft	1 poise	1 cal/g-mole = 1.8Btu/lb-mole
1 ft = 30.48 cm = 12 in	= 6.7197×10^{-2} lbm/ft-sec	1 amu = 1.66063 × 10^{-24}g
1 in = 2.54 cm	= 2.0886×10^{-3} lbf-sec/ft^2	1 eV = 1.6022 × 10^{-12}erg
1 m = 3.2808 ft	= 2.4191×10^2 lbm/ft-hr	1 radian = 57.3°
= 39.37 in	= 1 g/cm-sec	1 cm/sec = 1.9685 ft/min
1 nm = 10^{-9}m = 10 A		1 rpm = 0.10472 radian/sec

Table 1-8.   continued

Pressure	Constant	Mass
1 atm = 101325 N/m^2	h = 6.6262 × 10^{-27}erg-sec	1 kg = 2.2046 lb
= 14.696 psi	k = 1.38062 × 10^{-16}erg/°K	1 lb = 453.59 g
= 760 mmHg	N$_0$ = 6.022169 × 10^{23}	1 ton = 2000 lb
= 29.921inHg	C = 2.997925 × 10^{10}cm/sec	= 907.2 kg
(32 °F)	F = 96487 coul/eq	1 B ton = 2240 lb
= 33.91 ftH$_2$O	e = 1.60219 × 10^{-19}coul	= 1016 kg
(39.1 °F)	g = 980.665 cm/sec^2	1 tonne = 2205 lb
= 2116.2 lbf/ft^2	=32.174 ft/sec^2	= 1000 kg
= 1.0133 bar		1 slug = 32.2 lb
= 1033.3 gf/cm^2		= 14.6 kg
Area	**Power**	**Force**
1 m^2 = 10.76 ft^2 = 1550 in^2	1 HP = 550 ft-lbf/sec	1N = 1 kg-m/sec^2
1 ft^2 = 929.0 cm^2	= 745.48 watt	= 10^5 dyne
	1 Btu/hr = 0.293 watt	= 0.22481 lbf
		= 7.233 lbm-ft/sec^2
Transfer Coefficient	**Energy & Work**	
1 Btu/hr-ft^2 °F	1 cal = 4.184 Joule	
= 5.6784 Joule/sec-m^2 °K	1 Btu = 1055.1 Joule	
= 4.8825 Kcal/hr-m^2 °K	= 252.16 cal	
= 0.45362 Kcal/hr-ft^2 °K	1 HP-hr = 2684500 Joule	
= 1.3564x10^{-4}cal/sec-cm^2 °K	= 641620 cal	
1 lb/hr-ft^2	= 2544.5 Btu	
= 1.3562 × 10^{3}kg/sec-m^2	1 KW-hr = 3.6 × 10^6 Joule	
= 4.8823 kg/hr-m^2	= 860565 cal	
= 0.45358 kg/hr-ft^2	= 3412.75 Btu	
1 cal/g °C = 1 Btu/lbm °F	1 l-atm = 24.218 cal	
= 1 Pcu/lbm °C	1 ft-lbf = 0.3241 cal	
1 Btu/hr-ft °F	1 Pcu = 453.59 cal	
= 1.731 W/m °K	1 kg-m = 2.3438 cal	
= 1.4882 kcal/hr-m °K		

Table 1-9. Some Useful Constants

Atomic mass	$m_u \approx 1.6605402 \times 10^{-27}$
Avogadro's number	$N \approx 6.0221367 \times 10^{23}$ mol^{-1}
Boltzmann's constant	$k \approx 1.380658 \times 10^{-23}$ J K^{-1}
Elementary charge	$e \approx 1.60217733 \times 10^{-19}$ C
Faraday's constant	$F \approx 9.6485309 \times 10^{4}$ C mol^{-1}
Gas (molar) constant	$R = k \cong N \sim 8.314510$ J· mol^{-1} K^{-1}
	≈ 0.08205783 L· atm· mol^{-1} K^{-1}
Gravitational acceleration	$g = 9.80665$ m s^{-2}
Molar volume of an ideal gas at 1 atm and 25°C	$\overline{V}_{ideal\ gas} \approx 24.465$ L mol^{-1}
Permittivity of vacuum	$\varepsilon_0 = 8.854187 \times 10^{-12}$ C V^{-1} m^{-1}
Planck's constant	$h \approx 6.6260755 \times 10^{-34}$ J s
Zero of the Celsius scale	$0°C = 273.15$ K

Source: IUPAC, 1988.

REFERENCES

1-1   J. W. Moore and E. A. Moore, *Environmental Chemistry*, Academic Press, New York, 1976.

1-2   S. H. Maron and C. F. Prutton, *Principles of Physical Chemistry*, 4th ed., Macmillan, New York, 1965.

1-3   J. M. Smith and H. C. Van Ness, *Introduction to Chemical Engineering Thermodynamics*, 3rd ed., McGraw-Hill, New York, 1975.

1-4   J. S. Winn, *Physical Chemistry*, Harper Collins College Press, New York, 1995.

1-5   R. A. Albert and R.J. Silbey, *Physical Chemistry*, 2nd ed., Wiley, New York, 1997.

1-6   E. Grunwald, *Thermodynamics of Molecular Species*, Wiley, New York, 1997.

1-7   F. D. Rossini, *Chemical Thermodynamics*, Wiley, New York, 1950.

1-8   C. E. Dykstra, *Physical Chemistry*, A Modern Introduction, Prentice-Hall, Upper Saddle River, New Jersey, 1997.

1-9   J. B. Hudson, *Thermodynamics of Materials: A Classical and Statistical Synthesis*, Wiley, New York, 1996.

1-10   C. B. Skimmer, *Introduction to Chemical Kinetics*, Academic Press, New York, 1974.

1-11   S. W. Benson, *Foundations of Chemical Kinetics*, McGraw-Hill, New York, 1960.

1-12   K. G. Denbigh, *Thermodynamics of the Steady State*, Methuen, London, 1951.

1-13   A. M. Klotz, *Chemical Thermodynamics, Basic Theory and Methods*, Prentice-Hall, Englewood Cliffs, New Jersey, 1957.

1-14   H. J. M. Bowen, *Environmental Chemistry of the Elements*, Academic Press, London, 1979.

1-15   W. Stumm and J. J. Morgan, *Aquatic Chemistry*, 2nd ed., Wiley, New York, 1981.

PROBLEM SET

1. Generally for gases, the compressibility coefficient, k, the expansion coefficient, α, and the pressure coefficient, β, can be expressed by

$$\kappa = -\frac{1}{V}\left(\frac{\partial V}{\partial P}\right)_T \qquad \alpha = \frac{1}{V}\left(\frac{\partial V}{\partial T}\right)_P \qquad \beta = \frac{1}{P}\left(\frac{\partial P}{\partial T}\right)_V$$

a) What are their values if those gases are ideal gases?

b) Prove

$$\alpha = \kappa\beta P$$

c) Show that

$$\left(\frac{\partial P}{\partial T}\right)_V \left(\frac{\partial T}{\partial V}\right)_P \left(\frac{\partial V}{\partial P}\right)_T = -1$$

2. Calculate the maximum work done by the isothermal expansion of one mole of ideal gas at 0°C from 2.24 L to 22.4 L.

3. For a Carnot cycle as shown in the figure on the next page,

$$Q_2 = \int_a^b dQ = \int_a^b PdV = \int_a^b \frac{RT_2 dV}{V} = RT_2 \ln\left(\frac{V_b}{V_a}\right)$$

$$Q_1 = -\int_a^b dQ = RT_1 \ln\left(\frac{V_c}{V_d}\right)$$

Prove the efficiency is

$$n = 1 - \frac{Q_1}{Q_2} = 1 - \frac{T_1}{T_2}$$

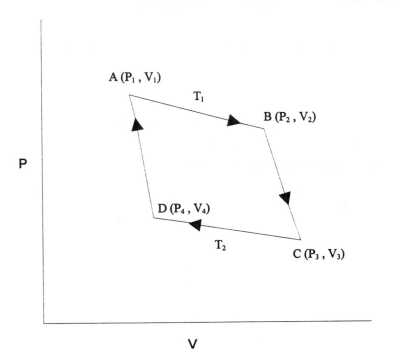

The Carnot cycle.

A to B is isothermal expansion, temperature is T_1 , volume change is V_1 to V_2 , and heat absorbed is Q_1.

B to C is adiabatic expansion, temperature is T_1 to T_2 , volume change is V_2 to V_3 , and heat absorbed is 0.

C to D is isothermal compression, temperature is T_2 , volume change is V_3 to V_4 , and heat absorbed is Q_2.

D to A is adiabatic expansion, temperature is T_2 to T_1 , volume change is V_4 to V_1 , and heat absorbed is 0.

4. For a consecutive reaction

$$A \xrightarrow{k_1} B \xrightarrow{k_2} C$$

If A(0) = A$_o$ and B(0) = 0 = C(0)

and

$$\frac{dA}{dt} = -k_1 A$$

$$\frac{dB}{dt} = k_1 A - k_2 B$$

$$\frac{dc}{dt} = k_2 B$$

calculate A, B, and C.

5. For ideal gas, derive

$$C_p - C_v = R$$

and

$$\gamma = C_p/C_v = 1.67$$

"Something mysteriously formed

Born before heaven and earth

In the silence and the void

Standing alone and unchanging

Ever present and in motion

Perhaps it is the mother of ten thousand things.

. . . .

. . . .

Being great, it flows

It flows far away

Having gone far, it returns."

Lao Tsu -- 700BC

-- Tao Te Ching

ORGANIC CHEMISTRY

*O*rganic chemistry deals with compounds of **carbon**, the organic materials usually present in liquid, solid, and gaseous wastes, that an environmental engineer will encounter in practice. Therefore, it is important that environmental engineers have a fundamental knowledge of organic chemistry. The aspects of organic chemistry with which an environmental engineer is concerned differ considerably from those with which an organic chemist is concerned. Organic chemists are more interested in the synthesis of compounds and the mechanisms of organic reactions. Environmental engineers, on the other hand, focus their attention on the removal, reduction, or the degradation of those compounds. In this chapter, emphasis will be put on the structures and properties of organic compounds, their reactivity and stability, their functional groups, and the methods of studying their structure activity relationships.

2.1 STRUCTURE AND PROPERTIES

Carbon, being the first element of Group IVA in the periodic table, normally has four covalent bonds that allow it to link with other atoms in a wide variety of ways through covalent
bonding. In this manner, a great variety of compounds can be formed, the most common of
which are **hydrocarbons**. The bond angle between two covalent bonds in a tetrahedron is
109°28′. This value can be obtained by the following calculation.

Here, point O is located in the center of a cube. Because

$$\overrightarrow{AO} \cdot \overrightarrow{BO} = |\overrightarrow{AO}||\overrightarrow{BO}|\cos\phi \qquad \text{[2-1]}$$

$$\overrightarrow{AO} \cdot \overrightarrow{BO} = (1,1,1)(-1,-1,1) = -1-1+1 = -1 \qquad \text{[2-2]}$$

$$|\overrightarrow{AO}| = |\overrightarrow{BO}| = \left(1^2 + 1^2 + 1^2\right)^{\frac{1}{2}} = \sqrt{3}$$

Thus,

$$\phi = \cos^{-1}\left(-\frac{1}{3}\right) = 109°28' \qquad \text{[2-3]}$$

Or from

$$|\overrightarrow{AO} \times \overrightarrow{BO}| = |\overrightarrow{AO}||\overrightarrow{BO}|\sin\phi \qquad \text{[2-4]}$$

Because

$$(i,j,k) \times (i',j',k') = \left(\begin{vmatrix} j & k \\ j' & k' \end{vmatrix}, \begin{vmatrix} k & i \\ k' & i' \end{vmatrix}, \begin{vmatrix} i & j \\ i' & j' \end{vmatrix}\right)$$

$$\overrightarrow{AO} \times \overrightarrow{BO} = \left(\begin{vmatrix} 1 & 1 \\ -1 & 1 \end{vmatrix}, \begin{vmatrix} 1 & 1 \\ 1 & -1 \end{vmatrix}, \begin{vmatrix} 1 & 1 \\ -1 & -1 \end{vmatrix}\right) = (2,-2,0) \qquad \text{[2-5]}$$

$$\left|\overrightarrow{AO}\right| \times \left|\overrightarrow{BO}\right| = \left(2^2 + (-2)^2 + 0^2\right)^{\frac{1}{2}} = 2\sqrt{2} \qquad [2\text{-}6]$$

$$\phi = \sin^{-1}\left(2\sqrt{\tfrac{2}{3}}\right) = 109°28' \qquad [2\text{-}7]$$

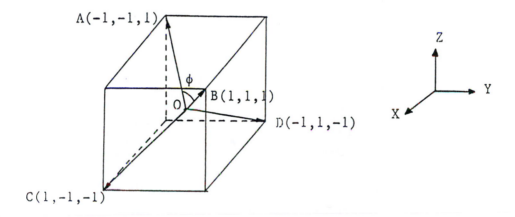

Figure 2-1. The tetrahedral angle at the center of a cube.

The **tetrahedral angle** by vector analysis is illustrated in Figure 2-1. This tetrahedral angle is important for developing the spatial relationships of chemical compounds. From elementary geometry, we know that any three points in a space determine a plane. As shown in Figure 2-2 on the next page, for notation, r_{ij} is the **bond length**, ϕ_{ijk} is the **bond angle**, and τ_{ijkl} is the **torsional angle** between planes *ijk* and *jkl*. Multiple atoms show the property of having the least distance between them, forming a chain structure that often consists of conformations behaving as a helical structure. For a helix where

a = radius of helix

n = atoms in one turn

l = identity period

θ = projection angle $(2\pi/n)$

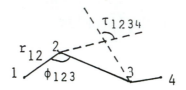

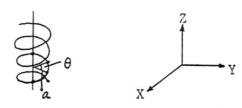

Figure 2-2.   The torsional angle and projection angle of a helical structure.

there are the following relationships:

$$x = a \cos \theta$$

$$y = a \sin \theta$$

$$z = \frac{l}{n} \qquad\qquad [2\text{-}8]$$

and

$$\vec{A} = (a \cos \theta, a \sin \theta, \frac{l}{n}) \qquad\qquad [2\text{-}9]$$

$$\vec{B} = (a \cos 2\theta, a \sin 2\theta, 2\frac{l}{n})$$ [2-10]

$$\vec{C} = (a \cos 3\theta, a \sin 3\theta, 3\frac{l}{n})$$ [2-11]

$$\vec{r}_{12} = (\vec{B} - \vec{A}) = \left(a \cos 2\theta - a \cos \theta, a \sin 2\theta - a \sin \theta, \frac{l}{n} \right)$$ [2-12]

$$|\vec{r}_{12}| = \left\{ 2a^2 (1 - \cos \theta) + \frac{l^2}{n^2} \right\}^{\frac{1}{2}}$$ [2-13]

$$\phi_{123} = \cos^{-1} \frac{a^2 (2 \cos \theta - 2 \cos^2 \theta + 1) \frac{l^2}{n^2}}{2a^2 (1 - \cos \theta) + \frac{l^2}{n^2}}$$ [2-14]

$$\tau_{1234} = \cos^{-1} \left(\frac{\vec{N}_2 \cdot \vec{N}_2}{|N_1||N_2|} \right)$$ [2-15]

Each plane is made from three successive atoms. The torsional angle is between the normals of two successive planes where

$$\vec{N}_1 = \vec{r}_{12} \times \vec{r}_{23}$$ [2-16]

$$\vec{N}_2 = \vec{r}_{23} \times \vec{r}_{34}$$ [2-17]

In this manner, for successive atoms in given molecules, the conformation of the molecules can be determined; for example, the torsional angles and the tecticities of the carbon chain can be determined. For the coordinates X_i, Y_i, Z_i transferred to $i - 1$ (the coordinates X_{i-1}, Y_{i-1}, Z_{i-1}) then

$$X_{i \cdot 1} = A X_i + B \tag{2-18}$$

$$A = \begin{bmatrix} -\cos\phi & -\sin\phi & 0 \\ \sin\phi\cos\tau & -\cos\phi\cos\tau & \sin\tau \\ \sin\phi\sin\tau & -\cos\phi\sin\tau & \cos\tau \end{bmatrix} \tag{2-19}$$

$$B = \begin{bmatrix} r \\ 0 \\ 0 \end{bmatrix} \tag{2-20}$$

for n-paraffins, $\tau = 180°$ (trans) or $\tau = \pm 60°$ (gauch); if $\tau = 180°$, then

$$A = \begin{bmatrix} -\cos\phi & -\sin\phi & 0 \\ -\sin\phi & \cos\phi & 0 \\ 0 & 0 & -1 \end{bmatrix} \tag{2-21}$$

Matrix A can be reduced to a trans (or syndiotactic) configuration for polymers. A relation for θ, τ, and ϕ can be

$$1 + 2\cos\theta = \cos\tau - \cos\phi\cos\tau - \cos\phi \tag{2-22}$$

For example, a polyethylene chain with a 3_1 helix will have a τ angle value of $60°$, because

$$4\cos^2\tau - 16\cos\tau + 7 = 0 \tag{2-23}$$

In the following pages, a method will be discussed for characterizing carbon compounds according to their bond types and the relationship of bond types to properties.

For a carbon compound there are four types of carbon atoms that may be characterized by their bonding to other carbon atoms: **primary**, **secondary**, **tertiary**, and **quaternary carbon** atoms. The number of carbon atoms for each bond type in a certain carbon compound are noted as k_1, k_2, k_3, and k_4 respectively. This carbon compound can be specified as $[k_1, k_2, k_3, k_4]$. For 2,2-dimethyl-3-ethyl heptane, the structure is in Figure 2-3, Structure A. By counting the numbers of different bond types, the structure can be represented as [5,4,1,1]. Table 2-1 lists some general formulas. The total number of carbon atoms in a compound, C, may be expressed as

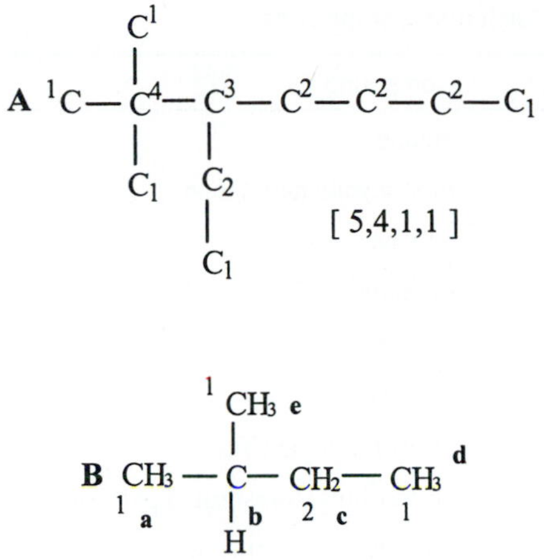

A $^1C - C^4 - C^3 - C^2 - C^2 - C^2 - C_1$

with C^1 above C^4, and C_1 and C_2 below C^4 and C^3 respectively, and C_1 below C_2.

[5,4,1,1]

B $CH_3 - C - CH_2 - CH_3$ with $^1CH_3$ (e) above the central C, and H below it.

labels: 1 a, b, 2 c, 1, d

Figure 2-3. Structure of (A) 2,2' -dimethyl-3-ethyl heptane and (B) 2-methyl butane.

$$C = \sum_{i=1}^{4} k_i \qquad [2\text{-}24]$$

If N_i is the summation of the i type bond, then

$$N_i = n_{ij} + \sum_{j=1}^{4} n_{ij} = ik_i \qquad [2\text{-}25]$$

The total number of bonds can be obtained

$$C - 1 = \frac{1}{2}\sum_{i=1}^{4} N_i = \frac{1}{2}\sum_{i=1}^{4} ik_i \qquad [2\text{-}26]$$

so

$$C - 1 = \frac{1}{2}\left(k_1 + 2k_2 + 3k_3 + 4k_4\right) \qquad [2\text{-}27]$$

but

Table 2-1.   Bond Types of Particular Compounds

Bond Type	Compound
$[k_1, 0, 0, 0]$	ethane
$[0, k_2, 0, 0]$	monocyclic naphthene
$[0, 0, k_3, 0]$	cubane
$[0, 0, 0, k_4]$	diamond
For combinations of two ($k_i \neq 0$) there are	
$[k_1, k_2, 0, 0]$	n-paraffin
$[k_1, 0, k_3, 0]$	all isobutyl paraffin
$[k_1, 0, 0, k_4]$	all tert-butyl-substituted paraffin (neopentylparaffin)
$[0, k_2, k_3, 0]$	multicyclic naphthene
$[0, k_2, 0, k_4]$	tricyclane
$[0, 0, k_3, k_4]$	polyspirocyclopentadiene
For $(3 - k_i) \neq 0$ there are	
$[k_1, k_2, k_3, 0]$	isoparaffins
$[k_1, k_2, 0, k_4]$	all ethyl-substituted paraffins
$[k_1, 0, k_3, k_4]$	all isopropyl-substituted paraffins
$[0, k_2, k_3, k_4]$	caged-fused naphthene
For $(4 - k_i) \neq 0$ (branched paraffins)	
$[k_1, k_2, k_3, k_4]$	

$$C = k_1 + k_2 + k_3 + k_4 \qquad \text{[2-28]}$$

By rearranging Equations [2-4] and [2-5], we obtain

$$k_1 = k_3 + 2k_4 + 2 \qquad \text{[2-29]}$$

[Example 2-1]   The elemental analysis for an isoparaffin is 84.9%C and 15.1%H, and the methyl content based on IR analysis is 42.5%. Find the number of branches (which are related to its solubility) and the methylene content ($-CH_2-$) of this isoparaffin.

The general formula for isoparaffins is C_nH_{2n+2}.

$$\frac{H}{C} = \frac{(2n+2)}{n} = 2 + \frac{2}{n}$$

$$n = \frac{2}{\left[\left(\dfrac{12\%H}{\%C}\right) - 2\right]} = 14.9 \sim 15$$

$$\frac{C_{methyl}}{C} = \frac{\left(\dfrac{\%\ methyl}{15}\right)}{\left(\dfrac{\%\ C}{12}\right)} = \frac{\left(\dfrac{42.5}{15}\right)}{\left(\dfrac{84.9}{12}\right)} = 0.4$$

$$k_1 = C_{methyl} = 0.4n = 6,\ n = 15$$

for isoparaffin $k_4 = 0$

$$k_1 = k_3 + 2k_4 + 2 = k_3 + 2$$

$$k_3 = k_1 - 2 = 6 - 2 = 4$$

thus four branches

$$n = k_1 + k_2 + k_3 + k_4$$

$$15 = 6 + k_2 + 4 + 0,\quad k_2 = 5$$

$$\frac{C_{methylene}}{C} = \frac{\left(\dfrac{\%\ methylene}{14}\right)}{\left(\dfrac{\%\ C}{12}\right)} = \frac{5}{15} = \frac{\left(\dfrac{\%\ methylene}{14}\right)}{\left(\dfrac{84.9}{12}\right)}$$

$$\%\ methylene = 33.01$$

$$\text{methylene content} = 14k_2/[12n + (2n + 2)] = 33\%$$

Table 2-2. Carbons and Their Isomer Numbers

No. of Carbon	Name	No. of Isomer
1	methane	1
2	ethane	1
3	propane	1
4	butane	2
5	pentane	3
6	hexane	5
7	heptane	9
8	octane	18
9	nonane	35
10	decane	75
20	eicosane	366,319
30	triacontane	4.11×10^9

In inorganic chemistry, a molecular formula is specific for one compound. This is not true for organic chemistry, for most molecular formulas do not represent any particular compound. Compounds having the same molecular formula are called **isomers**. Table 2-2 shows how the number of isomers increases with the carbon number.

Isomers of the same molecular formula often have different physical properties. One way to represent the difference between isomers is by their **bond type matrices**, as developed by Tatevskii. N_{ij} is the number of carbon bonds between i and j type atoms. The bond type matrix, N, is as follows:

$$N = \begin{bmatrix} n_{11}, & n_{12}, & n_{13}, & n_{14} \\ n_{21}, & n_{22}, & n_{23}, & n_{24} \\ n_{31}, & n_{32}, & n_{33}, & n_{34} \\ n_{41}, & n_{42}, & n_{43}, & n_{44} \end{bmatrix} \qquad [2\text{-}30]$$

Actually $n_{11} = 0$ and $n_{ij} = n_{ji}$, so there are nine significant values in the matrix.

$$N = \begin{bmatrix} n_{12}, & n_{13}, & n_{14} \\ n_{22}, & n_{23}, & n_{24} \\ 0 & n_{33} & n_{34} \\ 0 & 0 & n_{44} \end{bmatrix}$$

[2-31]

For example, for 2,2-dimethyl-3-ethyl heptane, the bond type matrix is

$$\begin{bmatrix} 2 & 0 & 3 \\ 2 & 2 & 0 \\ 0 & 0 & 1 \\ 0 & 0 & 0 \end{bmatrix}$$

[2-32]

The properties of carbon compounds are related to their structures by the general formula

$$P = \sum_{ij=1}^{4} n_{ij} P_{ij}$$

[2-33]

where

n_{ij} = the element of bond type matrix

P_{ij} = the element of property matrix

The data for a property matrix can often be found in some handbooks. Although the isomers can be represented by matrices, the product of Equation [2-33] is not by matrix multiplication, but rather by products of corresponding individual components. This is known as the Tatevskii's method.

[Example 2-2] Given the molar volume matrix, V_{ij}^{20}, as

$$\begin{bmatrix} V_{12} & V_{13} & V_{14} \\ V_{22} & V_{23} & V_{24} \\ V_{32} & V_{33} & V_{34} \\ V_{42} & V_{43} & V_{44} \end{bmatrix} = \begin{bmatrix} 41.472 & 33.979 & 29.695 \\ 16.002 & 6.479 & 1.003 \\ - & -5.356 & -12.624 \\ - & - & -22.596 \end{bmatrix}$$

find the densities of C_7 isomers.

Let us calculate the isomer, 2,2,3-trimethylbutane first.

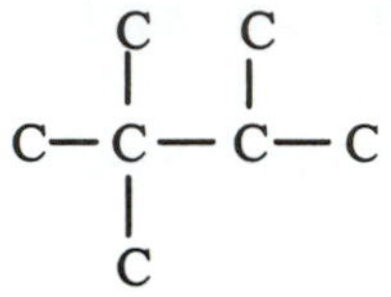

$$
\begin{array}{ccc}
& C & C \\
& | & | \\
C-C- & C-C \\
& | & \\
& C &
\end{array}
$$

The bond type matrix of this isomer is

$$
N = \begin{bmatrix}
0 & 0 & 2 & 3 \\
0 & 0 & 0 & 0 \\
0 & 0 & 0 & 1 \\
0 & 0 & 0 & 0
\end{bmatrix}
$$

$$
d_4^{20} = \frac{M}{\displaystyle\sum_{i \leq j=1}^{4} n_{ij} v_{ij}^{20}}
\qquad\qquad [2\text{-}34]
$$

$$
\sum_{i \leq j=1}^{4} n_{ij} v_{ij} = 2(33.979) + 3(29.695) - 12.624 = 144.419
$$

$$
\left(d_4^{20}\right)_{\text{cal}} = \frac{7(12.01) + 16(1.0079)}{144.419} = 0.6938
$$

The experimental value for this isomer is 0.6901. In this manner, the densities of other isomers can also be calculated out one by one. Table 2-3 lists the experimental and all the calculated densities of C_7 isomers by Tateveskii's method.

Similar methods can be applied to other physical properties, such as boiling point temperature.

Table 2-3.   Comparison of Experimental and Calculated Specific Gravities of Some Paraffins

Compound	d_4^{20}	
	Experimental (Rossini, 1953)	Calculated
n-Heptane	0.68376	0.6818
2-Methylhexane	0.67859	0.6773
3-Methylhexane	0.68713	0.6868
3-Ethylpentane	0.69816	0.6964
2,2-Dimethylpentane	0.67385	0.6789
2,3-Dimethylpentane	0.69508	0.6932
2,4-Dimethylpentane	0.67270	0.6730
3,3-Dimethylpentane	0.69327	0.6941
2,2,3-Trimethylbutane	0.69011	0.6937

$$t_{bp}^{\circ} = \frac{\lambda}{b - \log p} - 273.16 \qquad\qquad [2\text{-}35]$$

$$= \frac{\sum_{i \le j=1}^{4} n_{ij}\lambda_{ij}}{\sum_{i \le j=1}^{4} n_{ij}b_{ij} - \log P} - 273.16$$

where

λ = latent heat of vaporization

P = vapor pressure

2.2 FUNCTIONAL GROUPS IN ORGANIC COMPOUNDS

As discussed, hydrocarbons (the substitute sites of carbon are hydrogens) are the simplest class of organic compounds available; the typical example being the petroleum hydrocarbons. Basically, there are three major types of hydrocarbons. **Paraffins** are saturated chain-like molecules, typically of the form of C_nH_{2n+2} or RH, where R is C_nH_{2n+1}. If this saturated chain is folded into cyclic forms of 5- or 6- carbon-numbered rings, or the 6-numbered ring is further fused with other ring-forming methylene (CH_2) units to construct a condensed hexagonal system, then these hydrocarbons are termed **naphthenics**, represented by C_nH_{2n}; for example, cyclohexane n = 3 or fused-ring naphthenic. A simple example is a polyacene-type naphthenic such as perhydronaphthalene and perhydroanthracene. This naphthenic can be represented by $C_nH_{3(n/2+1)}$. Another major type is the **aromatics**, which are the unsaturated or dehydrogenated naphthenics. Starting with benzene (consisting of alternative double and single bonds to build the fused-ring aromatics), for example, the **polyacenes**, the **polyphenylenes**, and the regular R[m,n] type are illustrated in Figure 2-4.

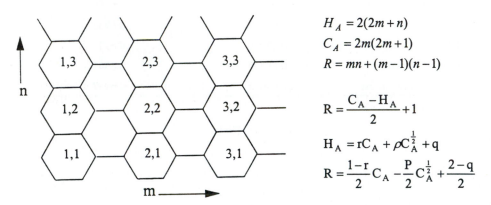

$$H_A = 2(2m+n)$$
$$C_A = 2m(2m+1)$$
$$R = mn + (m-1)(n-1)$$

$$R = \frac{C_A - H_A}{2} + 1$$

$$H_A = rC_A + \rho C_A^{\frac{1}{2}} + q$$

$$R = \frac{1-r}{2}C_A - \frac{P}{2}C_A^{\frac{1}{2}} + \frac{2-q}{2}$$

Figure 2-4.   The rectangular-type model R[m,n] represents polynuclear aromatic hydrocarbons. In this graph m or n is the index along the x- or y-axis. R[1,1] is benzene, R[1,2] is naphthalene, R[2,1] is biphenyl, R[2,2] is perylene, R[1,n] is polyacene, R[m,1] is polyphenylene, and R[m,n,] is a fused-ring aromatic hydrocarbon. (T. F. Yen, ref 2-7)

Polyacene $C_n H_{n/2+3}$

Polyphenylene $C_n H_{2n/3+2}$

Square fused aromatic $C_n H_{3n^{\frac{1}{2}} - \frac{3}{2}}$ (approximate value)   [2-36]

In a broad sense, all hydrocarbons can be represented by a general formula, $H_n C_m$ where the m values vary depending on the type.

The functional groups are derived from the substitution of one or more of the carbons or hydrogens of the $H_n C_m$ by **heterocyclic atoms**, such as N, O, S and X (X = F, Cl, Br, I).

The valance number of the heteroatoms are lower than four, which is the value of the carbon. Often these functional groups consist of unsaturated linkages. We will first discuss the oxygen groups.

2.2.1 Oxygen Functional Groups

As summarized in Table 2-4, the **alcohols** are important in that the hydrogens in the hydrocarbons (C_nH_{2n+2} or RH) are substituted by hydroxyl groups. ROH (where R is C_nH_{2n+1}) is the general formula for the paraffin series. The series begins with methanol (CH_3OH), ethanol (CH_3CH_2OH), propanol ($CH_3CH_2CH_2OH$), and so on. Similar to the bonding types, there is a primary alcohol, RCH_2OH, secondary alcohol, R_2CHOH, and tertiary alcohol, R_3COH, depending on the number of hydrogens remaining. The corresponding aromatic is phenol ArOH (Ar = C_6H_5), which exists in industrial wastewater derived from coal tar. Multiple OH groups substituted on one ring are also present, such as ortho- (catechol), meta- (resorcinol), and para- (hydroquinone) dihydroxybenzene. When hydrocarbons are partially oxidized, they can be converted into aldehydes such as those in automobile emissions.

$$RCH_3 \xrightarrow{\ [O]\ } RCHO$$

The condensation of two aldehydes, RC(H) = 0, will form a ketone, (R_2CO). The sharp odor of smog may originate from **aldehydes** and **ketones** formed by the oxidation of unsaturated hydrocarbons by ozone.

$$RCH{=}\,CHR' + O_3 \longrightarrow \overset{O}{RCH\diagup \diagdown CHR'} \xrightarrow{\ H_2O\ } RCHO + R'CHO + H_2O_2$$

The **carboxylic acids** RCOOH and their corresponding esters RCOOR' are also abundant; for example, in any landfill, cellulose is very easily converted to simple carboxylic acids before fermentation is initiated. Common monocarboxylic acids can be found in Table 2-5. Along with **dicarboxylic acids**, common names are also listed. These names are intermediates after the oxidation of complex organics. Finally, the **ethers** are those molecules in which oxygen serves as the bridge between two R groups, for example, ROR'.

Table 2-4. Substitution of Hydrocarbons (RH) by Functional Groups

Functional Groups	Name	Example
R-OH	alcohol	methanol (R=CH$_3$)
(secondary alcohol structure)	secondary alcohol	Isopropanol (R$_1$=R$_2$=CH$_3$)
(tertiary alcohol structure)	tertiary alcohol	t-butyl alcohol (R$_1$=R$_2$=R$_3$=CH$_3$)
(hydroxyl-benzene structure)	hydroxyl-benzene	phenol
	aromatic diols	catechol (o)
		reso cenol (m)
		hydroquinone (p)
R-COOH	carboxylic acid	acetic acid (R=CH$_3$)
		propionic acid (R=C$_2$H$_5$)
		butyric acid (R=C$_3$H$_7$)
RCOH	aedehyde	
R$_2$C=O	ketone	acetone, R=CH$_3$
ROR'	ether	diethyl ether, R=C$_2$H$_5$=R'
RX	halohydro carbons	THM(chloroform, CHCl$_3$)
		(CFC, Freon, CH$_2$F$_2$)
RCONH$_2$	amide	acetamide, R=CH$_3$
RCN	nitrile	HAN (chloroacetonitrile)
RNO$_2$	nitro	TNT (Trinitrotoluene)
RSH	mercaptan	skunk
RSR	thioether	
ArSO$_3$Na	sulfonates	Anionic surfactant, Cationic exchanger

Table 2-5. Names of Mono- and Di-carboxylic Acids

No. of R	RH	R Abr.	R(C_nH_{2n+1})	Monocarboxylic Acid*	Dicarboxylic Acid**
1	Methane	Me	CH_3	Formic	--
2	Ethane	Et	CH_3CH_2	Acetic	Oxalic
3	Propane	Pr	$CH_3(CH)_2$	Propionic	Malonic
4	Butane	Bu	$CH_3(CH_2)_3$	Butyric	Succinic
5	Pentane	Pn	$CH_3(CH_2)_4$	Valeric	Glutaric
6	Hexane	Hx	$CH_3(CH_2)_5$	Caproic	Adipic
7	Heptane	Hp	$CH_3(CH_2)_6$	Enanthic	Pimelic
8	Octane	Oc	$CH_3(CH_2)_7$	Caprylic	Suberic
9	Nonane	No	$CH_3(CH_2)_8$	Pelargonic	Azelaic
10	Decane	De	$CH_3(CH_2)_9$	Capric	Sebacic

*Formic acid is HCOOH, Acetic is the 2-carbon acid CH_3COOH; the remaining acids follow the formula R'COOH with R' being one less carbon than R(R' − 1).

** The first in the series is oxalic, $(COOH)_2$. The remaining ones are $(CH_2)_n(COOH)_2$ with n = R − 2.

2.2.2 Nitrogen Functional Groups

Similar to the oxygen functional groups, an important group of compounds are **amines**, which bear the substituted ammonia functions: -NH_2 the amino, =NH the imino, =N- and the nitrilo. The primary amine is RNH_2, the secondary amine is R_2NH, and the tertiary amine is R_3N. The physiological properties of amines vary with the positions; for example,

The last structure is very strong in carcinogenicity. Nitrogen can also participate in cyclic 5- or 6-membered systems; for example,

Pyrrole

Pyridine

These are called **heterocyclic compounds,** which involve one or more heterocyclic elements such as N, O, S in the ring system; for example, indole and skatol have unpleasant odors from putrefaction in sludge digestion. **Amino acids** contain two different functional groups in a hydrocarbon skeleton; the simplest being glycine, H_2NCH_2COOH. Amino acids are the foundation of certain biological molecules. The **amide** is a condensation product of carboxylic acid and ammonia.

$$RCOOH + NH_3 = RCONH_2 + H_2O$$

Nitrile, RCN, is important in that potable water will yield haloacetonitrile (HAN) as an undesirable contaminant after chlorination. **Nitro compounds,** RNO_2, are important because certain structures will yield hazardous compounds such as TNT or picric acid.

TNT

picric acid

These compounds can be found as soil contaminants for munitions operations.

2.2.3   Sulfur Functional Groups

Many sulfur compounds have the substituent of this group, -SH. These compounds are called **mercaptans,** and a well-known example is n-BuSH or n-$CH_3(CH_2)_3SH$ in the odor of skunk secretions, and nPrSH or $CH_3(CH_2)_2SH$ from freshly chopped onions. **Thioethers,** RSR', are similar to ethers, the S taking the place of O as a bridge. An important class of sulfur compounds is the sulfonates, $-SO_3Na$; for example, linear alkylbenzene sulfonate (LAS) is an efficient **anionic surfactant**. A similar compound, polystyrene sulfonate, is an excellent **cationic ion exchanger**. Both classes contain the $ArSO_3^-Na^+$ functions, depending on the applications concerning the anionic or the cationic portions of the molecule.

2.2.4 Others — the Halides and Organometallics

Group VII elements of the periodic table, such as F, Cl, Br, and I, are termed halides and are represented by the letter X. These elements can replace the hydrogens of hydrocarbons. The **alkyl halides,** such as RX, are made from the corresponding alcohols.

$$ROH \xrightarrow{PCl_3} RCl + P(OH)_3$$

Trihalomethanes (THMs) are found in drinking water after chlorine disinfectant treatment; for example CHX_3 such as chloroform. The chlorofluorocarbons (CFC) such as freons, CCl_2F_2, are refrigerants or aerosol propellants easily released into the atmosphere. When metals interact with organics, they may form **organometallics**. For example, dimethyl mercury (CH_3HgCH_3) is more toxic than mercury (Hg) alone. Alkyl mercury halides, RHgX, have been used as preservatives for seeds in crops. Metals can form complexes with the functional groups of organic compounds. If there is more than one functional group, they can chelate with metals and form **metal chelates**. Some of the important chelates are listed in Figure 2-5. They can readily form the calcium or lead chelates. One way to remove lead or mercury from the body as a result of lead poisoning is by ingesting EDTA or BAL. Many other similar metal complexes and chelates, such as porphyrins, are essential in the biosphere.

ethylenediaminetetraacetate

EDTA Anion

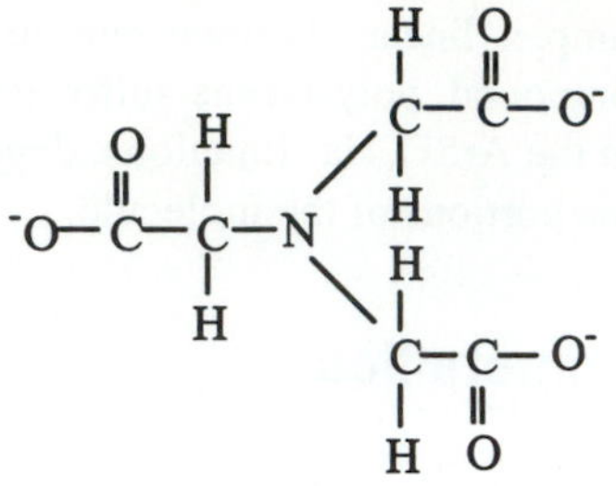

nitrilotriacetate anion

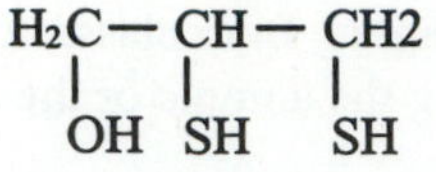

2,3-Mercaptopropanol
(BAL)
British anti lewisite

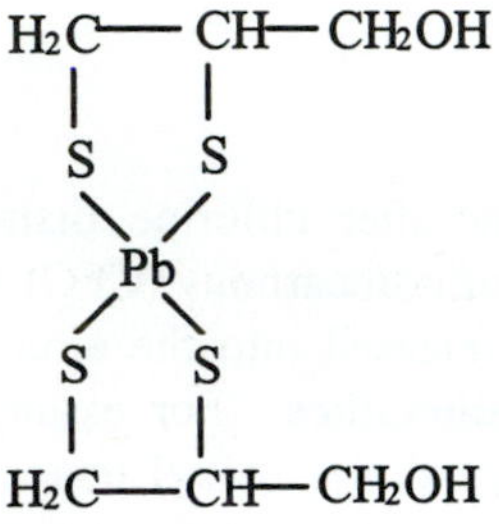

Pb bound to BAL 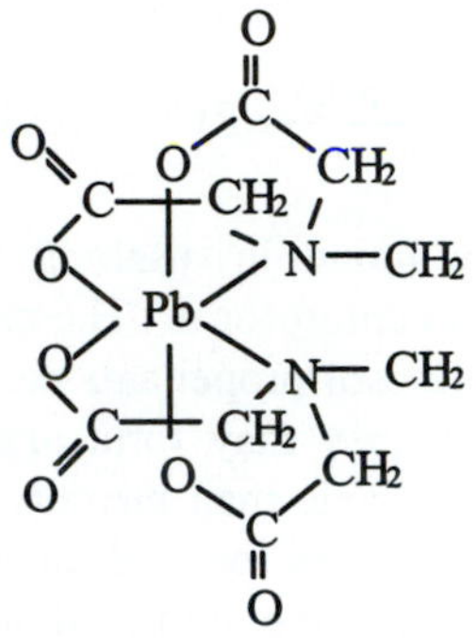   Pb bound to EDTA 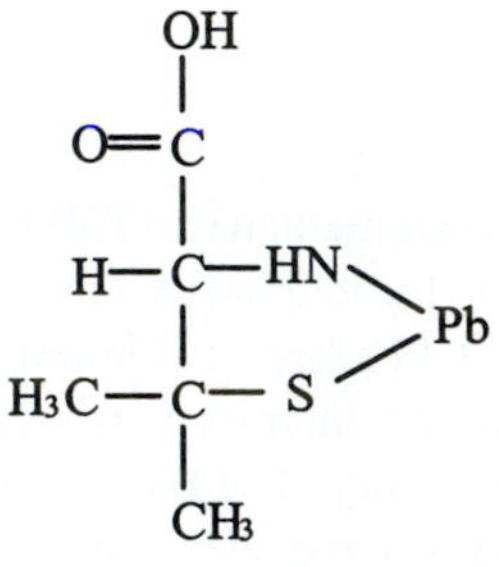   Pb bound to d-penicillamine

Ca^{2+} + NTA →

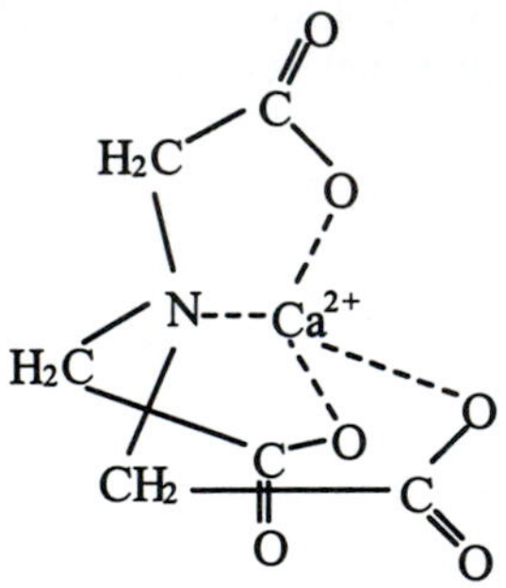

Figure 2-5.   Chelating agents.

2.3 STRUCTURE ACTIVITY RELATIONSHIP

In the preceding section, we discussed the influence of molecular structure on physical properties. In addition to physical properties, other characteristics such as stability, reactivity, and toxicity can be described and explained in molecular terms. Much creative effort has been devoted to the development of methods that measure properties in relation to the chemical structure. It is too much effort to go through each method in detail. Instead, following this paragraph are some examples to illustrate structure activity relationships. From the **structure activity relationship** (SAR) studies, highly efficient specific chemical can be produced. This opens the door for the recent molecular modeling investigations for many dynamic properties.

[**Example 2-3**]   Predict the composition of chlorinated compounds that result from the reaction between chlorine and isopentane in vapor phase, given the reactivity ratios of the structures as primary: secondary: tertiary = 1 : 3.3 : 4.4.

For chlorination

$$\equiv CH + X_2 \rightarrow \equiv CX + HX$$

The chlorinated products are formed by free radical mechanism. The radical activity is

$$A_{k_3} : A_{k_2} : A_{k_1} = 4.4 : 3.3 : 1$$

The molecular structure of isopentane shows us that there are nine primary atoms, two secondary atoms and one tertiary hydrogen atom that could be substituted by chlorine (refer to Fig. 2-3, Structure B). The distribution can be written as

$$(4 - i)k_i A_{k_i}$$

in such a way that the % k_i can be calculated as

		%
k_1	$(3)(3)(1) = 9$	45
k_2	$(2)(3.3) = 6.6$	33
k_3	$(1)(4.4) = 4.4$	22

For k_1, which can result in two different isomers, carbon **a** and **e** result in one isomer ($k_1' = 2$), carbon **d** results in another isomer ($k_1'' = 1$) (refer to Fig. 2-3, Structure B). In this manner, there are 30% of the k_1' type and 15% of the k_1'' type. The preceding example illustrates how the difference in reactivity affects the products of a reaction.

Hammett studied the inductive effects of substituents in the phenyl ring on the hydrolysis of ethyl benzoate.

$$Y\phi COOEt \xrightarrow{\quad OH^- \quad} Y\phi COOH + EtOH$$

He correlated that

$$\log K_\sigma = \log K + \sigma\rho \qquad\qquad [2\text{-}37]$$

where

K_σ = reaction rate for substituted benzoate (with Y)

K = reaction rate for unsubstituted benzoate (without Y)

σ = Hammett constant

ρ = constant of 2.56 (slope)

The equation can be rearranged as

$$\log K_\sigma/K = \sigma\rho \qquad\qquad [2\text{-}38]$$

The results are also shown in Figure 2-6 on the next page; for example, if it is ρ – OH (donating) $\sigma = -.357$; and if it is ρ – NO_2 (withdrawing) $\sigma = +.789$. A high value for the slope (+2.56) indicates that the reaction rate is enhanced by electron-withdrawing substituents.

Of the various parameters available for the study of SAR, those used to express electronic properties of steric factors, lipophilicity, are by far the most important. Quite often, therefore, a biological event will be described with the aid of the following **Hansch equation** to find the **quantitative structure activity relationship (QSAR)**:

$$\log BR = - a(\log P)^2 + b\log P + \sigma + cE_s + d \qquad\qquad [2\text{-}39]$$

where

BR = biological response

P = partition coefficient of the organic molecule examined

σ = summation of the Hammett constants of the various substituents

E_s = summation of their steric Taft parameters

and a, b, p, c, and d are constants. The preceding equation is for the use of DDT, as shown in Figure 2-7.

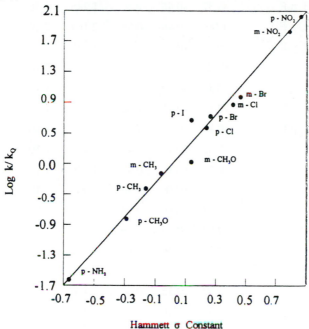

Figure 2-6.   Hammett plot for the substituents on benzoate.

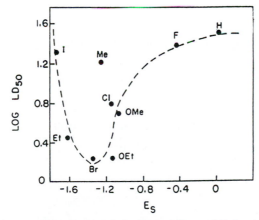

Figure 2-7.   Relationship between toxicity and E_s for 1,1,1-trichloro-p-methyl-p'-x-diphenylethanes.

Table 2-6.   Structure, Physical Properties, and Potency of Gamma Carbolines

X	Y	σR	Esp	Es8	Obs.	$pEd50_{Eq.\,A}$
6CH$_3$	(CH$_2$)$_3$COC$_6$H$_4$-p-F	-0.14	-0.46	0.00	1.917	1.71
5CH$_3$, 8F	(CH$_2$)$_3$COC$_6$H$_4$-p-F	-0.32	-0.46	-0.46	1.745	1.50
8CN	(CH$_2$)$_3$COC$_6$H$_4$-p-F	1.00	-0.46	-0.55	2.167	2.16
H	(CH$_2$)$_3$COC$_6$H$_4$-p-F	0.00	-0.46	0.00	1.627	1.79
8CF$_3$	(CH$_2$)$_3$COC$_6$H$_4$-p-F	0.61	-0.46	-2.40	1.491	1.48
8OCH$_3$	(CH$_2$)$_3$COC$_6$H$_4$-p-F	-0.43	-0.46	-0.55	1.400	1.42
8Br	(CH$_2$)$_3$COC$_6$H$_4$-p-F	-0.16	-0.46	-1.10	1.377	1.42
8CH$_3$	(CH$_2$)$_3$COC$_6$H$_4$-p-F	-0.14	-0.46	-1.20	1.372	1.40
8F	(CH$_2$)$_3$COC$_6$H$_5$	-0.32	0.00	-0.46	1.441	1.10
8F	H	-0.32	0.00	-0.46	1.124	1.10
8F	CH$_2$C$_6$H$_5$	-0.32	0.00	-0.46	0.926	1.10
8Cl	H	-0.18	0.00	-0.98	1.134	1.04
8F	(CH$_2$)$_4$C$_6$H$_4$-p-F	-0.32	-0.46	-0.46	1.528	1.50
8F	(CH$_2$)$_4$COC$_6$H$_4$-p-F	-0.32	-0.46	-0.46	1.417	1.50
8F	(CH$_2$)$_3$CN	-0.32	0.00	-0.46	0.805	1.10
8F	a	-0.32	-0.55	-0.46	1.426	1.58
8F	(CH$_2$)$_3$CHOHC$_6$H$_4$-p-F	-0.32	-0.46	-0.46	1.449	1.50
8F	(CH$_2$)$_3$OC$_6$H$_4$-p-F	-0.32	-0.46	-0.46	1.589	1.50
8Cl	(CH$_2$)$_3$COC$_6$H$_4$-p-F	-0.18	-0.46	-0.98	0.90[b]	1.43
8F	(CH$_2$)$_3$COC$_6$H$_4$-p-F	-0.32	-0.46	-0.46	2.18[b]	1.50
8F	(CH$_2$)$_3$C$_6$H$_4$-p-NO$_2$	-0.32	-2.52	-0.46	<0.50	3.27
8F	(CH$_2$)$_3$COC$_6$H$_4$-p-C(CH$_3$)$_3$	-0.32	-2.78	-0.46	0.80	3.49
8F	(CH$_2$)$_3$COC$_6$H$_4$-p-NH$_2$	-0.32	-0.61	-0.46	1.09	1.63
8F	(CH$_2$)$_3$COC$_6$H$_4$-p-CH$_3$	-0.32	-1.24	-0.46	<0.50	2.17
8F	(CH$_2$)$_3$COC$_6$H$_4$-p-Cl	-0.32	-0.97	-0.46	<0.50	1.94
8F	(CH$_2$)$_3$COC$_6$H$_4$-p-NO$_2$	-0.32	-2.52	-0.46	<0.50	3.27

a $\log(1/ED_{50}) = 1.39 + 0.52\sigma R - 0.86\,Esp + 0.26\,Es8$; Eq. A $R^2 = 0.77$, s = 0.17, n = 18

b   Not included in calculation

For another example, Hansch found a simple correlation in the study of narcosis

$$\log 1/C = 0.94 \log P + 0.87 \qquad\qquad [2\text{-}40]$$

where C is the molar concentration necessary to produce narcosis in case of α-carbolines. Table 2-6 shows the steric effects.

2.3.1   Polycyclic Aromatic Hydrocarbons

The next example shows the thermostability of a **polycyclic aromatic hydrocarbon** (PAH), which often refers to polynuclear aromatics (PNA), the general structure of which is shown in Figure 2-4.

The **number of unexcited forms of configuration**, N, is a qualitative measurement of either the boiling point or the thermal reactivity of these compounds. In general, the larger the N value, the higher the boiling point will be. Lower N values seem to indicate greater thermal reactivity. The number of unexcited configurations can be related to the number of rings in the system $[m,n]$ and the type of bonding — that is, biphenyl or naphthalene — according to the classification scheme shown in Figure 2-4. In this model, m indicates the number of biphenyl-type linkages along the x-axis, and n indicates the number of naphthalene-type linkages along the y-axis. It can readily be seen that, for polyacene, $R[1,n]$, $R = n$; and similarly for the polyphenylene, $R[m,1]$, $R = m$. In this model, the estimation of N can be obtained from

$$N = (n + 1)^m$$

Hence, for the polyacene series, N is equal to n + 1, and for the polyphenylene series, N is equal to 2^m. For an equal number of rings, it can be shown that the polyphenylene has the highest value of N, while the polyacene has the least. Thus, it can be generalized that quinquephenyl is considerably more stable than pentacene, because the N value for the former is equal to 2^5 and for the latter it is only 6. In the polyphenylene family, N increases rapidly as it is equal to 2^R, and it is used as a nuclear coolant. Free rotation of a single bond is allowed in the longitudinal axis of the polyphenylene compound without a change of shape, and this molecular flexibility contributes to its stability. Boiling point of PAH can be related to stability. As shown in Figure 2-8 on the next page for the pentacyclic aromatic hydrocarbons, the N values correlate well with the stability.

In conclusion, we must point out the two isomeric 5-ring polycyclic aromatic hydrocarbons (PAH's), **benz(a)pyrene** and **benz(e)pyrene,** as shown in Figure 2-9. The former is a strong carcinogen and the latter is inactive (refer to Fig. 2-9). It is interesting to correlate the SAR, because there are a number of plausible mechanisms that will be found if one examines the K-region (kink) and the L-region (meso).

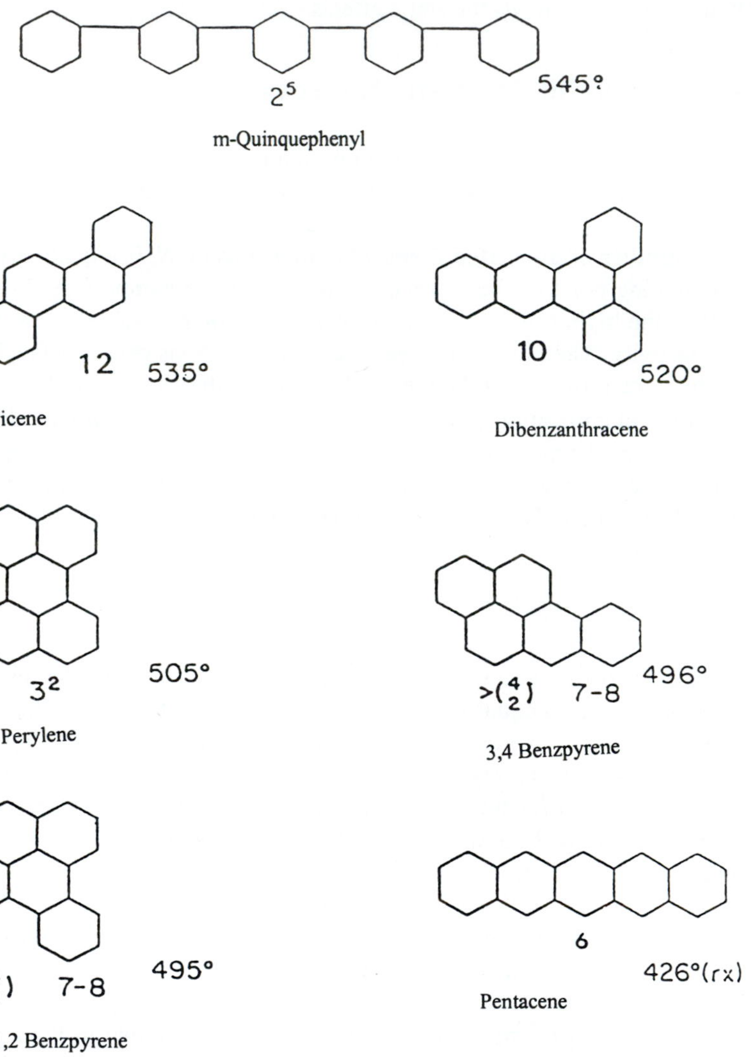

2^5 545°

m-Quinquephenyl

12   535°

Picene

10

520°

Dibenzanthracene

3^2 505°

Perylene

$>(\substack{4\\2})$ 7-8

496°

3,4 Benzpyrene

$>(\substack{4\\2})$ 7-8   495°

1,2 Benzpyrene

6

426°(rx)

Pentacene

Figure 2-8.   Boiling point (in °C) of some pentacyclic aromatic hydrocarbons. The N values are given under each structure (2).

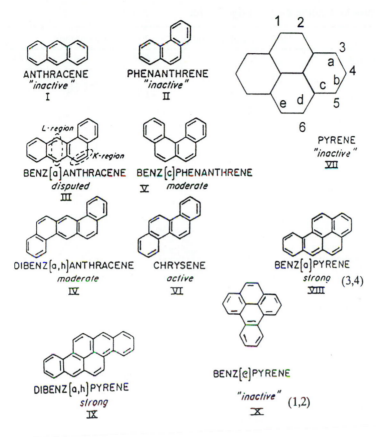

ANTHRACENE
"inactive"
I

PHENANTHRENE
"inactive"
II

PYRENE
"inactive"
VII

BENZ[a]ANTHRACENE
disputed
III

BENZ[c]PHENANTHRENE
V *moderate*

DIBENZ[a,h]ANTHRACENE
moderate
IV

CHRYSENE
active
VI

BENZ[a]PYRENE
strong (3,4)
VIII

DIBENZ[a,h]PYRENE
strong
IX

BENZ[e]PYRENE
"inactive" (1,2)
X

Figure 2-9. Carcinogenic properties of fused ring aromatics.

2.4 METHODS FOR STUDYING STRUCTURE ACTIVITY RELATIONSHIP

Three methods are generally used to study the structure activity relationship: molecular connectivity, factor analysis, and pattern recognition.

One topic in organic chemistry is the reaction mechanism. We purposely omit it here, due to a number of specialized books that are available (for example, R.A. Larson and E.J. Weber, *Reaction Mechanisms in Environmental Organic Chemistry*, Lewis Publishers, Boca Raton, Florida, 1994.). Some mechanisms are mentioned in Chapters 13, 14, 16, 22, 23, and 24.

Table 2-7.   Procedure for Finding Sum of Edge Terms

Steps	2,2,3-trimethylbutane	2,4-dimethylpentane
Write structural formula		
Draw hydrogen-suppressed graph		
Write valence at each vertex		
Compute product of end point valences for each edge		
Compute each edge term as the reciprocal square root product		
Sum of edge terms:	2.943	3.126

2.4.1   Molecular Connectivity

Molecular connectivity is an approach to the quantitative evaluation of molecular structure. This information is a nonempirical derivation of numerical values that encode within them sufficient information to relate them to many physicochemical and biological properties. The basic idea assumes that significant properties of a molecule may be represented as bonds connecting the atoms in a molecule. Table 2-7 shows the detailed procedure for the calculation of the **connectivity index**, which will be used to predict the properties.

2.4.2   Factor Analysis

Factor analysis is a method that correlates experimental results with important parameters. The famous Hansch equation is a good example of this method. Figure 2-10 on the next page shows the stepwise procedure of factor analysis.

2.4.3 Pattern Recognition

Pattern recognition determines to which class a given pattern of chemical activity belongs. The decision rule is based on some statistical concepts of similarity between cases as determined by their properties. Patterns are merged into an existing class or cluster. The measure of similarity between patterns is their distance in property space as

$$d_{ij} = \left[\sum_{k=1}^{m} \left(x_{ik} - x_{jk} \right)^2 \right]^{\frac{1}{2}} \tag{2-41}$$

similarity $= s_{ij} = 1 - (d_{ij}/D_{ij})$

where d_{ij} is the minimum distance between two patterns and D_{ij} is the maximum. Figure 2-11 shows the flow diagram of pattern recognition techniques.

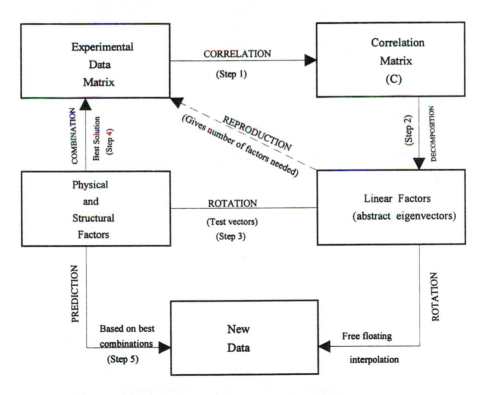

Figure 2-10. Factor analysis.

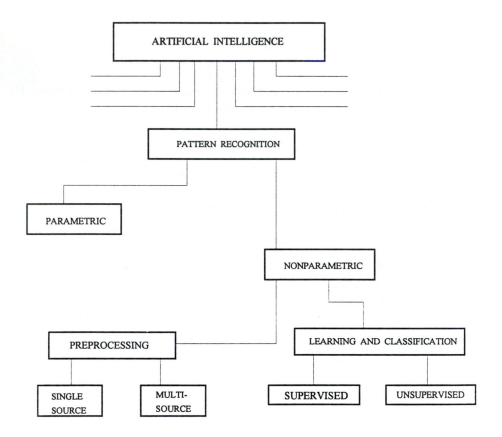

Figure 2-11.   Flow diagram of pattern recognition techniques.

REFERENCES

2-1   J. A. K. Buisman, *Biological Activity and Chemical Structure*, Elsevier Science, New York, 1977.

2-2   L. B. Kier and L. H. Hall, *Molecular Connectivity in Chemistry and Drug Research*, Academic Press, New York, 1976.

2-3   D. F. Rossini, *Selected Values of Physical and Thermodynamic Properties of Hydrocarbons and Related Compounds*, Pittsburgh, Pennsylvania, Carnegie Press, pp. 1050, 1953.

2-4   V. M. Tatevskii, V. A. Benderskii, and S. S. Yarovoi, *Rules and Methods for Calculating the Physico-Chemical Properties of Paraffinic Hydrocarbons* (M. F. Mullins, translator), Pergamon Press, Elmsford, New Jersey, 1961.

2-5   T. F. Yen, and G. V. Chilingarian, "Note on Hydrocarbon 1. Saturated Hydrocarbons," *Energy Sources*, *9*:71–74 (1987).

2-6   T. F. Yen, J. F. Kuo, and G. V. Chilingarian, "Note on Hydrocarbon 2. Naphthenic Hydrocarbons," *Energy Sources*, *9*:125–132 (1987).

2-7   T. F. Yen, "Resonance topology of Polynuclear Aromatic Hydrocarbons," *Theoret. chim.*, Acta Berlin, *20*, 399–404 (1971).

2-8   T. F. Yen, "Terrestrial and Extraterrestrial Stable Organic Molecules," in *Chemistry in Space Research* (R. F. Landel and A. Rembaum, ed.), Am. Elsevier, New York, 1972, pp. 105–153.

2-9   R. A. Y. Jones, *Physical and Mechanistic Organic Chemistry*, 2nd ed., Cambridge University Press, London, 1984.

2-10 C. D. Johnson, *The Hammett Equation*, Cambridge University Press, London, 1973.

2-11 S. R. Hartshorn, *Aliphatic Nucleophilic Substitution*, Cambridge University Press, London, 1973.

2-12 W. H. Saunders and A.F. Cockerill, *Mechanisms of Elimination Reactions*, Wiley-Interscience, New York, 1973.

2-13 J. Miller, *Aromatic Nucleophilic Substitution*, Elsevier, Amsterdam, 1968.

2-14 R. A. Rossi and R.H. deRossi, *Aromatic Substitution by the $S_{RN}I$ Mechanism*, American Chemical Society, Washington, 1983.

2-15 H. J. Shine, *Aromatic Rearrangements*, American Elsevier, New York, 1967.

2-16 T. M. Lowry and K.S. Richardson, *Mechanism and Theory in Organic Chemistry*, 2nd ed., Harper and Row, New York, 1981.

2-17 R. A. Jackson, *Mechanism: An Introduction to the Study of Organic Reactions*, Clarendon, Oxford, 1972.

2-18 C. K. Ingold, *Structure and Mechanism in Organic Chemistry*, 2nd ed., Bell, London, 1964.

2-19 S. Ege, Organic Chemistry, Structure and Reactivity, 3rd ed., D.C. Heath, Lexington, Massachusetts, 1994.

2-20 G. Klopman, *Chemical Reactivity and Reaction Path*, Wiley-Interscience, New York, 1974.

2-21 N. Bondard, *Pattern Recognition*, Spartan-Macmillan, New York, 1970.

2-22 T. F. Yen, "A Scheme for Memorizing Thermodynamic Functions", *J. Chemic. Edu.* 31, 610 (1954).

2-23 K. G. Joreskog, J. E. Klovan and R. A. Regment, *Geological Factor Analysis*, Elsevier, Amsterdam, 1976.

PROBLEM SET

1. What are the vapor phase nitration products of heptane, assuming that NO_2 can be attacked at any position of the molecule? Further bond-breaking would result in all the possible isomeric forms being less than 7-C units. Predict the product distribution, assuming the approximate ratios of the reaction rates at primary, secondary, and tertiary positions are 1.0 : 3.3 : 4.4 at 300°C.

2. Using Tatevskii's method, calculate the density of all heptane isomers.

3. For fused aromatics, prove

$$H_A = 3C_A^{\frac{1}{2}} - 3/2$$

4. Use some different methods to compute tetrahedron angles.

They could not drink of the waters of Ma'rah, for they were bitter...
And he cried unto the LORD, and the LORD shewed him a tree,
which when he had cast into the waters, the waters were made sweet.

Exodus 15:23-25

This marks the first example of ion exchange in Old Testament times. When the Israelites came out of Egypt, Moses cast a tree into the waters and they became sweet because of the action of ion exchange between the water and the wood. The aged, old tree trunk serves especially well as an excellent exchanger for nitrate and other ions.

C H A P T E R **3**

ANALYTICAL CHEMISTRY

*Q*uantitative measurements of one sort or another serve as the keystones of engineering practices. Environmental engineering is perhaps the most demanding in this respect, for it requires the use of not only the conventional measuring methods employed by engineers, but also many of the techniques and methods of measurements used by chemists, physicists, and biologists.

Measurements play a key role in the protection of the environment. They are needed to identify problems and to monitor the effectiveness of control and abatement technology. Decisions on vital questions such as the habitability of an area, the safety of drinking water, and the continued operations of an industrial plant are often based on measurement data. Equipment and technology for quantitative measurement are increasingly better developed these days, enabling us to identify new problems that may have existed for a long time. Consequently, stringent regulations can be set, and a cleaner environment can be assured with suitable enforcement. In this chapter, acid-base chemistry, instrumental analysis, separation science, and the quality assurance of environmental measurements will be addressed.

3.1 ACID-BASE CHEMISTRY

A thorough examination of acid-base chemistry is important when studying aqueous chemistry in order to understand water and wastewater treatment processes. In this section, we will discuss some important acid-base chemistry concepts, such as pH, acidity, and alkalinity, which relate to environmental engineering practices.

According to **Bronsted and Lowry's definition**, an **acid** is any substance that can donate a proton to any other substance. A **base**, then, is any substance that can accept a proton from an acid.

$$H^+ + OH^- = H_2O$$

An even broader theory of acids and bases has been proposed by **G.N. Lewis**. According to him, a **base** is any substance that donates a pair of electrons to the formation of a coordinate bond. In turn, an **acid** is any substance that accepts a pair of electrons to form such a bond.

$$R_2O : + BF_3 = R_3O : BF_3$$

Usanovich enlarged this concept to include the coordination, and examples are illustrated here:

$$
\begin{array}{ccccccc}
B^- & + & HA & = & HB & + & A^- \\
(B1) & & (A1) & & (A2) & & (B2)
\end{array}
$$

$$
\begin{array}{ccccccc}
HCl & + & C_5H_5N & = & Cl^- & + & C_5H_5NH^+ \\
(A1) & & (B1) & & (B2) & & (A2)
\end{array}
$$

$$
\begin{array}{ccccccc}
HCl & + & H_2O & = & H_3O^+ & + & Cl^- \\
(A1) & & (B1) & & (A2) & & (B2)
\end{array}
$$

$$
\begin{array}{ccccccc}
CO_3^{2-} & + & H_2O & = & OH^- & + & HCO_3^- \\
(B1) & & (A1) & & (B2) & & (A2)
\end{array}
$$

According to Usanovich neutralization will form a secondary acid and base species. Water is described as amphoteric because it can be both an acid and a base; thus, water is an ampholyte.

The intensity of the acid or alkaline condition of a solution is universally expressed by the term **pH**. It is a way of expressing the hydrogen-ion activity, and it is important in almost every phase of environmental engineering practice.

$$pH = -\log (H^+) = \log [1/(H^+)] \qquad\qquad [3\text{-}1]$$

For water in the absence of other substances, $(H^+) = (OH^-)$ as required by electroneutrality, and at 25°C

$$H_2O = H^+ + OH^-$$

$$(H^+)(OH^-) = K_w = 10^{-14} \qquad\qquad [3\text{-}2]$$

or

$$pH + pOH = 14 = pK_w$$

It is easily seen that, under neutral conditions,

$$pH = pOH = 7 \qquad\qquad [3\text{-}3]$$

A value of pH lower than 7 indicates that $(H^+) > (OH^-)$ and the water is acidic; when pH is greater than 7, the water is basic. If a strong acid such as nitric acid is added to the water with known concentration, C, then the pH of the water can be easily determined due to the neutrality requirement; for example,

$$(H^+) = (NO_3^-) + (OH^-)$$

or

$$(H^+) = C + K_w/(H^+) \qquad\qquad [3\text{-}4]$$

and the equation can be expressed as

$$(H^+)^2 - C(H^+) - K_w = 0$$

and

$$(H^+) = 1/2\, [C \pm (C^2 + 4\,K_w)^{1/2}] \qquad\qquad [3\text{-}5]$$

For an HNO_3 concentration of 10^{-7} M, the pH is calculated to be 6.79.

For weak acids such as acetic acid, which are not completely ionized like a strong acid, incomplete ionization will take place.

$$\frac{(H^+)(A^-)}{(HA)} = K_a = 1.8 \times 10^{-5} \qquad\qquad [3\text{-}6]$$

Again neutrality

$$(H^+) = (OH^-) + (A^-) \qquad\qquad [3\text{-}7]$$

and mass balance for a known concentration take place.

$$(HA) + (A^-) = C \qquad\qquad [3\text{-}8]$$

Using four equations (including K_w)(Equations [3-6], [3-7], [3-8], and [3-2]), we can solve four different species in the solution. By substituting the preceding equations, we get

$$(H^+)^3 + K_a(H^+)^2 - (K_aC + K_w)(H^+) - K_aK_w = 0 \qquad\qquad [3\text{-}9]$$

Given C is 10^{-2} M, the following are obtained

$(H^+) = 4.15 \times 10^{-4}$

$(OH^-) = 2.42 \times 10^{-11}$

$(HA) = 9.59 \times 10^{-3}$

$(A^-) = 4.15 \times 10^{-4}$

In many instances, an approximation can be made instead of the exact solution of the equation. In water supply, this is a factor that must be considered, whether in chemical coagulation, disinfection, water softening, or corrosion control. In wastewater treatment employing biological processes, pH must be controlled within a range favorable to the particular organisms involved. Chemical processes used to coagulate wastewater, dewater sludges, or oxidize certain substances such as cyanide ions, require that the pH be controlled within rather narrow limits.

Although pure water should have a pH of 7, the water in the atmosphere is not neutral. Most natural waters, domestic sewage, and many industrial wastes are buffered principally by a carbon dioxide-bicarbonate system. Carbon dioxide is a normal component of all natural waters. It may also enter surface waters by absorption from the atmosphere. Carbon dioxide may also be produced in water, particularly in polluted water, through the biological oxidation of organic matter. The acidity of rain can be significantly increased by industrial pollutants, and acid rain is an environmental hazard. Acid waters are of concern because of their corrosive characteristics and the expense involved in removing or controlling these corrosion-producing substances. The corrosive factor in most waters is carbon dioxide, but in many industrial wastes it is mineral acidity. Carbon dioxide must be reckoned within water-softening problems where the lime or lime-soda ash method is used.

The **alkalinity** of a water is the measurement of its capacity to neutralize acids. Bicarbonates represent the major form of alkalinity, because they are formed in considerable amounts from the action of carbon dioxide upon basic materials in the soil. A few organic acids are quite resistant to biological oxidation; for example, humic acid-formed salts that add to the alkalinity of natural water. In polluted or anaerobic waters, salts of weak acids such as acetic, propionic, and hydrosulfuric acid may be produced and may also contribute to alkalinity. In other cases, ammonia or hydroxides may contribute to the total alkalinity of a water. Details of more principles in alkalinity and carbonic systems will be discussed in Chapter 18.

In practice, the alkalinity can be conveniently expressed in terms of $CaCO_3$. In all cases, the multiplier is either 50 mg $CaCO_3$/meq, or 100 mg $CaCO_3$/mM. The following example can be illustrated. In general, where A_i^- is an anion and A_i^+ is a cation

$$T = \sum A_i^- - \sum A_i^+ \qquad \text{[3-10]}$$

[Example 3-1] A pH = 10 natural water contains 100 mg/L carbonate and 75 mg/L bicarbonate. Compute the alkalinity as expressed in $CaCO_3$.

For CO_3^{2-}

$$(100/60) \times 100 = 167 \text{ mg/L as } CaCO_3$$

and for HCO_3^-

$$(75/61) \times 100/2 = 61 \text{ mg/L as } CaCO_3$$

At pH = 10,

$$(H^+) = 10^{-10} \text{ M}$$

Thus expressed in mg/L

$$= 10^{-10} (10^3)(1) = 10^{-7} \text{ mg/L}$$

or

$$10^{-7} \times 100/2 \times 1 = 5 \times 10^{-6} \text{ mg/L as CaCO}_3$$

$$(OH^-) = K_w/H^+ = 10^{-14}/10^{-10} = 10^{-4}$$

Thus

$$(OH^-) = 10^{-4}10^{3}(17) \times 100/(17 \times 2) = 5 \text{ mg/L as CaCO}_3$$

Thus

$$\text{alkalinity} = T = \Sigma A_i^- - \Sigma A_i^+ = 61 + 167 + 5 - (5 \times 10^{-6}) = 233 \text{ mg/L as CaCO}_3$$

3.1.1   Titration Curve

If a strong acid or base is titrated with a strong base or acid, a typical S-shape or inverse S-shape results as shown is Figure 3-1(a) and Figure 3-1(b). When a weak acid is titrated with a strong base, the character of the titration curve depends on whether the acid is monobasic (monoprotic) or polybasic (polyprotic); that is, whether the acid will yield one or more hydrogen ions (for example, the curves shown on Figure 3-1(c) and Figure 3-1(d) with its middle portion flattened out). Considering a weak monobasic acid being titrated with a strong base

$$HA = H^+ + A^-$$

$$(HA) = [C - (A^-)] \tag{3-11}$$

$$K_a = \frac{(H^+)(A^-)}{(HA)} \tag{3-12}$$

under neutrality condition

$$(H^+) + (B^+) = (A^-) + (OH^-) \tag{3-13}$$

In the beginning stage of titration, $(B^+) = 0$, pH is low, and $(OH^-) \ll (H^+)$. Thus,

$$(H^+) \approx (A^-)$$

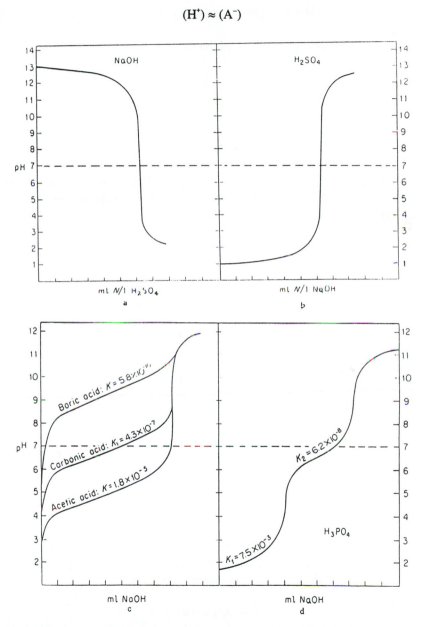

Figure 3-1. Titration curves for (a) strong base, (b) strong acid, (c) weak acids, and (d) weak bases.

and after substituting into the K_a equation (Equation [3-12]),

$$(H^+) \approx [K_a(HA)]^{1/2} = \{K_a[C-(A^-)]\}^{1/2} \qquad [3-14]$$

In many cases, at the beginning of titration $(A^-) \ll C$, so

$$(H^+) \approx (K_aC)^{1/2}$$

and

$$pH \approx 1/2\ (pK_a - \log C) \qquad [3-15]$$

At the midpoint of titration (A^-) increases and (HA) decreases; when the neutralization is 50% completed, $(B^+) = (1/2)C$, both (B^+) and (A^-) become significant.

Since $(H^+) \ll (B^+)$ and $(OH^-) \ll (A^-)$,

$$(B^+) \approx (A^-) \approx (1/2)C$$

and

$$(HA) + (A^-) = C$$

Hence

$$(HA) \approx (1/2)C$$

Substituting into the K_a equation (Equation [3-12]), then

$$(H^+) \approx K_a$$

or

$$pH \approx pK_a \qquad [3-16]$$

At the stoichiometric endpoint of titration (also called the equivalence point), the equivalents of the bases added equal those of the acids, and as $(B^+) = C$, pH becomes high in such a way that $(H^+) \ll (OH^-)$; the neutrality equation becomes

$$C \approx (A^-) + (OH^-)$$

Since

$$C - (A^-) = (HA)$$

then

$$(HA) \approx (OH^-) = K_w/(H^+)$$

Substituting into the K_a equation (Equation [3-12]),

$$1/(H^+) = [(A^-)/K_w K_a]^{1/2}$$

At the end of titration

$$(A^-) \approx C$$

So

$$pH \approx 1/2 \,(\log C + pK_a + pK_w) \qquad [3\text{-}17]$$

For a weak base being titrated with a strong acid, such as

$$Ac^- + H_2O = HAc + OH^-$$

then

$$K_b = \frac{(OH^-)(HAc)}{(Ac^-)} \qquad [3\text{-}18]$$

In this instance

$$pK_a = pK_w - pK_b$$

Again, as before, in the beginning (H^+) is small, (OH^-) is important, $(OH^-) \approx (HAc)$, and $Ac^- \approx C$, so $(OH^-) \approx K_b^{1/2}C^{1/2}$ and

$$\frac{1}{H^+} = \frac{K_b^{\frac{1}{2}}C^{\frac{1}{2}}}{K_w}$$

Hence

Initial $$pH \approx pK_w - 1/2\ pK_b + 1/2\ \log C$$

Midpoint $$pH \approx pK_w - pK_b \qquad\qquad\qquad [3\text{-}19]$$

Endpoint $$pH \approx 1/2\ (pK_w - pK_b - \log C)$$

For more discussions of system point and equivalence point please refer to Section 18.3. The following is a summary:

pH	Weak Acid Versus Strong Base	Weak Base Versus Strong Acid
Initial	$1/2\ (pK_a + pC)$	$pK_w - 1/2\ (pK_b + pC)$
Midpoint	pK_a	$pK_w - pK_b$
Equivalence	$1/2\ pK_w + 1/2\ (pK_a - pC)$	$1/2\ pK_w - 1/2\ (pK_b - pC)$

3.1.2   Buffers and Buffer Index

The word **buffer** may be defined as substances introduced in a solution that offer resistance to change in pH as acids or bases are added to that solution. Buffer solutions usually contain a weak acid and its salt (conjugate base) or a weak base and its salt (conjugate acid). At some point, the smallest changes in pH occur, and consequently at that point the buffering capacity is the greatest.

Weak acids and bases and their salts are used as buffers at a pH near the pK value; that is, within ± 1 pH unit of the pK value. The effectiveness can be demonstrated as follows; for example, a weak acid

$$pH = pK_a + \log \frac{(salt)}{(acid)}$$

In a solution of 0.1 M of sodium acetate to 0.1 M of acetic acid

$$pH = 4.75 + \log \frac{0.1}{0.1} = 4.75$$

Now if a small amount of HCl is added, equivalent to 10% of the acetate present (that is, 0.01 M), and the new salt concentration is 0.11 M, then

$$pH = 4.75 + \log \frac{0.09}{0.11} = 4.57 - 0.087 = 4.66$$

The pH has only decreased by 0.09 units, whereas if unbuffered, the amount of HCl added to the water (0.01 M) would change 5 units from pH = 7 to pH = 2. The reagent commonly used as a buffer near pH = 7 is phosphoric acid, whose ionization constant is near pH = 7. The salts, KH_2PO_4, and K_2HPO_4 are widely utilized for biochemical applications in nature.

The **buffering capacity** of a solution can be indicated quantitatively by the **buffering index**, β, which is defined as the slope of the titration curve pH versus the concentration of strong base added, C_B. On the other hand, the concentration of strong acid, C_A, can also be used.

$$\beta = \frac{dC_B}{dpH} = -\frac{dC_A}{dpH} \qquad [3\text{-}20]$$

If the concentration of the solution is given, this can be calculated. For a monoprotic acid

$$C_B + (H^+) = (OH^-) + (A^-)$$

$$(HA) + (A^-) = C$$

Substituting this into the K_a equation (Equation [3-6]), then

$$(HA) = \frac{C(H^+)}{K_a + (H^+)}$$

and

$$(A^-) = \frac{CK_a}{K_a + (H^+)}$$

Finally, the charge-balance equation becomes

$$C_B = \frac{K_w}{(H^+)} - (H^+) + \frac{CK_a}{K_a + (H^+)}$$

Hence

$$\frac{dC_B}{d\text{pH}} = \frac{dC_B}{d(\text{H}^+)} \frac{d(\text{H}^+)}{d\text{pH}}$$

Because pH = $-\ln(\text{H}^+)/2.303$

$$\frac{d(\text{H}^+)}{d\text{pH}} = -2.303(\text{H}^+)$$

$$\beta = \frac{dC_B}{d\text{pH}} = -2.303(H^+)\left[\frac{dC_B}{d(\text{H}^+)}\right]$$

$$= 2.303\left[\frac{\text{K}_w}{(\text{H}^+)} + (\text{H}^+) + \frac{CK_a(\text{H}^+)}{\text{K}_a + (\text{H}^+)^2}\right] \qquad [3\text{-}21]$$

This will numerically calculate the concentration of base needed to increase per pH unit, and usually β (increment of pH) will provide one with information of the concentration required to raise the pH value. Also β of a polyprotic acid or base is known.

3.2 INSTRUMENTAL ANALYSIS

A variety of sensitive instruments has been developed in recent years; these instruments have considerably increased the engineer's ability to measure and characterize pollutants with increasing complexity. An instrumental measurement is also called a physical method of analysis, since it is based on the differences between the physical properties of elements or compounds. Figure 3-2 is valuable for depicting the relationships between electron voltage E, wavelength λ, frequency ν of the radiant energy, and also the operational ranges in which major analytical instruments function. At this time, we will describe some common instruments used in the field of environmental engineering. Based on the electromagnetic series of energy, Figure 3-3 is a simple diagram for the function of an analytical instrument. A good reference for all the major instruments can be found in the practice written by H.H. Wilard, L.L. Merritt Jr., J.A. Dean, and F.A. Settle, Jr., Instrumental Methods of Analysis, 6th ed., 1981. Following discussion about instruments is based on the electromagnetic series, with the highest energy first and followed by decreasing energies.

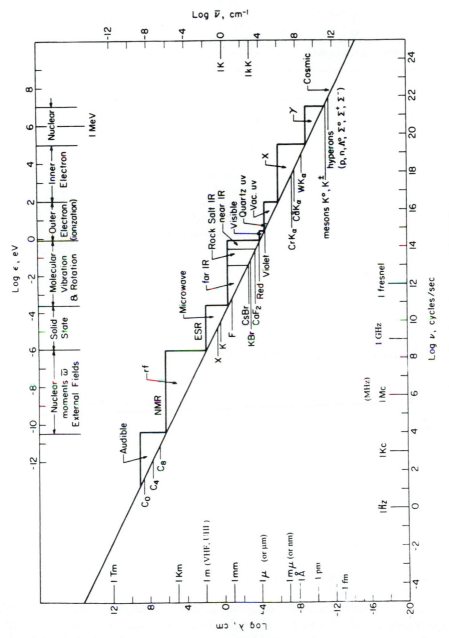

Figure 3-2. Generalized electromagnetic series.

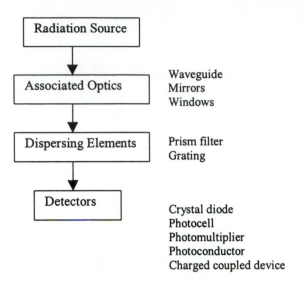

Figure 3-3.   Sketch of an instrument.

3.2.1 Gamma-Ray Spectrometry

Gamma-ray spectrometry is useful for the analysis of decayed elements or radioisotopes. It is routinely used for the measurement of radioactivity in the environment or in research studies that make use of radioactive tracers.

3.2.2 X-Ray Diffraction

X-ray diffraction (XRD) is primarily used for the study of crystalline material. X-rays are reflected off the surfaces of crystals, and by studying the reflection as the crystalline material is rotated in the path of x-rays, much information about the structure of the material can be obtained. Equation [3-1] is applied in the following analysis:

$$n \lambda = 2d \sin \theta \qquad\qquad\qquad [3\text{-}22]$$

where d is the range of interest that determines spacing between two centers and depends on the target material used. For very small angles, both small angle x-ray diffraction (SAXD) and small angle neutron scattering (SANS) are used to measure d-distance to 50–200 Å range. Another x-ray analysis commonly used is x-ray photoelectron spectroscopy (XPS), also called Electron Spectroscopy for Chemical Analysis (ESCA). To investigate the bonding pattern, an x-ray is applied to excite photons on a surface.

3.2.3 Mass Spectrometry

Mass spectrometry is an instrument that sorts out charged gas molecules or ions by bombardment with rapidly moving electrons. The ions formed are pulled from the gas stream by an electric field. A suitable detector can then record the particles of different mass either qualitatively, quantitatively, or both. Mass spectrometry when used with gas chromatography (GC/MS) can give positive identification and quantification for a large number of samples that are identified individually from the differences in their retention time when passed through a chromatographic column. Figures 3-4 to 3-6 show some typical mass spectra, and Figures 3-7 and 3-8 show typical gas chromatograms.

3.2.4 Ultraviolet/Visible Spectrophotometry

When a molecule absorbs radiant energy in either the **ultraviolet (UV)** or the **visible (vis)** **region**, **valence** or **bonding electrons** in the molecule are raised to high-energy orbits. The result is that fairly broad absorption bands are usually observed in both the ultraviolet and the visible region. The measurement of **UV absorption spectra** is primarily used to detect the presence of conjugated hydrocarbons. It is particularly suitable to have the selective measurement of low concentrations of organic compounds, such as benzene-ring-containing compounds or unsaturated straight-chain compounds containing a series of double bonds. **Beer's Law** is often used.

$$A = \log(I_o/I) = Ecb \qquad\qquad [3\text{-}23]$$

where

A = absorbance = optical density

E = molar absorptivity or extinction coefficient

c = concentration in moles/L

b = path length of sample cell in cm

I = resultant radiation

I_o = incident radiation

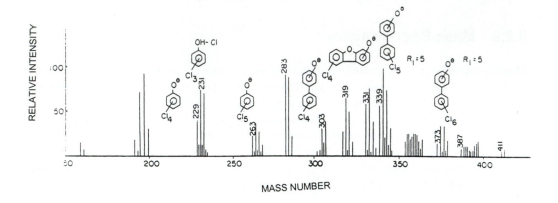

Figure 3-4.   Negative chemical ionization mass spectra of a Baltic Sea seal extract.

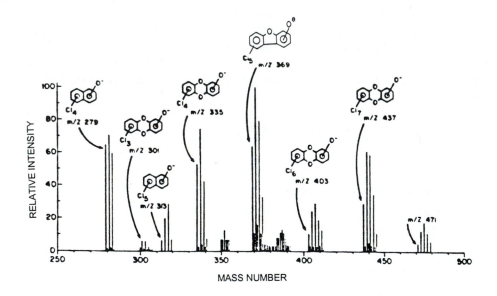

Figure 3-5.   Negative chemical ionization mass spectra of an extract from Tittabawas-see River bass caught near Dow Dam.

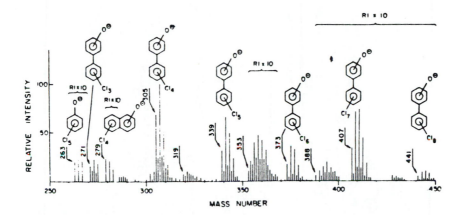

Figure 3-6.   Negative chemical ionization mass spectra of a turtle caught in the
Hudson River, NY.

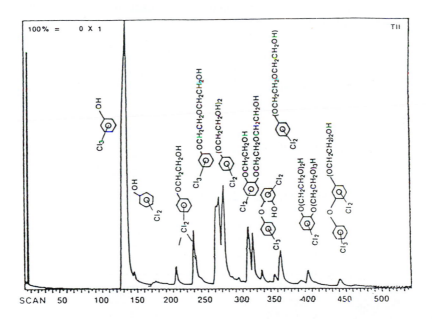

Figure 3-7.   Reconstructed gas chromatogram for base-soluble fraction after extraction with 15% MeCl₂/PhH.

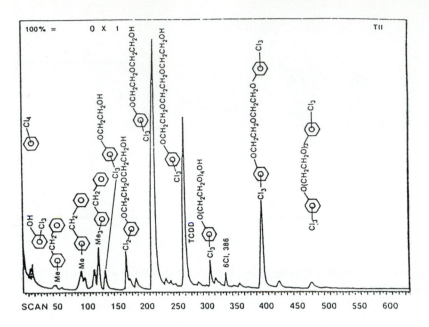

Figure 3-8.   Reconstructed gas chromatogram for fraction of waste extracted into 15% methylene chloride/benzene.

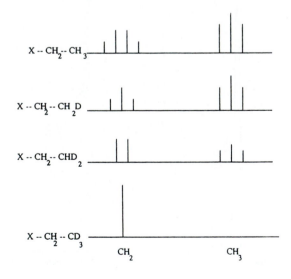

Figure 3-9.   Schematic NMR spectra of deuterated ethyl derivatives. The righthand set of lines is always a triplet when observable because of the two protons of the X-CH$_2$- group.

3.2.5   Infrared Spectrophotometry

Nearly all organic chemical compounds show a marked selective absorption in the infrared region. Infrared radiation is of low energy and its absorption by molecules causes all sorts of subtle changes in the vibrational or rotational energy of the molecule. **Infrared (IR) spectra** can be used to identify particular atomic groupings present in an unknown molecule. Because of the complexity of infrared spectra, it is highly unlikely that any two different compounds will have identical spectra. This fact has made **infrared spectroscopy** a valuable aid in the identification of pesticides and other complex organic chemicals. **Fourier Transform Infrared (FTIR)** technique is used to convert time-domain spectra into frequency domain spectra with the aid of a computer to enhance the signal-to-noise ratio by performing signal averaging. Far IR can be used to determine the bonding of metal to carbon, whereas near IR can detect a large group oscillation.

3.2.6   Nuclear Magnetic Resonance

Nuclear Magnetic Resonance (NMR) is used to detect and distinguish between the nuclear particles present in a sample. It measures the changes in the nuclei of materials when placed in a fixed magnetic field and then subjected to an alternating magnetic field. A nucleus can be considered a spinning charged particle that has an associated magnetic moment. In the presence of a magnetic field, the magnetic moments can align themselves either with or against the field. The higher energy state, against the field, is somewhat less populated than the lower energy state, with the field, and the nuclei can be promoted from the lower to the higher state by the application of radio frequency energy. It is the absorption of this energy that we observed in the NMR experiment. Table 3-1 lists properties of common nuclei.

Many common nuclei have no magnetic moments and thus will not exhibit any magnetic resonance absorption. These include ^{12}C, ^{16}O, and ^{32}S because they have a nuclear spin of zero. But the spins of their isotopes are not zero and can be detected by NMR. Figure 3-9 shows typical NMR spectra. Similar to NMR, the electron spin resonance (ESR) in the microwave frequency range is used to detect free radicals or certain transition metals.

Finally, it should be noted that for analysis of complex mixtures, usually more than one method is involved. A good example of the use of multiple instruments in identification of a complex hydrocarbon mixture in soil is illustrated by Figure 3-10. By a number of analytical approaches from puzzle-fitting, a final picture of the structure can be realized as shown in Figure 3-11.

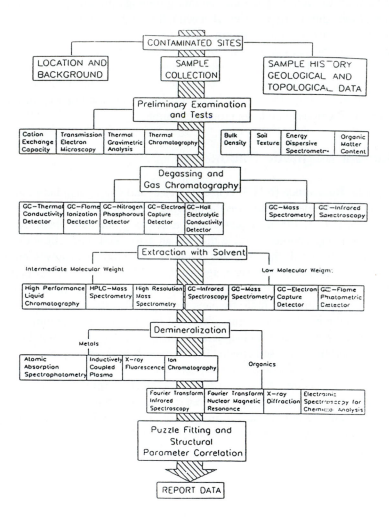

Figure 3-10.   Analytical scheme for complex hydrocarbons mixtures in soil (Yen, 1988).

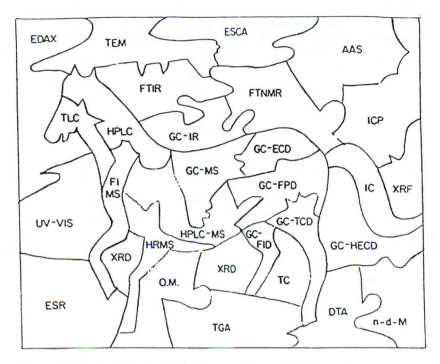

Figure 3-11.   Analytical methods for complex molecule puzzle.

3.3 SEPARATION SCIENCES

Separation is a common practice in environmental engineering; for example, during the absorption of pollutants from air streams and the filtration of particulates from water streams. A simplified schematic diagram is given in Figure 3-12.

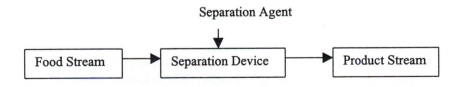

Figure 3-12. Schematics of a separation device.

Table 3-1.   Properties of Nuclei

Particle	Natural Abundance %	Relative Sensitivity for Equal Number of Nuclei (Constant Field)	Magnetic Moment (Nuclear Magnetons)*	Spin (Units of h 2τ)
electron			1840	$\frac{1}{2}$
^{1}H	99.98	1.000	2.793	$\frac{1}{2}$
^{2}H	0.016	9.6×10^{-3}	0.857	1
^{12}C	99	0	0	0
^{13}C	1.11	1.59×10^{-2}	0.702	$\frac{1}{2}$
^{14}N	99.6	1.01×10^{-3}	0.404	1
^{16}O	99.996	0	0	0
^{17}O	3.7×10^{-2}	2.91×10^{-2}	-1.893	$\frac{5}{2}$
^{19}F	100	0.834	2.627	$\frac{1}{2}$
^{32}S	99.3	0	0	0
^{31}P	100	6.6×10^{-2}	1.130	$\frac{1}{2}$
^{35}Cl	75.4	4.7×10^{-3}	0.821	$\frac{3}{2}$
^{37}Cl	24.6	2.7×10^{-3}	0.683	$\frac{3}{2}$

*Nuclear Magneton — 5.049×10^{-22} erg/gauss

A parameter, the **separation factor**, α, is often used in the field of separation. It is defined as

$$\alpha_{ij} = \frac{\dfrac{x_{i1}}{x_{j1}}}{\dfrac{x_{i2}}{x_{j2}}}$$

[3-24]

where 1 and 2 denote the phases or products, while i and j denote the components. Therefore, X_{i1} represents the mole fraction of component i in phase 1 or product 1. If the separation factor $\alpha_{ij} = 1$, no separation will occur. If it is greater than unity, component i tends to be concentrated in product 1. On the other hand, if the separation factor is less than unity, component j tends to be concentrated in product 1.

Table 3-2.   Processes Unit Operations and Principles

Type	Unit Operation	Principle
Equilibrium process	Distillation	Volatility
	Adsorption	Solubility
	Extraction	Solubility
	Crystallization	Crystal structure
	Gel filtration	Molecular size
Rate process	Gas diffusion	Diffusion rate
	Thermal diffusion	Diffusion rate
	Dialysis	Membrane transport
	Electrophoresis	Mobility
Mechanical process	Filtration	Size
	Settling	Density
	Centrifugation	Density
	Electrostatic	Charges
	Precipitation	Charges

For separation processes, as shown in Table 3-2, based upon the equilibration of immiscible phases, it is helpful to define the quantity

$$K_i = \left(\frac{X_{i1}}{X_{i2}} \right) \text{ at equilibrium}$$

K_i is called the equilibrium ratio for component i. The separation factor can then be written as

$$\alpha_{ij} = \frac{K_i}{K_j} \qquad\qquad [3\text{-}25]$$

For a vapor-liquid system, if the components of the mixture obey Raoult's and Dalton's Laws,

$$P_i = Py_i = P_i^o x_i \qquad\qquad [3\text{-}26]$$

In such a case

$$K_i = \frac{y_i}{x_i} = \frac{P_i^0}{P}$$

$$K_j = \frac{y_j}{x_j} \quad ,(1 = y, 2 = x) \tag{3-27}$$

So

$$\alpha_{ij} = \frac{K_i}{K_j} = \frac{P_i^0}{P_j^0} \tag{3-28}$$

The **separation factor** in a gaseous diffusion process is based on different rates of molecular gas-phase transport. The gas mixture to be separated is located on one side of a porous barrier, as shown in Figure 3-13. A pressure gradient is maintained across the barrier, with the pressure on the feed (left) side being much greater than that on the product (right) side. This pressure gradient causes a flux of molecules from the gaseous mixture to be separated across the barrier from left to right. If the barrier has sufficiently small pores and a sufficiently low gas pressure, the mean free path of the gas molecules will be large compared to the pore dimensions. As a result, the molecular flux will occur in what is called the **Knudsen flow**, as described by Equation [3-29].

$$N_i = \frac{a(P_1 y_{1i} - P_2 y_{2i})}{\sqrt{M_i T}} \tag{3-29}$$

where

N_i = flux of component i across the barrier

P_1 = pressure of the high-side

P_2 = pressure of the low-side

y_{1i} = mole fraction of component i on the high-pressure side

y_{2i} = mole fraction of component i on the low-pressure side

T = temperature

M_i = the molecular weight of component i

a = geometric factor depending only upon the structure of the barrier

In continuum of particles diffusion, a dimensionless parameter known as Knusen number is defined as

$$Kn = \frac{2\lambda}{d}$$
[3-30a]

here λ is the mean free path of the particles in a medium and d is the aerosol particle diameter. If Kn << 1, a continum exists; if Kn >> 1, continuum does not exist. The mean free path is usually measured as

$$\lambda = \frac{\mu}{0.449P\left(\frac{8M_a}{\pi RT}\right)^{\frac{1}{2}}} \quad (\text{in } \mu\text{m})$$
[3-30b]

where

μ = viscosity of the medium (Pa-s)

P = pressure (Pa)

M_a = molar mass of medium (kg/mol)

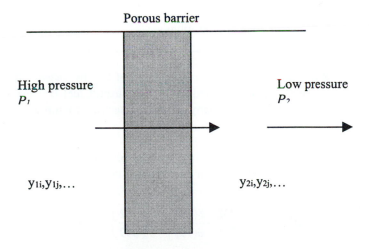

Figure 3-13. Simplified gaseous diffusion process.

We shall now presume that the composition of the high-pressure side does not change appreciably through depletion of one of the gas species. The material on the low-pressure side has all arrived through the steady-state transport process so that

$$N_i = \frac{P_1 y_{1i}}{\sqrt{M_i T}}$$

$$N_j = \frac{P_1 y_{1i}}{\sqrt{M_j T}} \qquad\qquad [3\text{-}30c]$$

$$\frac{N_i}{N_j} = \frac{y_{1i} M_j^{\frac{1}{2}}}{y_{1j} M_i^{\frac{1}{2}}} = \frac{y_{2i}}{y_{2j}}$$

We shall also presume for simplicity that $P_2 \ll P_1$. Combining Equations [3-24] and [3.30], we have

$$\alpha_{ij} = \frac{y_{2i} y_{1j}}{y_{2j} y_{1i}} = \frac{M_j^{\frac{1}{2}}}{M_i^{\frac{1}{2}}} \qquad\qquad [3\text{-}31]$$

which is not dependent upon composition.

[Example 3-2]   Raw uranium is used for enrichment of U^{235} by gaseous diffusion process for an useful nuclear fuel. If the required U^{235} for the useful fuel is 2.1% and the natural abundance of U^{235} in ore is 0.7%, how many diffusion stages are required?

Raw uranium ore is converted first into the gaseous UF_6. Because the $U^{235}F_6$ is being separated from $U^{238}F_6$, the separation factor can be computed by Equation [3-31].

$$\acute{a}_{235-238} = \left[\frac{238 + 6(19)}{235 + 6(19)} \right]^{\frac{1}{2}} = \left(\frac{352}{349} \right)^{\frac{1}{2}} = 1.0043$$

The improvement from 0.7% to 2.1% is three fold and this improvement can be evaluated by

$$\alpha^t = \text{times of improvement}$$

and n is number of stages. Therefore

$$(1.0043)^n = \frac{2.1}{0.7} = 3$$

Hence, $n = 263$, which requires 263 successive diffusion stages to perform this enrichment.

3.4 CHEMICAL MEASUREMENTS

Two of the essential principles that govern measurements are: the statistical methods for treating the measured numbers, and confidence and acceptability of measured system.

3.4.1   Precision, Errors, Data Reduction

Precision is a measure of agreement among individual measurements of the same property, under prescribed similar conditions. **Accuracy** is a measure of the closeness of an individual measurement or the average of a number of measurements to the true value. Another term used is **bias**, which is a systematic error inherent in a method or caused by some artifact or idiosyncrasy of the measurement. Temperature effects are the examples of the first kind. Blanks, mechanical losses, and calibration errors are examples of the latter. There are various ways to analyze or reduce the data generated from measurements. The common method is through the use of frequency distribution curves, as shown in Figure 3-14.

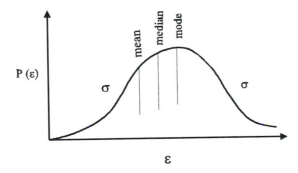

Figure 3-14.   Error function.

An error function can be expressed in a probability function, P (ε), as shown here:

$$\int_{-\infty}^{\infty} P(\varepsilon)d\varepsilon = 1 \qquad\qquad\qquad [3\text{-}32]$$

where ε is the measured error and

$$P(\varepsilon) = \frac{1}{\sqrt{2\pi}\sigma} \exp\left(\frac{-\varepsilon^2}{2\sigma^2}\right) \qquad\qquad\qquad [3\text{-}33]$$

where σ is standard deviation

$$\sigma = \left(\frac{1}{n}\sum_{i=1}^{n}\varepsilon_i^2\right)^{\frac{1}{2}} \qquad\qquad\qquad [3\text{-}34]$$

for a group of measurements of

$$x_i\,(i = 1, 2 \dots n)$$

and a frequency, f, as the frequency of the x_i value, is identical with the n population.

Statistics commonly use measures of (a) central tendency, giving the location of typical value, (b) describing the shape of distribution which deals with symmetry and peak, and (c) of dispersion, showing the degree to which values vary and scatter.

For the central tendency, the following are important:

mode — most common measurement.

median — 50% of accumulated frequency or P_{50}, the 50th percentile.

arithmetic mean — $\overline{X} = \dfrac{\sum f_i X_i}{n}$, if frequency is not used, $\overline{X} = \dfrac{\sum X_i}{n}$.

geometric mean — $m_g = \left(\prod X_i^{f_i}\right)^{\frac{1}{n}}$, or frequency can be omitted.

For the shape category, the **moment** of the curve is determined by the formula; for example, the j is the moment

$$m_j = \frac{\sum(x_i - \overline{x})^j}{n} \qquad\qquad\qquad [3\text{-}35]$$

the **skewness** is defined as

$$sk = m_3 / m_2^{3/2} \qquad\qquad\qquad [3\text{-}36]$$

and the **kurtosis** is

$$g_2 = (m_4 / m_2^2) - 3 \qquad\qquad\qquad [3\text{-}37]$$

For dispersion measures, the **variance** is defined as

$$s^2 = \frac{1}{(n-1)} \Sigma (x_i - \bar{x})^2 f_i \qquad\qquad\qquad [3\text{-}38]$$

the standard deviation is

$$\sigma = \left(\frac{1}{n-1} \Sigma (x_i - \bar{x})^2 f_i \right)^{1/2} \qquad\qquad\qquad [3\text{-}39]$$

the average deviation is

$$d = \frac{1}{n} \Sigma f_i |x_i - \bar{x}| \qquad\qquad\qquad [3\text{-}40]$$

and the **range** is

$$n = x_n - x_1 \qquad\qquad\qquad [3\text{-}41]$$

A number of correlations using standard tables to compare two data sets or designs are also available; for example, the t-tests. The standard error of the mean is defined as

$$SE_m = S / n^{1/2} \qquad\qquad\qquad [3\text{-}42]$$

The **confidence limit** for a mean is

$$CL = \bar{x} \pm 1.96\ SE_m \qquad\qquad\qquad [3\text{-}43]$$

The **confidence interval** for a mean can be located from a statistics table of the t

$$CI = \bar{x} \pm t\ SE_m \qquad\qquad\qquad [3\text{-}44]$$

where t is value from the table at a given level of confidence.

If only $n = 1$ observation was available, this observation would be the sample mean and would give us some idea of the underlying population mean. Since there is no spread in the sample, however, we would have absolutely no idea about the population spread.

Only the extent that n exceeds one can we get information about the spread. That is, there are essentially only $(n - 1)$ pieces of information for the spread, and this is the appropriate divisor for the variance.

For variance, there are $(n - 1)$ d.f. (degree of freedom). The statistics for chemical analysis are summarized below:

	Population	Sample
Sample number	N (large)	n (small)
Mean	$\bar{\mu} = \sum (\dfrac{X_i}{N})$	$\bar{X} = \sum (\dfrac{X_i}{n})$
Variance	$\sigma^2 = \sum \left[\dfrac{\left(X_i - \bar{\mu}\right)^2}{(N-1)} \right]$	$S^2 = \sum \left[\dfrac{\left(X_i - \bar{X}\right)^2}{(n-1)} \right]$
Standard deviation (S.E.)	σ	S
Degrees of freedom (d.f.)	$N - 1$	$n - 1$
Confidence level 95%	$\mu = \bar{\mu} \pm 1.96 \left(\dfrac{\sigma}{N^{\frac{1}{2}}} \right)$	$\mu = \bar{X} \pm t_{0.025} \left(\dfrac{S}{n^{\frac{1}{2}}} \right)$

3.4.2   Quality Assurance and Quality Control

Quality Assurance (QA) may be defined as those operations and procedures that are undertaken to provide measurement data of a stated quality with a stated probability of being right. The quality of data should be (1) scientifically valid, (2) legally defendable, and (3) of a known and accepted precision as well as accuracy. In general, the goal is the use of data from a stable measurement system (statistical) to provide probable confidence of achievement (assurance) of a desired level of acceptability (quality).

The basic ingredients of a good measurement program are appropriate methodology, adequate calibration, and proper usage. Therefore, proper documentation of all operations and proper maintenance of facilities and equipment are important aspects of **quality control (QC)**. The relation of QC with QA is illustrated in Figure 3-15.

The quality of analytical measurements may be evaluated in terms of the precision and accuracy attained when compared with the requirements for the data. **Precision** is evaluated by repetitive measuring. Evaluation with respect to measurement bias and, hence, assess ment of accuracy, is a more difficult process. **Accuracy** is infallible, always keeping an absolute standard. Measuring the same samples by several independent methods can identify measurement bias. Analyzing spikes, surrogates, or other internal standards can provide information on measurement bias. External evidence of measurement accuracy is usually desirable and is the easiest approach. Collaborative test exercises and proficiency tests using externally provided test samples are good ways to assess data quality and judge peer performance.

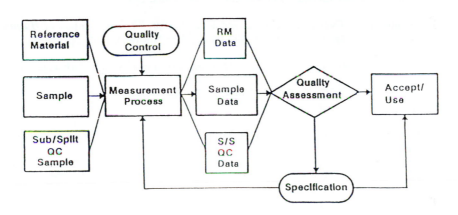

Figure 3-15.   Measurement process quality assurance.

REFERENCES

3-1   C. N. Sawyer and P. L. McCarthy, *Chemistry for Environmental Engineering*, 3rd ed., McGraw-Hill, New York, 1978.

3-2   V. L. Snoeyink and D. Jenkins, *Water Chemistry*, Wiley, New York, 1980.

3-3   C. J. King, *Separation Processes*, McGraw-Hill, New York, 1971.

3-4   J. W. Cooper, *Spectroscopic Techniques for Organic Chemists*, Wiley, New York, 1980.

3-5   J. K. Taylor and T. W. Stanley, *Quality Assurance for Environmental Measurements*, American Society for Testing and Materials, Philadelphia, Pennsylvania, 1985.

3-6   J. S. Devinny, L. G. Everett, J. C. S. Lu and R. L. Stollar, *The Composition of Hazardous Wastes in Subsurface Migration of Hazardous Wastes*, Van Nostrand, 1990, pp. 15–39.

3-7   J. K. Taylor, *Quality Assurance of Chemical Measurements*, Lewis, Chelsea, Michigan, 1989.

3-8   L. L. Havilcek and R. D. Crain, *Practical Statistics for the Physical Sciences*, American Chemical Society, Washington DC.

3-9   H. L. Finston and A. C. Rychtman, *A New View of Current Acid-Base Theories*, Wiley, New York, 1982.

3-10 T. F. Yen, *Electron Spin Resonance of Metal Complexes*, Plenum, New York, 1969.

3-11 L. H. Keith, *Advances in the Identification and Analysis of Organic Pollutants in Water*, Vol. 1 and 2, Ann Arbor Science, Ann Arbor, Michigan, 1981.

3-12 L. H. Keith, *Identification and Analysis of Organic Pollutants in Water*, Ann Arbor Science, Ann Arbor, Michigan, 1976.

PROBLEM SET

1. A number of replicate measurements of moisture content have been made of a lignite sample.

    15.2, 14.7, 15.1, 15.0, 15.3, 15.2, 14.9.

    (a) Calculate the mean, standard deviation, and degree of freedom.

    (b) Calculate the confidence interval based on standard deviation ($S = 0.11$) estimated from a data set ($x = 10.05$) of the seven measurements for a 95% level of confidence.

2. Obtain Pearson's product moment correlation coefficient for the two calorimetric methods for determination of Fe^{2+}.

Sample	Method 1	Method 2
1	12	13
2	10	12
3	4	5
4	4	6
5	5	6
6	10	13
7	7	9
8	4	6
9	8	8
10	11	11

Note:

$$r_{xy} = \frac{n\Sigma XY - (\Sigma X)(\Sigma Y)}{\left[n\Sigma x^2 - (\Sigma x)^2\right]^{\frac{1}{2}} \left[n\Sigma Y^2 - (\Sigma Y)^2\right]^{\frac{1}{2}}}$$

De longe te hei de amar
— da tranqüila distância
em que o amor é saudade
e o desejo, constância.

Do divino lugar
onde o bem da existência
é ser eternidade
e parecer ausência.

Quem precisa explicar
o momento e a fragrância
da Rosa, que persuade
sem nenhuma arrogância?

E, no fundo do mar
e Estrela, sem violência
cumpre a sua verdade
alheria à transparência.

— Cecília Meireles

This Portugese verse is from the Brazilian poet Cecília Meireles (1901-1964) in her book *Cançóes,* or *Songs.* The theme of this short poem, centered on the second stanza, is that permanent or eternal value is lacking. The essential point is in the next two stanzas:

Who needs to explain
the moment and the fragrance
of the Rose, which persuades
without any arrogance?

And at the bottom of the sea
the Star, without violence
fulfills its truth
oblivious of transparency.

Here, she evokes two lyrical objects, the Rose and the Star. The old cliché of the Rose as a symbol of beauty's transitoriness is transformed into the moment and fragrance of the Rose, while the Star fulfills itself through the action of something older than itself—the reflection of light upon water.

COLLOID AND SURFACE CHEMISTRY

*T*he concepts of colloid and surface chemistry in environmental science and engineering are enormously important. The five major spheres — atmosphere, hydrosphere, pedosphere, biosphere, and lithosphere — are each directly impacted by colloid and surface chemistry. A few obvious examples of this are the aerosol in air, the sedimentation process in water, the transport of nutrients across membranes, the erosion of soil, and many resource recovery processes.

We will leave the discussion about particles and the associated Newton and Stoke's laws for a later chapter. We will also discuss general coagulation and charge destabilization in another section, and we will examine sedimentation and flotation in later chapters.

This chapter will introduce some basic principles and definitions in colloid systems and especially in emulsions. Due to the increasing use of surfactants, we will group them with membrane-mimetic chemistry. Finally, we will address the electric double layer with repulsive and attractive potential energy for particle-particle interaction.

4.1 COLLOIDAL SYSTEM

In Chapter 1, we briefly reviewed the three bulk phases: gas (g), liquid (l), and solid (s). Surface chemistry is a study of the chemical processes that occur at the interfaces between these phases. An interface is the boundary between two phases encompassing the complete zone where their properties, whether electric charge or chemical composition, differ from those exhibited in either of the bulk phases. A total of five such interfaces exist, that is, g-l, g-s, l-l, l-s, and s-s. Notice that it is difficult to form a g-g interface.

Usually there are three types of colloidal systems:

- **Macromolecules** — such as humic materials or proteins existing in a solution form.

- **Colloidal dispersion** — discrete particles (disperse phase) suspended in a dispersing medium to form a two-component dispersion. In general, there are the following eight categories of disperse phase–dispersing medium systems:

  - l-g, liquid aerosol, fogs
  - s-g, solid aerosol, smokes
  - g-l, foam
  - l-l, emulsion
  - s-l, sol, hydrosol (l = water)
  - g-s, solid foam
  - l-s, gel, solid emulsion
  - s-s, solid suspension, solid sol

- **Associate colloids** — formed when the concentration of a surface-active agent, either called a surfactant or an amphophile, exceeds a critical value and aggregation occurs.

There are many other classifications of colloids. For example, **hydrophilic colloids** have an affinity toward water and tend to form stable suspensions in water. Naturally occurring proteins or synthetic polymers bearing functional groups such as O^-, $-OH_2^+$, and $-NH_3^+$, will form large ionic molecules. Conversely, **hydrophobic colloids** do not form stable suspensions in water. They are all electrically charged, either positive or negative (electrokinetic property). The processing charge may result from charged groups within the protected surface, or it may be gained by the adsorption of a layer of ions from the surrounding medium. A more general definition would be **lyophilic** and **lyophobic** colloids. The use of the prefix "lyo" instead of "hydro" includes other solvents and is not limited to water. In this manner, the colloids are termed protective colloids. Also, stability may give another classification to the unstable colloids that aggregate slowly, such as **diuturnal colloids**. The systems that aggregate rapidly are termed **cadicious colloids**.

4.2 COLLOIDAL RANGE AND ADSORPTION

The size of a colloidal particle is within the 1 nm–1 μm range. This is an arbitrary range that is located approximately between the dissolved solid in solution and the bacteria observed by light microscopy. Figure 4-1 shows airborne particles, and Figure 4-2 shows waterborne particles. An important feature of colloidal particles is the large surface area to volume ratio. Thus, the surface chemistry at the interface region controls the properties of the particle. The examples that follow indicate the extensive surface area of the small particles.

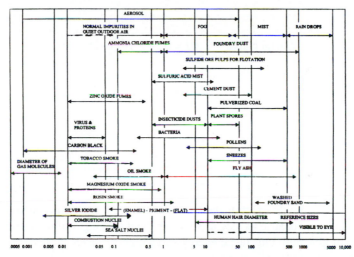

Figure 4-1. Sizes of airborne particles and contaminates (Redrawn, from Sources: J.A. Danielson, *Air Pollution Engineering Manual*, Environmental Protection Agency Research, Triangle Park, NC, 1973; Original prepared by Mines Safety Appliance Co., Pittsburgh, PA).

[Example 4-1] What is the surface area of 1 cm^3 of a colloid that consists of packing each side with (a) cubic particles of 10 nm size, and (b) a thread of 10 nm in radius.

(a) Because 10 nm = 10^{-6} cm, the cubic particles needed for packing are

$$\frac{1}{\left(10^{-6}\right)^{3}} = 10^{18}$$

There are six sides; thus, the total area is

$$6 \times \left(10^{-6}\right)^{2} \times 10^{18} \ \frac{1}{\left(30.48\right)^{2}} = 6500 \ \text{ft}^{2}$$

(b)   The total length of the thread is

$$l = \frac{1}{\pi \, r^{2}} = \frac{1}{\pi \left(10^{-6}\right)^{2}} = 0.34 \times 10^{12} \ \text{cm}$$

$$\text{Surface area} = 2 \ \pi r l = 0.34 \times 10^{12} \times 2\pi \times 10^{-6}$$

$$= 2 \times 10^{6} \ \text{cm}^{2} = 2167 \ \text{ft}^{2}$$

$$\approx 0.5 \ \text{acre}$$

   The colloidal particle exhibits the characteristic light-scattering phenomena of the so-called **Tyndall effect** because its size approaches the wavelength of the light. The extensive surface area will give high interfacial energy and a high surface/charge density ratio, both of which are the requirements of a catalyst.

   When a surface is created, there is work associated with the event. For a condensed phase, molecules in the interior will experience a spherical symmetry, attracting all adjacent molecules. Molecules at the interface will experience a net inward attraction around the surface. This force is usually called the **interfacial tension**, σ, but for air-liquid interfaces it is usually referred to as **surface tension**, γ. This attraction increases the intermolecular distances for the intermolecules. This process will eventually expand the surface area from the interior, A_{s}. The work will be

$$dw = \sigma \ dA_{s} \hspace{4cm} \text{[4-1]}$$

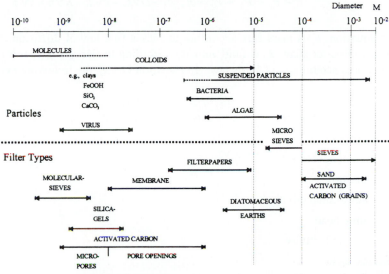

SIZE SPECTRUM OF WATERBORNE PARTICLES AND OF FILTER PORES

Figure 4-2.   Suspended Particles in natural and wastewaters vary in diameter from 0.005 to about 100 μm (5×10^{-9} to 10^{-4} m). For particles smaller than 10 μm, terminal gravitational settling will be less than about 10^{-2} cm sec^{-1}. Filter pores of sand filters, on the other hand, are typically larger than 500 μm. The smaller particles (colloids) can become separated either by settling if they aggregate or by filtration if they attach to filter grains. [Redrawn from W. Stumm, Environ. Sci. Technol., 11, 1066 (1977).]

The thermodynamic work done on a system for all possible forms of forces can be generalized as

$$dw = -PdV - \phi de + mgdh + \mu dn + \sigma \, dA_s \qquad\qquad [4\text{-}2]$$

where

ϕ = potential

e = charge

mg = force

h = head

and the expression ϕde in the electrochemical cell is $zFE \, dn$, where z is the charge per ion, F is Faraday (charge per mole), and dn is the variation in the ion mole number.

Equation [4-2] is similar to various fluxes experienced in Equation [4-2a]. Likewise, the various fluxes for a given material in water may be written as

$$F = F_1 + F_2 + F_3 + F_4 = -D\nabla C - \kappa \nabla T - K\nabla h + k\nabla \phi \qquad [4\text{-}2a]$$

In this equation, F_1 is mass flux according to Fick's first law of diffusion, F_2 is heat flux according to Fourier's law, F_3 is fluid velocity according to Darcy's law, and F_4 is electric current per area according to Ohm's law. In Equation [4-2a], the following symbols are used.

D = diffusion coefficient

C = concentration

κ = thermal conductivity

T = temperature

K = hydraulic conductivity

h = hydraulic head

k = electric conductivity

ϕ = electric field

and the ∇ gradient function is the partial derivatives over spatial and temporal coordinates; for example, $\partial/\partial x$, etc. Details of the laws are beyond the scope of this chapter, but those laws have appeared later in the book and are useful in environmental chemistry.

Going back to the discussion of thermodynamics, the Gibb's free energy may be expanded to involve the surface deformation.

$$dG = VdP - SdT + \Sigma \mu_i \, d \, n_i + \sigma \, dA_s \qquad [4\text{-}3]$$

At constant T, P, and n_i, then

$$dG = \sigma \, dA_s \qquad [4\text{-}4]$$

The surface tension of water at 20°C is 72.75 mNm^{-1}; for seawater (salinity = 35%) it is 73.53 mNm^{-1}; and for soil water it is only 45 mNm^{-1}. (Other amounts of surface tension include 1 erg/cm^2 = 10^{-3} J/m^2 = 10^{-3} N/m = mN/m; thus mNm^{-1} and erg cm^{-2} are interchangeable. Also because 1N = 10^5 dyne and 1mN = 10^2 dyne/m=dyne/cm, the units mNm^{-1} and dyne cm^{-1} are also interchangeable.) In general, electrolytes will increase, and surfactants (such as humic acid) will decrease the surface tension of a liquid.

The term **surface concentration,** or **surface excess,** Γ_i, is defined as the distribution of component i in the interface between the two adjacent phases α and β. If the total number of i moles is n_i, then the distribution is

$$n_i = n_{i,s} + n_{i,\alpha} + n_{i,\beta} \qquad [4\text{-}5]$$

In Equation [4-5], the first term is the concentration at the interface, whereas the second and third terms are the concentrations at phase α and phase β respectively. If concentration C and volume V are specified, then

$$n_{i,s} = n_i - C_{i,\alpha} V_\alpha - C_{i,\beta} V_\beta \qquad [4\text{-}6]$$

Moles at the interfaces can be taken as follows, assuming the interface is a plane:

$$\Gamma_i A_s = \eta_i - C_{i,\alpha} V_\alpha - C_{i,\beta} V_\beta \qquad [4\text{-}7]$$

Thus

$$\Gamma_i = \frac{n_{i,s}}{A_s} \qquad [4\text{-}8]$$

The above equation indicates that when $\Gamma_i > 0$, component i will accumulate at the surface, and adsorption is positive. Conversely, negative adsorption occurs when $\Gamma_i < 0$, and the solute will be excluded from the interface as in the case of salt in water. Either case will alter the surface tension, and, as exemplified by hydrocarbons in water, in the former case the attractive force between the solvent molecules will be greater than that between the solute and solvent molecules. At constant P and T, the surface concentration may be expressed as

$$\Gamma_i = \left(-\frac{d\gamma}{d\mu_i} \right)_{T,P} \qquad [4\text{-}9]$$

[Example 4-2]   Derive Equation [4-9].

From thermodynamics in Chapter 1, the internal energy is

$$E = TS - PV + \gamma A + \Sigma_i n_i \qquad [4\text{-}10]$$

Equation [4-10] can be written as

$$dE = TdS + SdT - PdV - VdP + \gamma dA + Ad\gamma + \Sigma \mu_i d n_i + \Sigma n_i d \mu_i \qquad [4\text{-}11]$$

Also from the first and second laws of thermodynamics

$$dE = TdS - PdV + \Sigma \mu_i \, d \, n_i \qquad\qquad\qquad [4\text{-}12]$$

Subtracting Equation [4-11] from Equation [4-12],

$$SdT - VdP + Ad\gamma + \Sigma n_i d \, \mu_i = 0 \qquad\qquad [4\text{-}13]$$

Using T and P as constant,

$$d\gamma = -\frac{\Sigma n_i}{A} d \, \mu_i = -\Gamma_i d \, \mu_i \qquad\qquad [4\text{-}14]$$

or,

$$\Gamma_i = -\frac{d\gamma}{d \, \mu_i} \qquad\qquad\qquad [4\text{-}9]$$

This chemical potential as Equation [4-9] may be expressed in terms of activity or called the **Gibb's adsorption isotherm**, because $\mu_i = \mu_i + RT \ln a_i$

$$\Gamma_i = -\frac{1}{RT}\left(\frac{d\gamma}{d \ln a_i}\right) \qquad\qquad [4\text{-}15]$$

or

$$\Gamma_i = -\frac{a_i}{RT}\frac{d \gamma}{d \, a_i} \qquad\qquad\qquad [4\text{-}16]$$

This equation correlates adsorption, surface tension and concentration because concentration is proportional to activity.

For a two-component system, the preceding equation is

$$-d\gamma = RT \, \Gamma_2 \, d \ln a_2 \qquad\qquad\qquad [4\text{-}17]$$

Assuming ideal behavior, then

$$-d\gamma = RT \, \Gamma_2 \, d \ln x_2 \qquad\qquad\qquad [4\text{-}18]$$

Usually at sufficiently low concentrations of surface-active solute, a surface tension isotherm is linear at constant temperature, such that

$$\pi = \sigma_0 - \sigma = m\,x_2 \qquad\qquad [4\text{-}19]$$

where m is the slope of the isotherm, π is the spreading pressure, and σ is the same as γ. However, at high concentrations the isotherm is no longer linear, and an empirical equation is developed, which is called the Szyskowski equation.

$$\pi = \sigma_0 - \sigma = RT\,\Gamma_m\,\ln\left(\frac{x_2}{a}+1\right) \qquad\qquad [4\text{-}20]$$

Now replacing σ with γ and differentiating Equation [4-20],

$$-\frac{d\gamma}{dx_2} = \frac{\Gamma_m\,RT}{x_2+a} \qquad\qquad [4\text{-}21]$$

where

Γ_m = moles of component 2 per unit area at saturated concentration

a = empirical constant

Also, we can write the Gibb's equation from Equation [4-18]

$$-\frac{d\gamma}{dx_2} = \frac{RT\,\Gamma_2}{x_2} \qquad\qquad [4\text{-}22]$$

Combining the two equations, we have

$$\Gamma_2 = \frac{\Gamma_m\,x_2}{a+x_2} \qquad\qquad [4\text{-}23]$$

which is identical to the Langmuir isotherm,

$$\theta = \frac{x_2}{a+x_2} \quad , \quad \Gamma_m = \Gamma \qquad\qquad [4\text{-}24]$$

This is a general adsorption equation where θ usually is normalized to Γ_2/Γ, Γ being total adsorption. When Γ_2/Γ is plotted versus x_2, an isotherm results.

$$\frac{x_2}{\Gamma_2} = \frac{a}{\Gamma} + \frac{x_2}{\Gamma}$$

[4-25]

Equation [4-25] represents a Langmuir isotherm, and when x_2/Γ is plotted versus x_2, linear lines are obtained.

[Example 4-3]   The surface tension of an aqueous solution of valeric acid can be expressed by $\gamma = \gamma^*_{(H20)} - a \ln (1 + bC_B)$, and a and b can be evaluated by experimental data as $a = 0.0131$ Nm^{-1}, $b = 0.01962$ m^3/mol. Calculate the surface concentration at $C_B = 200$m mol^{-3}. Then find the area of valeric acid adsorbed when the surface concentration is saturated.

$$\gamma = \gamma^*_{H_2O} - a \ln(1 + bC_B)$$

$$\left(\frac{\partial \gamma}{\partial C_B}\right)_{T,P} = -\frac{ab}{1 + bC_B}$$

(a)

From Equation [4-16] using concentration instead of activity,

$$\Gamma = -\frac{C_B}{RT}\left(\frac{\partial \gamma}{\partial C_B}\right)_{T,P} = \frac{abC_B}{RT(1 + bC_B)}$$

(b)

When $C_B = 200$ mol/m^3

$$\Gamma = \frac{(0.0131)(0.01962)(200)}{(8.314)(2922)(1 + 0.01962 \times 200)} \frac{\text{mol}}{\text{m}^2} = 4.30 \times 10^{-6} \frac{\text{mol}}{\text{m}^2}$$

From (b)

$$\Gamma = \frac{abC_B}{RT(1 + bC_B)}$$

When C_B is large, $bC_B \gg 1$ and $1 + bC_B \approx bC_B$

$$\Gamma_{max} = \frac{a}{RT}$$

(c)

Which is the saturated condition. Thus

$$\Gamma = \frac{0.0131}{(8.314)(292.2)} = 5.39 \times 10^{-6} \text{ mol/m}^2$$

and the area of valeric acid is

$$[(5.39 \times 10^{-6})(6.023 \times 10^{23})]^{-1} = 3.08 \times 10^{-19} \text{ m}^2$$

4.3 SURFACTANTS

Surfactants are surface-active agents; they are also referred to as detergents. They are organics or organometallics that form association colloids or micelles in solution. They are also called amphiphilic substances, or amphiphiles, which signifies that they possess distinct regions of hydrophobic and hydrophilic character. Due to their polarity, the surfactants are also described as amphipathic, heteropolar, or polar-nonpolar molecules. In general, there are four types:

- **Cationic surfactants** — typically the "onium" structures such as ammonium (N), sulfonium (S), and phosphonium (P). They can be represented by RnX^+Y^-, where the "onium" portion is X^+. An example is dodecyltrimethyl ammonium bromide $(CH_3)_3N^+ (CH_2)_9CH_3 Br^-$, a long chain quaternary compound.

- **Anionic surfactants** — typically the alkali or alkaline earth salts of mono- or polybasic carboxylic (fatty) acids of the $RX^- Y^+$ type. The X^- denotes the carboxylic, sulfonic, or phosphoric portion of the acid. An example illustrated will be sodium dodecylbenzene sulfonate, $CH_3 (CH_2)_9 \phi SO_3Na$, which again is a long-chain salt.

- **Nonionic surfactants** — most of these can be represented by the polyoxyethylene or the polyoxypropylene derivatives, or the polyalcohols, carbohydrate esters or fatty alkanol amides. An example is polyoxyethylated t-octylphenol, which is commercially available as Triton X-100 $t\text{-Oc-}\phi\text{-}(OCH_2\text{-}CH_2)_{10}\text{-OH}$. According to its name, this class of surfaces does not contain obvious ions or charges.

- **Ampholytic (zwitterionic) surfactants** — zwitterionic surfactants possess both cationic and anionic functional groups in the hydrophobic moiety. They can be either anionic, cationic, or neutral, depending on the pH of the solution. They generally come from N-alkyl or C-alkyl sultaines (sulfonic), betaines (carboxylic), or phosphatidyl amino alcohols and acids (phosphoric).

Table 4-1.   Surface-Active Agents

Anionic

   Sodium stearate

      $CH_3(CH_2)_{16}COO^-Na^+$

   Sodium oleate

      $CH_3(CH_2)_7CH=CH(CH_2)_7COO^-Na^+$

   Sodium dodecyl sulphate

      $CH_3(CH_2)_{11}SO_4^-Na^+$

   Sodium dodecyl benzene sulphonate

      $CH_3(CH_2)_{11}C_6H_4SO_3^-Na^+$

Cationic

   Dodecylamine hydrochloride

      $CH_3(CH_2)_{11}NH_3^+Cl^-$

   Hexadecyltrimethyl ammonium bromide

      $CH_3(CH_2)_{15}N(CH_3)_3^+Br^-$

Nonionic

   Polyethylene oxides

      $CH_3(CH_2)_7C_6H_4(OCH_2CH_2)_8OH$

   Spans (sorbitan esters)

   Tweens (polyoxyethylene sorbitan esters)

Ampholytic

   Dodecyl betaine

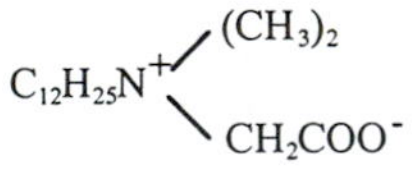

$$C_{12}H_{25}N^+ \begin{cases} (CH_3)_2 \\ CH_2COO^- \end{cases}$$

These chemical classifications are based on the charges that are carried by the surface-active portion of the molecules. Most of the surfactants are synthetic. The common types are listed in Table 4-1. Surfactants are also derived from naturally-occurring sources; these are called biosurfactants. The amphiphiles include lipids (e.g., carboxylic acid esters), complex lipids (e.g., simple lipids containing P^-, N^- bases, and/or sugars), and bile acids such as cholic and deoxycholic acid. The biosurfactants play an important role in vivo transport and membrane processes. Some examples of biosurfactants obtained from bacteria, which may be commercially viable, are listed in Figure 4-3. In general, the biosurfactants may be more valuable when compared with their synthetic counterparts. The biosurfactants have the following features:

- They are polymeric by nature, and more stable under heat and weathering.
- They are either heterodisperse or polydisperse, and never monodisperse. For the former, broad diffuse distribution in randomness will be confronted with a broad range of targets. The latter will contain a Poisson distribution around a mean and, again, will be used for a probability distribution of targets.
- They contain polar heads and long tails, portions of which often consist of peptide linkages in helical configurations for the accommodation of various conformations during transport.

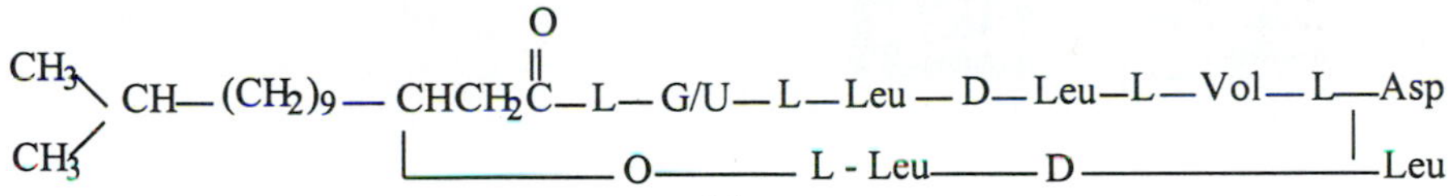

(a)

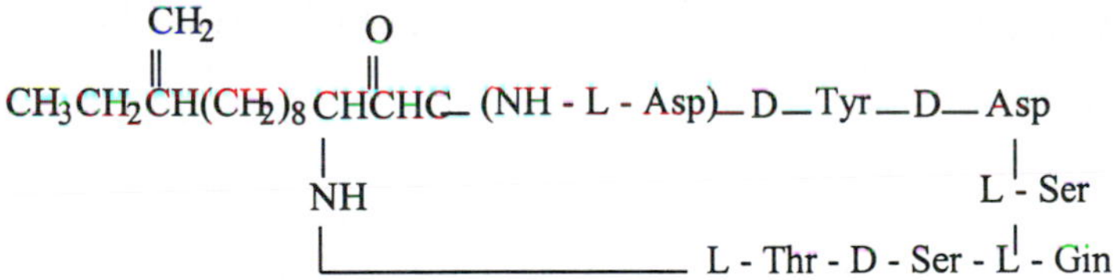

(b)

Figure 4-3. Two examples of biosurfactants. (a). the structure of surfactin or subtilysin, a lipopeptide isolated from *Bacillus subtilis*, (b). one of the surfactin analogs isolated from *Bacillus subtilis* containing a β-amino acid instead of a β–hydroxy fatty acid.

4.3.1 Emulsions

Next, we will discuss some phenomena related to the surfactants. An **emulsion** is defined as a mixture of particles of one liquid with some of a second liquid; and, because one of the liquids is often aqueous in nature, the two general types of emulsions are oil-in-water (O/W) and water-in-oil (W/O), the use of the word "oil" here denoting any water-insoluble fluid.

In these emulsions, the outer phase is continuous, whereas the inner phase is not. Illustrations of the two types of emulsions are in Figure 4-4. In general,

$$\frac{A}{B} = \frac{inner\ phase}{outer\ phase}$$

Now let

$$\frac{V_A}{V_B} = \phi \qquad\qquad\qquad [4\text{-}25a]$$

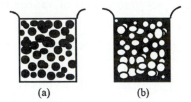

(a)   (b)

Figure 4-4. The two types of emulsion: (a) oil in water, O/W (b) water in oil, W/O.

In a dilute emulsion, the inner phase exists as spheres, and the Einstein limiting law is applicable,

$$\eta = \eta_0 (1 + 2.5\phi) \qquad\qquad\qquad [4\text{-}25b]$$

For a small ϕ value, the specific viscosity, η_{sp}, can be empirically related to ϕ by a power series

$$\eta_{sp} = \frac{\eta}{\eta_0} - 1 = a\phi + bd^2 + cd^3 + \ldots \qquad\qquad\qquad [4\text{-}25c]$$

where a, b, and c are empirical coefficients.

For a stable emulsion, a surfactant is required. In this case, the surfactant added is called an **emulsifier** (emulsifying agent). The purpose of the surfactant is to lower the interfacial tension. For example, the interfacial tension for an oil-water emulsion is 41 dyne/cm, but if a trace amount of sodium oleate is introduced, the interfacial tension is reduced to 7.2 dyne/cm. If NaCl is also introduced, the interfacial tension can reach 0.01 or even 0.002 dyne/cm. This is the principle for tertiary oil recovery in enhanced oil recovery or the abatement process for oil-spilled sands and soils. The aging processes of an emulsion can result in **flocculation** (inner phase clustering together) or **creaming** (inner phase undergoing gravity separation), and eventually will break the emulsion to yield two liquid layers as shown in Figure 4-5. Another process is called **inversion**, where A/B becomes B/A; for example, a W/O emulsion is stabilized by a monovalent ion soap, whereas an O/W emulsion is stabilized by a polyvalent ion soap — the latter agent being called an antagonistic agent. A de-emulsifier or breaking agent is usually a surfactant that is used to promote A/B emulsions and can be used to break B/A emulsions if the emulsifier is the B/A type.

An empirical method called the **hydrophile-lipophile balance** (HLB) has been set up to quantify the emulsion phenomena as previously discussed. For a given surfactant, an HLB number is assigned according to the structure. The HLB scale can correlate the surfactant solubility in water as well as its functional use as shown in Table 4-2. The HLB number of a dual surfactant mixture will be calculated according to the weight fraction of each surfactant. An empirical method has been used to compute the HLB number from the structural groups of the surfactant.

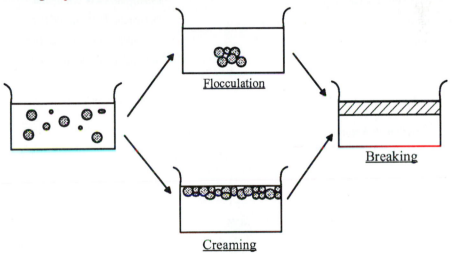

Figure 4-5. Types of emulsion instability.

$$HLB\ No. = 7 + n_h\ H + n_l\ L \qquad\qquad [4\text{-}26]$$

From the equation

n_h = number of hydrophilic groups

n_l = number of lipophilic groups

H = group contribution from hydrophilic

L = group contribution from lipophilic

The n_h, n_l, H, and L are listed in Table 4-3.

Table 4-2.   The HLB Scale

Surfactant Solubility Behavior in Water	HLB Number	Application
No dispersibility in water	0	
No dispersibility in water	2	W/O emulsifier
	4	W/O emulsifier
Poor dispersibility	6	
Milky dispersion; unstable	8	Wetting agent
Milky dispersion; stable	10	Wetting agent
Translucent to clear solution	12	Detergent, O/W emulsifier
Clear solution	14	Detergent, O/W emulsifier
Clear solution	16	Solubilizer, O/W emulsifier
Clear solution	18	Solubilizer, O/W emulsifier

Table 4-3.   Group HLB Numbers

Hydrophilic Groups	HLB	Lipophilic Groups	HLB
— SO_4Na	38.7	— CH —	−0.475
— COOK	21.1	— CH_2—	−0.475
— COONa	19.1	-CH_3-	−0.475
Sulfonate	about 11.0	— CH=	−0.475
— N (tetiary amine)	9.4	— (CH_2—CH_2—CH_2—O—)	−0.15
Ester (sorbitan ring)	6.8		
Ester (free)	2.4		
— COOH	2.1		
— OH (free)	1.9		
— O —	1.3		
— OH (sorbitan ring)	0.5		

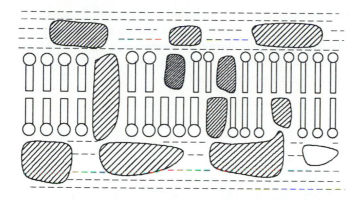

Figure 4-6. Schematic representation of a biological cell membrane. A bimolecular layer of phospholipid with hydrocarbon chains orientated to the interior and hydrophilic groups on the outside is penetrated by protein (shaded areas). Protein is also found adsorbed at the membrane surface.

4.3.2   Membrane-Mimetic Chemistry

Membrane-mimetic chemistry describes the chemistry processes in simple media that mimic aspects of biomembranes. Any arrangement of amphiphilic (or surfactant) molecules forming monolayers, bilayers, multilayers, micelles, reversed micelles, unilamellar vesicles, multilamellar vesicles, or polymerized vesicles can be related to biomembranes. The emerging scientific discipline concerned with the development and utilization of membrane-moderated (and inspired) processes in organized surfactant assemblies has a great amount of potential engineering applications, especially in the field of environmental engineering.

Most biological membranes consist of lipoprotein material. The classical model of lipid bimolecular layers has its foundation in hydrophobic bonding. The hydrophobic groups are always oriented toward the outside, as shown in Figure 4-6. The importance of membranes to the maintenance of life is essential due to the necessity for the regulation of transport across them. One important characteristic of lipids or fatty acids is that they can form clusters or islands on a surface. The polar ends will form a film extending towards a polar media, similar to the spreading of monomolecular films over the surface of water. For an environmental chemistry example, a monolayer of cetyl alcohol can enhance the rate of evaporation by as much as 40%. A sizable reduction in terms of water conservation can be made in this manner in fresh water lakes and reservoirs.

Solutions of highly surface-active materials, such as colloidal electrolytes, exhibit unusual physical properties. For example, abrupt changes in osmotic pressure, turbidity, electrical conductivity, surface tension, and so on, take place at well-defined concentrations. A typical colloidal electrolyte — sodium dodecyl sulfate — is shown in Figure 4-7. These changes interpret to the idea that aggregation of the colloidal electrolyte must happen at that point of abrupt change. This type of aggregation is called a **micelle** and the concentration of these abrupt changes is termed the **critical micelle concentration** (CMC). Micelles are narrowly dispersed in size and may contain 50 to 100 monomer units. They may be either spherical or lamellar in geometry as shown in Figure 4-8.

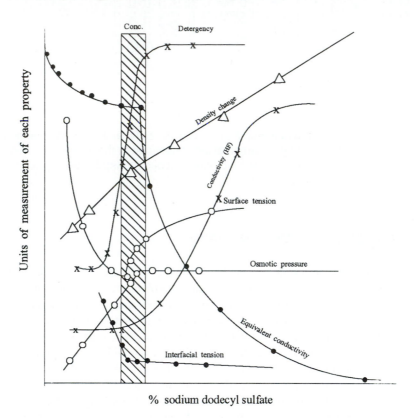

Figure 4-7.   Properties of surfactant near CMC.

Many micelles found in nonaqueous solvents are inverse (or reversed) in nature, in other words, the polar groups form the interior while the hydrophobic moieties are in contact with the nonpolar solvent. Asphaltene in oil behaves as a surfactant in a nonpolar medium and can be inverted by the use of ultrasound as shown in Figure 4-9. For a ternary system, normal micelles, inverse micelles, and liquid crystals may be formed, as shown in Figure 4-10. The vesicles can be single compartment or multicompartment lamellar; but most of them are liquid crystalline multilamellar vesicles that can be broken into unilamellar vesicles by ultrasound. The term vesicle describes spherical or ellipsoidal single- or multi-compartment closed bilayer structures. Vesicles can be composed of naturally-occurring or synthetic phospholipids, and may come from completely synthetic surfactants. Exploitation of vesicles for mimicking membrane functions has been prompted by the ease of their formation and stability.

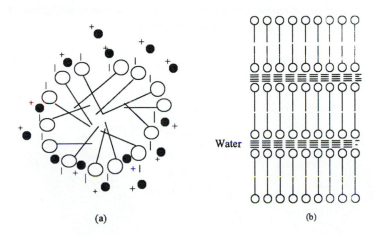

(a)   Water   (b)

Figure 4-8. Schematic representation of (a) a spherical micelle and (b) a lamellar micelle.

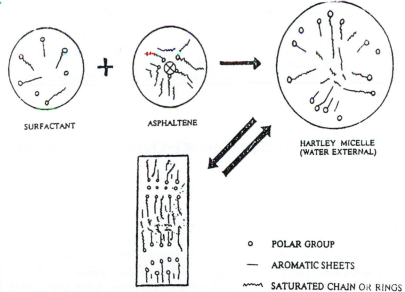

SURFACTANT   ASPHALTENE   HARTLEY MICELLE (WATER EXTERNAL)

o   POLAR GROUP

—   AROMATIC SHEETS

∿∿   SATURATED CHAIN OR RINGS

Figure 4-9. Interaction of surfactant with asphaltene to form Hartley micelle and the consequent formation of liquid crystals.

Membrane-mimetic chemistry has many applications in a variety of industries. With regards to environmental engineering, the following will serve as examples: the desulfurization of coal by multiphase biocatalysis, the maintenance of masking and demasking reactions during wastewater processing, the enzymatic treatment of industry wastewater via micelles, the decontamination of hydrocarbons from soil columns, the remediation of oil spills, the use of surfactant in enhanced bioremediaton, and so on.

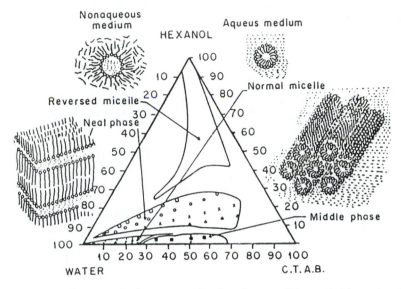

Figure 4-10.   Regions and structures for the phases of the water-hexadecyltrimethyl-ammonium bromide (CTAB)-hexanol system (Ahmad and Friberg, 1972).

4.4 DERJAGUIN-LANDAU-VERNEY-OVERBEEK (DLVO) THEORY

Derjaguin and Landau together with Verney and Overbeek have independently developed a quantitative theory in which the stability of lyophobic sols is treated in terms of energy changes that take place when particles approach one another. The theory involves the estimation of repulsive energy due to the overlap of electric double layers and the attractive energy of the London–van der Waals force in terms of the interparticle distance. **Colloid stability** is often interpreted in terms of the nature of the summation of total energy as a function of interparticle distance.   Theoretical calculations have been made in different geometrical arrangements, for example, between two parallel plates or between two charged spheres. We will attempt to introduce the forces of repulsion first followed by the forces of attraction. For the repulsive forces, a basic description is needed of the electric double layer and the associated electrokinetic phenomena. For the attractive forces, the concept of Hamaker constants should be understood. The combined summation of repulsive and attractive potential energies as a function of the distance between two interacting particles or surfaces can describe the colloid's stability. This type of diagram, often refered to as **potential energy curves** as illustrated by Figure 4-11 or Figure 4-12, can be used to predict the critical coagulation concentration. The various studies of potential energy curve types can yield useful applications, which are the essential component of the **DLVO theory**.

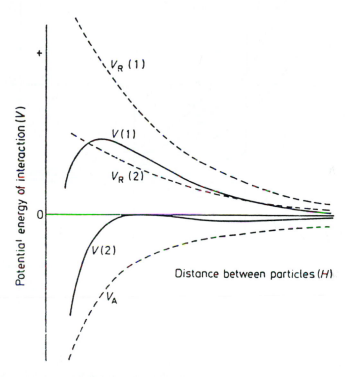

Figure 4-11. Total interaction energy curves, v(1) and V(2), obtained by the summation of an attraction curve, VA, with different repulsion curves, VR(1) and VR(2).

4.4.1 Electric Double Layer

When a substance is brought into contact with a polar (e.g., aqueous) medium, it generally acquires charges through ionization, ion adsorption, or ion dissolution. This acquisition of charges influences the charge distribution of nearby ions in the polar medium. Ions of opposite charge (counter-ions) are attracted toward the surface, while the ions of like charge

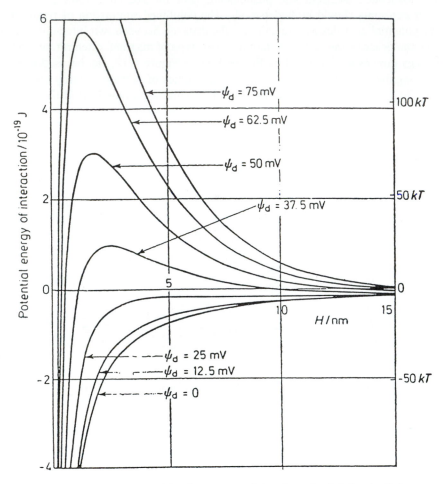

Figure 4-12.   The influence of the Stern potential, ψd, on the total potential energy of interaction of two spherical particles: $a = 10^{-7}$ m; $T = 298$ K; $s = 1$; $A_{11} = 2 \times 10^{-19}$ J; $A_{33} = 0.4 \times 10^{-19}$ J; $\varepsilon/\varepsilon_0 = 78.5$; $\kappa = 3 \times 10^8$ m^{-1}.

(co-ions) are repelled away from the surface. In this manner, a shell of a diffuse **double layer** as shown in Figure 4-13, will be formed. The first region is an inner region consisting of the original charge and the absorbed ions. In the second layer, however, the ions are distributed according to the influences of electric forces and random thermal motion. Gouy and Chapman independently have evaluated the potential of the double layer using the ion distribution function with the Poisson equation, which forms the basis of the Gouy-Chapman theory. Assuming that the electric potential is ϕ_0 at the surface and $\phi(x)$ at a distance x from the surface in the electrolyte solution, then the Boltzmann equation is

$$n_i = n_{io} \exp\left[-\frac{z_i e \phi(x)}{kT}\right]$$ [4-27]

where

n_i = concentration of ions of kind i where the potential is $\phi(x)$

n_{io} = concentration of ions in bulk solution

z_i = valency of ions of kind i

e = charge of an electron

A charge density ρ is used, which is the algebraic sum of the ionic charge per volume; that is,

$$\rho = \sum z_i e n_i$$ [4-28]

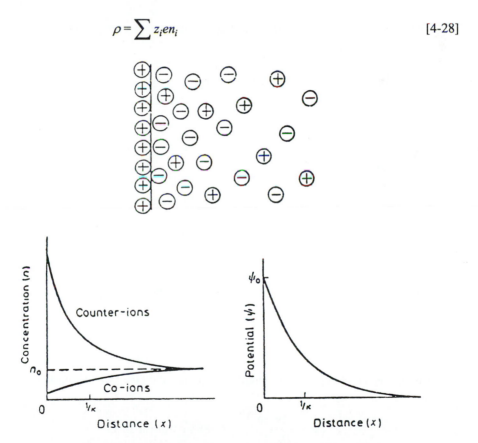

Figure 4-13. Schematic representation of a diffuse electric double layer.

and the n_i is defined by the previous Equation [4-27]. The volume charge density can also be expressed as $n_i = n_+ - n_-$

$$\rho = z\, e(n_+ - n_-)$$

$$= zen_0 \left(\exp\left[\frac{-ze\phi}{kT} \right] - \exp\left[\frac{ze\phi}{kT} \right] \right)$$

$$= -2zen_0 \sinh\left(\frac{ze\phi}{kT} \right) \qquad\qquad [4\text{-}29]$$

The Poisson equation can relate the charge density to electric potential

$$\nabla^2 \phi = -\frac{\rho}{D\,\varepsilon_0} \qquad\qquad [4\text{-}30]$$

where

D = dielectric constant

ε = permittivity of free space

For a symmetrical electrolyte, Equation [4-30] becomes

$$\nabla^2 \phi = -\frac{2zen_0}{D\varepsilon_0} \sinh\left(-\frac{ze\phi}{kT} \right) \qquad\qquad [4\text{-}31]$$

The solution of the preceding Poisson-Boltzmann equation is

$$\phi = 2\frac{kT}{ze} \ln \frac{1 + \gamma \exp(-\kappa x)}{1 - \gamma \exp(-\kappa x)} \qquad\qquad [4\text{-}32]$$

where κ is a unit of reciprocal length, and κ^{-1} is called the **Debye length**.

$$\kappa = \left(\frac{2n_0 ze}{D\varepsilon_0 kT} \right)^{\frac{1}{2}} = 3.288\, z\, c^{\frac{1}{2}} \text{ nm at } 25°C \qquad\qquad [4\text{-}33]$$

c = bulk electrolyte concentration in (m/L)

The addition of electrolyte will increase the value of κ, and consequently will decrease the κ^{-1}, the **double layer thickness**, thereby compressing the double layer.

Also, γ in Equation [4-32] is

$$\gamma = \tanh \frac{ze\phi_0}{4kT} \qquad\qquad [4\text{-}34]$$

or an approximation of the small surface potential is

$$\gamma \approx \frac{ze\phi_0}{4kT} \qquad\qquad [4\text{-}35]$$

For large distances, the approximation of the solution from Equation [4-31] can be reduced to

$$\phi = \frac{4\gamma kT}{ze} \exp(-\kappa x) \qquad\qquad [4\text{-}36]$$

For calculation of the free energy of repulsion, ΔG_R,

$$\Delta G_R = \int_d^\infty \pi_x \, dx \qquad\qquad [4\text{-}37]$$

where d is the midpoint of the double layer on which the Maxwell stress is highest. If n here signifies the number of excess ions per unit volume, then using the van't Hoff equation,

$$\Pi = nkT \qquad\qquad [4\text{-}38]$$

is osmotic pressure and as before

$$n = 2n_0 \left(\cosh \frac{ze\phi_d}{kT} - 1 \right) \qquad\qquad [4\text{-}39]$$

or

$$\Pi_d = 2n_0 kT \left(\cos h \, \frac{ze\phi_d}{kT} - 1 \right) \qquad \text{[4-40]}$$

After expanding the hyperbolic cosine and relating only the first term,

$$\Pi_d = 2 n_0 kT \left(\frac{ze\phi_d}{kT} \right)^2 \qquad \text{[4-41]}$$

Integrating the ΔG_R and substituting, then

$$\Delta G_R = \frac{64\, n_0 kT}{\kappa} \gamma^2 \exp(-2\kappa d) \qquad \text{[4-42]}$$

This is a key equation used for the DLVO theory.

4.4.2　Electrokinetic Phenomena

Four types of the electrokinetic phenomena are known which are caused by different field effects, such as electricity and so forth, at different solid surface:

- Electrophoresis — electric field on particles with motion of dispersed phase
- Sedimentation Potential — gravitational field on particles with potential gradient
- Electroosmosis — electric field on tube wall or packed bed with motion of the medium
- Streaming Potential — motion of medium on tube wall or packed bed with potential gradient

The relative motion between a charged surface and the bulk solution causes a potential difference, as indicated in Table 4-6. In each of the four cases, the shear plane between the double layer and the bulk medium is involved. The integration of net charge density out to infinity gives the total excess charge in solution per unit area. This charge is equal in magnitude but opposite in sign to the surface charge density, σ,

$$\sigma = - \int \rho \, dx \qquad \text{[4-43]}$$

Another expression of Poisson's equation, in comparison with Equation [4-30], is

$$\nabla^2 \phi = -4\pi \frac{\rho}{D} \qquad\qquad [4\text{-}44]$$

due to the factor that

$$\varepsilon = \frac{q_1 q_2}{4\pi\,\varepsilon_0\,Dx}$$

In the last section, we solved ϕ as

$$\phi = \frac{4\gamma kT}{ze}\, \exp(\text{-}\kappa x) \qquad\qquad [4\text{-}36]$$

$$= \phi_0\, \exp(\text{-}\kappa x)$$

After integration, Equation [4-44] and [4-43],

$$\sigma = \frac{D\kappa\,\phi_0}{4\,\pi} \qquad\qquad [4\text{-}45]$$

A **zeta potential**, ζ, is arbitrarily defined as the potential difference between a point away from the surface that is in the uniform diffuse medium and the plane of shear in relation to the double layer. To evaluate this potential, we use the same analogy as for the last equation, and therefore

$$\sigma = \frac{D\kappa\,\zeta}{4\,\pi} \qquad\qquad [4\text{-}46]$$

In electrophoresis, an electric potential gradient in solution is applied to determine the velocity of the charged particles. Then the force exerted on the surface per square cm is balanced by the viscous drag, and

$$\sigma F = \eta u \kappa \qquad\qquad [4\text{-}47]$$

where

F = field in voltz/cm

u = velocity

η = viscosity of the solution

or

$$u = \zeta DF/4\pi\eta \qquad\qquad [4\text{-}48]$$

In other words, the ζ potential or the $\sigma\kappa^{-1}$ — the electric moment per cm^2 — is proportional to the velocity per unit field. If the surface is located in a tube wall or packed bed, the mobile diffuse layer that moves under an electric field, will generate electroosmosis,

$$U = \pi r^2 u \qquad\qquad [4\text{-}49]$$

where

U = volume flow in mL/sec
r = radius of tube

then

$$U = \frac{r^2\eta DF}{4\eta} \qquad\qquad [4\text{-}50]$$

Experimentally, a field of about 1500 V/cm created by electrodes is needed to produce a velocity of 1 cm/sec of air bubbles in the capillary at the return path for a zeta potential of 100 mV in water at 25°C. The preceding formula is used to determine the zeta potential. Zeta potential has many environmental applications; for example, the ζ values of bacteria can be an important factor for their transport in porous media as shown in Table 4-4.

The reverse of electroosmosis is used so that a potential can be induced, and this potential is termed the **streaming potential**, E. If a stream line of flow is assumed, then by Poiseuille's equation the velocity at a radius x from the center of the tube is

$$u = \frac{P\left(r^2 - x^2\right)}{4\eta l} \qquad\qquad [4\text{-}51]$$

where

P = pressure
l = length of the tube

Table 4-4. Zeta Potential of *Bacillus subtilis* and *Pseudonomas putida* (ATCC 12633 as determined from the electrophoretic mobility measurements)

Species	Cultural Age	Suspending Medium	Zeta Potential (mV)
Bacillus subtilis	18 hrs	el*	33.6
a spore-forming Gram positive	18 hrs	A**	27.1
facultative anaerobe	18 hrs	B***	37.8
	3 days	A	47.0
	3 days	G****	51.8
	3 days	B	63.28
Pseudomonas putida	12 hrs	el	53.9
a nonsporeforming Gram negative	12 hrs	B	52.4
aerobe	15 hrs	G	58.3
	15 hrs	A	58.7
	3 days	A	56.9

*   Electrolyte solution containing 1,000 ppm NaCl

**   Buffer solution containing 0.0663 M KH_2PO_4 and 0.0267 M NaOH, pH=7.0

***   Buffer solution containing 0.0127 M KH_2PO_4 and 0.0054 M NaOH, pH=7.0

**** Cells remained in growth medium without further separation and resuspension in synthetic solutions

Source: L.K. Jang and T.F. Yen, *International Bioresources J.*, **1** 226–246 (1985)

The double layer is centered at

$$x = r - \kappa^{-1}$$ [4-52]

and its velocity is

$$u_d = \frac{\kappa^{-1} r P}{2\eta l}$$ [4-53]

When the κ^{-2} term is neglected, the current due to the motion of the double layer is

$$i = 2\pi r \sigma u_d$$ [4-54]

or

$$i = \frac{\pi r^2 \sigma \kappa^{-1} P}{\eta l}$$ [4-55]

The conductance of the liquid is

$$C = \frac{\pi r^2 k}{l}$$ [4-56]

and by Ohm's law, after substituting Equation [4-46],

$$E = \frac{i}{C} = \frac{\kappa^{-1} \sigma P}{\eta k} = \frac{\zeta PD}{4\pi \eta k}$$ [4-57]

From streaming potential data, one can also determine the zeta potential.

4.4.3   Hamaker Constants

London has used a simple harmonic oscillator theory to treat the dispersion energy or the attraction between two molecules separated by large distances.

$$u(r) = -\Lambda_{ab} r^{-6}$$

and

$$\Lambda_{ab} = \frac{3}{2} \left(\frac{h\nu_a \, h\nu_b}{h\nu_a + h\nu_b} \right) \alpha_a \alpha_b$$ [4-58]

where

ν = characteristic frequency
α = limiting polarizability
h = Planck's constant
Λ = London coefficient

Hamaker took London's expression of attraction for two molecules and integrated it for all the molecules in two separate particles to obtain the Gibb's free energy due to dispersion interactions,

$$\Delta G_{12}^d = - \int_{r_1} dv_1 \int_{r_2} \frac{\Lambda_{12}\rho_1\rho_2}{r_{12}^6} dv_2 \qquad [4\text{-}59]$$

where

v = volume element

ρ = molecular number densities (molecules per unit volume)

For planer parallel plates (slabs) with slab thicknesses of b_1 and b_2 separated by a distance of H, the free energy per unit area is

$$\Delta G_{12}^d = -\frac{\pi\Lambda_{12}\rho_1\rho_2}{12}\left[H^{-2} - \left(H + b_1 + b_2\right)^{-2} - \left(H + b_1\right)^{-2} - \left(H + b_2\right)^{-2}\right] \qquad [4\text{-}60]$$

now set

$$A_{12} = \pi^2 \rho_1\rho_2\Lambda_{12} \qquad [4\text{-}61]$$

If b_1 and b_2 are also large, then

$$\Delta G_{12}^d = -\frac{A_{12}}{12\pi H^2} \qquad [4\text{-}62]$$

A_{12} is termed the Hamaker constant between two particles. If there is an intervening substance between two bodies, say 1 and 3, then by the Archimedean buoyancy principle,

$$A_{123} = A_{13} + A_{22} - A_{12} - A_{23} \qquad [4\text{-}63]$$

If the intervening substance is between similar particles, then

$$A_{121} = A_{11} + A_{22} - 2A_{12} \qquad [4\text{-}64]$$

From Berthelot's principle,

$$A_{12} = \left(A_{11}A_{22}\right)^{\frac{1}{2}} \qquad [4\text{-}65]$$

Therefore, you can also include

$$A_{123} = \left(A_{11}^{\frac{1}{2}} - A_{22}^{\frac{1}{2}} \right)\left(A_{33}^{\frac{1}{2}} - A_{22}^{\frac{1}{2}} \right)$$ [4-66]

Some Hamaker constants A_{121} for nonretarded interaction across a film of water are illustrated by Table 4-5.

The summation of ΔG_{12} and ΔG_R — Equations [4-62] and [4-42] — is called the total potential energy that can be plotted in terms of H, the distance between two particles, a particle and a surface, or two surfaces. A typical example is demonstrated by Figure 4-11. A more detailed discussion of the potential energy curve will be conducted in Chapter 21.

Table 4-5.   Hamaker Constants A$_{121}$ for the Nonretarded Interaction across a Film of Water

Substance	Hamaker Constant, A_{121} (J) ($\times 10^{20}$)
Gold	33.5
Silver	26.6
Germanium	16.0
Silicon	11.9
Selenium	4.77
Alumina	4.12
Magnesia	1.60
Crystalline quartz	1.70
Fused quartz	0.833
Fused silica	0.849
Calcite	2.23
Calcium fluoride	1.04
Sapphire	5.32
Ionic crystals	0.31 – 4.85
Oxides	1.76 – 4.17
Metals	3 – 33.4
Polymers	(0.35)
Polyisoprene	0.743
Polymethyl methacrylate	1.05
Polystyrene, average of 2	0.931
Polystyrene	0.27
Polystyrene	0.35
Polytetrafluoroethylene	0.333

Table 4-5. continued

Substance	Hamaker Constant, A_{121} (J) ($\times 10^{20}$)
"Teflon FEP"	0.381
Polyvinyl chloride	1.30
Pentane	0.336
Hexane	0.360
Heptane	0.386
Octane	0.410
Nonane	0.435
Decane	0.462
Undecane	0.471
Dodecane	0.502
Tridecane	0.504
Tetradecane	0.514
Pentadecane	0.526
Hexadecane	0.540

REFERENCES

4-1   A. W. Adamson, *Physical Chemistry of Surfaces*, 4th ed., Wiley, New York, 1953.

4-2   D. J. Shaw, *Introduction to Colloid and Surface Chemistry*, 3rd ed., Butterworths, London, 1990.

4-3   D. A. Sabatini and R. C. Knox, *Transport and Remediation of Subsurface Contaminants*, American Chemical Society, Washington DC, 1992.

4-4   J. H. Fendler and E. J. Fendler, *Catalysis in Micellar and Macromolecular Systems, Academic Press*, New York, 1975.

4-5   J. H. Fendler, "Membrane Mimetic Chemistry," *Chem in Britain* 1098–1103 (1984).

4-6   S. Ross and I. D. Morrison, *Colloidal Systems and Interfaces*, John Wiley, New York, 1988.

4-7   J. H. Fendler, "Surfactant Vesicles as Membrane Mimetic Agents," *Acc. Chem. Res. 13*, 7–13 (1980).

4-8   M.-A. Sadeghi, K. M. Sedeghi, D. Momeni, and T. F. Yen, "Microscopic Studies of Surfactant Vesicles Formed during Tar Sand Recovery," *ACS Symp.* Ser. *396*, 391–407 (1989).

4-9   J. H. Fendler, *Membrane-Mimetic Chemistry*, Wiley, New York, 1982.

4-10 T. F. Yen, R. D. Gilbert and J. H. Fendler, *Membrane-Mimetic Chemistry*, Plenum Press, New York, 1994.

4-11 E. J. W. Verwey and J. Th. G. Overbeek, *Theory of the Stability of Lyophobic Colloids*, Elsevier, Amsterdam, 1948.

4-12 B. V. Derjaguin, L. Landau, "Theory of the Stability of Strongly Charged Lyophobic sols and of the Adhesion of Strongly Charged Particles in Solutions of Electrolyte," *Acta Physicchim. URSS, 14*, 733–762 (1941).

4-13 Y. Moroi, *Micelles, Theoretical and Applied Aspects*, Plenum, New York, 1992.

PROBLEM SET

1. Suppose we have a gram of crystalline silica. For simplicity, the crystals with the density of $\rho =$ 2.30 g/cm^3 are considered to be small cubes. Calculate the surface area in an cm^2/g at various particle sizes with the cube sides as 10^{-1}, 10^{-3}, 10^{-5}, 10^{-6}, and 10^{-7} cm.

2. Approximate the HLB (hydrophilic-lipophile balance) number for acetyl alcohol, $CH_3(CH_2)_{15}OH$.

3. The oil and water phase are emulsified using various proportions of surfactant mixture. A surfactant mixture having an HLB number of 12.3 should give a good water/oil emulsion. There are four surfactants listed in the following table. Suggest two possible surfactant mixtures that you may use for this particular system.

Surfactant Name	HLB
Span 65 (sorbital tristearate)	2.1
Span 85 (sorbital tristearate)	1.8
Tween 20 (polysoxyethylene sorbitan monolamate)	16.7
Tween 60 (polysoxyethylene sorbitan monolamate)	14.9

The Hungarian poet and nationalist Miklós Radnóti was executed by Fascists after a forced march from a labor camp where he was being held. His wife discovered a collection of poems in his trenchcoat pocket, written during his years of internment, which contained the following poem entitled "Gyökér," or "Root." In this poem, the nature of life is portrayed as ever-enduring. The concept of the root relates to the biosphere in representing the regenerating aspect of the life cycle.

A gyökérben erő surran,
esőt iszik, földdel él
és az álma hófehér.

Föld alól a föld fölé tör,
kúszik s ravasz a gyökér,
karja akár a kötél.

Gyökér karján féreg alszik,
gyökér lábán féreg ül,
a világ megférgesül.

De a gyökér tovább él lent,
nem érdekli a világ,
csak a lombbal teli ág.

Azt csodálja, táplálgatja,
küld néki jó ízeket,
édes, égi ízeket.

Gyökér vagyok magam is most,
férgek között élek én,
ott készül e költemény.

Virág voltam, gyökér lettem,
sulyos, sötét föld felettem,
sorsom elvégeztetett,
fűrész sír fejem felett.

Power glides in the root,
dirnking rain, living in the earth,
and its dream is white snow.

From underneath it rises and breaks through
the soil and crawls along secretly.
Its arm is like rope.

On the root's arm a worm sleeps
and a worm sticks to its leg.
The world is rotten with worms.

But the root goes on living below.
It is the branch, heavy with leaves,
that it lives for, not the world.

This is what it feeds and loves,
sending delicate tastes up to it,
sweet tastes out of the sky.

I am a root myself now,
living among worms.
This poem is written down there.

I was a flower. I became a root.
There is heavy black earth above me.
The workers on my life are done.
A saw wails over my head.

CHEMISTRY OF MAJOR SPHERES

THE LITHOSPHERE — FOSSIL FUELS

*T*he **lithosphere**, including the internal structure below the Earth's surface, is the part of the earth where all mineral resources originate. A number of illustration will be used to introduce the lithosphere. From the continental crust down, the structure of the mantle always provides the necessary energy to form compounds from iron and the elements associated with iron upwards above the upper mantle level, as shown in Figure 5-1. Different metamorphic facies are formed due to both the pressure and temperature gradients. Above the transition zone, especially in the continental margins, organic-rich sediments are formed, as shown in Figure 5-2. All mineral deposits in veins and domes accumulate at the tectonic plate boundaries, as shown in Figure 5-3. These can take the shape of belts or bands, as shown in Figure 5-4.

All energy on earth comes from the sun and is called **stellar energy**. When stellar energy is absorbed by the atmosphere and hydrosphere, the net result is the energy in winds, waves, ocean currents, tidal currents, hydroelectric power, and so on. When energy is absorbed by the biosphere and used in lifecycles by photosynthesis, the biomass produces decay that becomes buried in sediments, thereby producing fossil energy. Energy is absorbed by the lithosphere and is used in geochemical cycles and the conduction and convection from the earth's interior. These are called **geothermal** and **nuclear energies**; the latter of these is termed **fissile fuels**.

In the following chapters of this book, we will briefly discuss fossil fuels, followed by solar, wind, tidal, and other nonfossil fuels. In the last group, we will concentrate on nuclear power.

As the world has become increasingly industrialized and modernized, energy consumption has increased accordingly. After decades of careless exploitation of energy resources, the world has finally come to realize that the energy supplies that were once considered inexhaustible will shortly be nonexistent. Moreover, this increased energy consumption has resulted in an extremely adverse impact on the environment in the form of air, water, and other kinds of pollution. There are increasing conflicts between environmental conservationists, who are concerned with leaving a clean and healthy world for the future generations, and industrialists and businesses, who are pushing for a higher level of technological civilization and material consumption. In this chapter, we will explore the background of energy production and consumption with an emphasis on fossil energy. We will see that protecting the environment is not necessarily incompatible with meeting energy demands. We will begin with energy and power, and explain energy consumption. The introduction is followed by a brief classification of fossil fuels. Lastly, we will introduce some of the resource models used in energy technology. Energy conservation and the green process will be briefly discussed.

5.1 ENERGY AND POWER

Solar energy is the major source of the earth's energy system, in conjunction with two other small contributors: **tidal energy** and **geothermal heat**. The hydroelectric power we utilize results from rainfall, through a process in which sunlight provides energy to raise water up to the atmosphere. The food we eat is the end-product of food chains in which sunlight provides energy for photosynthesis. The fossil fuel we burn originates from these organic compounds created through the preceding process, to which solar power makes a great contribution. As shown in Figure 5-5, a quantity of $174,000 \times 10^{12}$ W of solar energy is intercepted by the earth. Of this quantity, about 30% is reflected or scattered back into space. This scattered fraction is called the **albedo**, and it determines the total energy balance of the earth. Another 47% of this solar energy is converted directly into heat. About 23% of the total energy intercepted is used to drive the **hydrologic cycle**, the massive evaporation and precipitation of water upon which we depend for our fresh water supplies. Only a very small fraction, 0.1%, is used by green plants and algae in photosynthesis, which is vital for our food supply. Figure 5-6 illustrates a detailed energy system.

As indicated in Chapter 1, various energy unit systems have been adapted for use by different groups of people. It is troublesome, however, for people to convert a value from one unit to another. For convenience, Table 5-1 and Figure 5-7 give some common energy equivalents and conversion factors.

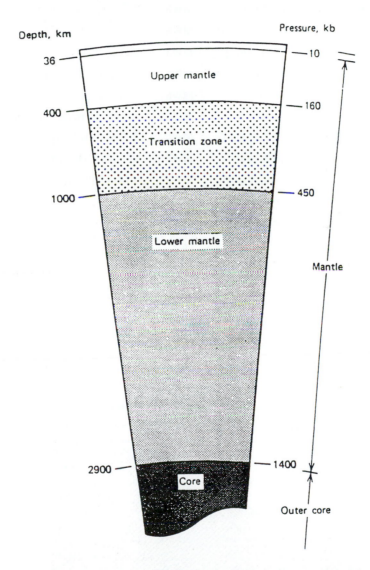

Figure 5-1. The internal structure of the Earth. (After B. Mason, *Principle of Geochemistry*, 1966)

Table 5-1.   Energy Equivalents and Other Conversion Factors

Unit	Equivalent		Remarks
1 kcal	$= 1.162 \times 10^{-6}$	MWh	
2 Hph (metric)	$= 7.355 \times 10^{-4}$	MWh	
1 BTU	$= 0.293 \times 10^{-6}$	MWh	
1 Q	$= 0.293 \times 10^{12}$	MWh	$1 Q = 10^{18}$ BTU
1 t hard coal	$= 8.134$	MWh	1 kg hard coal equivalent = 7,000 kcal
1 t petroleum products	$= 11$	MWh	varies according to raw material
$10^3 \ m^3$ natural gas	$= 10$	MWh	varies according to raw material
1 t U	$= 2.25 \times 10^7$	MWh	200 MeV/U atom
1 t Th	$= 2.30 \times 10^7$	MWh	200 MeV/Th atom
1 t D	$= 6.69 \times 10^7$	MWh	5 MeV/D atom
1 short ton U_3O_3	$= 0.7693$	t U	
1 kg U_3O_8	$= 0.8480$	kg U	
1 lb U_3O_8	$= 0.3847$	kg U	
1 short ton ThO_2	$= 0.7972$	1 Th	
1 kg ThO_2	$= 0.8788$	kg Th	
1 lb ThO_2	$= 0.3986$	kg Th	
1 lb	$= 0.4536$	kg	
1 short ton	$= 0.9072$	t	
1 U.S. barrel (petroleum)	$= 0.1590$	m^3	

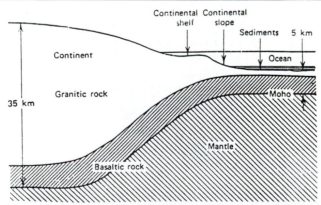

Figure 5-2.   The Earth's crust under the continents and oceans. The moho is Mo-horovicic discontinuity which separates the highly heterogenous crust from the more homogenous upper mantle.

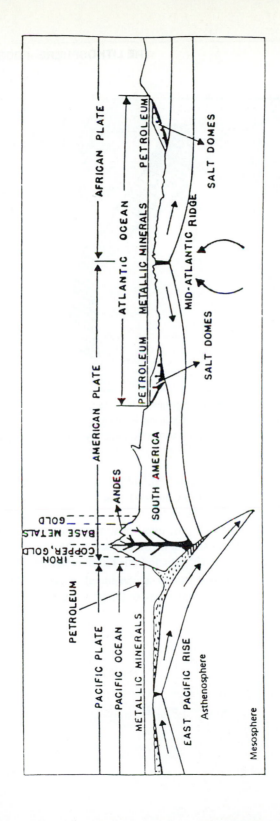

Figure 5-3.   The role of the plate boundaries in the accumulation of mineral deposits.

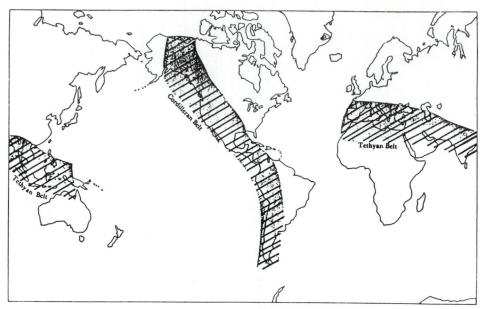

Figure 5-4.   Major world petroleum belts. [Source: T.F. Yen, Genesis and Degradation of Petroleum Hydrocarbons in Marine Environments in (T. M. Church ed.) *Marine Chemistry in the Coastal Environments*, ACS Symp. Series 18, Washington, DC, 1975 pp. 231-266.]

For energy, it is handy to know some of the abbreviations that are commonly adopted. In addition to the units discussed in Chapter 1, Table 1-6, both **Quad** (10^{15}) and **Quint** (10^{18}) were used in large numbers. In the field of studying energy demands, various units (tons of coal, barrels of oil, cubic feet of gas, gigawatts, and so on) are often encountered. To be consistent with other studies, Btu is sometimes used as the common unit of energy. On that basis, one Quad is equal to 1×10^{15} Btu and one Quint is equal to 1×10^{18} Btu.

Power is the rate at which energy is consumed or generated; for example, Joules are the energy unit, while Watts are Joules/sec, or the power unit.

$$P = \frac{dE}{dt} \qquad\qquad\qquad [5\text{-}1]$$

$$E_{year} = \int_{0}^{T} P_{inst}\, dt \qquad\qquad\qquad [5\text{-}2]$$

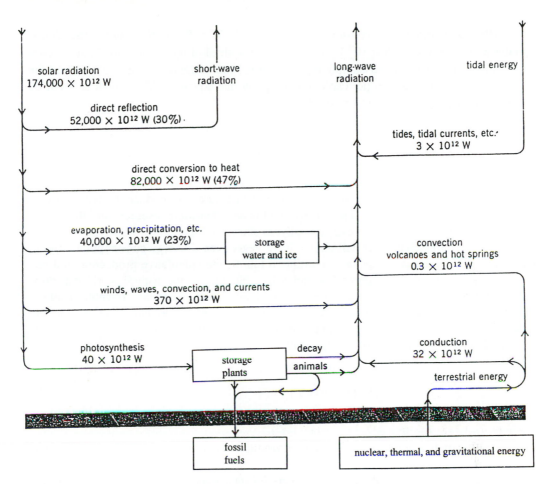

Figure 5-5. Energy flow-sheet for the Earth. [From M.K. Hubbert, U.S. energy resources: A review as of 1972, pt. 1, in A National Fuels and Energy Policy Study, U.S. 93d Congress, 2nd   Session, Senate Committee on the Interior and Insular Affairs, ser. no. 93-40 (92-75), 1974.]

and

$$P_{ar} = \frac{1}{T}\, E_{year} = \frac{1}{T}\int_{0}^{T} P_{inst}\, dt \qquad\qquad [5\text{-}3]$$

$$T = 3.15 \times 10^{2}\ \text{sec} \qquad\qquad [5\text{-}4]$$

Present world energy consumption = 7.1×10^{12} W = 5.3×10^{19} cal/y. The United States alone consumes 1.8×10^{16} kcal/y, which is one-third of the world's total energy consumption. The metabolic consumption per capita is 3100 kcal/day, or 150 Watts. Thus, the United States nonmetabolic per capita consumption rate equals 12 kW, which is about 80 times as great as the metabolic consumption.

5.2 TOTAL ENERGY CONSUMPTION

Humans are now consuming fossil energy faster than nature can produce it. We are living off the store of energy of past ages. Fossil fuel is an exhaustible resource, and the energy consumption by humans grows exponentially, as shown in Figure 5-8. This type of growth is inevitably unreasonable. It will double in 18 years even if energy consumption only increases by 4% per year. For an exhaustible resource, the cumulative production and rate production are shown in Figures 5-9 and 5-10. Nothing in the natural world can grow through too many doubling periods before it runs into some constraint. Eventually all exponential growth curves have to level off, and the growth of energy consumption is no exception. In the long run, energy inputs and outputs for human society must be in a steady state. Because population grows exponentially, our energy consumption is exponential in nature.

$$Q = Q_o \exp\left(\lambda T\right) \qquad\qquad [5\text{-}5]$$

where $\theta = 2.718$, T = time AD, λ=constant (yr^{-1}).

for example, our present total energy consumption is

$$Q^T = 1.85 \times 10^{-21} \, \theta^{.0282\,T} \, (\text{Quad/yr}) \qquad\qquad [5\text{-}6]$$

The following are some properties from the above exponential equation.

a. **doubling time**, T_2

$$T_2 = \frac{\ln 2}{\lambda} = \frac{.693}{\lambda} \qquad\qquad [5\text{-}7]$$

for example,

$$T_2 = \frac{.693}{.0282} = 25 \text{ yr}$$

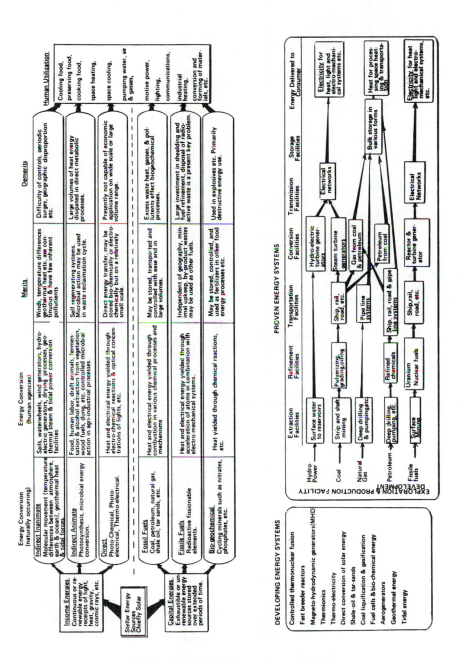

Figure 5-6. Energy Systems. Compiled from *Introduction to World Resources*, Praeger, New York, 1966 and *Inter-Department Energy Study*, Washington D.C., 1964.

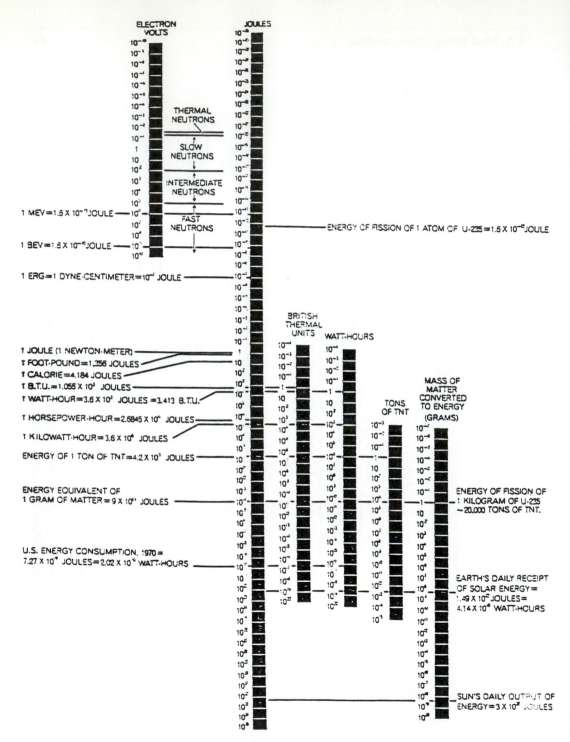

Figure 5-7.   Energy conversion factors.

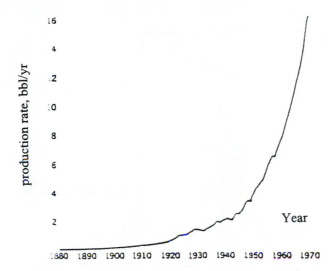

Figure 5-8.   World crude oil production (From Hubbert, op. cit., 1974).

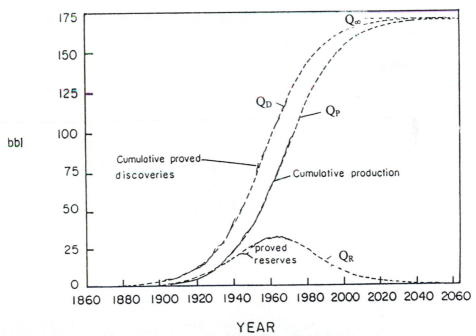

Figure 5-9.   Logistic equations and curves of cumulative production, cumulative discoveries, and proved reserves for crude oil from the conterminous United States 1900-1971 (From Hubbert, op. cit., 1974).

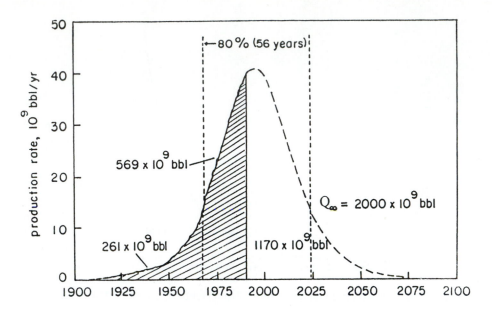

Figure 5-10.   Estimate as of 1972 of complete cycle of world crude oil production (From Hubbert, op. cit., 1974).

b. **yearly fractional increase,** R

$$R = \theta^\lambda - 1 \qquad\qquad [5\text{-}8]$$

for example,

$$\% \text{ increase} = \left(\theta^{.0282} - 1\right)(100) = 2.86\% \text{ per yr}$$

Derivation of R can be accomplished as follows:

$$R \approx \frac{dQ}{Q\,dt} \qquad\qquad [5\text{-}9]$$

or

$$R = \frac{Q - Q_o}{Q_o t} = \frac{Q}{Q_o} - 1$$

since $t = 1$, or

$$\frac{Q}{Q_o} = R + 1$$

$$\ln \frac{Q}{Q_o} = \ln (R + 1)$$

since

$$\ln \frac{Q}{Q_o} = \lambda$$

Thus

$$\ln (R + 1) = \lambda \qquad\qquad\qquad [5\text{-}10]$$

or

$$e^{\lambda} = R + 1$$

or

$$e^{\lambda} - 1 = R$$

c. **crossover**

$$Q_T = 1.85 \times 10^{-21}\, e^{.0282\,T} \qquad\qquad\qquad [5\text{-}11]$$

For example, the gas consumption has become increasingly rapid in recent years. Gas consumption has the potential to exceed the total energy consumption, and at its current rate it has increased from 6 Q in 1960 to 23 Q in 1980.

Thus

$$6 = Q_o\, e^{1960\lambda}$$

$$23 = Q_o\, e^{1980\lambda}$$

Solving

$$\lambda = .067 \; y^{-1}$$

$$Q_0 = 1.1 \times 10^{-56}$$

Hence,

$$Q_G = 1.1 \times 10^{-56} \; e^{.067T}$$

Solving, when $Q_G = Q_T$, $T = 2090$, the crossover will take place.

5.3 FOSSIL ENERGY

The fraction of sunlight (0.1%) used by plants in photosynthesis is converted to chemical energy and stored in the form of carbohydrates such as glucose, sucrose, and starch. The reduced carbon can be reoxidized into carbon dioxide during the process of respiration, providing for the energy needs of biological organisms. Plants themselves use up about 20% of their carbohydrates for their own energy needs. The remainder, which represents stored photochemical energy, is called the **net primary productivity.**

A small fraction of plant and animal matter, estimated at one part in 10,000, is buried in the earth and removed from contact with atmospheric oxygen. Some of these buried carbon compounds accumulated in deposits and were subjected to high temperatures and pressures in the earth's crust, becoming coal, petroleum, gas, oil shale, and tar sands. These are the **fossil fuels**. In the following sections, we will give some detailed descriptions of each of the fossil fuels.

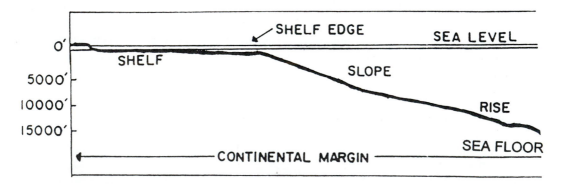

Figure 5-11.   Schematics for continental margins. (Source, T. F. Yen, *Chemistry of Marine Sediments*, Ann Arbor Sci.Pub., 1977, p.4)

5.3.1 Petroleum and Gas

Petroleum (rock-oil, derived from Latin "petra," meaning rock or stone, and Latin "oleum", meaning oil) occurs widely in the earth as a gas and a liquid. Gas is a part of petroleum, and petroleum is classified as a mineral according to the U.S. Department of Interior. Chemically, any petroleum is an extremely complex mixture of hydrocarbon compounds, with a minor amount of nitrogen, oxygen, and sulfur impurities. The various fractions can be separated by distillation to determine the overall composition, as shown in Table 5-2. Nearly all petroleum occurs in sediments. These sediments are chiefly of marine origin, and it follows that the contained petroleum is also most likely marine, or related to marine conditions, as shown in Figure 5-11. The process occurs as follows. A small portion of reduced carbon resulting from photosynthesis in the oceans settles to the bottom, where oxidation is negligible. The biological debris is covered by clay and sand particles and forms a compacted organic layer in a porous clay or sandstone. Anaerobic bacteria digest the protein, fat, and carbohydrates, releasing most of the oxygen and nitrogen. As the sediment with the remains, mostly lipid material, becomes buried deeper, the temperature and pressure acting on it rise. Bacterial action decreases, and organic disproportionation reactions are thought to occur through geochemical transformation. Figure 5-12 shows the comparison between reservoir rock and source rock as a function of depth.

Table 5-2. Petroleum Components

Components	Distillation Temperature (°C)	Structure
Gas	20	C_P; $C_1 - C_4$
Petroleum ether	20 – 60	C_P; $C_2 - C_6$
Ligroin (light naphtha)	60 – 100	C_P; $C_0 - C_7$
Natural gasoline	40 – 205	C_P, C_N; $C_6 - C_{10}$
Kerosene	175 – 325	C_P, C_N, C_A; $C_{12} - C_{18}$
Gas oil	Nonvolatile liquid	C_P, C_N, C_A; > C18
Lubricating oil	Nonvolatile semisolid	C_N, C_A, C_P, X; $\sim C_{20}$
Asphaltic bitumens	Nonvolatile	C_N, C_A, C_P, X; $C_{100} - C_{120}$

There are some other theories regarding the origin of petroleum; for example, "inorganic theories," which state that the primary source material for petroleum generation is inorganic. Theories that uphold the inorganic origin of petroleum have few supporters today. A solid proof for an organic origin was a C^{13} isotope mass spectroscopy experiment, which confirmed that the lipid content of marine microorganisms and that of petroleum have the same values, as shown in Figure 5-13.

The most immediate constraint on energy growth is the availability of petroleum and natural gas. The Industrial Revolution was initially fueled by coal, but oil and gas were increasingly substituted because they were cleaner fuels and were transported more easily. Petroleum and gas now constitute nearly 80% of the total energy consumption in the United States. Estimates of the ultimate amount of recoverable liquid petroleum worldwide range from 10,440 to 21,170 Quads (one Quad is equal to 10^{15} Btu). The world oil production until 1983 was approximately 2,800 Quads. In 1982 alone, the world production was about 110 Quads, which is equivalent to 19 billion barrels. Based on the 1982 rate of oil consumption, in the year 2000 our world's reserves of conventional petroleum will be exhausted. Fortunately, due to conservation measures, the rate has been reduced.

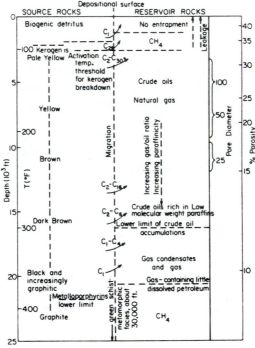

Figure 5-12.   Comparison between reservoir and source rock as a function of depth.(Yen, *Energy Sources*, 1973)

After production, petroleum is transported via pipeline and can be refined or upgraded into a lighter fraction called **gasoline** by the use of a cracking catalyst. Both production and recovery are termed upstream processes, and similarly both refining and upgrading are termed downstream processes.

Asphalt (or bitumen), the heavy or involatile fractions of petroleum, virtually controls many parameters of the production as well as refining processes. The asphaltic system is comprised of (a) asphaltenes, the dispersed or micellar phase, (b) resins, the peptizing agent (or surfactant), and (c) gas oil, the dispersed phase or intermicellar medium. These fractions can be separated by solvent cuts with appropriate Hildebrand's solubility parameters, as shown in Table 5-3.

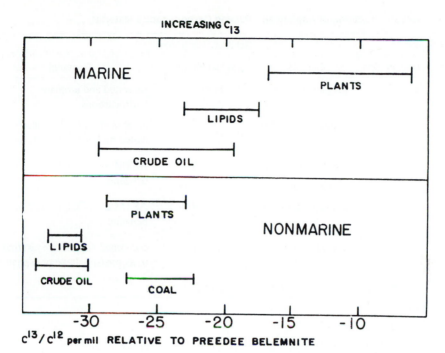

Figure 5-13.   Carbon isotope range of natural materials. (Source: S. R Silverman, 1971)

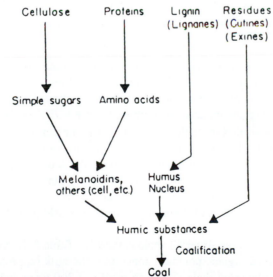

Figure 5-14.   Relation of melanoidins to coal as derived from cellulose and protein. [T. F. Yen, ACS Symp. Ser. *18*, 231-266 (1975)]

Table 5-3.   Solvent Fractions of Asphalt and Related Carbonaceous Material

Fraction			Solubility Parameter	
Number	Designation	Solubility	δ in hildebrands	Remarks
1	gas oil	propane soluble	below 6	saturated and aromatic hydrocarbons
2	resin	propane insoluble pentane soluble	6 – 7	combined 1 and 2 are also called maltene or petrolene
3	asphaltene	pentane insoluble benzene soluble	7 – 9	ASTM uses CCl_4 instead of benzene
4	carbene	benzene insoluble CS_2 soluble	9 – 10	ASTM uses CCl_4 instead of benzene
5	carboid	CS_2 insoluble pyridine soluble	10 – 11	combined 4 and 5 are referred to as preasphaltene or asphatol
6	mesophase	pyridine insoluble	above 11	

Volatile-free basis.

1 hildebrand = 2.04 $J^{1/2}/cm^{3/2}$ = 1 $cal^{1/2}/cm^{3/2}$.

Because of the flammability of CS_2, pyridine is preferred; fractions 4 and 5 can be combined.

Source: T. F. Yen in *Encyclopedia of Polymer Science and Engineering*, 1990, Wiley, New York.

5.3.2   Oil Shale

Oil shale is diverse fine-grained rock that contains refractory organic material that can be refined into fuels. The soluble fraction, called **bitumen**, constitutes about 20% of this organic material, whereas the remainder exists as an insoluble fraction, **kerogen**. However, most oil shales do contain inorganic minerals accounting from 80–20% of the bulk. All oil shales appear to have been deposited in shallow lakes, marshes, or seas that support a dense algal biota. The latter is a probable source for shale-bound organic precursors.

In Australia, France, and Scotland, oil shales have been the source of products similar to those obtained from petroleum for many years. In the United States, there are over 700 billion barrels of economically recoverable synthetic crude spread over the Green River Formation, located in Colorado, Utah, and Wyoming. The total world potential is estimated to be 30 trillion bbl of shale oil.

A typical composition of Green River oil shale is listed in Table 5-4. Kerogen, which can be viewed as a cross-linked organic polymer, constitutes the bulk (approximately 80%) of the available organic material in oil shale. Kerogen itself is 3,200 times richer in biomass than the total available bitumen and petroleum. The liberation of hydrocarbons depends on the degree to which kerogen can be degraded into liquid fuel precursors. Because kerogen is the most abundant organic carbon source in the world, it may be a potential food precursor in an age of food shortages, just as single cell proteins have been.

Table 5-5 shows the elemental and ash analyses of a number of raw fuels.

Table 5-4. Composition of a Typical Green River Oil Shale

General scheme of the oil-shale components

Inorganic matrix	Quartz
	Feldspars
	Clays (mainly illite and chlorite)
	Carbonates (calcite and dolomite)
	Pyrite and other minerals
Bitumens (soluble in CS_2)	
Kerogens (insoluble in CS_2)	
(containing U, Fe, V, Ni, Mo)	

Average chemical compositon of Green River oil shale, as determined by the writers for several samples from Rifle, Colorado.

FeS_2	0.86%				
$NaAlSi_2O_6 \cdot H_2O$ (analcite)	4.3%				
SiO_2 (quartz)	8.6%				
$KAl_4Si_7AlO_{20}(OH)_4$ (illite) Montmorillonite Muscovite	12.9%				
$KAlSi_3O_8$ (K-feldspar) $NaAlSi_3O_8$–$CaAl_2Si_2O_8$ (plagioclase)	16.4%				
O	22.2%	$CaMg(CO_3)_2$ (dolomite) And calcite	43.1%	Mineral matter 86.2%	Oil shale
Ca	9.5%				
Mg	5.8%				
C	5.6%				
S, N, O	1.28%	Bitumen	2.76%		
H	1.42%			Organic matter 13.8%	
C	11.1%	Kerogen	11.04%		

Source: T.F. Yen and G.V. Chilingarian. <u>Oil Shale</u>, Elsevier Sci. Pub. Amsterdam, 1976, p.3

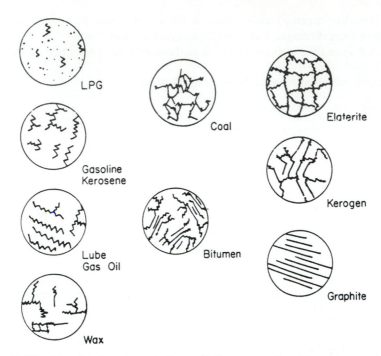

Figure 5-15.   Structural representations of bitumen, coal and kerogen, and their relations with LPG (liquified petroleum gas), gasoline, gas oil, and wax. Their interrelations among elaterite and graphite are also indicated. [Source: T. F. Yen, *Chemical Aspects of Interfuel Conversion*, Energy Sources *1(1)* 117-136 (1973)]

Table 5-5.   Elementary and Ash Analyses of Raw Fuels.

Sample	C(%)	H(%)	N(%)	S(%)	O(%)	Mineral and Ash(%)
Oil Shale (Colorado)	12.4		0.41	0.04		84.6
Oil Shale (Alaska)	53.9		0.30	1.50		34.2
Kerogen (Green River)	65.7	9.1	2.13	3.15	8.9	10.2
Lignite (Kincaid)	63.1	5.0	0.64	<0.04	21.5	9.3
Bituminous (Lower Freeport)	77.0	5.7	1.42	1.72	8.1	6.6
Anthracite (Pennsylvania)	87.1	3.8	0.60	<0.3	2.6	7.0
Gilsonite (Tarbor vein)	84.5	10.0	2.4	0.53	2.6	0.7
Residuum (Mid-continent)	87.7	6.6	0.90	0.75	1.6	1.3
Asphaltene (Baxterville)	84.5	7.4	0.80	5.60	1.7	0.5

Table 5-6. ASTM Classification of Coals by Rank (in Box) and Corresponding Bank Rank Parameters not Used in the ASTM Classification

ASTM Class	ASTM Group	Btu/lb (moist, mmf)	MJ/kg (moist, mmf)	Agglomerating	% VM (d, mmf)	Oil max. (vitrinite)	% Moisture (moist, mmf)
	Peat	3,000 – 4,000[a]	7.0 – 9.3	No	62 – 72	0.2 – 0.4	50 – 95[b]
Lignite	Lignite B	Undefined–6,300[a]	–14.6	No	40 – 65	0.2 – 0.4	45 – 60[b]
	Lignite A	6,300 – 8,300[a]	14.6 – 19.3	No	40 – 65	0.2 – 0.4	31 – 50[b]
Subbituminous	Subbituminous C	8,300 – 9,500[a]	19.3 – 22.1	No	35 – 55	0.3 – 0.7	25 – 38[b]
	Subbituminous B	9,500 – 10,500[a]	22.1 – 24.4	No	35 – 55	0.3 – 0.7	20 – 30[b]
	Subbituminous A	10,500 – 11,500[a]	24.4 – 26.7	No	35 – 55	0.3 – 0.7	18 – 25[b]
Bituminous	High volatile C bit.	10,500 – 13,000[a]	26.7 – 30.2	Yes	35 – 55	0.4 – 0.7	10 – 25[b]
	High volatile B bit.	13,000 – 14,000[a]	30.2 – 32.5	Yes	35 – 50	0.5 – 0.8[c]	5 – 12[b]
	High volatile A bit.	> 14,000	> 32.5	Yes	31 – 45	0.6 – 1.2[c]	1 – 7[b]
	Med. volatile bit.	> 14,000	> 32.5	Yes	22 – 31[b]	1.0 – 1.7[b]	< 1.5
	Low volatile bit.	> 14,000	> 32.5	Yes	14 – 22[b]	1.5 – 2.0[b]	< 1.5
Anthracitic	Semianthracite	> 14,000	> 32.5	No	8 – 14[b]	1.8 – 2.6[b]	< 1.5
	Anthracite	> 14,000	> 32.5	No	2 – 8[b]	2.2 – 5.0[b]	0.5 – 2
	Meta-anthracite	> 14,000	> 32.5	No	< 2	> 4.5[b]	1 – 3

After H.H. Damberger, R.D. Harvey, C.R. Ruch and J. Thomas in *Science and Technology and Coal Utilization*, Plenum Press, 1984.

[a] Air dried

[b] Well-suited for rank discrimination in range indicated.

[c] Moderately well-suited for rank discrimination.

5.3.3 Coal

Coal is composed of the remains of plant matter from the huge, thickly wooded swamps that flourished 250 million years ago during a period of mild, moist climate. Woody plants are made of lignin as well as cellulose and protein as shown in Figure 5-14. **Lignin** is a complex, three-dimensional polymer that contains aromatic groups. While aerobic bacteria rapidly oxidize cellulose when a plant dies, lignin is much more resistant to bacterial action. In swamps, lignin accumulates under water, compacting into a substance called **peat**. Over the geological ages, the peat layers of the primeval swamps were metamorphosed into coal. The first stage of coalification (the formation of coal) is termed **lignite**, where the %C value is 55-75 and the heating value in Btu/lb is 6300-8300. The next is **subbituminous**, where both %C and heating values increase. Next is **bituminous**, which can be divided into high volatile and low volatile types. The last stage can reach **anthracite**, which has a %C value of 87–97. The different stages of coal formation and the corresponding properties can be found in Table 5-6. Figure 5-15 shows the structural representations of bitumen, coal, and kerogen.

The recoverable reserves of coal are estimated to be about 7.4×10^{12} metric tons, with the United States and the former Soviet Union owning about 75% of the supply. Coal is substantially more abundant than oil or gas on a world basis. The size of U.S. coal reserves is also substantially larger than those of oil and gas.

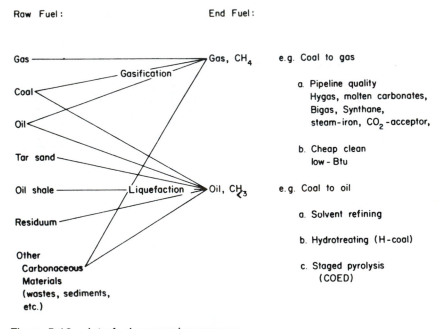

Figure 5-16.   Interfuel conversion process.

The major concern with coal is that it is a dirty fuel to burn. Of particular concern is the sulfur dioxide emitted, which causes serious health hazards in urban areas. In addition, being a solid, coal is much less convenient to use than petroleum or natural gas. Using the appropriate chemistry, it is possible to convert coal to liquid or gaseous fuels. The reduced carbon in coal, in which most of its energy content resides, can be transformed into hydro-carbon molecules that are either liquid or gaseous, depending on their molecular weight and structures. A simplified diagram for **interfuel conversion** is shown in Figure 5-16. (more discussion of this will be found in Section 5.5.1)

Production of Methane from Coal

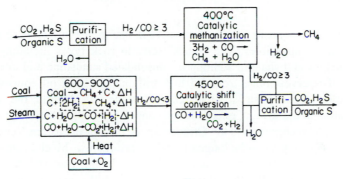

Production of Liquid Fuel from Coal by Fischer-Tropsch Synthesis

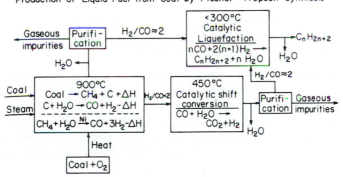

Production of Liquid Fuel from Coal by Direct Catalytic Hydrogenation

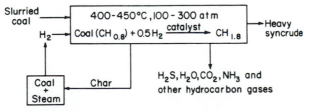

Figure 5-17. Coal conversion technology. (Source: Spiro and Stigliani, 1980)

The main problem in converting coal to liquid (coal liquefaction) or gaseous fuel (coal gasification) is finding an efficient way to combine hydrogen with solid carbon, which is a hydrogen-enriched method. The H/C atomic ratio is 4 for methane and about 2 for gasoline, but in coal it ranges from 0.3 to 0.8. Figure 5-17 shows a simplified flow diagram of current coal conversion technologies, including the **Fischer-Tropsch synthesis**. This process represents the synthetic fuel program of indirect conversion of coal program of the United States Department of Energy.

5.3.4   Tar Sands

Tar sands are petroleum deposits and are distinctive in that their bitumen is so viscous that primary production is impossible. The "sands" refer to rock types including limestone, dolomite conglomerate, and shale in addition to consolidated sandstone and unconsolidated sand. Estimates of reserves range from 2.5 to 6 trillion barrels of oil equivalence. The world's most known sand deposit is Athabasca, in Canada. In Alberta, the sands of the McMurray Formation of the lower Cretaceous age contain one billion barrels of oil in place. Next to this in size and recognition is the Orinoco heavy oil belt in eastern Venezuela. The biggest deposits of sand appear to be lodged in deltaic sediments. Mechanisms for turning migrating oil into heavy residue are still under debate, including bacterial degradation and meteoric water washing. Usually, these bitumen will have API gravities ranging from -10 to $+16$ degrees.

$$\circ\text{API} = \frac{141.5}{\text{specific gravity at } 60\,^\circ\text{F}} - 131.5 \qquad [5\text{-}12]$$

Viscosities range from 10,000 to more than one million centipoise (cp). Therefore, the bitumen cannot readily move through the carrying rock or the associated inorganic materials. The general methods for providing fuel from tar sands in-place are combustion and the injection of hot water or steam. Both methods are based on petroleum **enhanced oil recovery** (EOR) of the tertiary recovery schemes. The in-situ combustion method for tar sand recovery always encounters problems in formation permeability. Currently, commercial production of tar sands includes strip mining of the deposit and extraction with hot water (Suncor and Syncrude). One of the serious environmental problems is the gigantic volumes of the tailing ponds containing the oily residues and the abrasive, quartz-like inorganic particulates that currently cannot be disposed of.

5.4 RESOURCES MODELS

Of the available evaluations of our energy and resources on Earth, there have been many attempts to point out that all forms of resources are limited. This will affect the suppliers as well as the users; it also has an impact to government policies. In the following sections, we will discuss four such types of models.

5.4.1 Macroscopic Approach by King Hubbert

The essential feature of this model is based on the record of past discoveries and the production history records.

$$Q \text{ (resource)} = \int_{t_1}^{t_2} P \text{ (Production)} \, dt \qquad\qquad [5\text{-}13]$$

Initially, there is exponential growth and leveling off (refer to Figs. 5-9 and 5-10).

$$P = P_0 e^{\lambda t}$$

$$Q = \int_0^T e^{\lambda t} \, dt = \frac{P_0}{\lambda} e^{\lambda t} \Big|_0^t = \frac{P_0}{\lambda} \left(e^{\lambda t} - 1 \right)$$

$$t = \frac{1}{\lambda} \ln \left(\frac{\lambda Q}{P_0} + 1 \right) \qquad\qquad [5\text{-}14]$$

At the point of leveling off, the maximum production (P_m) is reached, suggesting a bell-shaped curve that can easily be represented by a probability curve.

$$Q_\infty = \int_{-\infty}^{\infty} P \, dt = \int_{-\infty}^{\infty} P_m \exp \left[-\frac{1}{2} \left(\frac{t - t_m}{\sigma} \right)^2 \right] dt$$

$$Q_\infty = \sqrt{2\pi} \, \sigma \, P_m$$

$$P_0 = P_m \exp\left[\frac{1}{2}\left(\frac{t_m}{\sigma}\right)^2\right]$$

or

$$t_m = \sigma\sqrt{2\ln\frac{P_m}{P_0}} \qquad [5\text{-}15]$$

where σ is standard deviation and t_m is the maximum time for production (notice also $t = 0$ for the preceding calculation). According to King Hubbert, energy resource and the proved reserves are equivalent as shown in Figure 5-18. If Q_D is from discovery and Q_P is from production, then $Q_D - Q_P = Q_R$ (resources). The rate of the increase of resources or approved reserves can be simply performed by a differential curve, as shown in Figure 5-19.

$$Q = \int_0^t \left(\frac{dQ}{dt}\right) dt = \text{resource} \qquad [5\text{-}16]$$

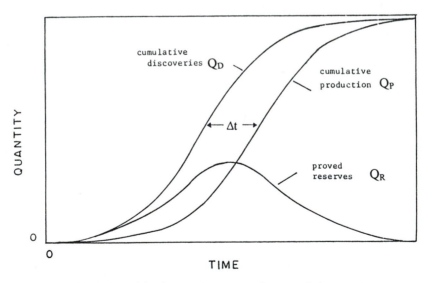

Figure 5-18.   Variation with of proved reserves Q_R, cumulative production Q_p, and cumulative proved discoveries Q_D, during a complete cycle of petroleum production. (Source: M.K. Hubbert, Energy Resources: A Report to the Committee on Natural Resources, Nat. Acad. Sci., Nat. Res. Counci. Publ. 1000-D, 1962: and Hubbert, op. cit., 1974)

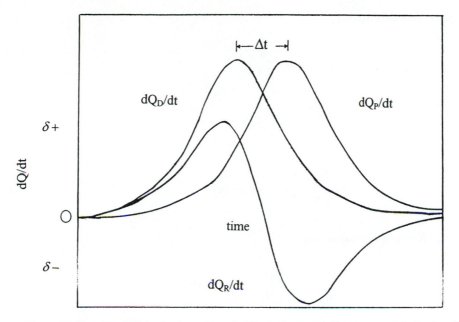

Figure 5-19. Variation of rates of production, of proved discovery, and of rate of increase of proved reserves of crude or natural gas during a complete production cycle. (After Hubbert, op. cit., 1962 and 1974)

$$\frac{dQ_D}{dt} - \frac{dQ_P}{dt} = \frac{dQ_R}{dt} \qquad [5\text{-}17]$$

When Q_R is max.,

$$\frac{d\,Q_R}{dt} = 0 \qquad [5\text{-}18]$$

then

$$\frac{d\,Q_D}{dt} = \frac{d\,Q_P}{dt} \qquad [5\text{-}19]$$

But

$$Q_D = \frac{Q_\infty}{1 + ae^{-bt}}$$

Q_∞ is ultimate discovery

$$t = 0, \quad Q_D = \frac{Q_\infty}{1+a}$$

$$t = \infty, \quad Q_D = Q_\infty$$

$$\log\left(\frac{Q_\infty}{Q_D} - 1\right) = \log a - bt \qquad\qquad [5\text{-}20]$$

a and b can be evaluated from

$$\log\left(\frac{Q_\infty}{Q_D} - 1\right) \text{ vs. } t \text{ plot}$$

In this regard, the fossil utilization is finite, only occurring as a short time interval when one considers a ±5000 year period. The fossil fuel use exploited by mankind is only a blink of time (Figure 5-20). Long-term reserves may come from nuclear fusion or solar power as indicated in Figure 5-21.

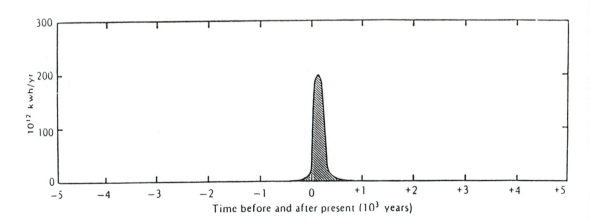

Figure 5-20.   Epoch of fossil-fuel exploitation in perspective of human history from 5,000 years in the past to 5,000 years in the future. (Modified from Hubbert, 1962)

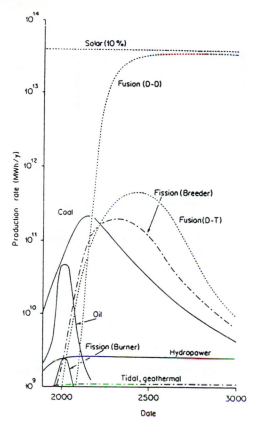

Figure 5-21.   Possible fuel consumption levels and projected availability of reserves.

5.4.2   McKelvey's Microanalytical Model

This model is based on cost and geological factors by a stepwise analysis of the deposit domains in a specific region. The analytical methods involve statistical approximations including a regressional analysis.

$$L = \frac{REI}{P}$$ [5-21]

Here

L = living standard

R = resource

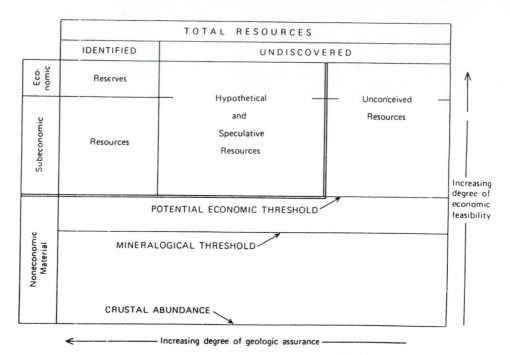

Figure 5-22.   The relation of resources to noneconomic mineral materials. (Source: Brobst, 1979)

E = energy

I = ingenuity (socioeconomic, political, and technological)

P = capita

$$\frac{E}{P} = a + b\,\frac{G}{P}$$

[5-22]

G = GNP

$$E_t = \frac{E_m}{g} + E_s$$

[5-23]

Here

E_t = total energy required

E_m = mining energy

E_s = smelting and refining energy

g = grade

Therefore, **Resource** depends on an increasing degree of both **geological assurance** (measured, indicated, inferred, hypothetical, speculative, and so on) and **economic feasibility** (submarginal, paramarginal, and so on), as shown in Figure 5-22. For each mineral there is a separate mineralogical barrier and threshold above crustal abundance, as shown here.

	%
Fe	5
Al	8.13
Cu	0.007

Such a barrier can be illustrated by Figure 5-23 for the copper ore. If it is below 0.007%, it is not economical to recover.

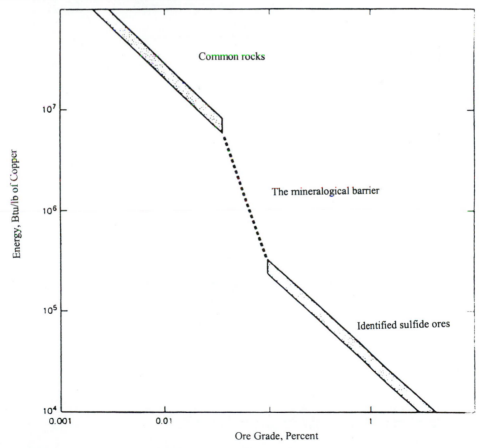

Figure 5-23.   The mineralogical barrier.

5.4.3   Dynamic Model of Meadows

Dennis Meadows's model concluded that reserves are finite, the usage rate will create substitution technology, and recycling is minor. He suggested a static reserve life index (s) and an exponential reserve life index (e), where

$$e = \frac{\ln{(Rs+1)}}{R}$$

[5-24]

in which R = annual fractional growth rate.

All resources are limited from 1980 to 2050 as shown in Figure 5-24.

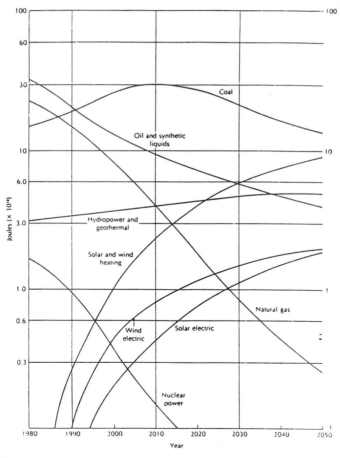

Figure 5-24.   Energy supply 1980 - 2050.

	s (yr)	*e* (yr)
coal	900	110
Fe	400	86
Al	175	60
Ni	140	55
Petroleum	70	35
Cu	40	26
Ag	20	16
Pb	15	12
Hg	13	11

5.4.4 Odum Ecological Model

Howard Odum proposed that the energy network is similar to electrical circuitry, as shown in Figure 5-25. All calculations can be performed as though it were systematic engineering. The essential points are as follows:

- Energy flows in the complex forest ecosystem, which includes all humans, such that

$$n = 1 + \frac{\left(\dfrac{\log E}{NPP}\right)}{\log \eta} \qquad [5\text{-}25]$$

where

n = trophic level

E = energy

NPP = net primary production

η = ecological efficiency

- Man's diverse work substitutes ecosystem variety in an agricultural system.
- Fossil fuel subsidized agriculture is a colonial member of technological society with maximum solar conversion.
- Energy is the organizing principle from which all economic, social, and political values are derived.

- Maximum power is in the middle of high rate and low efficiency, and vice versa for all competitors.

Finally, a diagram can illustrate the fossil energy flow in our ecosystem, as shown in Figure 5-26.

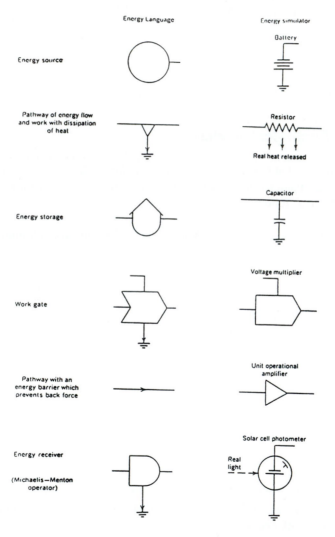

Figure 5-25.   Symbols for electric hardware items which are substituted for parts of the energy network diagram in making an energy simulator. (Source: Odum, 1976, Ref. 5-9)

a) self contained solar conversion

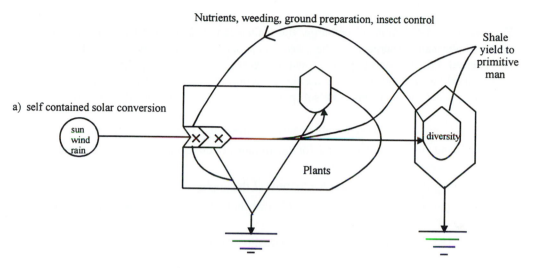

Man a minor part of the complex forest ecosystem.

b) Man's diverse work substituting
   for ecosystem variety.

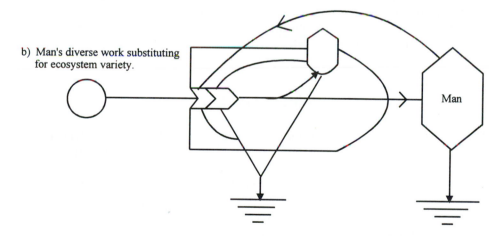

Man a major partner in an agricultural system on light alone.

Figure 5-26.   Forest ecosystem.

5.5 ENERGY CONSERVATION AND ITS CHEMICAL PERSPECTIVE

Following the 1973 Arab oil embargo, the United States developed technologies based on new and alternative sources. At the same time, social, economic, and political realizations had exerted influence on the public towards a **soft path** on energy policy instead of developing "hard" technology to accelerate the depletion of nonrenewable resources, as seen in the past. As defined by Lovins, the soft path consists of the following alternatives:

- relying heavily on renewable energy sources such as solar, and biomass
- being diverse and tailored for maximum effectiveness under specific circumstances
- being flexible and accessible to most of the public
- being matched in both geographic distribution and scale to prominent end use needs
- a good agreement between energy quality and end use

In 1991, the Union of Concerned Scientists and other conservation organizations united and issued three other scenarios (soft path) other than the U.S. government analysis, which anticipates a one-time increase of energy consumption by 2030 based on 1988. Even the market driven scenario of a GNP 2.1% annual growth is better. The softest scenario is the climate stabilization scenario, which is designed to achieve a 25% reduction of CO_2 emulsions by 2005 and a 50% reduction by 2030. Regardless, since the selecting of soft path, many technologies have been developed for the conservation of energy. They will be discussed in the following sections.

5.5.1   Intra, Inter and Combined Fuel Conversions

Intrafuel conversion signifies that a given raw fuel can produce more than one type of end-use fuel. For example, high volatile bituminous B coal can be used for liquefaction as well as gasification; thus, it can produce coal gas as well as coal liquid. The optimum yield of either product will depend on the type of raw coal that is fed to a given process. Furthermore, direct conversion or indirect conversion (such as Fischer-Tropsch Synthesis) can be evaluated (refer to Fig. 5-16). **Interfuel conversion** is the use of two or more raw fuels as feedstacks to derive one type of end fuel. Petroleum has been used with coal for a liquefaction process. The use of spent nuclear fuel as a catalyst for petroleum refining is another example. The **combined fuel conversion** is intended for the end use for two or more usages from one type of fuel. A good example is **cogeneration** in which both electricity and space heating can be achieved. The magnetohydrodynamics is another example where coal is thermally decomposed to obtain the energy in the meantime, during the same time iodine vapor is conditioned in the magnetic field to increase the current for yielding more electricity. The combined cycles for geothermal energy production to increase the efficiency is another example.

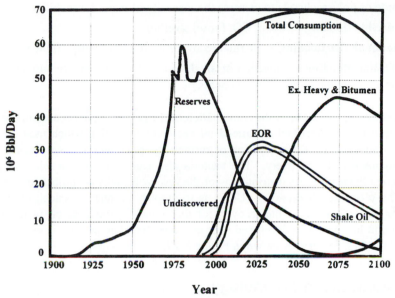

Figure 5-27.   World Crude Oil Supply from 1900 to 2100. (Source: from DOE, *Energy Outlook to the Year 2000 an Overview*, 1990, p.3)

5.5.2   Enhanced Oil Recovery (EOR) and Ultimate Oil Recovery (UOR)

When a petroleum oil field is discovered, the natural stored energy (expansion of natural gas or volatile component) assisted by pumping will produce oil. This stage is usually referred to as a **primary recovery**. As the energy is depleted, production declines and water is injected to the reservoir and this is called **secondary recovery**. When the water-to-oil production ratio of the field approaches an economic limit of operation — the net profit diminishes because the difference between the value of the produced oil and the cost of water injection and treatment becomes too narrow. The **enhanced oil recovery (EOR)** or the **tertiary recovery** begin. The combined total oil production of primary and secondary recovery is generally less than 40% of the original oil in place. The target setting for EOR is an additional 10–15%. In most cases, the oil well is shut down and about 50% of the oil can never be recovered.

Current EOR technology involves the following:

- **surfactant flooding** — reduction of interfacial tension assistance in emulsification

- **polymer flooding** — addition of water-soluble polymers such as polyacrylamide or polysaccharide to increase the viscosity of water for mobility control

- **miscible flooding** — use of CO_2 for oil swelling

- **steam or fire flooding** — thermal recovery to improve sweep efficiency

- **alkaline flooding** — injection of alkali to and from the in situ surfactant with the acid portion of the oil components

For recovery, either one or the combination of the preceding list is used in the field. A good example is the **microbial enhanced oil recovery** (MEOR), which uses the injected bacteria and nutrients for the production of surfactants, polymers, gases, solvents, and biomass simultaneously for recovery. The bacteria also can be used as a selective plugging agent for great heterogeneous distributions of the reservoir racks in propensity and permeability. The **ultimate oil recovery** (UOR) is to employ ultimate physical, chemical, and microbiological techniques to the recovery of the remaining residual oil in the reservoir. This technique has not been developed. At any rate the EOR process is essential for the duration of the 21st century, as shown in Figure 5-27.

5.5.3   Substitution Technology

Because waste can be looked upon as a resource, recycling becomes important. The problem is that based on the constraint of material, some resources cannot be recycled indefinitely; for example, paper can only be recycled up to 4 times — maybe a process involving an ink that will fade in a fixed duration so that paper can be reused is still needed to be invented. The consideration of material is essential to the proper recycling. This theory will be illustrated in the following example. In many communities, the use of styrofoam food containers has been banned because the material is nonbiodegradable. Yet, in a careful study of a styrofoam cup versus a paper cup on a per cup basis, the styrofoam cup has less environmental impact compared to a paper cup. This is due to the weight of the required raw material (polyfoam vs. paper cup, 1.59g vs. 10.1g). As resources deplete, especially for metals, new technology or substitution should be in place. In Figure 5-28 the chromium usage requires substitution. Recycling for metals plays an important role because it only requires a small fraction of energy compared to the energy used to extract and manufacture the metals from ores. Typically, the reprocessing of aluminum cans of soft drinks only requires 5% of the energy compared to the processing from aluminum ore. Some metals are higher; for example, steel requires 48%.

Due to the shortage and deprivation of nonrenewable resources, new substitution technology will be initiated. For example, carbon fibers will replace steel. In substitution, model economics becomes important. For example, the market share, F, of the introduction of new technology will rise exponentially in the beginning and reach a saturation lag phase.

$$\frac{dF}{dt} = \alpha F(1-F) = \alpha F - \alpha F^2 \qquad [5\text{-}26]$$

upon integration

$$F(t) = \frac{1}{\{1 + \exp[-(\alpha t + c)]\}} \qquad [5\text{-}27]$$

α determines the speed of the substitution process and c is the integration constant. The case is for two competing commodities. From system dynamics, it can also be stated as:

$$\frac{dF}{dt} = \frac{\alpha F(1-F)^2}{[\gamma F + (1-F)]} \qquad [5\text{-}28]$$

Now γ is time dependent to exogenous restrictions.

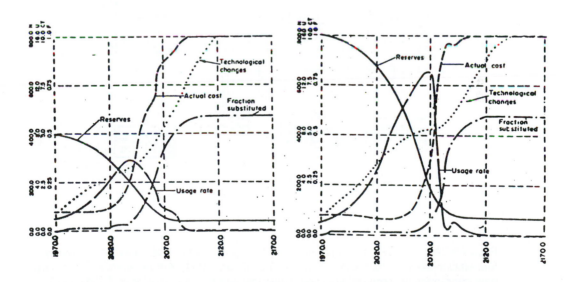

Figure 5-28.   Chromium usage patterns (a) with 1970 reserve (b) double the reserve U (usage), N (reserves), C (cost), T (technology), F (fraction substituted). (After Meadows et al., Ref. 5-6)

5.5.4   Environmentally-Benign Processing (Green Process)

In the 90s, energy efficiency is applicable to the most industrial processes. For example, automobile energy intensities in the United States (mJ per vehicle per km) and fuel economy (L/100 km) have been improved from 1970 to 1990. Improvement will be made for cutting the loss of efficiency due to aerodynamic drag and to breaking. An effort will also be made to reduce the weight by (maybe) using carbon fiber composites.(see Figure 5-29 for the "greener" vehicles). Research and development are centered on novel process designs and process improvement that would reduce the potential for environmental release. Also, for fossil fuel production, feedstock substitutions, alternative synthetic and separation procedures with efficient catalysts a new process that would minimize by-products formation and reduce waste at the source will be developed. Some areas are under consideration.

- more highly selective catalysts
- low temperature and pressure operations
- low-energy separation techniques
- synthesis that bypass toxic feedstock and solvents
- substitution of halogenated solvents

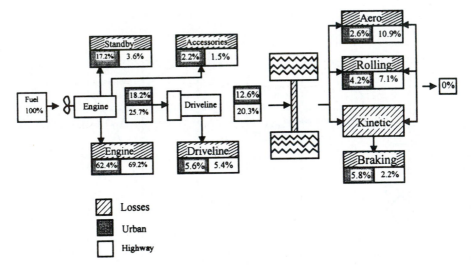

Figure 5-29.   Energy losses in automobile transport point to strategies for improving fuel efficiencies in automobiles. (Source: D.L. Illman (1994). Auto-makers move toward new generation of "greener" vehicles. *Chemical and Engineering News* 72(31): 8-16. Copyright 1994 by American Chemical Society. Reprinted with permission)

REFERENCES

5-1 T. F. Yen and G.V. Chilingarian (eds), *Oil Shale*, Elsevier Science, New York, 1976.

5-2 T. F. Yen, *Science and Technology of Oil Shale*, Ann Arbor Science, Ann Arbor, Michigan, 1976.

5-3 E. C. Donaldson, G.V. Chiligarian, and T.F. Yen, *Enhanced Oil Recovery*, *I*, *Fundamentals and Analyses*, Elsevier Science, New York, 1985.

5-4 R. E. Zimm, "Nuclear Energy Resources and Long-Term Energy Requirement," Angewandte Chem. 10, 1-19 (1971).

5-5 K. A. D. Inglis, *Energy, from Surplus to Sarcity?* Applied Science, Barking, Essex, UK, 1974.

5-6 D. H. Meadows, D. L. Meadows, J. Randers, and W. W. Behrens III, *The Limit to Growth: A Report for the Club of Rome's Project on the Predicament of Mankind*, Universe Books, New York, 1972.

5-7 Readings from Scientific American, *Chemistry in the Environment*, W.H. Freeman, San Francisco, California, 1973.

5-8 H. T. Odum, *Environment, Power, and Society*, John Wiley, New York, 1970.

5-9 H. T. Odum and E. C. Odum, *Energy Basis for Man and Nature*, McGraw Hill, New York, 1976.

5-10 C. A. S. Hall, C. J. Cleveland, and R. Kaufmann, *Energy and Resource Quality*, Wiley-Interscience, New York, 1986.

5-11 J. T. McMullan, R. Morgan, and Murray, *Energy Resources and Supply*, Wiley, London, 1976.

5-12 A. B. Lovin, *Soft Energetics: Toward a Durable Peace*, Harper and Row, New York, 1979.

5-13 Union of Concerned Scientists Alliance to Save Energy, American Concil for An Energy Efficient Economy, Natural Resources Defense Concil, American's Energy Choices, *Investing in a Strong Economy and a Clean Environment*, Union of Concerned Scientists, Cambridge, Massachusetts, 1991.

5-14 M. B. Hocking, "Paper Versus Polystyrene: A Complex Choice," Science, 251, 504-505, 1991.

5-15 T. F. Yen, "Chemical Aspects of Interfuel Conversion," Energy Sources, 117-136, 1973.

5-16 E. C. Donaldson, G. V. Chilingarian, and T. F. Yen, *Enhanced Oil Recovery, II, Process and Operation*, Elsevier Science, Amsterdam, 1989.

5-17   T. F. Yen, *Microbial Enhanced Oil Recovery: Principal and Practice*, CRC Press, Boca Raton, Florida, 1990.

5-18   M. K. Hubbert, Resources and Man, W.H. Freeman, San Francisco, California, 1973.

5-19   M. Christian and H. M. Groscarth, "Modeling Dynamic Substitution Process in Energy Supply Systems," Energy Sources, 17, 295-311 (1995).

5-20   Y. P. Hsia and T. F. Yen, "Evaluation of Coal Liquefaction Efficiency Based on Various Ranks," Energy Sources, 3, 46-53 (1976).

5-21   *The Institue of Fuel, Fuel and the Environment*, London, 1973.

5-22   L. H. Keith, *Energy and Environmental Chemistry, Fossil Fuels*, Ann Arbor Science, Ann Arbor, Michigan, 1982.

5-23   W. J. Mitsch, R. K. Rasade, R. W. Bosserman, and J. A. Dillon, Jr. *Energetics and Systems*, Ann Arbor Science, Ann Arbor, Michigan, 1982.

5-24   R. L. Seale and R. A. Sierka, *Energy Needs and the Environment*, University of Arizona Press, Tucson, Arizona, 1973.

5-25   J. K. Jacques, J. B. LeSourd and J. M. Ruiz, *Modern Applied Energy Conservation*, Ellis Horwood, Chichester, England, 1988.

5-26   W. J. Mitsch, R. K. Rasade, R. W. Bosserman and J. A. Dillon, Jr. *Energetics and Systems*, Ann Arbor Science, Ann Arbor, MI, 1982.

5-27   T. L. Shaw, D. E. Lennard, and P. M. S. Jones, *Policy and Development of Energy Resources*, Wiley, Chichester, England, 1884.

5-28   F. Benn, J. Edewor, and C. McAuliffe, *Production and Utilization of Synthetic Fuels--An Energy Economic Study*, Halsted, New York, 1981.

5-29   D. Trantolo and D. Wise, *Energy Recovery from Lignin, Peat and Lower Rank Coals*, Elsevier, Amsterdam, 1989.

5-30   E. M. Goodger, *Alternative Fuels: Chemical Energy Resources*, Wiley, New York, 1980.

5-31   E. W. Erikson and L. Waverman, *The Energy Question, An International Failure of Policy*, Vol. 1, *The Word*, Vol. 2. North America, University of Toronto Press, Toronto, 1974.

5-32   R. K. Hessley, J. W. Reasoner, and J. T. Riley, *Coal Science, An Introduction to Chemistry, Technology, and Utilization*, Wiley, New York, 1986.

5-33   R. F. Naill, *Managing the Energy Transition, a System Dynamics Search for Alternatives to Oil and Gas*, Ballinger, Cambridge, Massachusetts, 1977.

5-34 A. B. Lovins, *Soft Energy Patterns, Toward a Durable Peace*, Ballinger, Cambridge, Massachusetts, 1977.

5-35 B. R. Cooper and W. A. Ellingson, *The Science and Technology of Coal and Coal Utilization*, Plenum, New York, 1984.

5-36 G. V. Chillingarian and T. F. Yen, *Bitumen Asphalts and Tar Sands*, Elsevier, Amsterdam, 1978.

PROBLEM SET

1.   What is the temperature corresponding to a photosynthetic conversion (1.0 ev photons)? If a Carnot engine is running on radiant energy use by plant life, what is the efficiency? When carbohydrates burn, they release 112 kcal/g mole. Estimate the energy required to form the carbohydrate molecule.

2.   Differentiate between energy and power. Express the following energy terms in the two different units:

   a.   Earth's daily receipt of solar energy

   b.   daily output of the Hoover Dam

   c.   chemical energy in 100 barrels of oil

   d.   chemical energy in a gram of lignite

3.   Express the following power units in Watts:

   a.   average solar input to earth

   b.   a large gas guzzler

   c.   household washer

   d.   human heart

4.   Express the following energy sources in terms of a Quad and a Quin:

   a.   10 cubic miles of coal

   b.   10 sections of wheat growing for 3000 years (one crop per year)

   c.   1000 gallons of sea water for deuterium

   d.   2 trillion tons of Green River oil shale of 25 gal/ton grade

CHAPTER **6**

THE LITHOSPHERE — ALTERNATIVE ENERGY SOURCES

*I*n the preceding chapter, we focused our attention on fossil energy — petroleum, coal, oil shale, and tar sand. There are a number of alternatives to fossil fuels (such as solar, wind, tidal, geothermal, chemical, and nuclear energy) that are also important in helping us meet our energy demands. These are called **alternative energy sources**.

There are many different ways to classify different fuel types and at this time, there are quite a few types that warrant our attention. The first category is the improvement of conventional energy; a good illustration is enhanced oil recovery (EOR) or enhanced gas recovery (EGR). Magnetohydrodynamics (MHD), the most efficient use of coal, also belongs to this group. The next category is the interfuel refining and intrafuel optimization. Both categories are largely related to fossil fuels although the second type will include nuclear energy. The third category is the **nonrenewable energy** such as nuclear and geothermal energy. Then follows the **supplementary fuel** (auxiliary fuel) such as solar, tidal, wind, and ocean currency. The last important category is **chemical fuel** such as hydrogen and methanol. With regards to hydrogen, it is often called "ecofuel," signifying that it is compatible with the environment. The supplementary fuel and chemical fuel are **renewable energy**.

In this chapter, we will first spend some time discussing the thermal pollution problem, and then move to the main topic, the primary source — solar energy. Finally, we will look at other alternative sources of energy such as wind, tidal, geothermal, and chemical power.

6.1 WASTE HEAT

Even if we could be supplied with an unlimited amount of energy, there would still be difficulties associated with the ever-increasing use of energy. One general problem under the heading of thermal pollution is the disposal of all the heat that accompanies energy utilization. All energy generation, no matter what form it may take for the moment, eventually appears as a **heat burden** on the environment. A power station that generates electricity uses heat supplied by either the burning of fossil or nuclear fuels, to produce the steam that runs a turbine. Even if everything works with perfect efficiency, however, only a fraction of the heat can be converted to useful work. Throughout history, humans have tried their best to develop better heat engines as shown in Figure 6-1, but ultimate efficiency is still limited by their nature. These limits, expressed by the laws of thermodynamics, cannot be circumvented by clever engineering tricks. They represent the best we could do if everything went as well as possible. As illustrated in Figure 6-2, for a steam electric power plant, heat is delivered to a boiler at a temperature of T_2, and after driving the turbine, the steam is condensed at a lower temperature of T_1. The maximum efficiency, or the ratio of work output to heat input, is given by the temperature difference, $T_2 - T_1$, divided by the input temperature, T_2. This ratio is a consequence of the second law of thermodynamics and is a fundamental property of nature.

The first law of thermodynamics tells us that energy is conserved, so that

$$Q_s = Q_r + W \qquad\qquad [6\text{-}1]$$

where

Q_s = energy supplied to the heat engine

Q_r = heat rejected (waste heat) to the environment

W = quantity of work produced

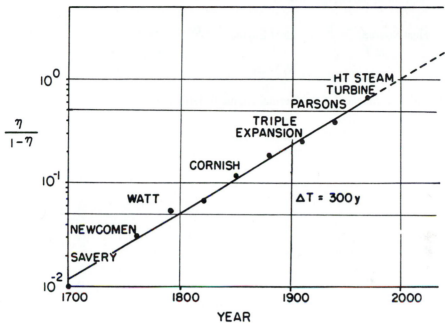

Figure 6-1. Efficiency of prime movers.

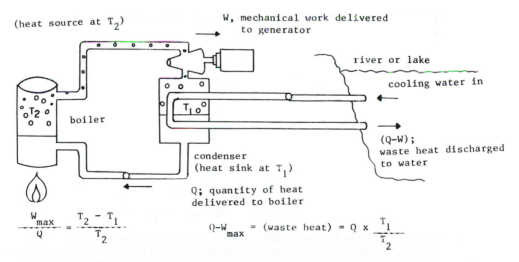

Figure 6-2. Maximum work and waste heat from steam electric power plant.

A diagram of the energy flow is

Heat Source $\xrightarrow{\ Q_s\ }$ Heat Engine $\xrightarrow{\ Q_r\ }$ Heat Sink

at T_s $\downarrow$ at T_r

W, Work

The ideal efficiency of the thermal engine is defined as

$$\eta = (W_{max}/Q_s) = (Q_s - Q_r)/Q_s = (T_s - T_r)/T_s \qquad [6\text{-}2]$$

So

$$W = \eta Q_s \qquad [6\text{-}3]$$

$$Q_r = (1 - \eta)\, Q_s \qquad [6\text{-}4]$$

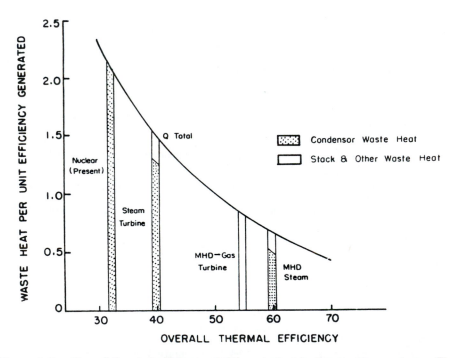

Figure 6-3.   Overall thermal efficiency of different electrical generating systems. The waste heat produced increases rapidly with decreasing efficiency. (Source: Richard J. Rosa, Avco Corp.)

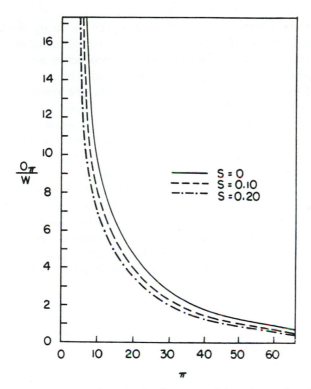

Figure 6-4.   The ratio of heat rejection to useful work as a function of overall plant efficiency. The effect of heat rejected in terms of stack loss (S) is also shown.

Similarly, the rate can be written $\dot{Q}_r = (1 - \eta)\, \dot{Q}_s$ The waste heat produced increases rapidly with decreasing efficiency as shown in Figure 6-3. If we also take the stack losses into consideration as shown in Figure 6-4, then

$$Q_r / W = (1 - \eta - s) / \eta \qquad\qquad [6\text{-}5]$$

Table 6-1.   Thermal Efficiencies of the Heat Engines Using Different Energy Sources

Energy Source	Q_r / W	η
Fossil fuel	1.75 – 1.6	0.36 – 0.33
Nuclear	2.33 – 2.0	0.30 – 0.33
Geothermal	4.2	0.19
Solar farm	2.33	0.30
Fusion	1.0	0.50

Table 6-1 shows the thermal efficiencies of heat engines using different energy sources. A plant operating at 40% efficiency produces 4 calories of useful work and 6 calories of waste heat for every 10 calories of fuel burned. This production means that for every calorie of useful work produced, 1.5 calories of waste heat have to be carried away.

Small portions of the waste heat from a fossil fuel plant are transferred to the environment through the hot gases emitted from the smokestack. A large fraction — 85% — is transferred via the condenser, which cools and condenses the hot steam. In a nuclear plant that has no smokestack, essentially all of the waste heat is rejected to the surroundings via the cooling water except the chemonuclear reactor concept. For large, modern, power stations, the volume of water required is enormous. It is estimated that 100,000 ft³/min of cooling water is required in a 1000 mega-watt power plant. Already more than 10% of the total water stream flow in the United States is used for this purpose. It is becoming increasingly difficult to find sites where this much water is available. Moreover, there are the ecological consequences of the cooling water stream flow to consider. For one thing, fish or other marine life can be sucked into the intake and killed. There is also concern that the increase in the temperature of the discharge water, as shown in Figure 6-5, may be harmful to aquatic life.

[Example 6-1]   Considering a coal plant for generation of 1400MW of power, calculate the required cooling water flow if the condenser temperature change is 20°F. Assume 85% of the waste heat is carried off by the condenser cooling water.

From Equation [6-4]

$$\dot{Q}_r = r(1-\eta)\dot{Q}_s \qquad\qquad (a)$$

here $\dot{Q} = \dfrac{dQ}{dt}$ and r is the plant efficiency.

One Btu raises the temperature one 1b of water for one °F, then the flow rate of water,

$$Q = \frac{\dot{Q}_r}{\Delta T} \qquad\qquad (b)$$

If we can express the power generated, P as KW, then from Equation [6-3], we have

$$P = \dot{W} = \eta\dot{Q}_s \qquad\qquad (c)$$

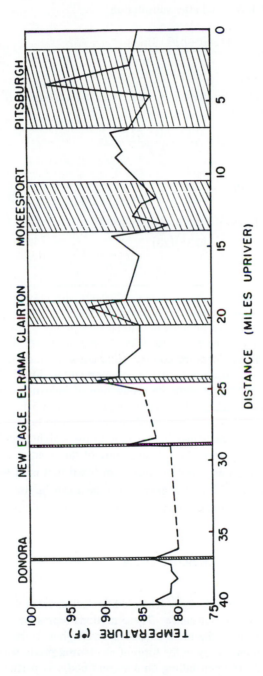

Figure 6-5. Water temperatures can become very high, particularly in summer, along rivers with concentrated industry. The chart shows the temperature of the Monongahela River measured in August, along a 40-mile stretch upriver from its confluence with the Ohio.

Because 3413 Btu = 1 KWH and after substitution

$$Q_r = \frac{3413r(1-\eta)P}{\eta} \quad \frac{\text{Btu}}{\text{hr}} \tag{d}$$

If we express by Q as cfs, then divided by 3600 (sec/ hr) × 62.4 (lb/ ft^3)

$$Q = \frac{0.152\, r\, (1-\eta)P}{\eta\, \Delta T} \quad \text{cfs}$$

Because $r = 0.85$, $\eta = 0.35$

$$Q = \frac{(0.152)(0.85)(0.65)(1.4\times10^6)}{(0.35)(20)} = 1680 \quad \text{cfs}$$

Measures have been taken to reduce the demand for cooling water. Dry cooling towers, using air as a coolant, have been adopted in some power plants. The disadvantages are more noise and less efficiency. There are also ways to use the waste heat from electrical plants purposefully, which also reduces the cooling water consumption. One way is to simply use the hot water outflow to heat residential or commercial buildings. Another possibility is to combine electrical generation with the production of industrial process heat. The latter is called **cogeneration**, which has been metioned in section 5.5.1, combing the water heat from electric generation to space heating. Research has also been done for applying waste heat to heat fish ponds. It was found that the ratio of the weight that the fish gained to the weight of feed food increases from 25% (temperature of the pond at 2°C) to 75% (temperature at 30°C). Most of the waste heat product from fossil fuel is of **low grade** (below 120°C) and fluctuate uncertainly. The low grade waste heat can be used as defrosting for fruits and plants to extend the growing season.

6.2 PLANK'S LAW AND ABSORPTION

Every object is a source of **radiant energy**. The radiation arises from the electron motions of the atoms and molecules of the substance. These motions represent the heat energy the object possesses. The hotter it is, the more extensive and higher in frequency the motion becomes. A heated body emits energy in the form of **electromagnetic waves**. This energy is radiated in all directions, and upon falling on a second body, is partially absorbed, partially reflected, and partially transmitted, as indicated in Figure 6-6. The fraction of the incident radiation absorbed is known as the **absorptivity** (*a*) and the fraction reflected, the **reflectivity** of the body. The reflectivity is also called **albedo** (*A*), which varies with surfaces, as shown in Table 6-2. The amount transmitted will therefore depend on the following two properties:

$$I = Ab + R + T$$

$$a = (1 - A) \qquad\qquad [6\text{-}6]$$

where *I* is incident energy, *Ab* is absorbed energy, *R* is reflected energy, and *T* is transmitted energy.

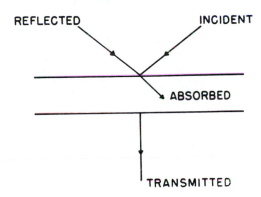

Figure 6-6. Reflection, adsorption, and transmission of radiation.

As previously mentioned, electromagnetic waves are emitted from hot surfaces — the higher the temperature of the surface, the greater the radiation energy flux leaving it, and the higher the frequencies of the departing electromagnetic waves. The way in which the energy in black body emissions is distributed over the wavelength spectrum could be explained by **Plank's quantum theory**. The emissive power of a black surface is

$$P(T) = \frac{2\pi\, hc^2}{\left[\lambda^5 \left(\exp\left(\dfrac{hc}{\lambda kT}\right)\right) - 1\right]} \qquad\qquad [6\text{-}7]$$

where

P = power density in W/m^3

λ = wavelength

T = absolute temperature

c = velocity of light

h = Plank's constant

k = Boltzmann constant

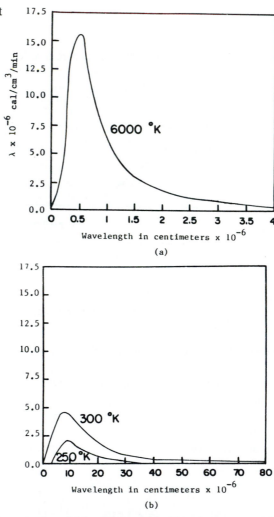

Figure 6-7.   Black-body emission of (a) a hot body such as the sun, and (b) a cool body such as the earth.

Table 6-2. Reflectivity or "Albedo" of Various Surfaces

Surface	% Reflected
Clouds (stratus) <500 ft thick	5 - 63
500 – 1000 ft thick	31 – 75
1000 – 2000 ft thick	59 – 84
average of all types and thicknesses	50 – 55
Concrete	17 – 27
Crops, green	5 – 15
Forest, green	5 – 10
Meadows, green	10 – 20
Ploughes dield, moist	14 – 17
Road, black top	5 – 10
Sand, white	34 – 40
Snow, fresh fallen	75 – 90
Snow, old	45 – 70
Soil, dark	5 – 15
Soil, light (or desert)	25 – 30
Water	8*

*Typical value for water surface, but the reflectivity increases sharply from less than 5% when the sun's altitude above the horizon is greater than 30°, to more than 90% when the altitude is less than 3°. The roughness of the sea surface also affects the albedo somewhat.

A comparison of the black body emission of a hot body and a cold body is shown in Figure 6-7. For any temperature, the distribution curve has a maximum value. The value of λ for which this maximum occurs may be found by determining $(dP/d\lambda)_T$ and finding what value of λ will make the derivative zero.

$$\left(\frac{\partial P}{\partial \lambda}\right)_T = 0 \qquad\qquad [6\text{-}8]$$

let

$$x = \frac{hc}{\lambda kT}$$

and substituting into Equation [6-7]

$$P = \frac{2\pi \, k^5 T^5}{h^4 c^3} \, \frac{x^5}{e^x - 1} \qquad\qquad [6\text{-}9]$$

$$\ln P = \ln \frac{2\pi \, k^5 T^5}{h^4 c^3} + 5 \ln x - \ln\left(e^x - 1\right)$$

then

$$\left(\frac{\partial \ln P}{\partial x}\right)_T = 0 + \frac{5}{x} - \frac{1}{e^x - 1}\frac{\partial(e^x - 1)}{\partial x} = \frac{5}{x} - \frac{e^x}{e^x - 1}$$

$$= \frac{5}{x} - (1 + e^{-x} + e^{-2x} + e^{-3x} + ...) = \frac{5}{x} - 1 - e^{-x} = 0 \qquad [6\text{-}10]$$

$$x + xe^{-x} = 5, \quad x = 4.9651 = \frac{hc}{\lambda kT} \qquad\qquad [6\text{-}11]$$

The result is that

$$\lambda T = 0.288 \text{ cm-degree K} \qquad\qquad [6\text{-}12]$$

which is **Wien's displacement law.**
Equation [6-12] can predict the wavelength of a black body; for example,

$$\lambda_{(sun)} = \frac{2880}{6000} = 0.48 \; \mu\text{m},$$

$$\lambda_{(earth)} = \frac{2880}{273} = 11 \; \mu\text{m}$$

The calculated value is in agreement with the earth's spectrum shown in Figure 6-7.

6.3 STEFAN-BOLTZMANN LAW AND EMISSIVITY

The rate at which a hot body radiates energy is proportional to the fourth power of its absolute temperature and is known as the **Stefan-Boltzmann Law**.

$$P = \sigma T^4 \qquad\qquad [6\text{-}13]$$

where

T = absolute temperature

σ = Stefan-Boltzmann constant, which has the value 5.67×10^{-8} W/m^{2}K^4

The solar flux incident on the earth, the **solar constant (S)**, can be estimated by equating the following two equations, Equations [6-14] and [6-15]:

$$\text{Power radiated by Sun} = 4\pi R_s^2 \sigma T_s^4 \quad \text{(based on black body)} \qquad [6\text{-}14]$$

where $R_s = 6.95 \times 10^8$m (radius of Sun)

$$\text{Power radiated by Sun} = 4\pi R_{SE}^2 S \quad \text{(based on } S \text{ from the earth)} \qquad [6\text{-}15]$$

where $R_{SE} = 1.49 \times 10^{11}$m (earth-sun distance)
Thus,

$$4\pi R_s^2 \sigma T_s^4 = 4\pi R_{SE}^2 S \qquad [6\text{-}16]$$

or

$$T_S = \left(\frac{R_{SE}}{R_S}\right)^{\frac{1}{2}}\left(\frac{S}{\sigma}\right)^{\frac{1}{4}} \qquad [6\text{-}16a]$$

In the preceding equation, if the average temperature of the sun is 6000K, then S can be calculated out as 1400 W/m^2. This value is equivalent to 2 cal/cm^2-min or 2 langleys/min. A simple schematic for those values can be found in Figure 6-8.

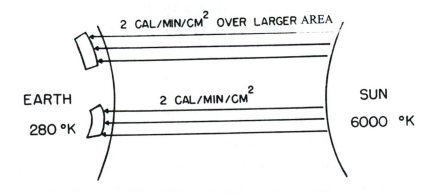

Figure 6-8.   The energy flux from the sun arriving at the earth's surface.

Table 6-3.   Emissivity of Surfaces Near T = 300°K

Material		ε (T ≈ 300°K)
Aluminum	Polished	0.04
	Rough plate	0.06
	Oxidized	0.15
Cast iron		0.50
Sheet steel		0.70
Wood, black lacquer, white enamel, plaster, roofing paper		0.90
Porcelain, marble, brick, glass, rubber, water		0.94

A **black body** is defined as one that absorbs all the radiation falling on it; that is, its absorptivity = 1. The **emissivity,** ε, of a body is a dimensionless factor related to the rate of thermal radiation from a particular surface. It varies with surface temperature, roughness, and color and is an important parameter for indicating the energy trapping ability, as shown in Table 6-3. The emissivity of the earth can be estimated by the following calculation, which sets Equation [6-17] equal to Equation [6-18]:

$$\text{Radiation energy absorbed by the earth} = (1 - A)\pi R_E^2 S \qquad [6\text{-}17]$$

(depending on earth's cross-sectional area)

$$\text{Energy emitted by the earth outward} = (4R_E^2)\,\varepsilon\,(\sigma T_E^4) \qquad [6\text{-}18]$$

$$\text{At equilibrium}\ \ (1 - A)\,\pi R_E^2 S = (4\pi R_E^2)\,\varepsilon\,(\sigma T_E^4)$$

then,

$$(1 - A)S = 4\varepsilon\sigma T_E^4 \qquad [6\text{-}19]$$

Taking $A = 0.35$ and $T_E = 286°K$ (13°C), we obtained $\varepsilon = 0.6$.

By slightly modifying Equation [6-19], one can easily estimate the effect of human utilization of energy on the earth's temperature.

[Example 6-2]   If the earth's average absolute temperature, T, is given by a balance between the absorbed solar energy, $s(1 - A)/4$, and black body radiation, σT^4, what would be the direction and magnitude of the temperature change of

a. the albedo increased by 1%, and

b. power that is generated from fossil or nuclear fuels at a rate equivalent to 1% of the incidental solar energy.

$$\frac{S\left(1-A\right)}{4} = \sigma T^4$$

$$T = \left[\frac{S(1-A)}{4\sigma}\right]^{\frac{1}{4}}$$

$$= \left[\frac{2\,\text{cal/min/cm}^2\,(1-0.4)}{4\left(1.43\times10^{-12}\,\text{cal/sec/cm}^2/°\text{K}\times60\,\text{sec/min}\right)}\right]^{\frac{1}{4}} = 244\ °\text{K}$$

a.

$$\frac{dA}{A} = 0.01\ , \qquad \frac{A}{1-A} = \frac{0.4}{0.6} = \frac{2}{3}$$

$$dT = \left(\frac{-1}{4}\right)\left(\frac{dA}{A}\right)\left(\frac{A}{1-A}\right)(T) = -0.25(0.01)(0.667)(244) = -0.4\ °\text{K}$$

b.

$$\frac{dS}{S} = 0.01$$

$$\frac{dT}{T} = \frac{1}{4}\left[\frac{S(1-A)}{4\sigma}\right]^{-1}\left(\frac{1-A}{4\sigma}\right)dS = \frac{1}{4}\frac{dS}{S}$$

$$dT = \frac{1}{4}\left(\frac{dS}{S}\right)T = \frac{1}{4}(0.01)(244°\,\text{K}) = +0.6°\text{K}$$

As we have seen, the sun provides us with a large input of energy every day. Solar energy is our largest and most lasting energy resource as shown in Table 6-4. To maintain a steady state, the earth must dispose of the energy that it receives from the sun. In section 6.2, we calculated that the earth emits a spectrum of energy with a peak wavelength of about 10,000 nm. If the heat influx to the earth increases or decreases, the outflux will adjust accordingly, and the average temperature of the earth will increase or decrease. It has been estimated that human consumption of energy in the form of fossil or nuclear fuels will equal the solar heat flux within another 14 doubling periods, which at the current rate of increase corresponds to about 320 years. Using Equation [6-19], it is easy to calculate that the average temperature would then increase by 19% or 46°C. Long before that, severe effects, including the melting of the polar ice caps, would be felt.

Human activity could also upset the heat balance by inadvertently changing the albedo. For example, the clearing of forest for agricultural land use increases the albedo from about 10% to 15%. If erosion sets in, leading to dust bowl and eventually desert conditions, the albedo is further increased to 30% (refer to Table 6-2).

Table 6-4.   Estimated World Energy Resources Q = 10^{14} Btu

Resource	Recoverable Quantity	Energy in Q
Oil	2500 billion barrels	15
Natural gas	12000 trillion cubic feet	12
Oil shale	2000 billion barrels	12
Tar sand	300 billion barrels	2
Coal	7600 billion tons	190 – 231
Uranium	1.3 million tons	100
Lithium	0.67 million tons	230
Deuterium	50×10^6 million tons	12×10^6
Photosynthesis on earth		1 Q/year
Solar energy on earth		4000 Q/year
Total solar output		13×10^{13} Q/year

6.4 Solar Technology

Solar energy is an immense resource. Enough sunlight falls yearly on each square meter of earth to equal the energy content of 420 pounds of high-grade bituminous coal. But it is also characterized by low energy density and intermittency. The most convenient and straightforward application of solar energy is the heating of buildings and water. These so-called passive energy systems often involve architectural designs that enhance the absorption of solar energy. The active energy systems require mechanical power such as pumps to circulate air, water, or other fluids from solar collectors to heat sink (for storage). In addition to these applications, there are two more difficult methods for generating electricity from sunlight. One is **solar thermal electric conversion (STEC)**, which indirectly transforms the solar energy into electrical energy; and the other, **photovoltaic energy conversion**, is a method of direct transformation.

6.4.1   Solar Thermal Electric Conversion

Solar thermal electric conversion (STEC) uses collected heat to run a boiler in a steam generator, as shown in Figure 6-9. To achieve sufficiently high temperatures for efficient operation, the sunlight must be focused from many collection units, as shown in Figure 6-10.

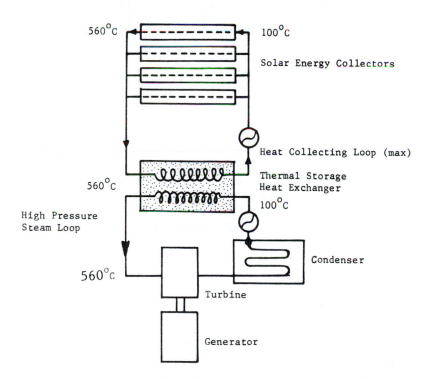

Figure 6-9.   Basic solar energy system using thermal conversion.

Approximately 90% of the solar spectrum is at wavelengths shorter than 1.3 μm, and the spectrum of the escaping infrared radiation, even at 900K, overlaps it very little, as shown in Figure 6-11. Thus, the selective surface for the collectors must be black for wavelengths shorter than 1.3 μm and mirror-like for longer wavelengths. Different materials have different absorption spectra. Figure 6-12 shows that for various gases, oxygen and ozone have strong absorptions of radiation at wavelengths shorter than 0.3 μm. Figure 6-13 shows the calculated optical performance of a thin-film stack for an absorber panel. The panel reflects most of the radiation for wavelengths greater than 1 μm, the reflectance value is close to unity, and the panel absorbs most of the radiation in shorter wave lengths. Silicon so far is the best material for the absorption, as shown in Figure 6-14.

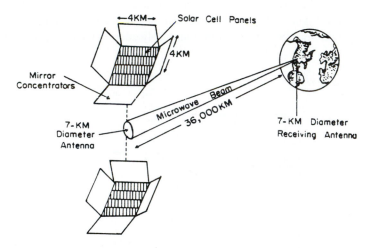

Figure 6-10.   A schematic drawing showing the approximate solar cell panel and antenna dimensions required, with present technology, to produce 10,000 Mw of electrical power on earth using solar cells in synchronous earth orbit.

The following is an example of how to find the temperature of a solar panel:

$$\text{Absorption by panel} = (1-A)S\,(A_p) \qquad\qquad [6\text{-}20]$$

$$\text{Radiation by panel} = \sigma T_p^4 \varepsilon\,(A_p) \qquad\qquad [6\text{-}21]$$

where A_p = area of panel and T_p = panel temperature.
At equilibrium

$$(1-A)S = aS = \sigma T_p^4 \varepsilon \qquad\qquad [6\text{-}22]$$

$$T_p = \left(\frac{aS}{\sigma \varepsilon} \right)^{\frac{1}{4}}$$

[6-23]

Therefore the properties of a collector must be

a) transparent to visible and UV
b) opaque to IR
c) high a and low ε values

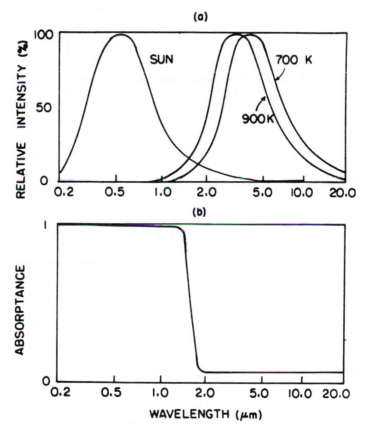

Figure 6-11.   (a) Relative intensities of solar emission and of thermal reradiation for two absorber temperatures. Approximately 90% of the solar spectrum is at wavelengths shorter than 1.3μm, and the spectrum of the escaping infrared radiation, even at 900k, overlaps it very little. Thus, the selective surface must be black for wavelengths shorter than 1.3μm and mirrorlike for longer wavelengths. (b) Spectral characteristic of an ideal selective absorber.

Assume $a = 80\%$, $\varepsilon = 50\%$, $S = 1000$ W/m^2, then $T_p = 125°C$. This temperature is too low. At 30°C, which is ambient, $\eta = (T_H - T_L)/T_H = 25.9\%$. There are two ways, using new film and a focusing mirror, that the panel temperature can be increased. In the case of **new film**, for example, Al coated with CdTe, $a = 90\%$, $\varepsilon = 3.9\%$, and the calculated $T_p = 526°C$. For a **focusing mirror** of 1000:1, $a = 90\%$, $\varepsilon = 1\%$, and the calculated value is $T_p = 6000°C$. For a solar farm, the temperature should reach 560°C.

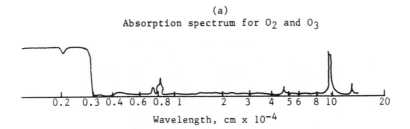

(a)
Absorption spectrum for O_2 and O_3

Wavelength, cm x 10^{-4}

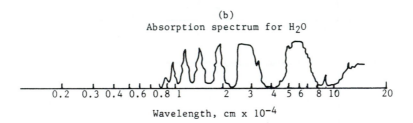

(b)
Absorption spectrum for H_2O

Wavelength, cm x 10^{-4}

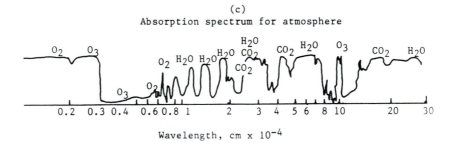

(c)
Absorption spectrum for atmosphere

Wavelength, cm x 10^{-4}

Figure 6-12.   Absorption of radiation at various wavelengths by (a) O_2 and O_3; (b) H_2O; and (c) the principal absorbing gases.

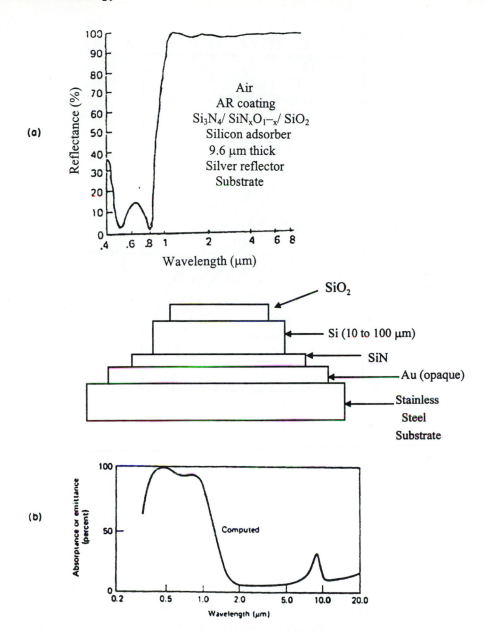

Figure 6-13. (a) Calculated optical performance of that film stack for absorber panel. (b) A possible frequency-selective solar absorption stack and its computed absorption curve. (Modified from A.B. Meinel and M.P. Meinel, "Physics Looks at Solar Energy," *Physics Today*, February, 1972)

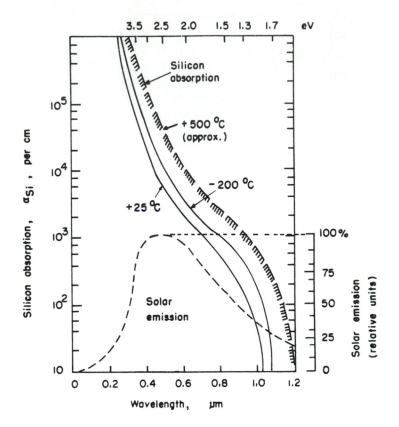

Figure 6-14.   Overlay of silicon absorption and solar emission spectra, indicating optimum thickness of 10 μm for the silicon layer.

6.4.2 Photovoltaic Devices

Photovoltaic devices convert light to electricity by means of a nonthermal process, using solar cells comprised of semiconductors such as silicon. The process works at ambient temperatures and produces no by-products other than heat from sunlight, which is not converted to electricity. Figure 6-16 indicates an overlay of silicon absorption and solar emission spectra. Silicon solar cells, developed for the space program, are the most successful current design. This design consists of a sandwich of p-type (positive) silicon semiconductors that conduct positive charges and n-type (negative) silicon semiconductors that conduct negative charges. A charge separation is developed across the junction between them, as shown in Figure 6-15. There are net positive and negative charges, and the field created is similar to a chemical complexation, as shown in Figure 6-16. If crystalline silicon is doped with boron atoms, a bonded negative charge results (B⁻) as well as free positive holes; on the other hand, if crystalline silicon is doped with arsenic atoms, a bonded positive charge results (As⁺) as well as free negative electrons. When a p-type semiconductor is joined with an n-type (p-n junction), the free charges move away from the interface because of repulsion by the fixed charges. This movement results in a separation of charge and create a potential across the interface. If a photoelectron strikes the p-type semiconductor, it will have the charge to accelerate across the interface before it combines with a hole. The silicon cell produces electricity reliably, but is quite expensive because high-grade crystalline silicon is required.

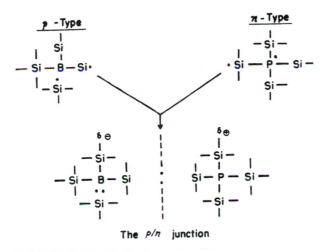

The *p/n* junction

Figure 6-15.   Origin of barrier field.

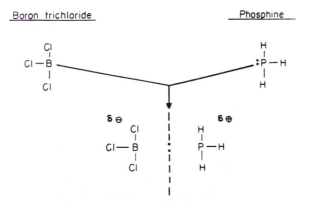

Figure 6-16.   Field creation similar to chemical complexation.

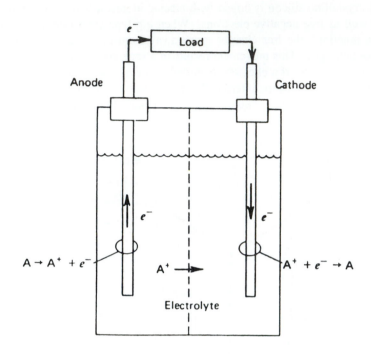

Figure 6-17.   General diagram of an electrochemical cell.

Table 6-5.   Heat Storage in Phase Change

Compound	Transition Temparature (°K)	Heat (J/g)
$CaCl_2 \cdot 6H_2O$	302 – 312	174
$Na_2CO_3 \cdot 10H_2O$	305 – 309	267
$Na_2HPO_4 \cdot 12H_2O$	309	265
$Ca(NO_3)_2 \cdot 4H_2O$	313 – 315	209
$Na_2SO_4 \cdot 10H_2O$	305	241
$Na_2S_2O_2 \cdot 5H_2O$	322 – 324	209

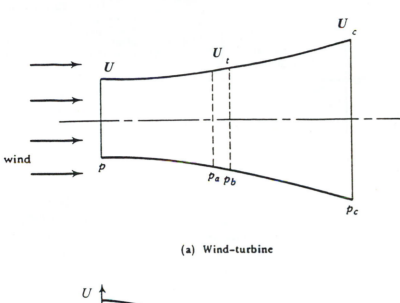

(a) Wind-turbine

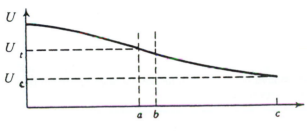

(b) Velocity

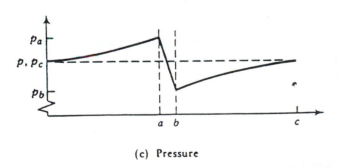

(c) Pressure

Figure 6-19.   An enclosed wind-turbine.

Table 6-6.   Summary of Current Battery Characteristics

	Specific Power (watts per kg)	Energy Density (watt-hours per L)	Specific Energy (watt-hours per kg)	Life (years)	Cycle Life[a] (80%DOD)	Ultimate Cost (\$ per kWh)
BATTERY GOALS[b]						
Mid-term goal	150	135	80	5	600	<150
Long-term goal	400	300	200	10	1,000	<100
CURRENT BATTERY STATUS						
Lead-acid	67 – 138[c]	50 – 82	18 – 56	2 – 3	450 – 1,000	70 – 100
Nickel-iron	70 – 132	60 – 115	39 – 70	na	440 – 2,000	160 – 300
Nickel-cadmium	100 – 200	60 – 115	33 – 70	na	1,500 – 2,000	300
Nickel-metal hydride	200	152 – 215	54 – 80	10	1,000	200
Sodium-sulfur	90 – 130	76 – 120	80 – 140	na	250 – 600	100+
Sodium-nickel chloride	150	160	100	5	600	> 350
Lithium-polymer	100	100 – 120	150	na	300	50 – 500

a cycle life = number of discharges in battery lifetime at 80% depth of discharge.

b USABC figures.

c CARB estimates 170 watts per kg.

na = not available.

Source: "The Keys to the Car: Electric and Hydrogen Vehicles for the 21ˢᵗ Century," World Resources Institute.

Table 6-7.   Energy Density in Storage

	Chemical Energy	Electric-Mechanical Energy
	kcal/c	watt-hr/lb (20% heat efficiency)
Gasoline	11.0	1,150
Lipid	9.3	
Methanol	5.2	550
Ammonia	4.8	510
Carbohydrate	4.1	
Protein	4.1	
Sodium-sulfur battery		385
Conceptual super flywheel		200
Lead acid battery		85
Super flywheel		40
Rubberband		1

Solar energy is a time-dependent energy resource. A means of storing energy is needed to provide an even and continuous supply. There are various methods of storing energy, such as the storage of compressed air in caverns, mechanical energy storage in fly-wheels, and direct electrical storage in large superconducting magnets. Materials that undergo a change of phase in a suitable temperature range may also be useful for energy storage. Table 6-5 lists some common materials used for heat storage. Batteries are also good devices for energy storage, representing chemical storage of electrical energy in a portable form. Table 6-6 lists characteristics for various rechargeable batteries. Although the chemical battery is very efficient in converting electrical energy to chemical energy and back, it is a heavy and expensive storage medium. The lithium-polymer battery is especially suitable for the future because it can easily be packaged in "credit card" form. One of the major energy supplies is in the fuel cell, which will be used for the transportation vehicles in the future, as shown in Figure 6-17. Table 6-7 lists some common energy densities in storage. Figure 6-18 illustrates the specific power and energy of various sources.

There are several points regarding pollution by solar energy that are worth mentioning, because utilizing solar energy is definitely not pollution-free. High temperatures near the solar panel may cause unfavorable air turbulence, resulting in the death of flying birds. So-called "optical pollution" of the solar farm is also felt by some people. In addition, toxic materials are generated in manufacturing the photovoltaic systems.

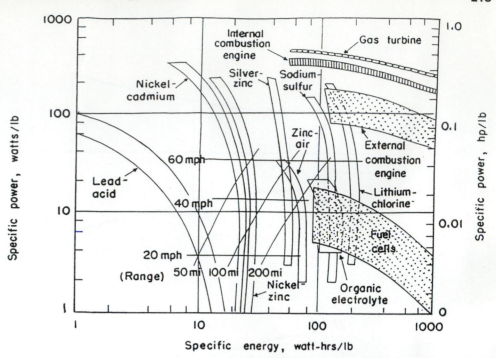

Figure 6-18.   The power and energy requirements for a 2000-lb vehicle utilizing a 500-lb motive power source for steady driving. Power and energy are assumed to be at the output of the device.

6.5 MISCELLANEOUS ENERGY SOURCES

This section is used to illustrate some of the supplementary energy sources such as wind and tidal waves. Furthermore, chemical fuels such as alcohol and hydrogen will be discussed under miscellaneous energy sources.

6.5.1   Wind Power

Wind power has a yearly energy potential of four times the current United States consumption. Windmills have a long history of use throughout the world, and there have been many technical advances in the design of windmills and wind turbines. It seems quite likely that wind power will be an additional economical source of electricity in the near future. The energy density, E, is in J/m^3.

The energy E' is $E' = (1/2) MU^2$ (in J), or $(1/2) \rho AXU^2$, the energy density, E, is

$$E = \frac{1}{2} \rho U^2 \quad \text{in} \left(\frac{\text{J}}{\text{m}^3}\right) \qquad [6\text{-}24]$$

where $\rho = \dfrac{M}{V}$, $V = \dfrac{RT}{P}$, U is velocity of wind, ρ is density, and V is volume.

The power density, P, is (power can be expressed as $P_w = dE'/dt = (1/2) \rho AU^3$ in (W))

$$P = EU = \frac{1}{2} \rho U^3 \quad \text{in (W/m}^2) \qquad [6\text{-}25]$$

Assuming velocities (U) and pressures (p) according to Figure 6-18 and Figure 6-19

U, p at entrance

U_t, p_t at turbine

U_c, p_c at exit

the axial force is

$$F = A\, p_t = \frac{1}{2} \rho A (U^2 - U_c^2) \quad \text{in (Newton)} \qquad [6\text{-}26]$$

which is derived from Bernoulli's equation.

Also, the flow rate,

$$Q = \rho A U_t \quad \text{in (kg/s)} \qquad [6\text{-}27]$$

$$U_t = \frac{1}{2} (U + U_c) \qquad [6\text{-}28]$$

$$F = QU - QU_c = \rho A U_t (U - U_c) \quad \text{in (kg - m/s}^2) \qquad [6\text{-}29]$$

Thus

$$\rho A U_t (U - U_c) = \frac{1}{2} \rho A (U^2 - U_c^2) = \frac{1}{2} \rho A (U - U_c)(U + U_c) \qquad [6\text{-}30]$$

Also

$$P = \frac{1}{2}QU^2 - \frac{1}{2}QU_c^2 = \frac{1}{2}\rho A U_t \left(U^2 - U_c^2\right) = \frac{1}{4}\rho A\left(U + U_c\right)\left(U^2 - U_c^2\right) \quad [6\text{-}31]$$

$$\frac{dP}{dU_c} = \left(-3U_c + U\right)\left(U_c + U\right) = 0 \quad\quad [6\text{-}32]$$

or

$$U_c = \frac{U}{3} \quad\quad [6\text{-}32a]$$

For maximum power density

$$P_{max} = \frac{8}{27}\rho A U^3 \quad\quad [6\text{-}33]$$

The P in the preceding equation is in W.
Because entrance wind flux is $1/2\ \rho A U^3$, $P_{max} = 16/27 = 59.3\%$ of wind speed.
Furthermore, P is power density in W/m^2, and

$$P(\text{W/m}^2)\ A(\text{m}^2) = \quad\quad E(\text{J/m}^3) \quad\quad U(\text{m/s}) \quad\quad A(\text{m}^2) \quad\quad [6\text{-}34]$$

$$\downarrow \quad\quad\quad \downarrow \quad\quad\quad \downarrow$$

$$\text{physical} \quad\quad \text{wind} \quad\quad \text{sail}$$

$$\backslash \quad\quad /$$

$$\text{Economic}$$

where E is the physical limit, and U and A are economic limits. Thus, for a windmill with four sails of total area $A = 80$ m^2, at a wind velocity of 10m/sec (and thus a kinetic energy density, E, of 50 J/m^3), the maximum wattage is $P_w = EUA$ is $50 \times 10 \times 80$ or 40 kilowatts. In this manner, the wind energy is controlled by physical and economic constraints. The maximum power that can be obtained by wind power as a function of wind speed is shown in Figure 6-20. At present, wind power can only be used as a backup energy source.

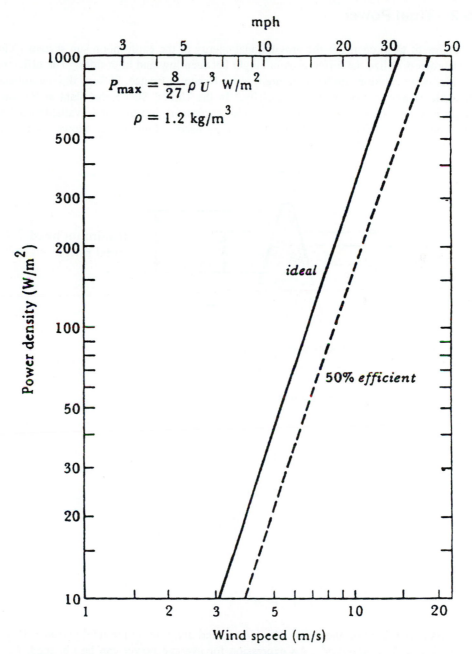

Figure 6-20. Maximum power density vs. wind speed.

6.5.2   Tidal Power

The source of **tidal** energy is the gravitational energy of the earth-moon-sun system. Tidal power projects utilize the differences in height between low and high tides. The efficiency of a tidal power station can be quite high; at La Rance in France, 25% of the theoretically obtainable power is generated as electricity. In the United States, the plant at Passama-quoddy Bay near Canadian–U.S. border is also successful, but the total available tidal energy is only a small fraction of the world's energy needs. Figure 6-21 shows a schematic diagram of a tidal power dam and turbine.

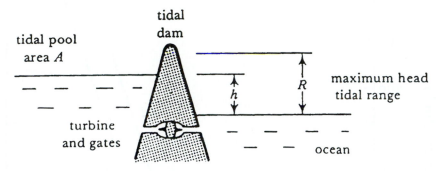

Figure 6-21. A tidal power dam and turbine.

$$dE = g\rho h dV \tag{6-35}$$

where h = head and R = tidal range.

$$dV = -Adh$$

$$E = \int_R^0 dE = -g\rho A \int_R^0 hdh = \frac{1}{2} g\rho AR^2$$

$$\therefore E_{period} = g\rho AR^2 \tag{6-36}$$

Assuming R = 5m, then E = .245 TJ/km^2, and dividing by the tidal period = 12 h 25 min, then P = 5.48 MW/km^2. An expression for average power can be obtained, P_{Ave} = 0.219 R^2 MW/km^2, which is determined by the tidal range.

Tidal energy does affect coastal waters by markedly changing the habits of fish.

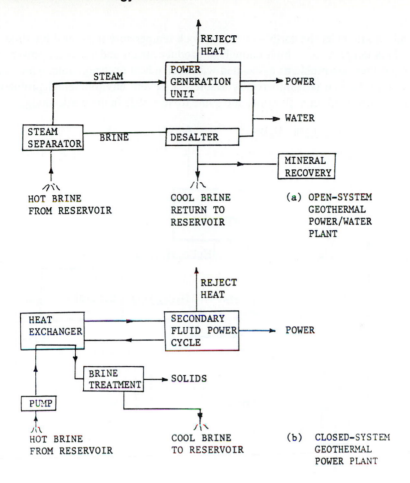

Figure 6-22. Open- and closed-system geothermal power plant cycles.

6.5.3 Geothermal Power

Geothermal energy is another source being discussed these days. It has been successfully used on a small scale in a number of volcanic areas around the world. Figure 6-22 gives schematic diagrams of open and closed system geothermal power plant cycles. Geothermal energy has substantial advantages for high-power energy production; that is, geothermal energy, unlike solar energy, can generate power continuously. In utilizing natural systems, pollution problems that occurred were the disposal of the condensed steam and the impurities extracted from it. Also, gaseous emissions, particularly hydrogen sulfide, often accompanied the production. The modern approach to geothermal power is based on the fact that between 10 and 15 km under the earth's crust, the rock temperature is several hundred degrees Celsius. This temperature is high enough to produce steam and generate power efficiently. However, there are problems associated with such a heat exchange rate, which need to be solved before the rate is commercially viable. A severe environmental problem is linked to the elimination of boron, fluorine, and some toxic metals in the waste sludge.

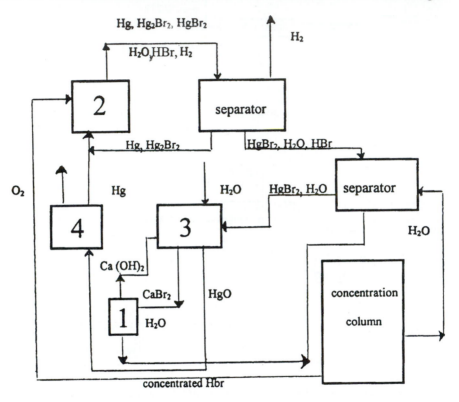

Figure 6-23. DeBeni-Marchetti's Mark-1 cycle schematics.

6.5.4   Hydrogen Fuel–"Eco-energy"

Hydrogen is portable enough that it can be transported through the existing natural gas system, and certainly it is clean enough that it can produce water upon combustion. For catalytic burners, it can be flameless even for central heating to have adjustable accomplished humidity of the circulated air. As a fuel, it can be suitable for aircraft with M > 1. It can even transform edible food such as *Hydrogenomonas* yeast. Hydrogen can also be easily stored as metal hydrides or intermetallic compounds. Hydrogen can be produced by electrolysis or direct photolysis, but the best way is by successive thermal decompositions through mineral cycles as long as there is **high quality waste heat** (about 730°C) available. One such cycle is illustrated here, with the schematics shown in Figure 6-23.

This scheme is termed the **De Beni-Marchetti's Mark-1 Cycle**, and proceeds as follows:

water splitting,	$CaBr_2 + 2H_2O \rightarrow Ca(OH)_2 + 2HBr$	at 730°C
Hydrogen switch,	$2HBr + Hg \rightarrow HgBr_2 + H_2$	at 250°C
Oxygen shift,	$HgBr_2 + Ca(OH)_2 \rightarrow CaBr_2 + H_2O + HgO$	at 100°C
Oxygen switch,	$HgO \rightarrow Hg + \frac{1}{2}O_2$	at 600°C
The net balance:	$H_2O \rightarrow H_2 + \frac{1}{2}O_2$	

All the chemicals are in a closed system. The only net result is water splitting to produce oxygen and hydrogen. The waste heat for nuclear power is well suited; for example, the **chemonuclear reactor** concept. In this manner the petrochemical stocks such as CO and H_2 can be produced from the undesirable CO_2 gas, as shown in Figure 6-24.

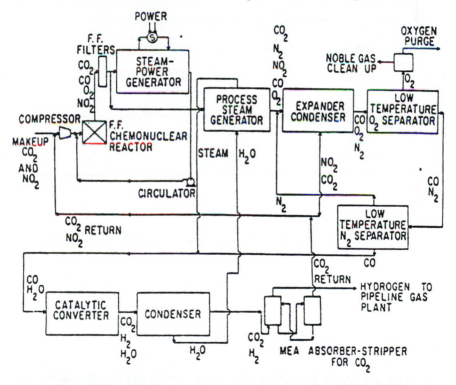

Figure 6-24. Fission-fragment chemonuclear reactor for production of CO and H_2 from CO_2 and for power production.

REFERENCES

6-1   A. P. Kapitza, "Physics and the Energy Problem," *New Scientists*, 7, 10 October (1976).

6-2   R. Wilson and W. Jones, *Energy, Ecology, and the Environment*, Academic Press, New York, 1974.

6-3   T. L. Brown, *Energy and the Environment*, Charles E. Merrill, Columbus, Ohio, 1971.

6-4   J. A. Duffie and W. A. Beckman, *Solar Energy Thermal Process*, Wiley, New York, 1974.

6-5   M. Steinberg, "A Review of Nuclear Sources of Non-Fossil Chemical Fuels," *Energy Sources 1*, 17-29 (1973).

6-6   J. Edmonds and J. M. Reilly, *Global Energy—Assessing the Future*, Oxford University Press, New York, 1985.

6-7   C. Starr, "Energy and Power," *Scientific American 225*, 37-49 (1971).

6-8   G. L. Johnson, *Wind Energy Systems*, Prentice-Hall, Englewood Cliffs, New Jersey, 1985.

6-9   J. H. Krenz, *Energy Conversion and Utilization*, Allyn and Bacon, Boston, Massachusetts, 1976.

6-10   S. S. Lee and S. Sengupta, *Waste Heat Management and Utilization*, Vol. 1-3, Hemisphere, Washington DC, 1979.

6-11   J. T. McMullan, R. Morgan, and R. B. Murray, *Energy Resources and Supply*, Wiley, London, 1976.

6-12   J. J. Kroushuar and R. A. Ristinen, *Energy and Problems of a Technical Society*, revised edition, Wiley, New York, 1988.

6-13   J. R. Williams, *Solar Energy: Technology and Applications*, Ann Arbor Science, Ann Arbor, Michigan, 1974.

6-14   S. W. Angrist, *Direct Energy Conversion*, 3rd ed., Allyn and Bacon, Boston, Michigan, 1976.

6-15   R. C. Bailie, *Energy Conversion Engineering*, Addison and Wesley, Reading, Michigan, 1978.

6-16   S. Sengupta and S. S. Lee, *Waste Heat: Utilization and Management*, Hemisphere, Washington D.C., 1983.

6-17   H. P. Garg, *Advances in Solar Energy Technology*, Vol. 3, *Heating, Agricultural and Photovoltaic Application of Solar Energy*, Reidel, Dordrecht, Holland, 1987.

6-18   H. Yiincii, E. Paykoc and Y. Yener, *Solar Energy Utilization*, Martinus Nijhoff, Dordrecht, Holland, 1987.

6-19   J. S. Hsieh, *Solar Energy Engineering*, Prentice-Hall, Englewood Cliffs, New Jersey, 1986.

6-20   A. deVos, *Endoreversible Thermodynamics of Solar Energy Conversion*, Oxford University Press, New York, 1992.

6-21   J. Schmid and W. Palz, *European Wind Energy Technology*, Reidel, Drodrecht, Holland, 1986.

6-22   R. J. Goldstick and A. Thumann, *The Waste Heat Recovery Handbook*, Fairmont Press, Atlanta, Georgia, 1983.

6-23   J. H. Krenz, *Energy: From Opulence to Sufficiency*, Praeger, New York, 1980.

6-24   P. Auer, *Advances in Energy Systems and Technology*, Vol. 1, Academic, New York, 1978.

6-25   T. F. Spiro and W. M. Stigliani, *Environmental Issues in Chemical Perspective*, State University of New York Press, Albany, New York, 1980.

PROBLEM SET

1.   The Rance River tidal power plant has the following characteristics:

a. tidal range: 14 m

b. time between successive high tides: 12 hours 20 min. (This allows two cycles of the plant, one on the incoming and one on the outgoing tide.)

c. area of reservoir 23 km^2

Assuming a net efficiency of conversion of 90% calculate the power rating of the plant.

2.   If the flux density is taken as W(joule/sec/cm^2) = V(cm/sec) U(joule/cm^3), where U is energy density and the Power $P = WA = UVA$, where A is area, what is the maximum wind power if there are 4 sails each of 80 m^2 and the wind velocity is 10 m/sec, assuming energy density of windmill is 50 joules/m^3? How many sails are needed to generate 360 kW of electricity?

3.   Assuming that the earth's core contains iron at an average density of 11.0 g/cm^3 and an average temperature of 3300 °K, how long could the current yearly energy consumption of 0.16×10^{21} J be sustained by geothermal energy (assuming that energy could be withdrawn at that rate)?

4.   Look up as many of the properties of TiH$_2$ as you can find. How would these properties affect its use as a storage medium for H$_2$? Using the density of TiH$_2$ calculate the mass and volume of a storage cell which could contain enough H$_2$ to drive an automobile 100 miles, (assuming that the car would have gotten 15 miles/gallon of gasoline, 1 gallon = 1.46×10^8 J, and H$_2$ can be burned at 50% efficiency in an Otto cycle engine).

Table 6-6.   Summary of Current Battery Characteristics

	Specific Power (watts per kg)	Energy Density (watt-hours per L)	Specific Energy (watt-hours per kg)	Life (years)	Cycle Life[a] (80%DOD)	Ultimate Cost ($ per kWh)
BATTERY GOALS[b]						
Mid-term goal	150	135	80	5	600	< 150
Long-term goal	400	300	200	10	1,000	< 100
CURRENT BATTERY STATUS						
Lead-acid	67 – 138[c]	50 – 82	18 – 56	2 – 3	450 – 1,000	70 – 100
Nickel-iron	70 – 132	60 – 115	39 – 70	na	440 – 2,000	160 – 300
Nickel-cadmium	100 – 200	60 – 115	33 – 70	na	1,500 – 2,000	300
Nickel-metal hydride	200	152 – 215	54 – 80	10	1,000	200
Sodium-sulfur	90 – 130	76 – 120	80 – 140	na	250 – 600	100+
Sodium-nickel chloride	150	160	100	5	600	> 350
Lithium-polymer	100	100 – 120	150	na	300	50 – 500

a cycle life = number of discharges in battery lifetime at 80% depth of discharge.

b USABC figures.

c CARB estimates 170 watts per kg.

na = not available.

Source: "The Keys to the Car: Electric and Hydrogen Vehicles for the 21ˢᵗ Century," World Resources Institute.

Table 6-7.   Energy Density in Storage

	Chemical Energy kcal/c	Electric-Mechanical Energy watt-hr/lb (20% heat efficiency)
Gasoline	11.0	1,150
Lipid	9.3	
Methanol	5.2	550
Ammonia	4.8	510
Carbohydrate	4.1	
Protein	4.1	
Sodium-sulfur battery		385
Conceptual super flywheel		200
Lead acid battery		85
Super flywheel		40
Rubberband		1

Solar energy is a time-dependent energy resource. A means of storing energy is needed to provide an even and continuous supply. There are various methods of storing energy, such as the storage of compressed air in caverns, mechanical energy storage in fly-wheels, and direct electrical storage in large surperconducting magnets. Materials that undergo a change of phase in a suitable temperature range may also be useful for energy storage. Table 6-5 lists some common materials used for heat storage. Batteries are also good devices for energy storage, representing chemical storage of electrical energy in a portable form. Table 6-6 lists characteristics for various rechargeable batteries. Although the chemical battery is very efficient in converting electrical energy to chemical energy and back, it is a heavy and expensive storage medium. The lithium-polymer battery is especially suitable for the future because it can easily be packaged in "credit card" form. One of the major energy supplies is in the fuel cell, which will be used for the transportation vehicles in the future, as shown in Figure 6-17. Table 6-7 lists some common energy densities in storage. Figure 6-18 illustrates the specific power and energy of various sources.

There are several points regarding pollution by solar energy that are worth mentioning, because utilizing solar energy is definitely not pollution-free. High temperatures near the solar panel may cause unfavorable air turbulence, resulting in the death of flying birds. So-called "optical pollution" of the solar farm is also felt by some people. In addition, toxic materials are generated in manufacturing the photovoltaic systems.

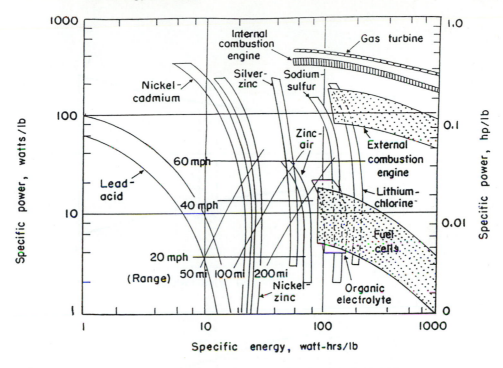

Figure 6-18. The power and energy requirements for a 2000-lb vehicle utilizing a 500-lb motive power source for steady driving. Power and energy are assumed to be at the output of the device.

6.5 MISCELLANEOUS ENERGY SOURCES

This section is used to illustrate some of the supplementary energy sources such as wind and tidal waves. Furthermore, chemical fuels such as alcohol and hydrogen will be discussed under miscellaneous energy sources.

6.5.1 Wind Power

Wind power has a yearly energy potential of four times the current United States consumption. Windmills have a long history of use throughout the world, and there have been many technical advances in the design of windmills and wind turbines. It seems quite likely that wind power will be an additional economical source of electricity in the near future. The energy density, E, is in J/m^3.

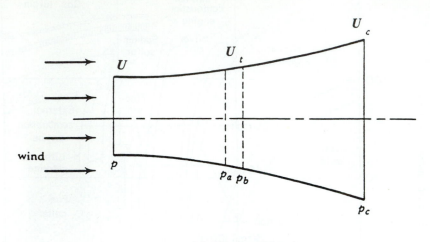

(a) Wind-turbine

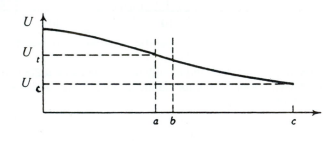

(b) Velocity

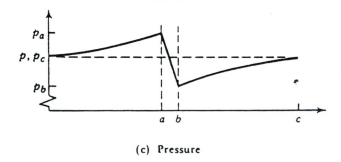

(c) Pressure

Figure 6-19.   An enclosed wind-turbine.

The energy E' is $E' = (1/2) MU^2$ (in J), or $(1/2) \rho A X U^2$, the energy density, E, is

$$E = \frac{1}{2}\rho U^2 \quad \text{in} \quad \left(\frac{J}{m^3}\right) \tag{6-24}$$

where $\rho = \dfrac{M}{V}$, $V = \dfrac{RT}{P}$, U is velocity of wind, ρ is density, and V is volume.

The power density, P, is (power can be expressed as $P_w = dE'/dt = (1/2)\,\rho A U^3$ in (W))

$$P = EU = \frac{1}{2}\rho U^3 \quad \text{in} \quad (W/m^2) \tag{6-25}$$

Assuming velocities (U) and pressures (p) according to Figure 6-18 and Figure 6-19

U, p at entrance

U_t, p_t at turbine

U_c, p_c at exit

the axial force is

$$F = A\,p_t = \frac{1}{2}\rho A\,(U^2 - U_c^2) \quad \text{in (Newton)} \tag{6-26}$$

which is derived from Bernoulli's equation.

Also, the flow rate,

$$Q = \rho A U_t \quad \text{in (kg/s)} \tag{6-27}$$

$$U_t = \frac{1}{2}(U + U_c) \tag{6-28}$$

$$F = QU - QU_c = \rho A U_t (U - U_c) \quad \text{in (kg-m/s}^2) \tag{6-29}$$

Thus

$$\rho A U_t (U - U_c) = \frac{1}{2}\rho A(U^2 - U_c^2) = \frac{1}{2}\rho A(U - U_c)(U + U_c) \tag{6-30}$$

Also

$$P = \frac{1}{2}QU^2 - \frac{1}{2}QU_c^2 = \frac{1}{2}\rho A U_t\left(U^2 - U_c^2\right) = \frac{1}{4}\rho A\left(U + U_c\right)\left(U^2 - U_c^2\right) \qquad [6\text{-}31]$$

$$\frac{dP}{dU_c} = \left(-3U_c + U\right)\left(U_c + U\right) = 0 \qquad [6\text{-}32]$$

or

$$U_c = \frac{U}{3} \qquad [6\text{-}32a]$$

For maximum power density

$$P_{max} = \frac{8}{27}\rho A U^3 \qquad [6\text{-}33]$$

The P in the preceding equation is in W.
Because entrance wind flux is $1/2\ \rho A U^3$, $P_{max} = 16/27 = 59.3\%$ of wind speed.
Furthermore, P is power density in W/m^2, and

$$P(\text{W/m}^2)\ A(\text{m}^2) = \qquad E(\text{J/m}^3) \qquad U(\text{m/s}) \qquad A(\text{m}^2) \qquad\qquad [6\text{-}34]$$

$$\downarrow \qquad\qquad \downarrow \qquad\qquad \downarrow$$

$$\text{physical} \qquad \text{wind} \qquad \text{sail}$$

$$\backslash \qquad\quad /$$

$$\text{Economic}$$

where E is the physical limit, and U and A are economic limits. Thus, for a windmill with four sails of total area $A = 80$ m^2, at a wind velocity of 10m/sec (and thus a kinetic energy density, E, of 50 J/m^3), the maximum wattage is $P_w = EUA$ is $50 \times 10 \times 80$ or 40 kilowatts. In this manner, the wind energy is controlled by physical and economic constraints. The maximum power that can be obtained by wind power as a function of wind speed is shown in Figure 6-20. At present, wind power can only be used as a backup energy source.

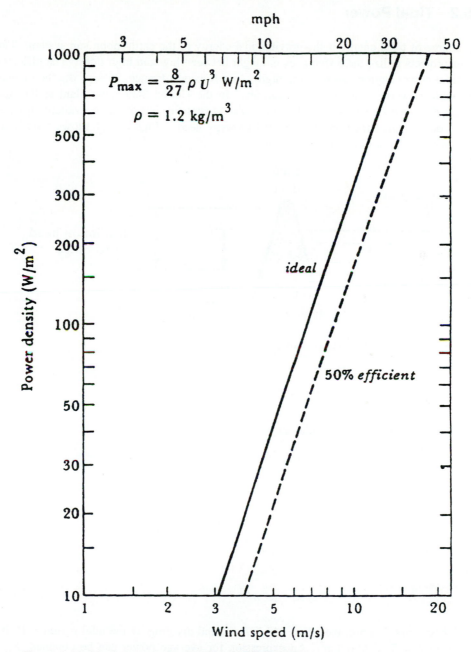

Figure 6-20. Maximum power density vs. wind speed.

6.5.2   Tidal Power

The source of **tidal** energy is the gravitational energy of the earth-moon-sun system. Tidal power projects utilize the differences in height between low and high tides. The efficiency of a tidal power station can be quite high; at La Rance in France, 25% of the theoretically obtainable power is generated as electricity. In the United States, the plant at Passamaquoddy Bay near Canadian–U.S. border is also successful, but the total available tidal energy is only a small fraction of the world's energy needs. Figure 6-21 shows a schematic diagram of a tidal power dam and turbine.

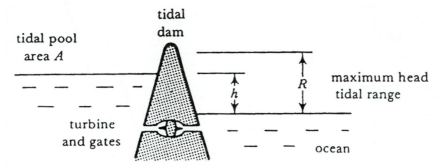

Figure 6-21. A tidal power dam and turbine.

$$dE = g\rho h dV \qquad\qquad [6\text{-}35]$$

where h = head and R = tidal range.

$$dV = -Adh$$

$$E = \int_{R}^{0} dE = -g\rho A \int_{R}^{0} h dh = \frac{1}{2} g\rho \, AR^2$$

$$\therefore E_{period} = g\rho \, AR^2 \qquad\qquad [6\text{-}36]$$

Assuming $R = 5$m, then $E = .245$ TJ/km^2, and dividing by the tidal period = 12 h 25 min, then $P = 5.48$ MW/km^2. An expression for average power can be obtained, $P_{Ave} = 0.219 \, R^2$ MW/km^2, which is determined by the tidal range.

Tidal energy does affect coastal waters by markedly changing the habits of fish.

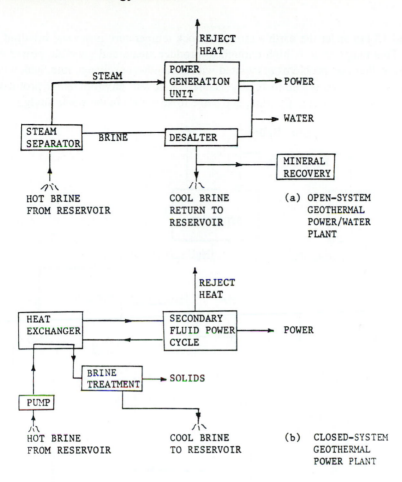

Figure 6-22. Open- and closed-system geothermal power plant cycles.

6.5.3 Geothermal Power

Geothermal energy is another source being discussed these days. It has been successfully used on a small scale in a number of volcanic areas around the world. Figure 6-22 gives schematic diagrams of open and closed system geothermal power plant cycles. Geothermal energy has substantial advantages for high-power energy production; that is, geothermal energy, unlike solar energy, can generate power continuously. In utilizing natural systems, pollution problems that occurred were the disposal of the condensed steam and the impurities extracted from it. Also, gaseous emissions, particularly hydrogen sulfide, often accompanied the production. The modern approach to geothermal power is based on the fact that between 10 and 15 km under the earth's crust, the rock temperature is several hundred degrees Celsius. This temperature is high enough to produce steam and generate power efficiently. However, there are problems associated with such a heat exchange rate, which need to be solved before the rate is commercially viable. A severe environmental problem is linked to the elimination of boron, fluorine, and some toxic metals in the waste sludge.

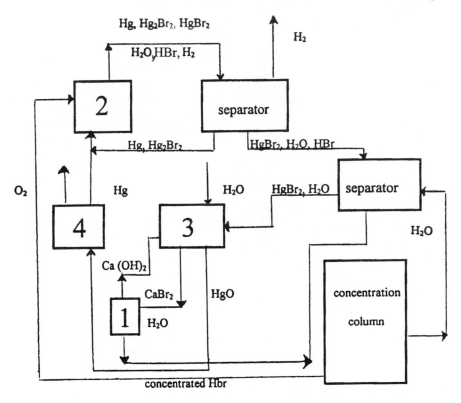

Figure 6-23. DeBeni-Marchetti's Mark-1 cycle schematics.

6.5.4   Hydrogen Fuel–"Eco-energy"

Hydrogen is portable enough that it can be transported through the existing natural gas system, and certainly it is clean enough that it can produce water upon combustion. For catalytic burners, it can be flameless even for central heating to have adjustable accomplished humidity of the circulated air. As a fuel, it can be suitable for aircraft with M > 1. It can even transform edible food such as *Hydrogenomonas* yeast. Hydrogen can also be easily stored as metal hydrides or intermetallic compounds. Hydrogen can be produced by electrolysis or direct photolysis, but the best way is by successive thermal decompositions through mineral cycles as long as there is **high quality waste heat** (about 730°C) available. One such cycle is illustrated here, with the schematics shown in Figure 6-23.

This scheme is termed the **De Beni-Marchetti's Mark-1 Cycle**, and proceeds as follows:

water splitting,	$CaBr_2 + 2H_2O \rightarrow Ca(OH)_2 + 2HBr$	at 730°C
Hydrogen switch,	$2HBr + Hg \rightarrow HgBr_2 + H_2$	at 250°C
Oxygen shift,	$HgBr_2 + Ca(OH)_2 \rightarrow CaBr_2 + H_2O + HgO$	at 100°C
Oxygen switch,	$HgO \rightarrow Hg + \frac{1}{2}O_2$	at 600°C
The net balance:	$H_2O \rightarrow H_2 + \frac{1}{2}O_2$	

All the chemicals are in a closed system. The only net result is water splitting to produce oxygen and hydrogen. The waste heat for nuclear power is well suited; for example, the **chemonuclear reactor** concept. In this manner the petrochemical stocks such as CO and H_2 can be produced from the undesirable CO_2 gas, as shown in Figure 6-24.

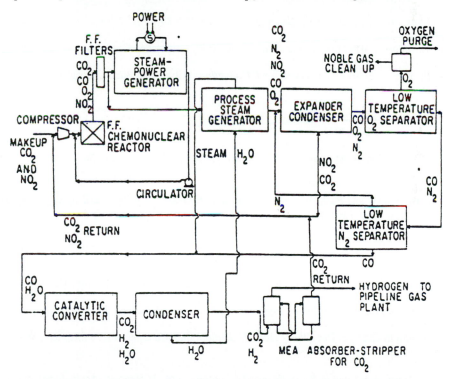

Figure 6-24. Fission-fragment chemonuclear reactor for production of CO and H_2 from CO_2 and for power production.

REFERENCES

6-1   A. P. Kapitza, "Physics and the Energy Problem," *New Scientists*, 7, 10 October (1976).

6-2   R. Wilson and W. Jones, *Energy, Ecology, and the Environment*, Academic Press, New York, 1974.

6-3   T. L. Brown, *Energy and the Environment*, Charles E. Merrill, Columbus, Ohio, 1971.

6-4   J. A. Duffie and W. A. Beckman, *Solar Energy Thermal Process*, Wiley, New York, 1974.

6-5   M. Steinberg, "A Review of Nuclear Sources of Non-Fossil Chemical Fuels," *Energy Sources 1*, 17-29 (1973).

6-6   J. Edmonds and J. M. Reilly, *Global Energy—Assessing the Future*, Oxford University Press, New York, 1985.

6-7   C. Starr, "Energy and Power," *Scientific American 225*, 37-49 (1971).

6-8   G. L. Johnson, *Wind Energy Systems*, Prentice-Hall, Englewood Cliffs, New Jersey, 1985.

6-9   J. H. Krenz, *Energy Conversion and Utilization*, Allyn and Bacon, Boston, Massachusetts, 1976.

6-10   S. S. Lee and S. Sengupta, *Waste Heat Management and Utilization*, Vol. 1-3, Hemisphere, Washington DC, 1979.

6-11   J. T. McMullan, R. Morgan, and R. B. Murray, *Energy Resources and Supply*, Wiley, London, 1976.

6-12   J. J. Kroushuar and R. A. Ristinen, *Energy and Problems of a Technical Society*, revised edition, Wiley, New York, 1988.

6-13   J. R. Williams, *Solar Energy: Technology and Applications*, Ann Arbor Science, Ann Arbor, Michigan, 1974.

6-14   S. W. Angrist, *Direct Energy Conversion*, 3rd ed., Allyn and Bacon, Boston, Michigan, 1976.

6-15   R. C. Bailie, *Energy Conversion Engineering*, Addison and Wesley, Reading, Michigan, 1978.

6-16   S. Sengupta and S. S. Lee, *Waste Heat: Utilization and Management*, Hemisphere, Washington D.C., 1983.

6-17   H. P. Garg, *Advances in Solar Energy Technology*, Vol. 3, *Heating, Agricultural and Photovoltaic Application of Solar Energy*, Reidel, Dordrecht, Holland, 1987.

6-18   H. Yiincii, E. Paykoc and Y. Yener, *Solar Energy Utilization*, Martinus Nijhoff, Dordrecht, Holland, 1987.

CHAPTER **7**

THE LITHOSPHERE — NUCLEAR POWER

Nuclear energy is a by-product of weapon research. The development of nuclear reactors began in earnest in 1942. In 1953, the United States launched the Atoms for Peace program with the intention of harnessing the destructive potential of nuclear power and dedicating it to supply energy to the world. The first unit of electricity from nuclear energy was experimentally generated in 1953. From commercial introduction in 1960, nuclear power expanded rapidly throughout the early 1970s. Nuclear power is presently the most highly developed alternative to energy supplied by coal. This chapter will begin with a summary of applicable nuclear phenomena, followed by a bird's-eye view on types of nuclear power reactors that have been developed. Fuel cycles of nuclear energy will be briefly discussed. Finally, the generation of nuclear waste, its impact on the environment, and management of the waste including separation and treatment technology will be addressed.

Radioactive dating will be discussed in Chapter 15 and radon and its environmental effect will appear in Chapter 16.

7.1 RADIOACTIVITY

Nuclear energy originally resides in the nuclei of **atoms**, the smallest particles of chemical elements. **Nuclei** are made of collections of protons and neutrons called **nucleons,** which are held together by strong nuclear forces. **Protons** are positively charged, while **neutrons** are neutral. The number of protons, P, determines the number of negatively charged **electrons** that surround the nucleus, which in turn determines the chemical properties of the element. An **element** in the periodic table could be characterized by $_z$Symbol^A, in which A is the number of nucleons in the nuclei, and Z corresponds to the **atomic number** and is equal to the number of electrons around the nucleus of a neutral atom. This symbol is commonly referred to as **nuclide**. The number of neutrons, N, is equal to the atomic weight, A, expressed as the nearest whole number less the number of protons: $N = A - Z$. **Isotopes** of the elements, such as $_{20}Ca^{40}$ and $_{20}Ca^{42}$, have the same number of protons but a different number of neutrons. **Isotones** such as $_{20}Ca^{40}$ and $_{19}K^{39}$ are elements that have same number of neutrons. Elements with the same number of nucleons, such as $_{20}Ca^{40}$ and $_{18}Ar^{40}$, are called **isobars**. **Isodiaspheres** are elements with same $N - Z$ values, such as $_{20}Ca^{40}$ and $_{19}K^{38}$. A summary is shown here:

$_z$Element^A

A = mass no. = no. of nucleons in nuclei

Z = atomic no. = no. of protons

A – Z = N = no. of neutrons

Isotope — same Z, $_{20}Ca^{40}$, $_{20}Ca^{42}$ (on vertical lines of Fig. 7-1)

Isotone — same N, $_{20}Ca^{40}$, $_{19}K^{39}$ (on horizontal lines of Fig. 7-1)

Isobar — same A, $_{20}Ca^{40}$, $_{18}A^{40}$

Isodiasphere — same $N - Z = A - 2Z$, $_{20}Ca^{40}$, $_{19}K^{38}$ (on 45° line of Fig 7-1)

    $A = 2Z$ proton and neutron are equal, for example, $_1H^2$, $_2He^4$, $_3Li^6$, $_5B^{10}$, etc.

Isomer — same Z, A, N; differ only in half-life

Nuclear forces increase as the number of nucleons increases, yet so does the electrostatic repulsion among the positively charged protons. To some degree the stability of a nucleus can be empirically related to the ratio of the number of neutrons to the number of protons it contains: N/Z. The values of N/Z range from 1 to 1.59. For stable light nuclei, N/Z is approximately 1 (see Figure 7-1). The highest nuclear stability is associated with atoms of intermediate atomic weight in the vicinity of the element iron. For heavier elements, the repulsive forces among protons gradually become more important, and elements heavier than bismuth, with 83 protons, are unstable. The shakedown of an unstable nucleus to a more stable form results in the natural process of **nuclear decay** and the ejection of particles or radiation from the nucleus. Some of these heavy elements can also undergo **spontaneous fission**, in which they are split into two daughter atoms of intermediate atomic weights, with the release of a great deal of energy.

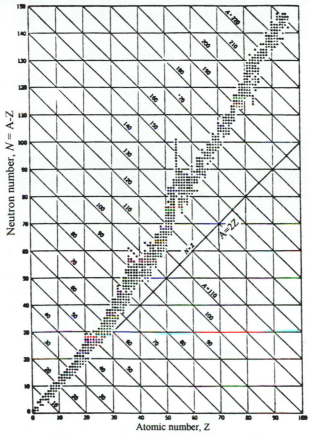

Figure 7-1. Nuclidic chart. Stable, negatron emitter, positron emitter (or electron capture), and alpha emitter are illustrated, where a nuclide has more than one mode of disintegration, the predominant mode has been used. The sloping lines represent constant A values (isobars).

7.1.1 Nuclear Binding Energy

The mass of a nucleus is less than the sum of its separate constituent particles, protons, and neutrons. The difference is called **mass defect**. The mass is lost in forming the nucleus and appears as energy, the **binding energy**. The amount of binding energy can be related to the mass defect by Einstein's famous energy formula, $E = mc^2$, where c is the velocity of light in a vacuum. It has been calculated that 1 **a.m.u. (atomic mass unit)** is equivalent to 931.14 MeV (million electron volts). Binding energy per nucleon is greatest near the nucleus of iron (A = 56). The nuclei in this region are the most strongly bound of all, or, in nuclear terminology, the most stable. Most of the energy goes off as gamma rays, and a little as the kinetic energy of the atom recoil.

[Example 7-1]   Compute the binding energy of $_{25}Mn^{55}$ if the mass measured by mass spectrum is 54.9558 a.m.u.

This nuclide has 30 neutrons, 25 protons, and 25 electrons.
Total mass = 30(1.00898) + 25(1.00758) + 25(0.00055)= 55.47265 a.m.u.
Mass defect = 55.47265 – 54.9558= 0.517 a.m.u.= 0.517(931.14) = 48/MeV
Mass defect per nucleon = 481/(30 + 25) = 8.7 MeV

7.1.2 Nuclear Reactions

Early workers with radioactive materials were cognizant of the presence of only one form of radiation, and its properties were similar to those of X rays. Actually, there are several different types of nuclear reactions. The following symbols are used: $_2\alpha^4$ (α-ray here $_2\alpha^4$ is equivalent to $_2He^4$), $_0\gamma^0$ (γ-ray), $_{-1}\beta^0$ (β-ray), $_{-1}e^0$ (electron), $_1\beta^0$ (positron), $_0n^1$ (neutron), $_1p^1$ (proton), $_1d^2$ (deutron), and $_1t^3$ (triton). In general, six types of nuclear reactions are presented here:

(1) **Alpha Emission** (α-decay)

$$_ZX^A \rightarrow \, _{Z-2}X^{A-4} + \, _2\alpha^4 \qquad\qquad [7\text{-}1]$$

for example

$$_{88}Ra^{226} \rightarrow \, _{86}Rn^{222} + \, _2\alpha^4 \qquad\qquad [7\text{-}2]$$

Alpha radiation is not true electromagnetic radiation as are light and X rays; it consists of particles of matter. **Alpha particles** are actually doubly charged ions of helium with a mass of 4 ($_2He^4$). Although they are propelled from the nuclei of atoms at velocities of about 10% of the speed of light, they do not travel much more than 10 cm in air at room temperature. They ionize half the atoms in their path. If an alpha emitter is ingested into the body (the likeliest route is via inhalation of dust particles that carry radioisotopes), it produces a high density of localized damage, with an appreciable potential for cancer induction.

(2) **Beta Emission** (β-decay)

$$_{z}X^{A} \rightarrow _{z+1}X^{A} + _{-1}\beta^{0}$$
[7-3]

for example

$$_{15}P^{32} \rightarrow _{16}S^{32} + _{-1}\beta^{0}$$
[7-4]

(3) **Beta-Positron Emission**

$$_{z}X^{A} \rightarrow _{z-1}X^{A} + _{1}\beta^{0}$$
[7-5]

for example

$$_{53}I^{121} \rightarrow _{52}Te^{121} + _{1}\beta^{0}$$
[7-6]

A **beta ray** is actually an energetic electron. For an element having a large N/P ratio, neutrons tend to be converted to protons by releasing $_{-1}\beta^{0}$. On the other hand, if the N/P ratio is small, protons have a tendency to become neutrons by releasing $_{1}\beta^{0}$. Because of the low mass, the ionizing power of beta radiation is much weaker than that of alpha radiation.

(4) **Electron Capture**

$$_{z}X^{A} + _{-1}e^{0} \rightarrow _{z-1}X^{A}$$
[7-7]

for example

$$_{26}Fe^{55} + _{-1}e^{0} \rightarrow _{25}Mn^{55}$$
[7-8]

One element can be bombarded by high energetic electrons and transformed into another element.

(5) **Neutron Capture**

$$_{z}X^{A} + _{0}n^{1} \rightarrow _{z}X^{A+1}$$

$$_{28}Ni^{56} + _{0}n^{1} \rightarrow _{28}Ni^{57}$$

(6) **Proton Release** (α-bombardment)

$$_{Z}X^{A} + {_2}\alpha^{4} \rightarrow {_{Z+1}}X^{A+3} + {_1}p^{1}$$
[7-9]

for example

$$_{7}N^{14} + {_2}\alpha^{4} \rightarrow {_8}O^{17} + {_1}p^{1}$$
[7-10]

Table 7-1.   Nuclear Reactions Used to Produce Neutrons

Incident radiation	Reaction	Lowest Neutron energy, Mev
Alpha particles	^{9}Be (α,n) ^{12}C	5.71
	^{11}B (α,n) ^{14}N	
	^{7}Li (α,n) ^{10}B	
Deutrons	^{2}H (d,n) ^{3}He	2.45
	^{3}H (d,n) ^{4}He	14.05
	^{9}Be (d,n) ^{10}B	
Protons	T (p,n) ^{3}He	1.19
	^{9}Be (p,n) ^{9}B	
	^{7}Li (p,n) ^{7}Be	1.88
Photons	D (γ,n) H	0.3
	^{9}Be (γ,n) ^{8}Be	0.16
	^{238}U (γ,n) ^{237}U	6.0
	^{2}H (γ,n) ^{1}H	0.1

Protons can be released resulting from bombardment of alpha particles. The short-hand notation for the preceding reaction is $N^{14}(\alpha,p)O^{17}$ — usually the Z is omitted and sometimes the A can be written on the left side, for example N^{14} or ^{14}N. Another way to express $_{Z}E^{A}$ is to use $_{Z}^{A}E$, E being the elements. For upper layers of the atmosphere, the following reactions are important:

$$N^{14} (\gamma, \beta) C^{14}$$

$$N^{14} (n, t) C^{12}$$

$$N^{14} \, (n, p) \, C^{14}$$

Can you compute the power necessary for the following nuclear reaction? What do you name this reaction?

$$O^{16} \, (\gamma, \alpha) \, C^{12}$$

We tentatively name it as the Christ equation! The energy can change water to wine — a transmutation of O^{16} in water to C^{12} in alcohol. In addition to preceding reaction, there are some reactions used to produce neutrons as shown in Table 7-1. The particles that are generated from the above reactions — that is, alpha particles, beta particles, neutrons, and protons, could induce nuclear reactions by bombarding other atoms. Gamma emission is a high-energy photon, often released as energy by nuclear transformations or shifts of orbital electrons.

7.1.3 Radioactive Decay

A **radioactive element** emits radiation spontaneously. Radioactive decomposition is a true unimolecular reaction and its rate is not affected by external circumstances such as temperature, pressure, or even chemical combination. If we start with a certain amount of a radioactive element and arrange to measure its activity as a function of time, we find that the activity steadily diminishes. The quality of the radiation — that is, the energy of each alpha, beta, or gamma ray — does not change, but the quantity decreases.

The decomposition of a radioactive element is a true first-order reaction. In such a reaction the rate of decomposition is directly proportional to the amount of undecayed material. If the initial concentration is N_o at time $t = 0$, and if at some later time, t, the concentration has fallen to N, the following relationship is valid:

$$\frac{dN}{dt} = -\lambda N$$

$$N = N_0 \exp(-\lambda t) \tag{7-11}$$

where λ is the decay constant. For radioactive substances, it is customary to express decomposition rates in terms of **half-life** $(t_{1/2})$, or the time required for the amount of substance to decrease to half its initial value. Then

$$\lambda = \frac{0.693}{t_{1/2}} \tag{7-12}$$

For example, the half-life of I^{131} is 8 days, and the decay constant = (0.693)/8 = 0.087 day^{-1}. Half-lives of the radioactive elements vary from fractions of a second to around 10^{12} years.

For successive decays,

$$N_1 \xrightarrow{\lambda_1} N_2 \xrightarrow{\lambda_2} N_3$$
$$t_{\frac{1}{2}}(1) \qquad t_{\frac{1}{2}}(2)$$

[7-13]

$$\frac{dN_1}{dt} = -\lambda_1 N_1, \quad \frac{dN_2}{dt} = \lambda_1 N_1 - \lambda_2 N_2$$

[7-14]

solve,

$$N_2 = \frac{\lambda_1 N_{01}}{\lambda_2 - \lambda_1} \left(e^{-\lambda_1 t} - e^{-\lambda_2 t} \right)$$

[7-15]

if $\lambda_2 \gg \lambda_1$

$$\lambda_2 N_2 \approx \lambda_1 N_{01} e^{-\lambda_1 t} = \lambda_1 N_1$$

[Example 7-2]   The nuclide $_{34}Se^{70}$ decays by beta emission to $_{33}As^{70}$ and again $_{33}As^{70}$ decays in the same manner to $_{32}Ge^{70}$. The decay constants for the selenium nucleide is 0.0158 min^{-1} and for the arsenic nuclide is 0.0133 min^{-1}. Assuming the original $_{34}Se^{70}$ is 10^{10} atoms, how many atoms of $_{33}As^{70}$ is formed in 10 min?

From the problem we can write the following:

$$_{34}Se^{70} \rightarrow {_{33}As^{70}} + {_1\beta^0}$$

$$_{33}As^{70} \rightarrow {_{32}Ge^{70}} + {_1\beta^0}$$

Writing out the kinetics, we get

$$\frac{dN_{As}}{dt} = \lambda_{Se} N_{Se} - \lambda_{As} N_{As}$$

(a)

and

$$-\frac{dN_{Se}}{dt} = \lambda_{Se} N_{Se} \tag{b}$$

Integrating (b), we get

$$\int_{N_{Se}}^{N_0} \frac{dN_{Se}}{N_{SE}} = \int_{t}^{0} -\lambda_{Se}\,dt$$

or

$$N_{Se} = N_0 \exp\left(-\lambda_{Se} t\right) \tag{c}$$

Substituting (c) to (a), we get

$$\frac{dN_{As}}{dt} + \lambda_{As} N_{As} = \lambda_{Se} N_0 \exp\left(-\lambda_{Se} t\right) \tag{d}$$

In order to solve (d), we assume

$$a(x) = \lambda_{As}, \; Q(x) = \lambda_{Se} N_0 \exp\left(-\lambda_{Se} t\right)$$

Then,

$$e^{\int a(x)dx} = \exp\left(\int \lambda_{As}\,dt\right) = \exp(\lambda_{As} t)$$

Thus,

$$\int Q(x) e^{\int a(x)dx}\,dx = \int \lambda_{Se} N_0 \exp\left(-\lambda_{Se} t\right) \exp\left(\lambda_{As} t\right) dt$$

$$= \frac{\lambda_{Se} N_0}{\lambda_{As} - \lambda_{Se}} \exp\left[\left(\lambda_{As} - \lambda_{Se}\right) t\right]$$

After integration,

$$N_{As} \exp(\lambda_{As} t) = \frac{\lambda_{Se} N_0}{\lambda_{As} - \lambda_{Se}} \exp[(\lambda_{As} - \lambda_{Se})t] + c \qquad \text{(e)}$$

When $t=0$, $N_{As} =0$, we can evaluate the constant c

$$c = \frac{-\lambda_{Se} N_0}{\lambda_{As} - \lambda_{Se}}$$

Substituting into (e),

$$N_{As} = \frac{\lambda_{Se} N_0}{\lambda_{As} - \lambda_{Se}} \left[\exp(-\lambda_{Se} t) - \exp(-\lambda_{As} t) \right]$$

$$= \frac{0.0158 N_0}{(0.0133 - 0.0158)} \left(e^{-0.158} - e^{-0.133} \right) = 0.136 N_0$$

Because $N_0 = 10^{10}$, $N_{As} = 1.36 \times 10^9$ atoms.

7.1.4   Units of Radioactivity

The unit of radioactivity is the **curie**. It was formerly considered to be the number of disintegrations occurring per second in 1 gram of pure radium. Now it is defined to be a fixed value of 3.7×10^{10} disintegrations per second as the standard curie (Ci). The curie is a fairly large unit; therefore, smaller units such as pico-curie (pCi) are more commonly used (1 pCi = 2.2 disintegrations/min). Derivation of the basic unit is shown here

$$\text{Ci (Curie)} \longrightarrow \text{1g of Ra}^{226} \ (t\tfrac{1}{2} \longrightarrow 1590 \text{ yr})$$

$$\lambda = \frac{0.693}{1590} \text{ yr}^{-1} = 1.38 \times 10^{-11} \text{ sec}^{-1}$$

$$-\frac{dN}{dt} = \lambda N = \lambda \frac{1}{226} \left(6.02 \times 10^{23} \right) = 3.7 \times 10^{10} \text{ disintegration/sec.}$$

One disintegration/sec (dis/sec) is called 1 Bq (**Becquerel**), and some common units are summarized in Table 7-2.

Table 7-2. Radiation Quantities and Units

Quantity	SI Units	Equivalents
Activity (Becquerel)	Bq	$1 \text{ curie} = 3.7 \times 10^{10} \text{ Bq}$
		$1 \text{ pCi} = 0.037 \text{ Bq}$
Concentration	Bq m^{-3}	$1 \text{ pCi } 1^{-1} = 37 \text{ Bq } 1^{-1}$
Equilibrium Equivalent	EEC$_{222}$	$1 \text{ WL} = 3{,}740 \text{ Bq m}^{-3}$
Concentration	EEC$_{220}$	$1 \text{ WL} = 276 \text{ Bq m}^{-3}$
Absorbed dose (Gray)	Gy	$1 \text{ Gy} = 100 \text{ rad}$
Dose equivalent (Sievert)	Sv	$1 \text{ J kg}^{-1} = 100 \text{ rem}$
Working Level	WL	$1 \text{ WL} = 1.3 \times 10^5 \text{ MeV } 1^{-1}$
Working Level Month	WLM	$1 \text{ WLM} = \text{WL (hours/170)}$
Potential Alpha Energy Concentration (no longer in use)	PAEC	$1 \text{ PAEC} = 1 \text{ J m}^{-3}$

For example, mCi, μCi, nCi, and so on.

$$1 \text{pCi} = 0.037 \text{ dis/sec} = 2.2 \text{ dis/min} = 3.7 \text{ m Bq}$$

The **roentgen (r)** is a unit of gamma or X ray radiation intensity. It is of value in the study of the biological effects of radiation that result from ionization induced within cells by the radiation. One roentgen is defined as the amount of gamma or X ray radiation that will produce 1 electrostatic unit (esu) of electricity in 1 cubic centimeter of dry air at standard conditions.

With the advent of atomic energy involving exposure to neutrons, protons, and alpha and beta particles, which all have effects on living tissues, it has become necessary to have other means of expressing ionization produced in cells. Three methods of expression have been used.

The **roentgen-equivalent-physical (rep)** is defined as the quantity of radiation that the ionization produces in 1 gram of human tissue and is equivalent to the quantity produced in air by 1 roentgen (33.8 ergs of energy). The **roentgen-absorption-dose (rad)** is a unit of radiation corresponding to an energy absorption of 100 ergs per gram of any medium. One **gray** (Gy) is equivalent to 100 rads. It was found that 1 roentgen is approximately equivalent to 100 ergs/g of tissue. The term **roentgen-equivalent man (rem)** has been specially developed for man. It corresponds to the amount of radiation that will produce an energy dissipation in the human body that is biologically equivalent to 1 roentgen of radiation of X rays, or approximately 100 ergs/g. One **sievert** (Sv) is equivalent to 100 rems. The recommended **Maximum Permissible Dose (MPD)** for radiation workers is 5 rem/year and for nonradiation workers 0.5 rem/yr. Table 7-3 shows the dosages of some common exposures. A summary is expressed here:

R (Roentgen) — quantity of radiation that can produce 1 stat coulomb ($1/3 \times 10^{-9}$ coulombs) of ionized charge in 1 cm^3 of dry air at standard conditions (34 eV for each collision).

$$E = (34\text{eV})\,N = 34\,\frac{\left(\frac{1}{3} \times 10^{-9}\right)}{\left(1.6 \times 10^{-19}\right)} = 7.083 \times 10^{10}\ \text{eV/cm}^3 = 1.133 \times 10^{-8}\ \text{J/cm}^3$$

$$= 8.76 \times 10^{-3}\ \text{J/kg} = 87.6\ \text{ergs/g or air}$$

rep (Roentgen-equivalent-physical)

$$E = 93\ \text{ergs/cm}^3\ \text{in tissue}$$

rad (radiation dosage)

$$E = 100\ \text{ergs/g in any media}$$

rem (Roentgen-equivalent-man)

$$E = (\text{rad})(\text{QF})\quad (\text{QF is quality factor for } \gamma,\ \beta = 1,\ \text{and QF for n, neutron} = 3)$$

for example, Natural background ~ 120 mrem/yr

Table 7-3.   Levels of Exposure

Exposures	Dosage (milli rem)
Chest X ray	10-2000
Watching color T.V.	.002
Flight from New York to San Francisco	1

7.1.5   Natural Radiation

Most of the presently existing atoms on earth are stable, but some are radioactive. **Naturally occurring radioactive materials** (NORM) generally contain radionuclides found in nature. The largest terrestrial sources of radiation are ^{40}K, ^{238}U, ^{235}U, and ^{232}Th. The last three are alpha emitters, while ^{40}K is a beta emitter. ^{232}Th and ^{238}U are both quite abundant in the earth's crust. ^{235}U, which is the naturally occurring isotope that can undergo fission, has become scarce. The total energy emission from ^{40}K in the earth's crust is estimated to be 4 ×

10^{12}W. The heat generated by the decay of these elements has resulted in a much slower cooling of the earth than would have otherwise been the case.

Unstable isotopes can also be created by the interaction of stable nuclei with neutrons or with high-energy particles. As shown in Table 7-4, many radioactive materials are generated inside the nuclear reactors by the bombardment of neutrons or protons, making it difficult to manage radioactive waste. Bombardment of the earth with radiation from outer space also converts some stable atoms to radioactive ones. A good example is the production of ^{14}C from ^{14}N by cosmic rays, which are charged particles entering the earth's atmosphere at high velocities. All living forms are kept uniformly radioactive with ^{14}C because atmospheric carbon, which contains this produced material, is the primary source of carbon for life; this is the basis of the **radiocarbon dating method** (see Section 15.2 in Chapter 15).

Table 7-4. Typical activation Products That Appear in Wastes from Power Reactors

Radionuclide	Half-life	Mechanisms of formation			Activated source
Light-water-cooled reactors					
^{16}N	7 sec	^{16}O	(n,p)	^{16}N	water
^{17}N	4 sec	^{17}O	(n,p)	^{17}N	water
^{19}O	30 secs	^{18}O	(n,p)	^{18}O	water
^{3}H (tritium)[b]	12.0 yrs	^{6}Li	(n,α)	^{3}H	lithium hydroxide
^{16}F	1.8 hrs	^{18}O	(p,n)	^{18}F	water
^{36}Na	15.0 hrs	^{28}Na	(n,y)	^{24}Na	sodium in water
		^{27}Al	(n,α)	^{34}Na	aluminum
^{28}Al	2.0 mins	^{17}Al	(n,y)	^{28}Al	aluminum
^{31}Si	2.8 hrs	^{31}P	(n,p)	^{31}Si	water treatment with phosphates
^{41}Ar	1.8 hrs	^{40}Ar	(n,y)	^{41}Ar	air
^{53}Mn	300 days	^{53}Fe	(n,p)	^{54}Mn	steel
^{56}Mn	2.6	^{55}Mn	(n,y)	^{56}Mn	steel
		^{50}Fe	(n,p)	^{54}Mn	steel
^{55}Fe[b]	29 yrs	^{54}Fe	(n,y)	^{55}Fe	steel
^{59}Fe[b]	45.0 days	^{58}Fe	(n,y)	^{59}Fe	steel
		^{58}Co	(n,p)	^{59}Fe	steel
^{18}Co[b]	71.0 days	^{57}Co	(n,y)	^{38}Co	steel and stellite
		^{18}Ni	(n,p)	^{58}Co	steel
^{60}Co	5.2 yrs	^{18}Co	(n,y)	^{44}Co	steel

Table 7-4. continued

Radionuclide	Half-life	Mechanisms of formation			Activated source
^{44}Cu	12.8 hrs	^{61}Cu	(n,y)	^{64}Cu	17-4 ph steel
^{64}Cu	4.6 mins	^{65}Cu	(n,y)	^{66}Cu	and Cu-Ni alloy
^{68}Ni	2.6 hrs	^{64}Ni	(n,y)	^{65}Ni	steel
^{51}Cr^{b}	27.0 days	^{50}Cr	(n,y)	^{51}Cr	steel
^{96}Zr	65 days	^{94}Zr	(n,y)	^{94}Zr	zirconium fuel structure
^{192}Hf	40 days	^{190}Hf	(n,y)	^{13}Hf	halfnium control rods
^{182}Ta^{b}	111.0 days	^{181}Ta	(n,y)	^{182}Ta	steel
^{187}W	24.0 hrs	^{186}W	(n,y)	^{187}W	stellite
sodium-cooled reactors					
^{41}Ar	1.8 hrs	^{40}Ar	(n,y)	^{41}Ar	impurity in nitrogen
^{21}Na^{b}	15.0 hrs	^{23}Na	(n,y)	^{24}Na	sodium
^{22}Na^{b}	2.6 yrs	^{23}Na	(n,2n)	^{22}Na	sodium
^{86}Ru^{b}	19.5 days	^{85}Rb	(n,y)	^{84}Rb	collant impurities
^{121}Sb^{b}	60.0 days	^{127}I	(n,α)	^{124}Sb	coolant impurities

[a]
Source: from *Radioactive Waste Handling in the Nuclear Power Industry*, Electric Institute, 750 3rd Ave., N.Y., 1960.

[b]
Isotopes likely to be most prevalent and that can be important in waste-handling operations.

　　　Radioactive changes involve the transmutation of one element into another, such as the radioactive decay of U to stable Pb. Such a change cannot occur in one step, and many intermediate steps are involved. In addition, many intermediate products are generated, as shown in Figure 7-2. Natural radiation is rather high in some parts of the world; for example, 0.2–2 roentgen/yr in Morrode Ferro, Brazil. Karala, India registered 2.6 R/yr. The nuclei present are $_{19}K^{40}$, $_{37}Rb^{87}$, $_{75}Re^{187}$.

　　　The radioactivity occurs in nature are:

$$U^{238} \xrightarrow{\alpha} Th^{234} \xrightarrow{\beta^-} Pa^{234} \xrightarrow{\beta^-} U^{234} \xrightarrow{\alpha} Th^{230} \xrightarrow{\alpha}$$

$$Ra^{226} \xrightarrow{\alpha} Rn^{222} \xrightarrow{\alpha} Po^{218} \xrightarrow{\alpha} Pb^{214} \xrightarrow{\beta^-}$$

$$Pb^{214} \xrightarrow{\beta^-} Po^{214} \xrightarrow{\beta^-} Po^{214} \xrightarrow{\alpha} Pb^{210}$$

The sequence of fallout can be expressed as follows:

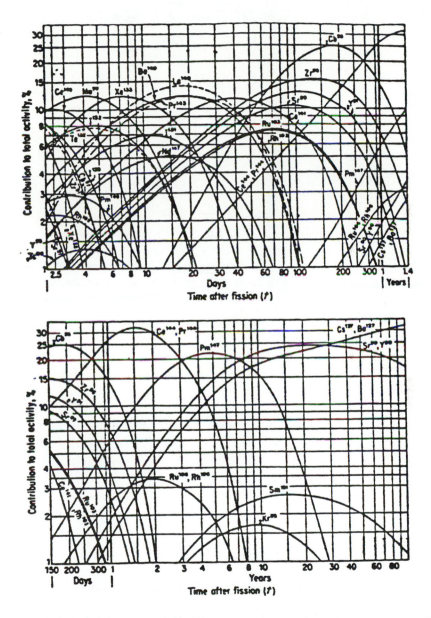

Figure 7-2. Yields of the principal radionuclides form the slow-neutron fission of ^{235}U.
(Source: Hunter and Ballou, 1951)

in bone,

$$_{38}Sr^{90} \xrightarrow[\text{28.1 y}]{\beta^-} {}_{39}Y^{90} \xrightarrow[\text{64 hr}]{\beta^-} {}_{40}Zr^{90}$$

in muscle,

$$_{55}Cs^{137} \xrightarrow[\text{30 y}]{\beta^-} {}_{56}Ba^{137}$$

and in thyroid,

$$_{53}I^{131} \xrightarrow[\text{8 d}]{\beta^-} {}_{54}Xe^{131}$$

Currently, there are no federal regulations (U.S.) concerning NORM which include the uranium and other radioactive elements in coal ash, oil, gas production wastes, and so on.

7.1.6 Nuclear Fission

The principle is illustrated here:
    Bombardment with a neutron

$$_{92}U^{235} + {}_0n^1 \rightarrow {}_{92}U^{236} + {}_0\gamma^0 \quad \text{(Absorption)}$$

Fragmentation

$$_{92}U^{235} + {}_0n^1 \rightarrow {}_{56}Ba^{142} + {}_{36}Kr^{91} + 3{}_0n^1$$

or

$$_{92}U^{235} + {}_0n^1 \rightarrow {}_{57}La^{139} + {}_{40}Zr^{95} + 5{}_{-1}\beta^0 + 2{}_0n^1$$

In general, 2.5 neutrons are gained from the two fragments or

$$_{92}U^{235} + {}_0n^1 \rightarrow {}_zX^A + {}_{z'}Y^{A'} + [(z + z') - 92]{}_{-1}\beta^0 + [236 - (A + A')]{}_0n^1 + \text{energy}$$

Also, the principle of a breeder reaction is discussed here:

$$_{92}U^{238} + {}_0n^1 \rightarrow {}_{92}U^{239} + {}_0\gamma^0 \xrightarrow{\beta^-} {}_{93}Np^{239} \xrightarrow{\beta^-} {}_{94}Pu^{239}$$

$$_{90}Th^{232} + {}_0n^1 \rightarrow {}_{90}Th^{233} + {}_0\gamma^0 \xrightarrow{\beta^-} {}_{91}Pa^{233} \xrightarrow{\beta^-} {}_{92}U^{233}$$

but for the liquid metal-cooled fast breeder (LMFBR), the following is valid:

$$_{11}Na^{23} + {}_0n^1 \rightarrow {}_{11}Na^{24} + {}_0\gamma^0 \xrightarrow{\beta^-} {}_{12}Mg^{24}$$

7.1.7 Nuclear Fusion

In contrast to fission, where a large atom can be split into a smaller atom resulting in the release of energy, **fusion** is when light atoms are combined so that energy can be released. The principle of nuclear fusion is outlined here: A simple example of fusion can illustrated by the proton (p) attack of the deuteron nucleus (p,n) which will essentially form the He^3 (2p,n) nucleus with a release of energy.

Hydrogen burning — Sun

$$H^1 \, (p, \, \beta) \, H^2$$

$$H^2 \, (p, \, \gamma) \, He^3$$

$$He^3 \, (p, \, \beta) \, He^4$$

$$4p \rightarrow \alpha + 2\beta + \gamma$$

D-D and D-T reaction

$$H^2 \, (d, \, n) \, He^3$$

$$H^2 \, (d, \, p) \, H^3$$

$$H^3 \, (d, \, n) \, He^4$$

$$He^4 \, (d, \, p) \, He^4$$

$$6d \rightarrow 2\alpha + 2p + 2n, \text{ or } 3d \rightarrow \alpha + p + n$$

Li Breeding (from seawater)

$$H^3 \text{ (d, n) } He^4$$

$$\text{either } Li^6 \text{ (n, } \alpha\text{) } H^3$$

$$\text{or } Li^7 \text{ (n, } \frac{\alpha}{n}\text{) } H^3$$

$$d + Li^6 = 2\alpha$$

or

$$d + Li^7 = 2\alpha + n$$

7.2 NUCLEAR REACTORS

In using nuclear energy, heat is again generated to produce steam to drive a steam turbine to generate electricity. Due to the size and complexity of "burners" for either nuclear fission or nuclear fusion, they can only be used in the largest factories or for electricity generation. Here we will focus on electricity generation. The fusion of two or more light atomic nuclei to form the nucleus of a heavier element generally produces more energy than the fission of heavy elements. Research conducted to produce a **controlled fusion reaction** for power production has proven unsuccessful up to the present, so the discussion here will be focused on nuclear fission reactors.

In general, there are two types of fission reactors. One is called a **thermal type reactor** and the other a **breeder type reactor**. Three main types of thermal reactors have been developed: the **boiling water reactor (BWR)**, the **pressurized water reactor (PWR)**, and the **high temperature gas-cooled reactor (HTGR)**, as shown in Figure 7-3. The first two are commonly called **light water reactors (LWR)**. The breeder type reactors are more advanced systems and there are three main types: the **liquid metal fast breeder reactor (LMFBR)**, the **gas-cooled fast breeder reactor (GCFBR)**, and the **molten salt breeder reactor (MSBR)**.

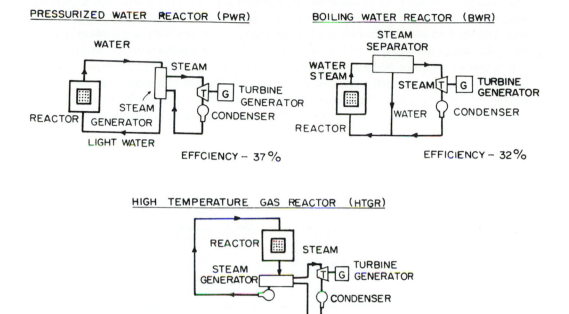

Figure 7-3. Basic thermal reactor concepts.

7.2.1 Thermal Reactors

The major difference between the two types of light water reactors is that the PWR circulates highly pressurized water (2200 psi) through the system, whereas the BWR uses boiling water instead. The BWR concept was developed because of the desirable reduction in pressure and plant costs by eliminating the large temperature drops and the expense associated with the steam generators of the PWR. Also, BWR pressure vessels may have thinner walls. Disadvantages arise mainly from radioactivity in the cooling water and in the steam circulating through the turbine and other parts of the heat-power loop, thus potentiating large releases to the atmosphere. The efficiencies are pretty close: 31% for PWR and 32% for BWR.

The lower part of Figure 7-4 shows the operating principles of a pressurized light water reactor. The reactor itself consists of a number of metal tubes containing pellets of uranium or uranium oxide. The reactor is controlled by adding material that absorbs (captures) neutrons and prevents more than one neutron per fission from causing further fissions. Such a material could be boron or cadmium, a solid that can be conveniently placed on a control rod. Control rods are lowered automatically among the fuel rods to a level that adjusts the neutron flux so that the chain reaction is maintained but does not run out of control. Surrounding the fuel and control rods is a bath of water, which acts both as a **coolant** to carry away the energy generated in the fission reaction and also as a **moderator** — that is, a substance that slows down the neutrons to increase the fission probability. Neutrons, released by the fission, travel at such high velocities that, in the absence of a moderator, they would escape before inducing further fission. The water circulates through a heat exchange that generates steam from a secondary coolant. This steam is then used to drive a turbine to generate electricity.

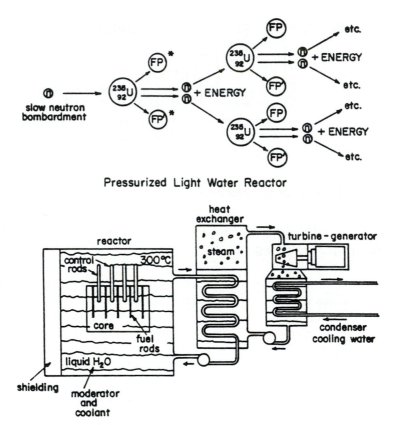

Figure 7-4.   Chain reaction by induced with slow (thermal) neutrons; pressurized light water reactor. FP and FP' are fission products. (Source: Spiro and Sriglianti, 1980.)

The reactor components are summarized below:

Fuel	initial fissile material U^{235}, Pu^{239}
	fertile material Th^{232}, U^{238}
Moderator	H_2O, D_2O, C, Be
Coolant	H_2O, air (Ar, Kr), CO_2, He, Na, Bi, Na-K,
	organic (polyphenylenes)
Reflector	Be, C
Shielding	Concrete (Si, Na, Ca), steel, Pb, H_2O (P, Cl)
Control Rod	Cd, B, Hf, Zr
Structure	Al, steel (Co, Ni, Cr, W, Ta, Mn, Cu)

The HTGR, using helium instead of water to transfer heat, permits the use of graphite and other materials at elevated temperatures. These materials provide thermal and mechanical stability and allow the transfer of heat at temperatures up to 850°C. This feature affords higher heat power efficiency (40%), the option of steam or gas turbines for power production, and the use of heat for chemical processing.

7.2.2 Breeder Reactors

Although U-235 represents an extremely concentrated form of energy, there is not a great deal of it present in the world. While U-235 is the only naturally occurring fissionable isotope, isotopes of other heavy elements can also undergo induced fission. Of particular interest is plutonium-239, which can be made by neutron bombardment of uranium-238, the abundant form of uranium. As shown in Figure 7-5 it is feasible to convert inactive uranium-238 to fissionable plutonium-239, thereby converting all the uranium to nuclear fuel.

The breeder reactor is designed to extract power from the fission of either U-235 or Pu-239, but at the same time to produce plutonium from U-238 at a fast rate so that more fuel is produced than is consumed. The breeder reactor usually uses **fast neutrons** so that few neutrons are captured by surrounding material, and the number of neutrons per fission is greater. The heat-transfer material in a fast-neutron reactor cannot be water, for that would slow the neutrons down. It must therefore be either a gas or another liquid. Molten sodium is usually chosen because it does not slow down the neutrons, has good heat transfer properties, and is a liquid over a wide temperature range, 98–808°C.

The use of breeder reactors would stretch the supply of uranium fuel by at least a factor of 50. However, the technology of the breeder reactor is far more complex and is still in the process of being developed.

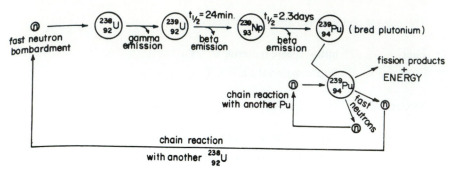

Liquid Sodium Breeder Reactor

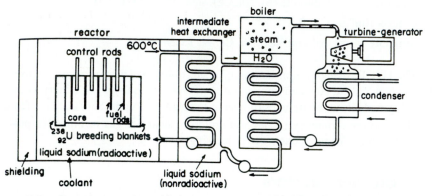

Figure 7-5.   Breeder reaction with fast neutrons and liquid sodium breeder reactor.
(Source Spiro and Sriglianti, 1980)

7.3 NUCLEAR FUEL CYCLE

The amount of energy concentrated in uranium is vastly greater than that contained in coal
or oil. One gram of uranium-235 is equivalent to about 2 metric tons of high-grade coal or
12 barrels of oil. But is it a cheap energy source to use? As discussed before, natural U-235
is in dilute form and needs to be concentrated for reactors. A lot of energy has to be spent in
the **separative work (SW)**, which can be represented as a separation factor, α where:

$$\alpha = \frac{\left(\dfrac{N'}{1-N'}\right)}{\left(\dfrac{N}{1-N}\right)} = \frac{R'}{R}$$

where N= concentration fraction of desired, N'= undesired, and R= abundance

From the separation factor, the following terms are used in the nuclear science and technology that include:

Process difference , ε,

$$\varepsilon = \alpha - 1$$

$$\alpha \approx \left(\frac{m_2}{m_1}\right)^{\frac{1}{2}}$$

Separation power $\propto \varepsilon^2$

Separation potential, $V(N)$,

$$V(N) = (2N-1)\ln\left(\frac{N}{1-N}\right) + AN + B$$

Separative work, SW, $SW = m_p\, V(N_p) + m_w\, V(N_w) - m_f\, V(N_f)$

Where the subscripts indicate p — products; w — wastes; f — feeds

A **unit of separative work (SWU)** refers to the energy required to double the U-235 content in 1 kg of uranium (output). The use of gas diffusion, centrifugation, or the recently-developed laser technology still requires a lot of energy to separate U-235. Table 7-5 lists the energy consumption in some of the nuclear centers around the world. The electricity used in Oak Ridge, Tennessee, for example, is approximately 6,000 million watts per year, the sum of the total electricity consumption of Philadelphia, San Francisco, and Denver. A fuel cycle for the enrichment of U-235 is shown in Figure 7-6.

Table 7-5. Energy Consumption in Some of the World's Nuclear Centers

Location	10^6 SWU/ yr.
Oak Ridge, TN	4.7
Portsmouth, OH	5.2
Paducah, KY	7.3
Capenhurst, (U.K.)	0.4
Pierrelatte (FRANCE)	0.2

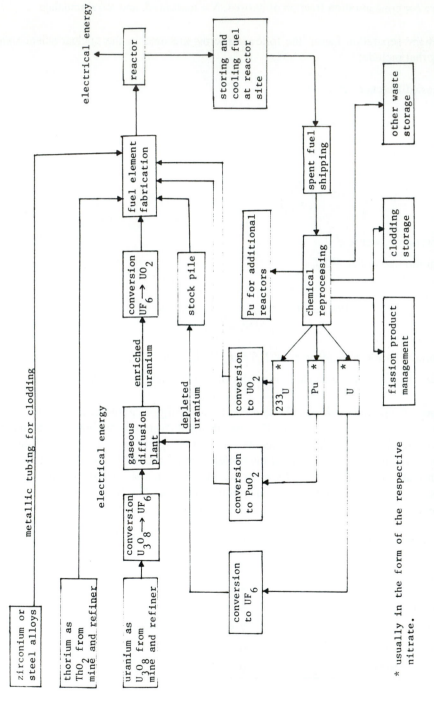

Figure 7-6. Schematic representation of the nuclear-fuel cycle. Each box represents a stage in the processing of materials from their raw state to their reuse or management as radioactive wastes.

7.3.1 Nuclear Accident

At Hiroshima and Nagasaki, A-bombs with yields of approximately 20 kT were used, and they exploded about half a mile each in the middle of both cities. An H-bomb with a yield of 1 MT can destroy everything and everyone within 7 miles. The intercontinental missiles were equipped with over 3-MT of thermonuclear warheads. Nuclear power is not only used for destruction, it also allows for peaceful use. Some of the examples for the peaceful use of nuclear energy are presented here. In the past, Project Handcar (yield 10 kT) was designed for the exploration of carbonate rocks at the Nevada testing sites. Project Gas Buggy (yield 26 kT) was used for stimulation of natural gas in the San Juan Basin, which supported by the El Paso Natural Gas Co. Project Rulison (yield 40 kT) was for the exploration of gas at Garfield, CO by the CER Geonuclear Corp. Project Branco, which was for the exploration of oil shale, never took place. There were also some other practical uses including the construction of harbors and waterways, blockcave mining, and aggregate production.

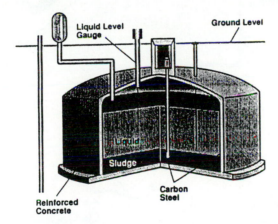

Single-Shell Tanks

- 149 tanks constructed 1943 to 1964
- ~210 m^3 to 3,800 m^3 capacity (55 kgal to 1 Mgal)
- Bottom of tanks at least 50 m (150 feet) above groundwater
- No waste added to tanks since 1980
- Tanks currently contain: ~136,800 m^3 (36 Mgal) of salt cake, sludge and liquid ~555×10^{16} Bq (150 MCi)
- 67 are assumed to have leaked ~3,800 m^3 (~1 Mgal)

Figure 7-7.   A cutaway view of a typical single-shell tank at the Hanford Site.

According to the Rasmussen Report, the risk of major accidents or calamities for nuclear reactors is extremely rare when compared with other accidents. Nevertheless, Three Mile Island and Chernobyl accidents do occur. From WASH 740, the maximum hypothetical accident of a 500 MW (t) reactor in a population center of 1 M and a population density of 500/ miles^2 will result in 3,400 deaths, 43,000 injuries, and property damage of \$7B. Modern reactor technology has been built based on the safety principles of redundancy (if single failure), separation, and diversity to avoid the core melt due to the **loss of coolant accident** (LOCA). To prepare for this event, modern reactors are provided with the **emergency core-cooling system** (ECCS) to allow rapid shutdown of reactor transient.

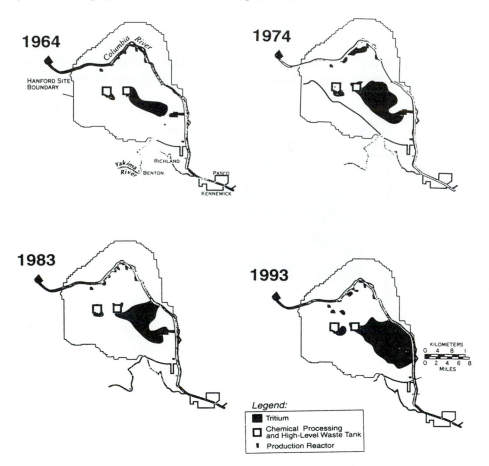

Figure 7-8.   Spreading tritium contamination at the Hanford Site in Washington. The shaded areas on these maps show how tritium contamination in concentrations above safe drinking-water standards have spread over time. (Source: US DOE, "Closing the Circle on the Splitting of the Atoms," 1996)

The transportation of radioactive material, including wastes, are of some concern. During the past, thousands of rail shipments containing radioactive materials resulted in 26 shipping accidents. None of them caused overexposure or injury to the public. The most serious accident was the storage of radioactive waste. For example, in the 74 MG of high-level waste stored at Hanford operation, 10 out of 149 underground tanks developed leaks which resulted in 227,400 gal to ground. For the 17 MG stored at Savannah River site, four tanks developed leaks. All these leaks will contaminate the soil and surface water, as shown in Figure 7-7. For example, the spreading of tritium contamination in concentrations above safe drinking-water standards has increased steadily from 1964 to 1993 in Hanford site, as shown in Figure 7-8.

7.4 RADIOACTIVE NUCLEAR WASTE

As the utilization of nuclear power expands, more radioactive wastes are generated either from the separative work of U-235 or from fission reactions in the reactors. Table 7-6 gives the amount of radioactive wastes as a result of the expanding use of nuclear power in the United States.

Table 7-6. Radioactive Wastes as a Function of Expanding U.S. Nuclear Power*

	Calender Year		
	1970	1980	2000
Installed nuclear capacity, MW(e)	11,000	95,000	734,000
Volume high-level liquid waste[a,b]			
Annual production, gal/yr	23,000	510,000	3,400,000
Accumulated volume, gal[c]	45,000	2,400,000	39,000,000
Accumulated fission products, megacuries[b]			
Sr^{90}	15	750	10,800
Kr^{35}	1.2	90	1,160
H^3	0.04	3	36
Total for all fission products	1,200	44,000	860,000
Accumulated fission products, tons	16	388	5,350

*Source: Snow, 1967

aBased on 100 gallons of high-level acid waste per 10,000 thermal megawatt days (MWd) irradiation.

bAssumes 3-yr lag between dates of power generation and waste production.

cAssumes wastes all accumulated as liquids.

Table 7-7. An Example of Annual Discharge of Radioactive Waste (Noble Gases)

Country	Facility	Discharge Limit (Ci/a)	Activity Released (Ci/a) 1969	1970	1971	1972
FED. REP.	VAK	8.8×10^4	1,750	3,340	2,455	—
GERMANY	AVR	51.6	18	32	27	30
	KRB	1.9×10^6	11,400	7,350	6,780	11,105
	MZFR[a]	3×10^3	—	—	526	955
	KWL	3.1×10^6	166,000	114,000	9,000	5,300[b]
	KWO	8×10^4	5,560	7,700	1,456	3,202
	KWW	3.2×10^4	—	—	—	594
	KKS	6.1×10^4	—	—	3	2,445
	BR-3		—	26,680[c]	—	252
	Chinon	$4 \times 10^{5\ d}$	12,300	8,085	4,225	11,515
	SENA	$2.5 \times 10^{6\ d}$	—	3	4,500	31,342
	EL-4	$4 \times 10^{5\ d}$	46	72	53,810	144,450[e]
	St-Laurent-des-Eaux	$4 \times 10^{5\ d}$	1,900	305	3,425	3,863
	Bugey	$4 \times 10^{5\ d}$	—	—	—	841
	Latina	5×10^3	1,500	2,500	2,470	3,660
	Garigliano	6.3×10^5	140,000	275,000	640,000	290,000
	Trino	5×10^5	—	19	585	1,031
	Dodewaard	3×10^5	—	~3,000	~3,000	8,400

UNITED KINGDOM   CEGB Power Stations: gaseous activity not measured routinely [f]

a In addition, MZFR discharged the following amounts of tritium into the atmosphere: in 1969 1300 Ci; in 1970 1190 Ci; in 1971 1130 Ci; in 1972 542 Ci. The discharge limit is 4000 Ci/ a.

b Shut-down of power station for 8 months.

c Exceptional discharge due to reactor operation experimentally with faulty fuel elements.

d At this discharge level, assuming an atmospheric dilution factor of 1.5×10^{-5} s/m3 and a probability of over 20% that the wind is blowing in one direction, the maximum concentration in air at ground level is equal to the MPC to population in air.

e In addition, EL-4 discharged 83 Ci of tritium into the atmosphere.

f In the CEGB power stations, gas activity (Ar-41) is not systematically measured. Occasional measurements have shown that at the Bradwell, Hinkley Point, and Trawsfynydd power stations the annual discharge is approximately 40,000 Ci, 200,000 Ci and 130,000 Ci respectively.

Spent reactor fuels are usually reprocessed. This process involves cutting up the old fuel rods, chemically extracting the uranium and plutonium from the fission products, and preparing the products for radioactive waste disposal. Maintenance and safety problems are much more severe than those in the operation of a nuclear reactor, and the possibilities for the accidental release of radioactivity are much greater. Transportation of nuclear fuels between stations also has a great potential for environmental hazard.

Although the radiation released from nuclear reactors in normal operation is quite low, the reactors themselves contain a large quantity of intense radioactivity. Concerns that the system might fail in an actual crisis situation were raised considerably after the Three Mile Island accident (discussed in Section 7.3.1). Although there are several barriers inside the reactor to keep all product activity under control, a small amount of fission product gases (krypton, xenon, and iodine) does leak through pinhole leaks to the primary coolant circuit. They are usually released to the environment through a stack, along with hot air to make them rise and disperse. Nevertheless, these gases are radioactive, as shown in Table 7-7.

7.4.1 Nuclear Waste and Waste Types

Any activity that provides radioactive materials generates radioactive waste. The waste will include mining, nuclear power generation, and various processes in the industry. It is especially included in the defense industry, which can use a gas, liquid, or solid form and can remain radioactive for a few hours, months, or over thousands of years. Currently in the United States alone, a minimum of over 45,300 sites handle radioactive material; of these sites a single complex may have as high as 1,500 contaminated sites. During the past 50 years of nuclear weapon production, vast quantities of hazardous materials and radionuclides have been released into the air, groundwater, surface water, sediments and soils, as well as vegetation and wildlife. Data and description of vast amounts of buried waste within the contaminated pits, ponds, and lagoons stated that the migration of the contaminants to water are presently unknown, except for a small number of examples.

Nuclear wastes can be categorized into **high-level waste** (HLW) and spent nuclear fuel, **transuramic** (TRU) **waste**, **low-level waste** (LLW), and **mixed waste**. The HLW includes fissionable product elements, active nuclide and their daughter elements. The temperature of these wastes can reach up to 930°C and take 5 years for cooling. The half-life of the element and its daughter compound can be very long-lived (refer to Figure 7-2). Much of HLW was generated by defense activities and stored in underground storage tanks at the Savannah River site, the Idaho National Engineering Laboratory, and the Hanford site. Spent nuclear fuel from commercial utilities has to be reprocessed to recover materials for defense purposes. The remaining is handled similarly as HLW in the sites. TRU is a waste contaminated with alpha-emitting radionuclides, with an atomic number greater than 92 (U), a half-life greater than 20 years, and in concentrations greater than 100 nCi per gram of waste. The LLW can have a radioactivity level that is less than 10μCi and up to a 1 m Ci/L level, and can be discarded after dilution with water. Usually, if the dilution extent reaches the **decontamination factor** (DF), then it can be considered clean. (DF is the ratio of impurity concentration relative to the desired product before processing to that concentration after processing. Mixed waste happens when radioactive wastes are also contaminated with hazardous wastes.) Mixed waste also contain hazardous materials with HLW and LLW.

As indicated by Table 7-6, the increase in HLW is in exponential growth. The amount of HLW currently in storage (in m^3) has been summarized by U.S. DOE in 1991 as:

Savannah River Site	132,000
Hanford Site	254,000
Idaho Chemical Processing Site	12,000
West Valley Demonstration Project	1,230

7.4.2   Biological Concentration of Radioactive Elements

Some substances will be biologically concentrated. Of those potentially emitted by power stations, iodine, strontium, radium, plutonium, and cesium are probably the most important. For example, iodine can fall on grasslands and be eaten by cows; it will then be concentrated in milk. The milk, when ingested by humans, will lead to radioactive iodine concentrated in the thyroid. Figure 7-9 illustrates the $^{129}I/^{127}I$ atom ratio in various material showing the change in the pathway from air to food. These indicate the risk to the biosphere and especially to mankind.

Microbial processes for nuclear waste treatment can result in

- the removal, recovery, and stabilization of radionuclides,
- the biodegradation of organic constituents to binolous products, and
- the overall reduction of the volumes of waste for disposal under proper conditions.

Microorganisms bring about dissolution or immobilization of radionuclides and toxic metals by one or more of the following mechanisms:

- redox reactions that affect solubility
- changes in pH and Rh that affect the valence or ionic states
- solubilization and leaching of certain elements by metabolites or decomposition products such as organic acid metabolites, dielates, or specific sequestering agents
- volatilization due to alkylation (biomethylation)
- immobilization leading to formation of stable minerals or bioaccumulation by microbial biomass

In a flow-through bioreactor, *Pseudomonas aeroginosa* immobilized within a matrix of calcium alginate, can reduce uranium levels in a simulated wastewater from 10 ppm to 6.8 ppb. Over 350 column volumes before breakthrough occurred and the uranium can be recovered by dilute HNO_3 of 5 colune volumes. Biosorption is unique for removal of trace uranium in wastewater because its high solubility is water.

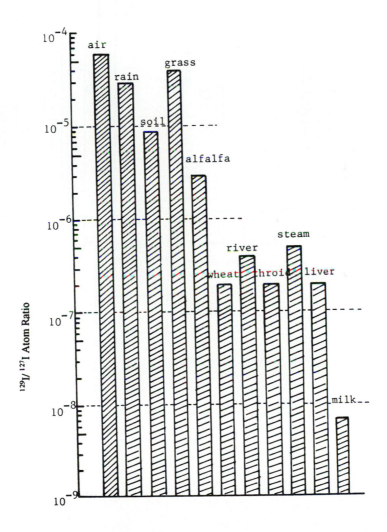

Figure 7-9. $^{129}I/^{127}I$ in various materials showing the change in the pathway from air to food.

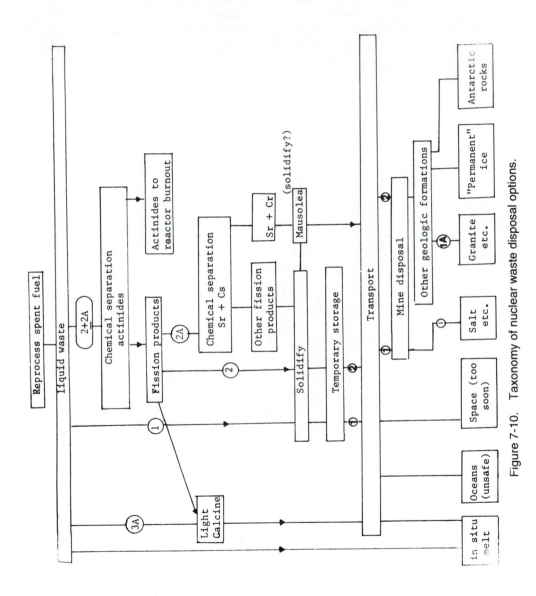

Figure 7-10. Taxonomy of nuclear waste disposal options.

7.5 NUCLEAR WASTE DISPOSAL AND TREATMENT TECHNOLOGY

The cost estimate for nuclear waste cleanup in the United States has been rising rapidly. It has increased from \$200 B to \$500 B, and in 1995, the estimate for the total cleanup costs can reach 1 trillion dollars and 30 years to complete! This surely is a serious matter as much of the treatment technology is handicapped by the limited information available about the contamination profile. For example, U.S. DOE has been identified as particularly intractable for the following:

- groundwater contamination at almost all sites
- plutonium in soil (for example at Rocky Flats and Mound Plant)
- silos containing uranium processing residuals at Fernald
- single-shell tanks containing HLW at Hanford
- buried TRU waste at INEL

Disposal of radioactive wastes is difficult because there is no way to render them non-radioactive. They must be kept isolated from the biosphere until they decay to the background level, requiring about 10 half-lives and perhaps isolation for hundreds of years. Figure 7-10 shows the taxonomy of nuclear waste disposal options. Possible options are storage in salt vaults, geologically secure strata of the earth, and granite layers.

Recently, after significant institutional and political maneuvers, the Yucca Mountain Project in the United States is proceeding with the characterization of the volcanic tuft for development as a repository. Historically, nuclear repository has always undergone controversy. One of the most famous cases is at the salt dome in Lyons, Kansas. Allowing 3 years for licensing and 6 years for construction, operations for Yucca Mountain is scheduled to begin by 2010. The repository would have a capacity of 70,000 metric tons of uranium (MTU), which is equivalent to nuclear waste that can contain only a fraction of current stockpiles.

Much of the treatment and cleanup technology of nuclear waste remains in conceptual and research phases only. The following section gives a brief account of the effort, except the biological ones, which were covered in section 7.4.2 .

7.5.1 Transmutation

This concept involves the elemental changes of the waste constituents into elements with shorter radioactive lives or even into nonradioactive elements through nuclear reactions by a reactor or an accelerator. Actinides burning (refer to Fig. 7-10), also called waste partitioning-transmutation (P-T), is an advanced method for radioactive waste management based on the idea of destroying the most toxic components in the waste. It consists of:

- selective removal for the most toxic radionuclides from HLW
- conversion of these radionuclides into less toxic radioactive elements and/or stable elements.

Transmutation of key fission products of long-lived Tc^{99} and I^{129} is feasible as a thermal reactor. For example, both the long-lived radioactive nuclides are converted by neutron capture and beta decay into stable products as shown here:

$$Tc^{99} + n \rightarrow Tc^{100} \rightarrow Ru^{100} + n \rightarrow Ru^{101} + n \rightarrow Ru^{102}$$

$$(165h)\beta \text{ stable} \qquad \text{stable} \qquad \text{stable}$$

$$I^{129} + n \rightarrow I^{130} \rightarrow Xe^{130} + n \rightarrow Xe^{131} + n \rightarrow Xe^{132}$$

$$(12.4 \text{ h})\beta \text{ stable} \qquad \text{stable} \qquad \text{stable}$$

$$I^{127} + n \rightarrow I^{128} \rightarrow Xe^{128} + n \rightarrow Xe^{129} + n \rightarrow Xe^{130}$$

$$\text{stable} \qquad (25m)\beta \text{ stable} \qquad \text{stable} \qquad \text{stable}$$

The main product from TRU is Pu^{239}, which can fission well by neutron capture to Pu^{240} and end with high mass isotopes of Pu, Am, and Cm. With complexity and several competing routes, the anticipated goal is difficult to achieve. The extent of the depletion of TRU by transmutation is measured by the depletion ratio $\chi(t)$.

$$\chi(t) = \frac{\text{total amount of TRU supplied}}{\text{TRU in transmuter and its waste}}$$

7.5.2   Polymer Extraction

This method is the use of water-soluble chelating polymers containing multiple hydroxamine acid functional groups to retain certain metal ions of interest while the unbound metal ions are removed with the bulk of the aqueous solution as they permeate by membrane ultrafiltration. For actinides, selective retention of americium (III) and plutonium (III) from dilute solution high in salt content has been achieved. Chelators also have been used to bind tetravalent plutonium and thorium over trivalent ions for the TRU wastes. Chelating ligands include polyhydroxamates, bis(acylpyrazdones), and malonamides. Functionalized adsorption particles ($1\text{-}15\mu$) with a magnetic core and polymer coating of adequate ligands have been developed for in situ groundwater treatment when a magnetic filter "wall" is installed.

7.5.3 Aqueous Extraction for Separation

Two major aqueous processes have been developed. The first is the **PUREX** (plutonium-uranium extraction) process, which separates U(VI) and Pu(IV) from fission product species in nitric acid solution by solvent extraction with tributyl phosphate (TBP). Americium, curium, and neptuniun (most cases) remain in waste stream. The second is the **TRUEX** (transuranic extraction) process, which is a solvent extraction procedure that can efficiently separate TRU elements, (for example Np, Pu, Am and Cm) from aqueous nitrate or chloride containing wastes. The key extractant is actyl (phenyl) N,N-diisobutylcarbamoyl-methylphosphine oxide (CMPO) (refer to Fig. 7-9). This is combined with TBP and a diluent such as a normal paraffinic hydrocarbon (C_{12}-C_{14} mixture) or a nonflammable chlorocarbon (tetrachloroethylene) to formulate the TRUEX solvent.

There are also other processes developed for removal of TRU that are more efficient; for example, the use of DMDBTDMA shown in Figure 7-11, for mostly the Am(III). If the TRU constant can be lowered to below 100 nCi/g of solid, the waste can be classified as non-TRU. If ^{137}Cs and ^{90}Sr can also be reduced to an acceptable level, then the effort of decontamination is complete. Many extraction processes also employ coextractions of both actinides and lanthanides with HDEHP (refer to Fig. 7-11), and, with the help of DTPA, have been successfully attempted.

CMPO

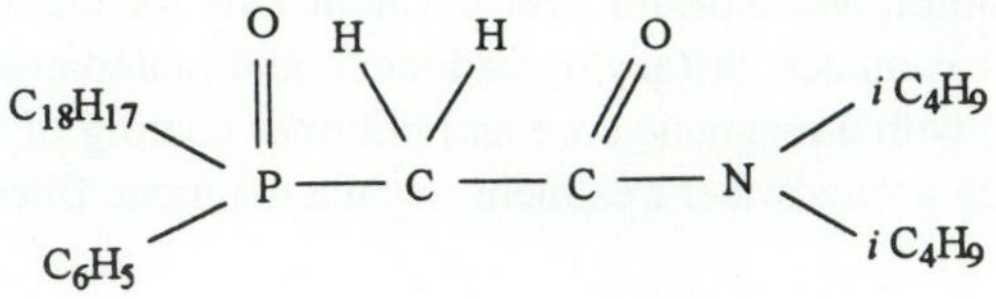

DMDBTDMA

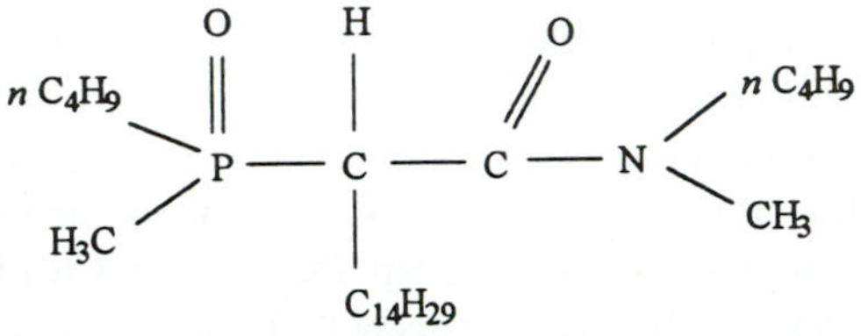

TBP

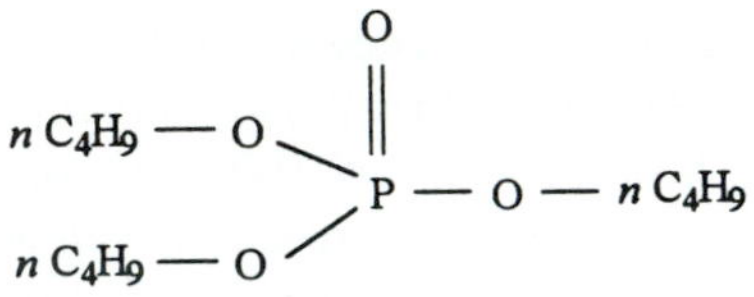

HDEHP

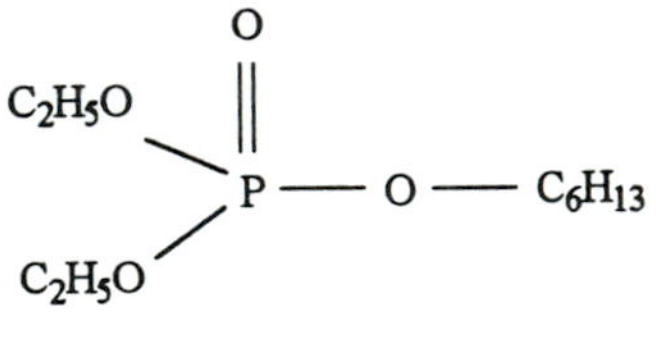

DTPA

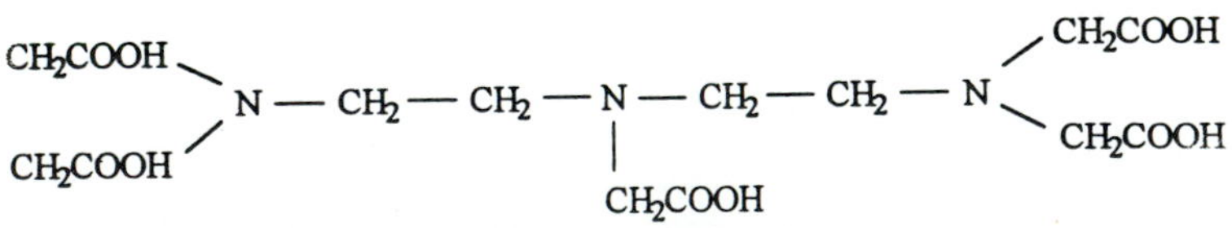

Figure 7-11. Chemicals for solvent extraction of radioactive metals in nuclear wastes.

REFERENCES

7-1   J. Edmondo and J. M. Reilly, *Global Energy-Assessing the Future*, Oxford University Press., New York, 1985.

7-2   N. C. Rasmussen, *Reactor Safety Study, An Assessment of Accident Risks in U.S. Commercial Nuclear Plants*, WASH-1400, U.S. Nuclear Regulatory Commission, 1975.

7-3   D. Bodansky, *Nuclear Energy*: *Principles, Practices and Prospects*, AIP, Woodbury, New York, 1996.

7-4   R. Wilson and W. J. Jones, *Energy, Ecology, and the Environment*, Academic Press, New York, 1974.

7-5   J. J. Duderstadt, *Nuclear Power*, Marcel Dekker, New York, 1979.

7-6   S. S. Penner (ed.), *Energy, Vol. III, Nuclear Energy and Energy Policies*, Addison-Wesley, London, 1976.

7-7   M. W. Firebaugh and M. T. Ohanian, *An Acceptable Future Nuclear Energy System*, Oak Ridge Associated Universities, Oak Ridge, Tennessee, 1980.

7-8   D. Faude, M. Helm, and W. Weisz, *Fusion and Fast Breeder Reactors*, International Institute for Applied System Analysis, Luxenburg, Australia, 1977.

7-9   J. G. Kemeny, *The Accident at Three Mile Island*, Pergamon, New York, 1979.

7-10   F. C. Williams and D. A. Deese, *Nuclears Non-proliferation: The Spent Final Problem*, Pergamon, New York, 1979.

7-11   R. Noyes, *Nuclear Waste Cleanup Technology and Opportunities*, Noyes, Porkridge, New Jersey, 1995.

7-12   National Council Research, *Nuclear Wastes-Research Technologies for Separations and Transmutation*, National Academy Press, Washington DC, 1996.

7-13   V. Jain, *Environmental Issues and Waste Management Technologies in the Ceramic and Nuclear Industries*, American Ceramic Society, Westerville, 1996.

7-14   International Atomic Energy Agency, *Peaceful Nuclear Explosions III, Applications, Characteristics and Effects*, IAEA, Vienna, 1994.

7-15   G. Friedlander and J. W. Kennedy, *Introduction to Radioactivity*, Wiley, New York, 1949.

7-16   D. Halliday, *Introductory Nuclear Physics*, Wiley New York, 1950.

7-17   N. Tsoulfanidis, *Measurement and Detection of Radiation*, Hemisphere, Washington DC, 1983.

PROBLEM SET

1. A certain radioactive substance (which has no radioactive parents) has a half-life of 8 days.

    a. What fraction of this initial amount will be left after 16 days? After 24 days?

    b. The half-life of Na^{24} is 14.9 hr. Calculate the decay constant.

    c. $_3Li^6$ emits α particles when bombarded with neutrons. Write a balanced equation for the nuclear reaction involved. What is a short-hand abbreviation form for this equation?

    d. Complete the following:

        (i) $_1H^2 + ? \rightarrow ? + _0n^1$

        (ii) $_0n^1 \rightarrow p + ?$

        (iii) $_{13}Al^{27} + ? \rightarrow _{15}P^{30} + _0n^1$

        (iv)   Write down the short-hand form for (i) and (iii).

    e. Consider the reaction

    $$_5B^{10} + _2He^4 \rightarrow _0n^1 + _7N^{13}$$

    Calculate the energy release of the reaction.

2. Through a sequence of α- and β-decay, $_{92}U^{235}$ becomes the stable $_{82}Pb^{207}$. Assuming there are four β-decays, how many times does the α-decay take place?

8.1 STRUCTURE OF THE ATMOSPHERE

C H A P T E R **8**

ATMOSPHERE — STRUCTURE AND PROPERTIES

The gaseous envelope surrounding us is the Earth's atmosphere. It is the working fluid of the Earth's heat engine. Most of the radiant energy arriving from the sun is converted into atmospheric heat energy before it is reradiated into space. The fluctuations of the atmospheric system cause weather and climate changes, which form an important part of the earth's history. The **ozone layer**, also part of the atmospheric system, shields the surface of the earth from harsh radiation. In addition to these varied traits, the atmosphere provides an indispensable element of life in the air we breathe. In this chapter, we will address some topics related to the structure and properties of atmosphere that are of an environmental engineering concern, such as the composition and structure of the atmosphere, the greenhouse effect, global warming, natural ice periods, the ozone layer, stratosphere chemistry, and the nature of thermosphere (ionosphere). In the next chapter, troposphere, air pollution, control technology, automotive emission, and meteorology will be discussed.

8.1 STRUCTURE OF THE ATMOSPHERE

The atmosphere is divided into regions based on the profile of temperature as a function of altitude. These layers are depicted in Figure 8-1. The lowest layer, which is the region from the surface of Earth to about 12 km, is called the **troposphere**. The troposphere is where the most action is, or at least where most of the action we can observe take place. Thunder and lightning, rain and rainbows, hail, snow, and spectacular sunsets are all derived from processes occurring in this layer. It is heated from below by solar radiation absorbed at the earth's surface, so its temperature decreases with increasing altitude. This process is referred to as the **lapse rate** (more detail will be given in the latter part of this section). The lapse rate for the troposphere is about −1°C/100 meters. This rate leads to cold air masses overlying warmer air masses. The troposphere is unstable and has rapid convection motions. It is also a region of much turbulence due to the global energy flow that results from imbalances of heating and cooling rates between the equator and the poles. These give rise to what is commonly referred to as weather and result in a rapid vertical mixing of gases that enter the troposphere.

A positive lapse rate reflects a region of stability with respect to convection, because warm air overlies cool air. The change from a negative to a positive lapse rate is called a **temperature inversion**, and the point at which this change occurs marks a stable boundary between two physically distinct layers of air. The tropopause marks the boundary between the troposphere and the stratosphere. The **stratosphere** is the region from about 12 to 50 km. In this region, the ozone absorbs solar ultraviolet radiation with wavelengths from about 200 to 300 nm leading to a temperature inversion. This positive lapse rate makes the stratosphere very stable in vertical mixing. Usually, the residence times of molecules or particles in this layer are measured long on a scale of years.

Because the atmosphere is in the Earth's gravitational field, its density falls with altitude. The mathematical relationship between them will be examined shortly. The troposphere contains 70% of the mass of the atmosphere. Above the stratosphere, extending from 50 to 85 km, lies the **mesosphere**, an intermediate region in which the atmosphere grows continuously thinner. Due to the very low pressures, not enough ozone can be formed from molecular oxygen to maintain the temperature inversion. At the top of the mesosphere the temperature is only about −120°F, and the pressure is only about 1/1000 of 1 atm.

The **thermosphere**, also known as the **ionosphere**, is the region from about 85 km to the top of the earth's atmosphere. Here, the temperature rises due to the absorption of solar rays in the far ultraviolet region by atmospheric gases, principally oxygen. These far ultraviolet rays, X rays and cosmic rays are sufficiently energetic to ionize molecules and break them into their constitute atoms. An appreciable fraction of the gases in this region exists as atoms or ions.

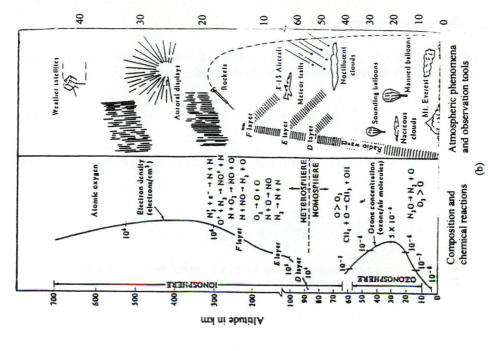

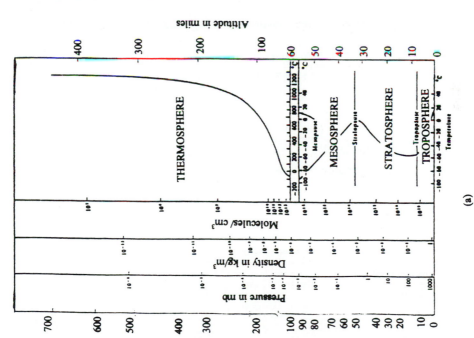

Figure 8-1. Vertical distribution of atmospheric properties and phenomena.

8.1.1   Barometric Formula

The pressure at any height z in the atmosphere is due to the weight of the air above. Thus, the change of pressure in the vertical direction obeys the relation

$$\left(\frac{dP}{dz}\right) = -\rho_{fluid}\, g \qquad\qquad [8\text{-}1]$$

where ρ_{fluid} is the density of the air. If air is considered to be an ideal gas, the density of the air at any point in the atmosphere can be expressed by

$$\rho_{fluid} = \left(\frac{M}{RT}\right)P = \frac{M}{V} \qquad\qquad [8\text{-}2]$$

Combining the two preceding equations from, we obtain the general relation between pressure and temperature at any height z :

$$\left(\frac{dP}{dz}\right) = -\left(\frac{M}{RT}\right)gP \qquad\qquad [8\text{-}3]$$

If T were constant with height, the equation could be integrated directly to yield

$$P = P_0 \exp\left(\frac{-gMz}{RT}\right) \qquad\qquad [8\text{-}4]$$

where
M = molecular weight of air (28.97)

P_0 = pressure at ground level

g = gravitational acceleration (9.80 ms^{-2})

The following illustrates how the atmospheric pressure decreases as the altitude increases (from Equation 8-4):

Layers of the Atmosphere	
Altitude (km)	P (atm)
10	0.3
30	0.03
50	0.003

8.1.2   Adiabatic Lapse Rate

From Chapter 1 on thermodynamics we have

$$dH = dE + PdV + VdP \qquad\qquad [1\text{-}10]$$

We also have the definition

$$C_p dT = dH \qquad\qquad [1\text{-}28]$$

the first law

$$dE = dq - dW = dq - PdV \qquad\qquad [1\text{-}7,8]$$

or

$$C_p dT = dq - PdV + PdV + VdP$$

Thus,

$$dq = C_p dT - VdP \qquad\qquad [8\text{-}5]$$

where C_p the specific heat at constant pressure. Assuming it is under **adiabatic conditions**, no heat goes in or out of the system ($dQ = 0$), and we reach

$$C_p dT = Vd \qquad\qquad [8\text{-}6]$$

That is

$$\left(\frac{dT}{dP}\right) = \left(\frac{V}{C_P}\right)$$

Because

$$\left(\frac{dT}{dz}\right) = \left(\frac{dT}{dP}\right)\left(\frac{dP}{dz}\right)$$

and from Equation [8-3]

$$\left(-\rho_{\text{fluid}}g\right)\left(\frac{dT}{dz}\right) = -\left(\frac{Mg}{V}\right)\left(\frac{V}{C_P}\right) = -\frac{Mg}{C_P} \qquad [8\text{-}7]$$

The specific heat of dry air is about 7.0 cal/mole°K. By substituting C_P into the equation, the adiabatic elapse rate (dT/dz) is determined to be about 1°K per 100 meters. Calculated values for dry adiabatic lapserate (sometimes indicated by F_d) for Venus, Earth, Mars, and Jupiter are respectively 10.7, 9.8, 4.5, and 20.2 K km^{-1}.

8.2 GREENHOUSE EFFECT

The three major constituents of dry air are nitrogen, oxygen, and argon, which account respectively for 78%, 21%, and 0.9% by volume. The remaining constituents of air are present in small amounts that are generally given in parts per million. The most abundant of them is carbon dioxide, forming 0.03% of the total air, while the rest together make up less than 0.01% of the total. The composition of dry air is remarkably constant over the globe, but the amount of water vapor in the atmosphere varies widely, ranging from 4% by volume to a few ppm. The water vapor pressure is highest at the surface and diminishes very rapidly with increasing height; for example, it is only on the order of a few ppm at the tropopause.

All of the gaseous constituents are transparent to most of the Sun's rays. Referring back to the previous chapter, we see that none of them absorbs light significantly in the visible region of the spectrum. The situation is different in the infrared region where ozone, water vapor, and carbon dioxide are the principal absorbers. These gases tend to block a large fraction of the Earth's emitted radiation. Therefore, it has often been remarked that the atmosphere is much like the glass walls of a greenhouse, which are transparent to the incoming short-wavelength solar radiation, but which retain (through absorption and reradiation) the long wavelength infrared rays.

Ozone does not play a large role in the atmospheric greenhouse effect because its infrared absorptions are not very extensive, and its total presence in the atmosphere is not large. However, the absorption of the Earth's rays by carbon dioxide and water is of great importance to the climate on our planet. The overall **greenhouse effect** phenomenon, shown in Figure 8-2, heats up the Earth's surface so that the light absorbed by carbon dioxide and water can be emitted again. Part of the radiation returns to the surface and raises the surface temperature to be warmer than what it would be in the absence of an atmosphere. From the Earth's radiation balance, it is found that the estimated average temperature of the earth (T_e) should be at 253°K. But actually the surface temperature (T_s) is higher by 13°C (286°K) due to the greenhouse effect.

$$S(1-A)\pi R^2 = \sigma 4\pi R^2 T_E^2 \qquad [8\text{-}8]$$

which is

(Solar radiation received by a body) = (Irradiation power by a body)

where

$$T_e = \left[\frac{S(1-A)}{4\sigma} \right]^{\frac{1}{4}} = \text{estimated temperature} \qquad [8\text{-}9]$$

T_s = measured surface temperature

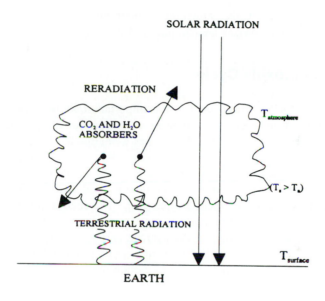

SOLAR RADIATION

RERADIATION

CO$_2$ AND H$_2$O ABSORBERS

$T_{atmosphere}$

$(T_s > T_e)$

TERRESTRIAL RADIATION

$T_{surface}$

EARTH

Figure 8-2.   The greenhouse effect.

The greenhouse effect coefficient is defined as T_S / T_E. The following table illustrates the coefficient for several bodies:

Body	S-W/m²	A	T_e(K)	T_s(K)	Coefficient
Earth	1372	.3	255	286	1.13
			253		
Venus	2613	.75	232	700	3
			(265)		(2.6)
Mars	583	.15	217	220	1.01

The coefficient is an indication of whether or not the greenhouse effect is taking place.

Several mathematical models have been proposed to predict the dependence of the surface temperature on the concentration of carbon dioxide (C). A function $E(C,T_s,W)$ was used to express their relationship, where W is the water vapor pressure. Because the water vapor pressure is a function of T_s, E could be rewritten as $E(C,T_s)$. If the function is exact

$$\left(\frac{\partial E}{\partial C}\right)dC + \left(\frac{\partial E}{\partial T_s}\right)dT_s = 0 \qquad\qquad [8\text{-}10]$$

It is found $(dT_s) = (3.8°C)dC$, which means doubling the atmospheric carbon dioxide would raise the global mean surface temperature by 3.8 degrees Celsius.

8.2.1 Carbon Dioxide Cycle

As far as we surface-dwellers are concerned, it is important to know if the greenhouse effect would be magnified by the increasing amounts of carbon dioxide produced by the rapid burning of fossils. The burning of fossil fuels has a negligible effect on the total oxygen content of the atmosphere, but an appreciable effect has imposed on the carbon dioxide content. As shown in Figure 8-3, carbon dioxide is only a small portion on the carbon balance sheet of the Earth. The industrial carbon dioxide production increased exponentially during the last century at a rate of about 3% per year. The concentration of carbon dioxide in the atmosphere at a site in Iceland has been measured continuously since 1958, as shown in Figure 8-4. This process shows that the average carbon dioxide content of the atmosphere has risen more than 5% since 1958 (the current rate is about 1.5 parts per million per year) which is equivalent to 3.18 peta grams of carbon per year. Detailed calculations can be seen as follows:

C (Pg/yr) for Fossil Fuel and Biomass Decomposition

Petroleum	Gas	Coal	Biomass	$\sum$
2.5	1	2.2	1	6.7

In the United States consumption is 1.2 Pg/yr., [per capita $\approx$ 14 kg/day (US)]. Past records show that CO_2 increased at a rate of 1.5 ppm/yr. Since the Industrial Revolution which was 280 ppm, the CO_2 concentration increases every year and at present it is 360 ppm.

$$360\,\text{ppm of } CO_2 = \frac{\left(360\,\text{m}^3\,CO_2\right)}{\left(1\times10^3\,\text{air}\right)}\frac{(\text{mole})}{(22.4\times10^{-3}\,\text{m}^3\,CO_2)}\frac{(44\,\text{g})}{(\text{mole})} = .707\,\frac{\text{g}}{\text{m}^3}\,\text{of } CO_2$$

$$= \frac{(.707 \text{g CO}_2)}{(\text{m}^3 \text{ air})} \frac{(12 \text{ g of C})}{(44 \text{ g of CO}_2)} \frac{\left(5.1 \times 10^{18} \text{ kg air}\right)}{\left(1.29 \dfrac{\text{kg}}{\text{m}^3} \text{ air}\right)} = 762 \text{ Pg of C} \quad [8\text{-}11]$$

Therefore,

$$1 \text{ ppm of CO}_2 = \frac{762}{360} = 2.12 \text{ Pg of C} \quad\quad\quad [8\text{-}12]$$

and the airborne fraction of $CO_2 = \dfrac{1.5 \text{ ppm/yr}}{\left[(6.7 \text{ Pg/yr}) \Big/ (2.12 \text{ Pg/ppm})\right]} \approx 0.5$

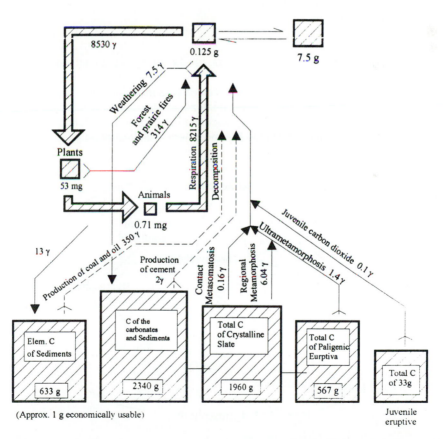

Figure 8-3.   The carbon distribution and carbon cycles on Earth (from Dietrich, 1963).

Carbon dioxide levels in the

atmosphere are increasing exponentially.

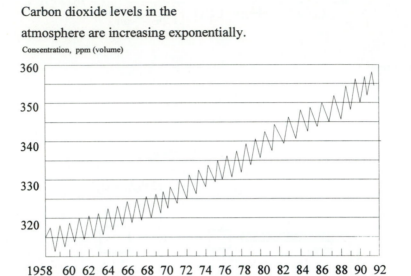

Figure 8-4.   Concentration of carbon dioxide was measured with a continuous recording nondispersive infrared gas analyzer at Mauna Loa Observatory, Hawaii. The dots indicate average monthly concentrations. (Sources: Scripps Institution of Oceanography, National Oceanic & Atmospheric Administration.)

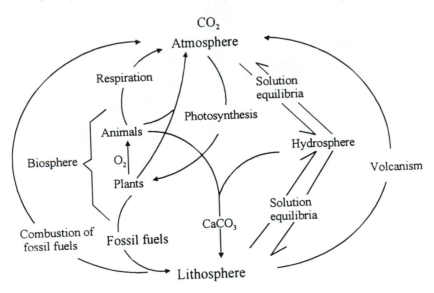

Figure 8-5.   The carbon dioxide cycle.

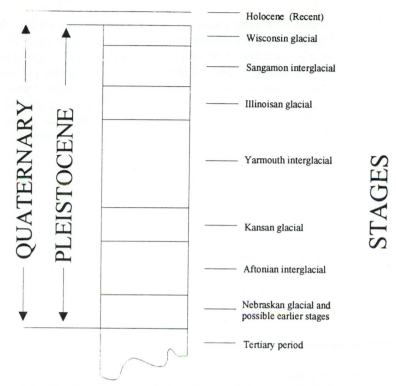

Figure 8-6. The Quaternary period and its subdivisions in North America.

However, the rate increase is only 50% of that expected if all the carbon dioxide emitted by human activity (including cement making) during those years were added to the total. Evidently, 50% of the carbon dioxide produced does not stay in the atmosphere. Figure 8-5 shows the Earth's carbon dioxide cycle. Much of the carbon dioxide added to the atmosphere is absorbed by the oceans, which contain large amounts of carbon dioxide in the form of bicarbonate ions. Other possible uptakers are the living green plants themselves, the biomass. Experimental studies have shown that plant growth increases in the presence of increased carbon dioxide concentration.

8.2.2   Global Warming and Ice Periods

The mean global temperature has been increasing gradually throughout the first half of this century, a rise which correlates the increase in carbon dioxide production since the Industrial Revolution. It has been suggested that the greenhouse effect is responsible. However, nature also goes through its own cycles; for example, ice periods. Table 8-1 gives the geologic time scale. Figure 8-6 illustrates the Quaternary period (0.01 million of years before the present) and its subdivision in North America. The average temperature can be traced back over a longer period of time using a variety of geophysical techniques as well as fossil records, as shown in Figure 8-7. One paleothermometer is the ratio of oxygen 18 to oxygen 16 in the Greenland ice core recorded by Vostok for the 160,000 year temperature record , as shown in Figure 8-8. Another example is that the oil yields (in gallon per ton GPT) of the oil shale from the different buried depths corresponding to the geological time scale vary greatly. The higher organic material content of the oil shale would correspond to higher earth temperatures, which, in turn, imply a higher growth rate of algae, as shown in Figure 8-9. A summary of the different methods for studying ice periods is as follows:

- Greenland Ice Core

  — Vostok (East Antarctica)

  O^{16}, O^{18} isotope ratio

  160,000 year temperature record

- Tree Ring Research

  (recent year only)

- Ocean Beds — Foraminifera

  amino acids racemization

  using optical activity of carbohydrates

- Green River Oil Shale Core

  since Eocene time (50 M year – now)

  Oil yield (GPT) from kerogen

- Sun Spots

  (maybe Little Ice Age)

  22-yr. cycle and 100-yr. cycle (80 + 180-yr. cycle)

- Milankovitch Cycle (Earth)

	10^3 years
stretch	90–100
	(Illinoisan, Kansan)
roll	40
	(Wisconsin)
wobble	21
	(Mankato, Tazewell)

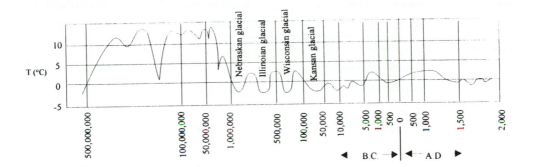

Figure 8-7. Temperature variations in the northern hemisphere (40°N–90°N) as a function of time. (modified after J. E. Oliver, "Climate and Man's Environment," 1973.)

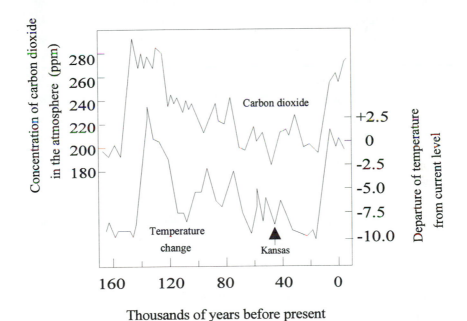

Figure 8-8. CO_2 Concentrations (ppm) and Antarctic temperatures (°C) plotted against age in the Vostok record. Temperatures are referenced to current Vostok surface temperature. (Source: Barnola et al. Reprinted by permission from *Nature*, Vol. 329. 1987, Macmillan Magazines Ltd.)

Table 8-1.   Approximate Scale of Geological Time[1]

Era	Period or Epoch	Beginning and End, In 10^6 Years	Approximate Duration In 10^6 Years
Cenozoic[4]	Quarternary		
	Contemporary	0-1	0.8-1.2
	Pleistocene	1-10	1
	Tertiary		69
	Pliocene	1-10	9
	Miocene	10-25	15
	Oligocene	25-40	15
	Eocene	40-60	20
	Paleocene	60-70	10
Mesozoic[4]	Cretaceous	70-140	70
	Jurassic	140-185	45
	Triassic	185-225	40
Paleozoic[4]	Permian	225-270	45
	Carboniferous	270-320	50
	Devonian	320-400	80
	Silurian	400-420	20
	Ordovician	420-480	60
	Cambrian	480-570	90
Pre-Cambrian	Pre-Cambrian IV (Riphean)[2]	570-1200	630
	Pre-Cambrian III (Proterozoic)[3]	1200-1900	700
	Pre-Cambrian II (Archean)	1900-2700	800
	Pre-Cambrian I (Catarchean)	2700-3500	800
	Pregeological era	3500-5000	1500

[1]Based on the geochronological scale of the Commission for Determining the Absolute Age of Geological Formations, published in *Izv. AN SSR*, Geological Series, No. 10, 1960.

[2]Proterozoic II.

[3]Proterozoic I.

[4]total duration of Cenozoic, Mesozoic and Paleozoic is 570×10^6 years.

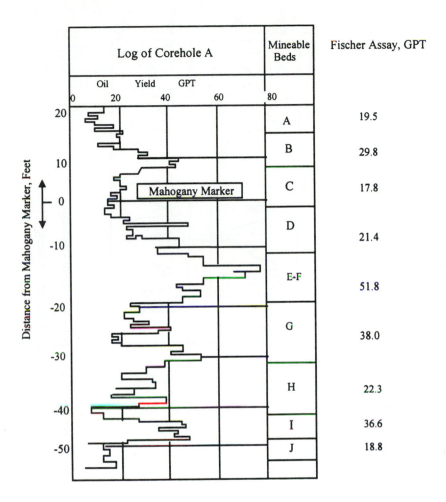

Figure 8-9.   Core intervals and minable beds at Anvil Points Mine. Rifle, Colorado.

The Milankovitch cycle is responsible for most of the ice periods occurring on Earth. As shown in Figure 8-10, it correlates quite well for the past 700,000 yrs. The stretch, roll, and wobble of the Earth are shown in Figure 8-11.

The assessment of human impacts on the climate must be superimposed on this large natural variation. Figure 8-8 shows an attempt to do this for the carbon dioxide greenhouse effect. In this model, a 3°C per 100% increase in carbon dioxide concentration was added to a projection of the natural temperature fluctuations obtained from an examination of the temperature record over the past several hundred years. If this approach is correct, then the current cooling trend should soon level off and be followed by a rather steep rise in temperature.

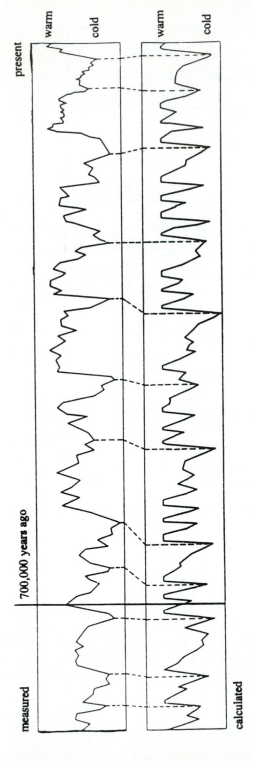

Figure 8-10. Measured and calculated ice periods for 700,000 years ago.

(Permission obtained from N. Calder, *The Weather Machine*, Viking Press, 1974.)

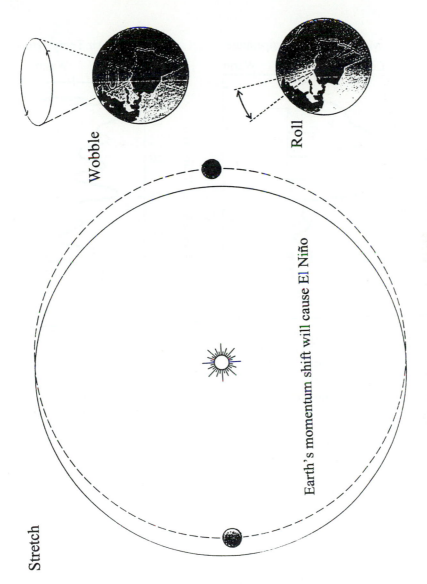

Figure 8-11.   Stretch, roll, and wobble of Earth as Milankovitch cycle.

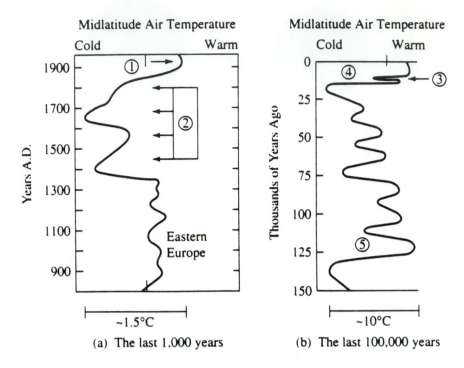

Figure 8-12.   Long-term and short term natural fluctuations in Earth's temperature. (1) Thermal maximum of 1940s, (2) Little Ice Age, (3) Cold interval, (4) Present interglacial (Holocene), (5) Las previous interglacial (Eemian). [From National Research Council. *Understanding Climatic Change, a Program for Action,* Washington, DC, National Academy Press, 1975.]

Relatively small changes of average temperature could disrupt world food production, and unless there are radical changes in the approach to energy conservation, it seems quite probable that the continued generation of carbon dioxide will be very substantial in the future. The implications seem clear enough; carbon dioxide will be an important factor in changing the nature of the Earth's climate. A long-term model prediction is included in Chapter 15.

The culture and economic import of the Little Ice Age are quite clear. The Golden Period of the Tang Dynasty in China (warm, 700–900 AD) and the Dark Ages in Europe (cold, 1200–1600 AD) can be seen in Figure 8-12. Japan has made a correlation of the GNP index to the short-range temperature change, as shown in Figure 8-13.

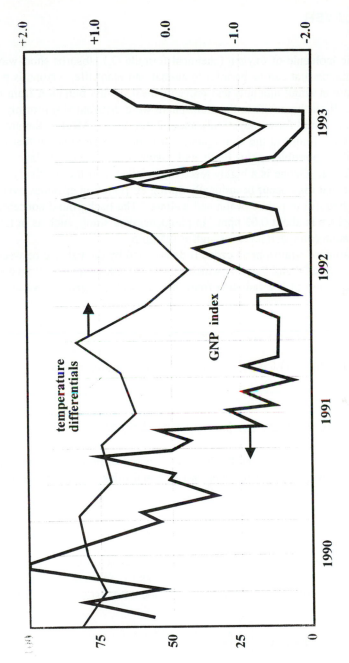

Figure 8-13. The relationship of GNP index and temperature differentials for 1990-1994 in Japan. 50% mark of GNP index is normal, >50% good, and <50% poor. The unusual cold summer in 1993 is a good example.

8.3 OZONE LAYER

Ozone, the triatomic molecule of oxygen (chemical formula O_3), absorbs short-wavelength ultraviolet solar radiation that can be harmful to animal and plant life. Ozone is present in the upper atmosphere in small amounts and prevents most of this radiation from reaching the Earth's surface. If all the ozone in the atmosphere were distributed uniformly over the surface at sea level, it would form a layer only about 3 mm thick. Most of the atmospheric ozone (roughly 95%) is found in the stratosphere. It is this ozone window that made life forms as we know them possible on this Earth, and a depletion of the ozone layer is a threat to these same life forms. Ozone is a highly reactive chemical, and the relatively high concentrations of ozone that may occur occasionally during air pollution episodes over parts of North America are harmful to public health and welfare. The background concentration of ozone in the troposphere is about 0.03 ppm. In photochemical smog, such as in Los Angeles, ozone concentration can reach levels as high as 0.5 ppm.

The concentration of stratospheric ozone is determined by the balance between the reactions by which it is created and those by which it is destroyed. Ozone is formed as a consequence of the interaction of UV radiation from the Sun with oxygen to give atomic oxygen (O):

$$O_2 + \text{sunlight } (h\nu < 242\text{nm}) \rightarrow 2\,O$$

This reaction is followed by the subsequent reaction of atomic and molecular oxygen.
$$O_3 + O \rightarrow 2\,O_2$$

8.3.1   Beer-Lambert Law and Chapman Layers

Absorption of radiation is governed by the interaction between photons and matter. If radiation of intensity I traverses an absorber of unit area and thickness of dz, the decrease of intensity is given as

$$-dI = \ln k_a\ dz \qquad\qquad [8\text{-}13]$$

where n is the number density of absorbers, usually can be used as concentration of a given absorber and k_a is a constant having the units of area, and is referred to as the absorption cross-section. Integration of Equation [8-13] for an incident intensity, I_0, is as follows:

$$I = I_0 \exp\left(-\int_0^z k_a\, dz\right) \qquad\qquad [8\text{-}14]$$

Because n is independent of z

$$I = I_0 \exp\left(-n k_a z\right) \qquad [8\text{-}15]$$

This equation is termed Beer-Lambert Law and used in spectrosophy. If it is expressed in transmittance and the concentration is in molar concentration then

$$T = \frac{I}{I_0} = \exp\left(-\varepsilon\, z\right) \qquad [8\text{-}16]$$

where ε is termed molar absorbance (extinction coefficient) and Figure 8-14 is a spectrum of ozone.

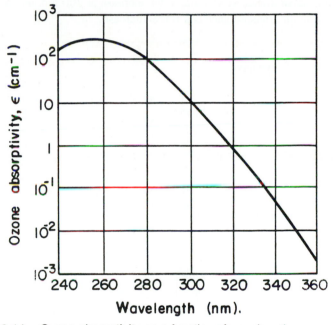

Figure 8-14. Ozone absorptivity as a function of wavelength.

[Example 8-1] If there is a 1% decrease of ozone in our ozone layer, what percentage of increase in ultraviolet transmittance is for our exposure.

The equivalent thickness of ozone at 0°C and 1 atm is 0.34 cm. on the average.

Differentiate Equation [8-16]

$$dT = -\varepsilon \exp\left(-\varepsilon\, z\right) dz \qquad\qquad\text{(a)}$$

or

$$\frac{dT}{T} = -\varepsilon\, dz = -\varepsilon\, z\, \frac{dz}{z} \qquad\qquad\text{(b)}$$

after dividing by Equation [8-16]. For the critical regime of sunburn and skin cancer, the wavelength falls between 310 and 290 nm. In Figure 8-14 the product of εz (value of the absorptivity times 0.34) ranges from 1 to 10 for the wavelengths of 310 nm and 290 nm. Therefore, from the above equation (b), a 1% decrease in the ozone layer gives a 1% increase in ultraviolet transmittance at 310 nm, a 3% increase at 300 nm, and a 10% increase at 290 nm. At 260 nm, the transmittance is a 100% increase.

From Equation [8-4], we have

$$P = P_0 \exp\left(\frac{-Mgz}{RT}\right)$$

If we express into molecular scale

$$\rho = \frac{MP}{RT} = \frac{mP}{kT}$$

or $R = NR$ (see Chapter 1), then

$$P = P_0 \exp\left(\frac{-Mgz}{kT}\right) \qquad\qquad [8\text{-}17]$$

in Boltzmann distribution form
Because the quantity (kT/mg) has the units of length and represents a characteristic length, or

$$P = P_0 \exp\left(\frac{-z}{H_s}\right) \qquad\qquad [8\text{-}18]$$

$$H_s = kT/mg = \text{scale height}$$

Let atmospheric number density n replace P, then

$$n = n_0 \exp\left(\frac{-z}{H_s}\right) \qquad [8\text{-}19]$$

Also an increase in altitude dz, the atmospheric path that the Sun's rays have to traverse, is decreased by $dz \sec \theta$ for a zenith angle θ or Equation [8-13] becomes

$$dI = \ln k_a \left(dz \sec \theta\right) \qquad [8\text{-}20]$$

Combine with Equation [8-19], and we get the following:

$$\frac{dI}{I} = d\left(\ln I\right) = n_o k_a \sec \theta \exp\left(\frac{-z}{H_s}\right) \qquad [8\text{-}21]$$

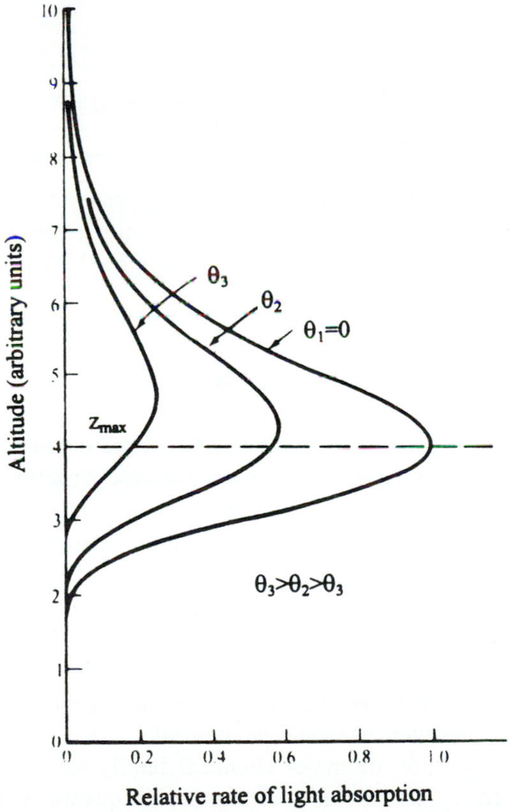

Figure 8-15. Photochemical energy deposition in Chapman layers.

On integration and set the boundary condition as

$$I = I_\infty \quad \text{at } z = \infty$$

then

$$I = I_\infty \exp\left[-n_o\, k_a\, H_s \sec\theta \exp\left(\frac{-z}{H_s}\right)\right] \qquad [8\text{-}22]$$

the rate, P, at which the energy is removed from decrease in intersisity per unit path traversed is

$$P = \frac{dI}{dz \sec\theta} = \left(\frac{dI}{dz}\right)\cos\theta$$

$$= I_\infty\, n_o\, k_a \cos\theta \exp\left[-\frac{z}{H_s} - n_o\, k_a\, H_s \sec\theta \exp\left(-\frac{z}{H_s}\right)\right] \quad [8\text{-}23]$$

This rate is called the Chapman layer function, because the equation will define the shape of the ozone layer. A plot of this function for 3 zenith angles can be found in Figure 8-15. This clearly indicates that the ozone concentrates on 35 km above our atmosphere (refer to Fig. 8-1).

8.3.2   Depletion of the Ozone Layer

In the early 1970s, it was realized that human activities result in the addition of certain chlorine, nitrogen, and other catalyst species to the stratosphere, upsetting the balance between production and destruction processes and leading to changes in the total amounts of ozone above the Earth's surface. Over the past two decades, the stratospheric ozone concentration has been declining with the so-called Antarctic ozone hole. Among the chemical agents considered to have the potential to affect stratospheric ozone in various ways are nitrogen oxides (NO_x), chlorofluorocarbons (CFCs), nitrous oxide (N_2O), methyl chloroform (CH_3CCl_3), carbon tetrachloride (CCl_4), methane, and carbon dioxide. A reduction in the stratospheric ozone would lead to an increase in the intensities of UV light reaching the Earth's surface, and the consequences would be harmful.

The oxides of nitrogen are the major chemical family responsible for the ozone decrease in the stratosphere. The addition of significant quantities of NO_x to the stratosphere—for example, from an increasing concentration of N_2O, detonation of nuclear weapons, or substantial numbers of supersonic aircraft—would result in substantial decreases in the total amount of ozone. Chlorofluoromethanes are used as aerosol propellants and refrigerants because they are inert. Because of the inertness, they survive in the atmosphere to be transported to the stratosphere, where they are photochemically dissociated to give atomic (Cl). These chlorines, as well as OH and NO, can destroy ozone without a loss of the reactant species. They work as catalysts in chemical reactions.

The ozone destruction can be explained by the **Molina-Rowland scheme**, as follows:

$$CCl_3F + h\nu \rightarrow CCl_2F + Cl$$

$$Cl + O_3 \rightarrow ClO + O_2$$

$$ClO + O \rightarrow Cl + O_2$$

$$\overline{}$$

$$O_3 + O \rightarrow 2O_2$$

or

$$O(^1D_2) + H_2O \rightarrow 2OH$$

$$OH + O_3 \rightarrow HO_2 + O_2$$

$$HO_2 + O \rightarrow OH + O_2$$

$$\overline{}$$

$$O_3 + O \rightarrow 2O_2$$

Fate of Cl – rainout

$$Cl + HO_2 \rightarrow HCl + O_2$$

$$Cl + CH_4 \rightarrow HCl + CH_3$$

What would be the effect of a depletion of the order of 5% of the total ozone? In some estimates, the associated increase in UV radiation reaching the surface of the Earth could produce a 10% increase in nonfatal skin cancers. A correlation of melanoma mortality rates and latitudes has been found and is indicated in Figure 8-16.

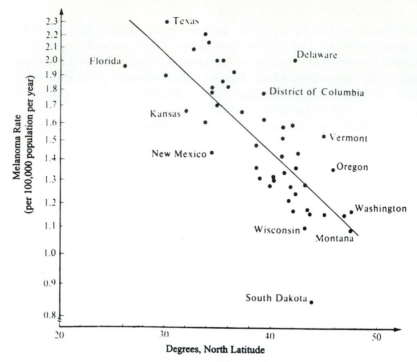

Figure 8-16. Variation with latitude of human death due to skin melanoma among white males in the United States excluding Alaska and Hawaii. [From Rowland, F.S., Chapter 4.6 in Coyle, J.D., Hill R. R., and Roberts, D.R. (eds) *Light, chemical change and life*, Open University Press, 1982.]

8.3.3   Fate of Halomethanes

Two classes of saturated halocompounds are of importance; the first is chlorofluorocarbons (CFCs), and the second includes both hydrochlorofluorocarbons (HCFCs) and hydrofluorocarbons (HFCs), the latter of which do not contain any chlorine. The CFCs, HCFCs, and HFCs have a nomenclature system; for example, CFC-11, CFC-113, and so on. These numbering systems are based on the following:

Number after CFC + 90 = abc (3 digits)

a = No. of C

b = No. of H

c = No. of F

Balance the carbon valence requirement with No. of Cl.

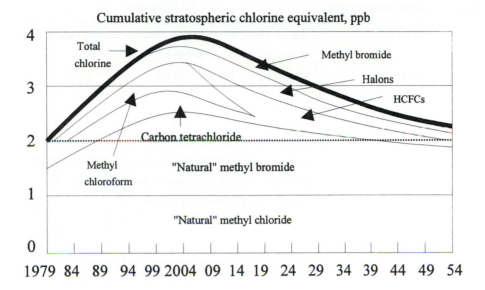

Note: Ozone-depleting effects of bromine atoms in halons and methyl bromide have
been converted to their chlorine equivalents.

Figure 8-17.   Levels of chlorine in stratosphere will decrease slowly under Montreal
protocol. (Source: DuPont)

For example,

CFC – 12, $12 + 90 = 102$ $\therefore CF_2Cl_2$

CFC – 115, $115 + 90 = 205$ $\therefore CF_3\text{-}CF_2Cl$

CFC – 113, $113 + 90 = 203$ $\therefore CCl_2F\text{-}CClF_2$

CFC – 11, $11 + 90 = 101$ $\therefore CFCl_3$

The CFCs have a long atmospheric lifetime, being also a stronger absorber within the
7 to 13μm atmospheric window. The lifetime of HCFCs is shorter and their breakdowns are
relatively quick. They have a modest potential to affect ozone. The same is true for the
HFCs; they contain no chlorine atoms to threaten the ozone layer, but they contribute to
affect global warming. According to the *Montreal Protocol on Substances That Deplete the
Ozone Layer*, all CFCs will be banned by 1996 and all HCFCs by 2030. HFCs will be restricted if other alternatives exist, as shown in Figure 8-17 and Table 8-2.

Table 8-2.   EPA Plans to Phase Out HFC's in Stages

Date [a]	Compounds Affected	Restriction
1994	All HCFCs	Ban on use in aerosols (except medical devices) and plastic foams (except foam insulation).
2003	HCFC-141b (CH_3CCl_2F, ODP^b=0.12)	Ban on production and imports.
2010	HCFC-22 ($CHClF_2$, ODP=0.05) HCFC-142b (CH_3CClF_2, ODP=0.06)	Production and imports frozen at 1989 baseline levels. Ban on use of virgin chemical, unless used as feedstock or for servicing refrigeration or air-conditioning equipment manufactured before Jan.1, 2010.
2015	All other HCFCs	Production and imports frozen at 1989 baseline levels. Ban on use of virgin chemical, unless used as feedstock or for air-conditioning equipment manufactured before Jan.1, 2010.
2020	HCFC-22 HCFC-142b	Ban on production and imports.
2030	All other HCFCs	Ban on production and imports.

Note: HCFCs = Hydrochlorofluorocarbons.

a Effective date is Jan. 1 of the given year.

b ODP = Estimated ozone depletion potential, which depends on chlorine content and atmospheric lifetime.

   Potentials are relative to CFC-11, which is assigned a value of 1.0.

Source: *Federal Register*. March 18, 1993. Page 15.014 and Sept. 27, 1993. Page 50.464.

Most of the halomethanes are used in refrigeration. The second largest uses in industry are the blowing agents for foams; others could be dry-cleaning agents. Some recent technological advances include air-conditioning systems that use no refrigerants or compressors—for example, the desiccant system. Actually, this is a combination of evaporative cooling and desiccant drying, as shown in Figure 8-18.

Other types of halomethanes (termed halons) are used in firefighting; they are composed of brominated fluorocarbons, particularly CF_3Br. It seems at present that the fluoroiodocarbon (FIC) CF_3I is a good substitute because the short life will be unlikely to contribute to ozone depletion or global warming.

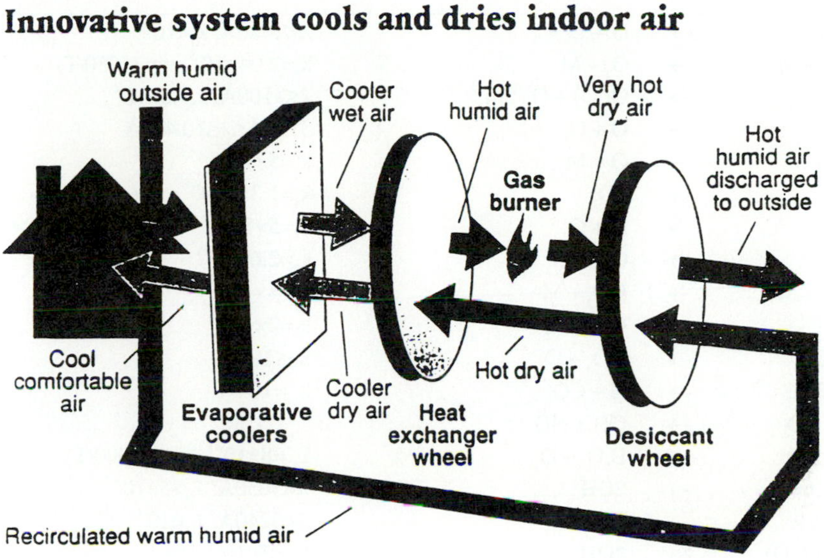

Innovative system cools and dries indoor air

Figure 8-18. Innovative system cools and dries indoor air. (After P.S. Zurer, C and EN, Nov. 15, 1993.)

8.4 STRATOSPHERIC CHEMISTRY

Stratospheric chemistry involves a bewildering number of chemical reactions and catalytic cycles. Many key stratospheric reactions involve radicals. Table 8-3 lists some of the reactions and their reaction coefficients. In terms of predicting the effect of a given perturbation on ozone, the primary question is the balance among various species that interact extensively. Current modeling work incorporates as many as 140 reactions with the aid of computers.

In the stratosphere, ozone behaves as a UV shield.

$$O_2 + h\nu \rightarrow 2O \quad (^3P_2 \text{ and } ^1D_2)$$

$$O + O_2 \rightarrow O_3$$

$$O_3 + h\nu \rightarrow O_2 + O(^1D_2)$$

Table 8-3.   Reactions and Reaction Coefficients in cm-molecule-sec Units

$O_2 + h\nu$	$\rightarrow$	$O + O$	$\lambda < 2420\text{Å}$, $k_1 < 10^{-6}$
$O + O_2 + M$	$\rightarrow$	$O_2 + M$	$k_2 = 2.04 \times 10^{-26} \exp(1050/T)$
$O_2 + h\nu$	$\rightarrow$	$O(^1D) + O_2(^1\Delta_g)$	$\lambda \leq 3100\text{Å}$, $k_{2a} < 5 \times 10^{-6}$
$O_2 + h\nu$	$\rightarrow$	$O + O_2$	$3100\text{Å} \leq \lambda \leq 10{,}400\text{Å}$
$O(^1D) + M$	$\rightarrow$	$O + M$	$k_4 = 5 \times 10^{-11}$
$O + O_1$	$\rightarrow$	$2O_2$	$k_5 = 1.33 \times 10^{-11} \exp(-2100/T)$
$O + OH$	$\rightarrow$	$H + O_2$	$k_6 = 5 \times 10^{-11}$
$H + O_2$	$\rightarrow$	$OH + O_2$	$k_7 = 2.6 \times 10^{-11}$
$H + O_2 + M$	$\rightarrow$	$HO_2 + M$	$k_8 = 4 \times 10^{-12}$
$HO_2 + O$	$\rightarrow$	$OH + O_2$	$k_9 = 2 \times 10^{-11}$
$OH + O_2$	$\rightarrow$	$HO_2 + O_2$	$k_{10} \leq 10^{-16}$
$OH + CO$	$\rightarrow$	$H + CO_2$	$k_{11} = 10^{-12}$
$HO_2 + NO$	$\rightarrow$	$OH + NO_2$	
$HO_2 + HO_2$	$\rightarrow$	$H_2O_2 + O_2$	$k_{13} = 8 \times 10^{-11} \exp(-1000/T)$
$H_2O_2 + h\nu$	$\rightarrow$	$2OH$	$\lambda < 5650\text{Å}$; $J_{14} > 5 \times 10^{-4}$
$H_2O + h\nu$	$\rightarrow$	$H + OH$	$\lambda < 2240\text{Å}$; $J_{15} < 10^{-4}$
$H_2O + O(^1D)$	$\rightarrow$	$2OH$	$k_{14} = 3 \times 10^{-16}$
$H_2O + h\nu$	$\rightarrow$	H_2O	$\lambda = 1.4\mu m$
$H_2O + O$	$\rightarrow$	$2OH$	
$OH + OH$	$\rightarrow$	$H_2O + O$	$k_{19} = K_{13}$
$OH + HO_2$	$\rightarrow$	$H_2O + O_2$	$k_{20} \geq 10^{-11}$
$OH + H_2O_2$	$\rightarrow$	$HO_2 + H_2O$	$k_{21} = 6 \times 10^{-12} \exp(-600/T)$
$NO + O_2$	$\rightarrow$	$NO_2 + O_2$	$k_{22} = 1.33 \times 10^{-12} \exp(-1250/T)$
$NO_2 + O$	$\rightarrow$	$NO + O_2$	$k_{23} = 1.67 \times 10^{-11} \exp(-300/T)$
$NO_2 + O_3$	$\rightarrow$	$NO_3 + O_2$	$k_{24} = 10^{-11} \exp(-3500/T)$
$NO_3 + h\nu$	$\rightarrow$	$NO + O_2$	$J_{21a} = 10^{-2}$ (?)
$NO_2 + h\nu$	$\rightarrow$	$NO_2 + O$	$J_{21b} = 10^{-2}$, $\lambda < 5710\text{Å}$
$NO_2 + h\nu$	$\rightarrow$	$NO + O$	$J_{26} = 5 \times 10^{-8}$, $\lambda < 4000\text{Å}$
$NO_2 + NO$	$\rightarrow$	$2NO_2$	$k_{27} = 10^{-11}$
$NO + h\nu$	$\rightarrow$	$N + O$	$J_{28} < 5 \times 10^{-6}$
$N + NO$	$\rightarrow$	$N_2 + O$	$k_{29} = 2 \times 10^{-11}$
$N + O_2$	$\rightarrow$	$NO + O$	$k_{30} = 1.2 \times 10^{-11} \exp(-3525/T)$
$N + O_2$	$\rightarrow$	$NO + O_3$	$k_{31} = 3 \times 10^{-11} \exp(-1200/T)$
$N + OH$	$\rightarrow$	$NO + H$	$k_{32} = 7 \times 10^{-11}$
$N_2O + O(^1D)$	$\rightarrow$	$2NO$	$k_{33a} = 1 \times 10^{-10}$
$N_2O + O(^1D)$	$\rightarrow$	$N_2 + O_2$	$k_{33b} = 1 \times 10^{-10}$
$N_2O + h\nu$	$\rightarrow$	$N_2 + O$	$J_{34} < 5 \times 10^{-7}$, $\lambda < 3370\text{Å}$

Source: Crutzen, 1972.

8.4.1 Photochemistry

By far the most abundant photochemical reaction in the stratosphere is the photolysis of molecular oxygen. For a detailed discussion of photolysis, please refer to Chapter 23. The bond dissociation energy of oxygen (5.1 eV) corresponds to a photon of wavelength 243nm. Ultraviolet absorption is weak at 200nm and the excited molecular states can be dissociated into two ground state $^3P_2$ oxygen atoms.

$$O_2 \xrightarrow{\text{200 nm}} 2\, O(^3P_2)$$

Below 200nm, excitation leads to dissociation to one ground state $^3P_2$ oxygen atom and one excited $^1D_2$ oxygen atom.

$$O_2 \xrightarrow{\text{<176 nm}} O(^3P_2) + O(^1D_2)$$

As the ultraviolet wavelength continues to decrease, the highest excited states of $^1S_0$ will result.

$$O_2 \xrightarrow{\text{<130 nm}} O(^3P_2) + O(^1S_0)$$

$$O_2 \xrightarrow{\text{<92.3 nm}} 2O(^1S_0)$$

Furthermore, the ionization potential of oxygen molecules is 12.15 eV, which corresponds to a photon wavelength of 102nm. Thus, a more likely reaction below 102nm is photoionization.

$$O_2 \xrightarrow{\text{<102 nm}} O_2^+ + e^-$$

followed by dissociative recombination

$$O(^1S_0) + O(^3P_2) + 64.3 \text{ Kcal}$$

$$O_2^+ + e^- \Big\langle$$

$$O(^1S_0) + O(^1D_2) + 19.1 \text{ Kcal}$$

This reaction plays a role in the photochemical smog cycle. Similar types of reactions occur from the forbidden radiative transitions, as shown in Figure 8-19.

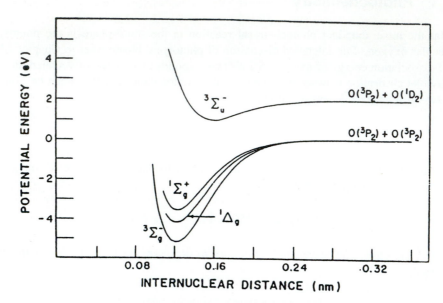

Figure 8-19.   Potential energy curves from O_2. [Curves drawn from data of F. R. Gilmore, *J. Quant. Spectrosc. Radiat. Transfer 5*, 369 (1965)]

$$O_2(^1\Sigma_g^+) \rightarrow O_2(^3\Sigma_g^-) + h\nu\,(762\text{nm})$$

$$O_2(^1\Delta_g) \rightarrow O_2(^3\Sigma_g^-) + h\nu\,(1270\text{nm})$$

These reactions turn out to be the most intense bonds in the atmospheric dayglow and are the auroral displays. The aurora spectra lines are expressed in the following:

		Å
O	$^1S_o \rightarrow {}^1D_2$	5577 (gr)
	$^1D_2 \rightarrow {}^3P_2$	6300
		6363
		6392
N	$^2P_{3/2} \rightarrow {}^4S_{3/2}$ via $^2D_{5/2}$	3466
O_2	$^1\Sigma_g^+ \rightarrow {}^3\Sigma_g^-$	7620
	$^1\Delta_g \rightarrow {}^3\Sigma_g^-$	12700
N_2	$^3\pi \rightarrow {}^3\Sigma$	14700–50300

8.4.2 Term Symbols

The **term symbol** designation can be repeated by $^{2S+1}L_J$, where $S = \sum m_s$, $L = \sum m_l$, and $J = L + S$ or $L + S - 1$; and when $L = 0,1,2,3$, the designation is S,P,D,F. The m_s and m_e are obtained from atomic orbitals. Similarly, an oxygen ion, O^+, or a nitrogen atom can have three states: $^4S_{3/2}$, $^2D_{3/2}$, and $^2P_{3/2}$. For general use, the J value can be eliminated.

These values are used for the sketch below. For O, we have $2s^2$, $2p^4$ (only consider outer orbit). For $2p^4$, we have 4 electrons distributed in 3 p-orbitals, which can be seen as follows:

^2P

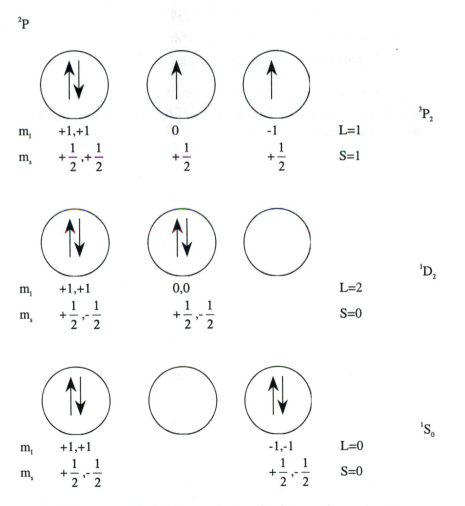

Therefore the O atom will have the 3 forms, $^3P_2$, $^1D_2$, and $^1S_0$ and stability of those term symbols are as follows:

$${}^3P_2 > {}^1D_2 > {}^1S_0$$
$$\leftarrow \quad \text{stability}$$

for example,

$$O_2 \xrightarrow{\;200\,nm\;} 2O\,({}^3P)$$

$$O_2 \xrightarrow{\;<176\,nm\;} O\,({}^3P) + O\,({}^1D)$$

$$O_2 \xrightarrow{\;<92\,nm\;} 2O\,({}^1S)$$

According to above equations for photo desociation of oxygen molecules, the shortest UV will produce the most unstable species.

Alternatively, the term symbol and stability for N(or O^+), $2s^2$, $2p^3$ are explained as follows:

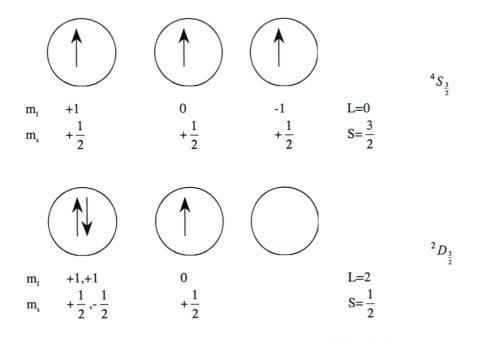

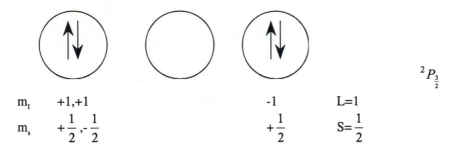

$$^2P_{\frac{3}{2}}$$

$$
\begin{array}{lll}
m_l & +1,+1 & -1 \quad\quad L=1 \\
m_s & +\dfrac{1}{2},-\dfrac{1}{2} & +\dfrac{1}{2} \quad\quad S=\dfrac{1}{2}
\end{array}
$$

In this fashion, for N,

$$^4S_{3/2} > {}^2D_{3/2} > {}^2P_{3/2}$$

Notice that the term symbol for a diatomic or linear polatomic electronic state is $^{2S+1}\Lambda_G$ plus the symmetry — for example, g (gerade) for no change in inversion symmetry, u (ungerade) for the opposite; + for no change in reflection symmetry, – for the opposite. $\Omega = |\Lambda + \Sigma|$, where Λ can have values 0,1,..., L, which are desingated repectively Σ, π, Λ...states, analogous to s, p, d...for the atoms.

For O_2,

$$^3\Sigma_g^- > {}^1\Delta_g > {}^1\Sigma_g^+$$

8.5 THERMOSPHERE AND IONOSPHERE

The purpose of the ionosphere is the production of ions and electrons. The function of the thermosphere is the production of exothermic reactions. Actually, they can be considered as one sphere, as shown in Figure 8-20.

The following is a summary of the chemistry of both thermosphere and ionosphere. Chemical species in those regions are extremely dilute. The names are derived from the properties reflected in these regions.

Production of electron — E-layer

$O + h\nu \rightarrow O^+ + e$

$O_2 + h\nu \rightarrow O + O^+ + e$

$N_2 + h\nu \rightarrow N + N^+ + e$

Production of ions — ionosphere

$O^+(^4S) + N_2 \rightarrow NO^+ + N$

$$O^+ + O_2 \rightarrow O_2^+ + O$$
$$NO^+ + e \rightarrow N + O$$
$$O_2^+ + e \rightarrow O + O$$
$$O^+(^2D) + N_2 \rightarrow N_2^+ + O$$
$$N_2^+ + e \rightarrow 2N$$

Chemical heating (exothermic reaction) — thermosphere
$$O_2^+ + e \rightarrow 2O(^3P) + 6.95 \text{ eV}$$
$$\rightarrow O(^3P) + O(^1D) + 4.98 \text{ eV}$$
$$N(^4S) + O_2 \rightarrow O + NO + 1.4 \text{ eV}$$
$$N(^2D) + O_2 \rightarrow O(^1P) + NO + 1.84 \text{ eV}$$
$$O(^1D) + N_2 \rightarrow O(^3P) + N_2 + 1.96 \text{ eV}$$

Altitude, km

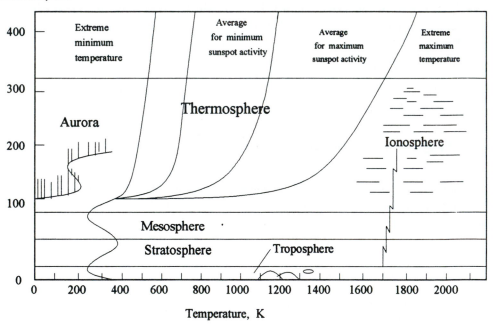

Figure 8-20. Temperature varies more in thermosphere than in low regions of the atmosphere. (Modified and redrawn from R.G. Roble, *Chem. Eng. News*, June 16, 1986).

REFERENCES

8-1. W. Strauss and S. J. Mainwaring, *Air Pollution*, Edward Arnold Ltd., London, 1984.

8-2. H. C. Perkins, *Air Pollution*, McGraw-Hill, New York, 1974.

8-3. J. H. Seinfeld, *Air Pollution*, McGraw-Hill, New York, 1975.

8-4. Enviornmental Studies Board, National Research Council," Causes and Effects of Changes in Stratospheric Ozone: Update 1983", National Academy Press, Washington DC, 1984.

8-5. T. L. Brown, *Energy and the Environment*, Charles E. Merrill, Columbus, OH, 1971.

8-6. J.H. Seinfeld, *Atmospheric Chemistry and Physics of Air Pollution*, Wiley, New York, 1986.

8-7. R. M. Baum, "Stratospheric Science Undergoing Change," *C & EN*, September, p. 21 (1982).

8-8. R. Revelle, "Carbon Dioxide and World Climate," *Scientific Amer.*, *247(2)*, 35 (1982).

8-9. G. M. Woodwell, "The Carbon Dioxide Question," *Scientific Amer.*, *238(1)*, 34 (1978).

8-10. A. P. Ingersoll, "The Atmosphere," *Scientific Amer.*, *249(3)*, 162 (1983).

8-11. D. G. Torr, "The Photochemistry of Atmosphere: Earth and Other Planets and Comets," Academic Press, New York, 1985.

8-12. R. G. Noble, "Chemistry in the Thermosphere and Ionosphere," *C & EN*, June 16, 23–38 (1986).

8-13. R.P. Wayne, *Chemistry of Atmospheres*, 2nd ed., Clerendon Press, Oxford, 1991.

8-14. T.G. Spiro and W.M. Stigliani, *Chemistry of the Environment*, Prentice-Hall, Upper Saddle River, NJ, 1996.

8-15. A. D. Danilov, *Chemistry of the Ionosphere*, Plenum, New York, 1970.

8-16. R. W. Bonbel, D. L. Fox, B. D. Turner, and A. C. Stern, *Fundamentals of Air Pollution*, Academic Press, San Diego, 1994.

8-17. B. M. Smirnov, *Reviews of Plasma Chemistry* Vol. 1, Plenum, New York, 1991.

PROBLEM SET

1. Use Stoke's Law to calculate the settling rate in water of an Fe_2O_3 particle whose radius is 10 μm. What is the settling rate for a one μm-particle which settles in air?

2. Calculate the tropospheric residence time for methylene chloride, given an estimated global anthropogenic emission rate of 0.35 Tg/yr, and a mean tropospheric concentration of 30 ppt (by weight). Assume the mass of the troposphere to be 4 billion Tg.

ATMOSPHERE — AIR POLLUTION

Air pollution may be defined as any atmospheric condition in which substances are present at concentrations high enough above their normal ambient levels to produce a measurable effect on people, animals, vegetation, or materials.

The pollutant types can be generally divided into five categories: carbon monoxide, NO_x, hydrocarbons, SO_x, and particulates. The following table is a summary of their toxicity and residence time.

This chapter is divided into the following sections: particulates, sulfur dioxide, automotive emissions, and tropospheric chemistry. Each section covers the five major air pollutants (SO_x, CO, NO_x, hydrocarbon, and particulates). Topics such as the nature of their formation, their effects on the environment, and methods of coping with them will also be addressed.

Pollutant Types	CO	NO_x	HC	SO_x	Particulates
Mobile Source* (M ton/yr)	63.8	8.1	16.6	0.8	1.2
Stationary Source*	119	10.0	0.7	24.4	8.9
Tolerance Level ($\mu g/m^3$)	40,000	514	19,300	1,430	375
Relative Toxicity (weighing factor)	1	77.8	2.07	28.0	106.7
Residence Time (yr)	0.1	0.25	2	days to weeks	?

*United States only, both have the same unit.

9.1 PARTICULATES

The first widely recognized form of air pollution was smoke—fine carbon particles arising from the incomplete combustion of fuels, and inorganic ash arising from the noncombustible matter in the fuel. Particulates form a major part of the emissions of air pollutants and come from such diverse sources as cars, steel mills, cement plants, and local dumps. Volcanos, forest fires, and ocean spray aerosols are among the largest natural sources of world particulate emissions. "**Particulates**" is a general term for something that exists in the form of minute separate particles, either solid or liquid. Table 9-1 gives the sizes of airborne particulates.

Some necessary definitions are given here:

Aerosol: A dispersion of solid or liquid particles of microscopic size in gaseous media, such as smoke, fog, or mist.

Dusts: Solid particles predominantly larger than colloidal particles, and capable of temporary suspension in air or other gases. They will settle under the influence of gravity.

Fly ashes: Finely divided particles of ash entrained in flue gases arising from the combustion of fuel.

Fumes: The solid particles generated by condensation from the gaseous state and often accompanied by a chemical reaction such as oxidation.

Smokes: Finely divided aerosol particles, which consist mainly of carbon and other combustible material, resulting from incomplete combustion.

Table 9-1. Relation of size to properties of particulate matter (With permission from J.W. Moore and E.A. Moor, *Environmental Chemistry*, Academic Press, 1976, Harcourt Brace Jovanovich Publishers.)

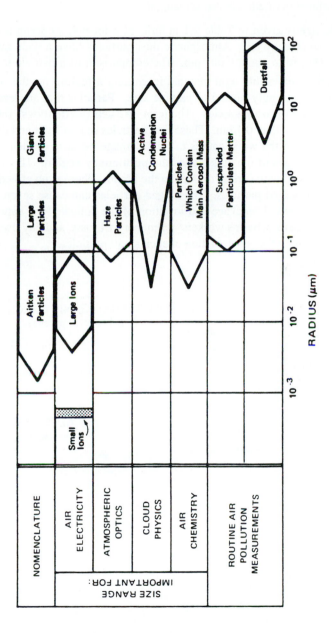

Soot: Agglomerations of particles of carbon impregnated with tar, formed by the incomplete combustion of carbonaceous material.

Particle size is given in Table 9-1 in units of **microns**; a micron is one millionth of a meter and is denoted by μm. Atmospheric dust particles have a wide range of sizes, from greater than 100   m to about 0.001 μm. The comparison of a particle to a human hair and to the wavelength of visible light may aid in gaining a feeling for the size of particulates. Health effects are strongly related to particle size. Particles that are less than 1 micron in size are called **submicron particles**. The term **"Aitken particulates"** refers to those particles with radii of less than 0.1 μm. These fine particles scatter light and thereby reduce visibility. They are also the worst causes of lung damage because of their ability to penetrate the innermost passages of the lung, called the **pulmonary region**. This is the region where oxygen is exchanged with carbon dioxide in the blood. There is no effective mechanism for removal of these lodged particles. The lodged particles can cause severe breathing impairment simply by physical blockage and irritation of the delicate lung capillaries. Coal miners' blacklung disease, asbestos workers' pulmonary fibrosis, and city dwellers' emphysema are all associated with the accumulation of such small particles.

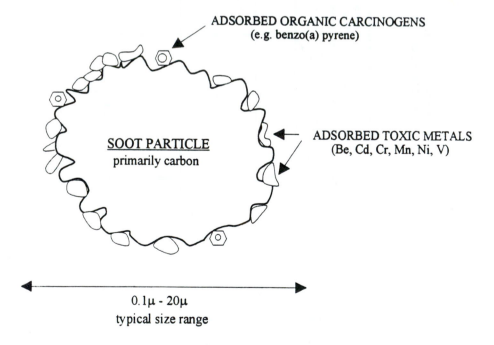

Figure 9-1.   Soot particle from the combustion of fossil fuels (Source: Spiro and Stigliani).

Pneumoconiosis is a lung disease cause by prolonged inhalation of metallic or mineral dusts. The fly ashes emitted from coal combustion equipment consist largely of silica (SiO_2), alumina (Al_2O_3), and iron oxide (Fe_2O_3), as shown in Table 9-2. Beryllium oxide (BeO) may come out of a spark plug while driving. Heavy metals, such as mercury, that are often used as fungicides in the paper industry may accompany the ash generated from smoking cigarettes. Some particles are especially dangerous because they may carry toxic chemicals that can interact directly with lung tissue. Soot is finely divided carbon with a loose structure that possesses a large surface area, as shown in Figure 9-1. It is often associated with toxic trace metals such as beryllium, cadmium, chromium, manganese, nickel, and vanadium adsorbed on its surface. Moreover, soot serves as a carrier for toxic organic molecules such as benzo(a)pyrene, which has been implicated as a **carcinogen**, a cancer causing agent. Table 9-3 lists the sources, annual emissions, and health effects of minor air pollutants in the United States.

Particulate matter is removed from the air naturally by **fallout**, frequently referred to as **sedimentation**. Small particles grow to larger ones via collisions and aggregation and gradually settle out. The **settling velocity** in wind-free air is determined by the balance of two forces: frictional forces and gravitational forces. The drag force on a spherical particle of radius r moving at a steady speed u through a fluid of density ρ and viscosity η can be seen in the following equation:

$$F_{friction} = -6\pi r \eta u$$

The gravitational force on the particle is

$$F_{gravitation} = \frac{4}{3}\pi r^3 (\rho_{part} - \rho)g$$

Table 9-2. Chemical Analysis of Fly Ash (%)

Chemical Components	Subbituminous Coal	Bituminous Coal
SiO_2	50.50	43.5-57.0
Al_2O_3	33.70	18.0-28.0
Fe_2O_3	6.85	7.9-16.0
CaO	2.80	4.0-10.0
MgO	1.50	1.0-5.5
SO_3	0.75	0.9-3.3
Combustion losses	2.85	(Na_2O+K_2O)

Source: Nowak 1973, Table 1, p. 225.

Table 9-3.   Sources, Annual Emissions, and Health Effects of Minor Air Pollutants

Substance	Sources[a]	Emissions[a] (tonnes/ year)	Health Effects[b]
Lead	Auto exhaust, industry, solid waste disposal, coal combustion, paint	208,250	Brain damage, behavioral disorders, convulsions, death
Fluorides	Industry, coal combustion	150,400	Mottled teeth, weakening of bone, weight loss, thyroid and kidney injury, death
Vanadium	Coal and petroleum combustion, industry	18,440	Inhibits formation of phospholipids and S-containing amino acids
Manganese	Industry, coal combustion	16,230	Fever, pneumonia
Arsenic	Industry	9,570	Dermatitis, melanosis, perforation of nasal septum, possible carcinogen
Nickel	Coal combustion, industry	6,625	Dermatitis, dizziness, headaches, nausea, carcinogenesis [also $Ni(CO)_4$]
Asbestos	Industry	6,080	Scarring of lungs, lung cancer
Cadmium	Industry	1,962	Gastrointestinal disorder, respiratory tract disturbances, carcinogenic and mutagenic
Mercury	Coal combustion, commercial, industry	777[c]	Tremor, skin eruption, hallucinations
Beryllium	Coal combustion, industry	156	Lung damage, enlargement of lymph glands, emaciation
Selenium	Ore refining, sulfuric acid manufacture, coal combustion	—	Depression, jaundice, nose-bleed, dizziness, headaches

[a] Data from U.S. Environmental Protection Agency, "Air Pollution Emission Factors," AP-42, 2nd ed. USEPA, Research Triangle Park, North Carolina, 1973.

[b] Data from G.L. Waldbott, "Health Effects of Environmental Pollutants." Mosby, St. Louis, Missouri, 1973.

[c] Emissions may be larger than this estimate; see C.E. Billings and W.R. Matson, *Science*. 176, 1232-1233 (1972).

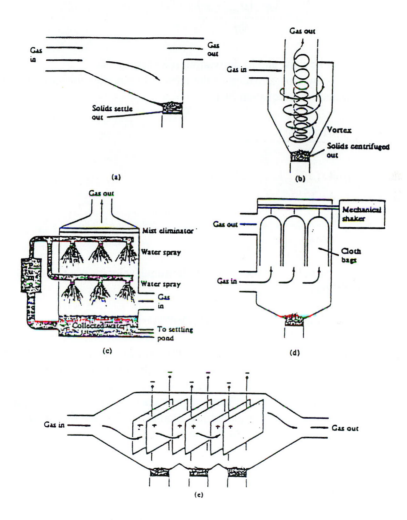

Figure 9-2.   Collection devices for particulate matter and minimum particle sizes for which they give efficient removal: (a) settling chamber (d > 50μm); (b) centrifugal separator (d > 1μm); (c) wet scrubber (several other designs also used : d > 0.05 μm; can also collect water-soluble gases); (d) baghouse filter (d > 0.01 μm); and (e) electrostatic precipitator (d > 0.005 μm).

When the particle moves at a steady velocity, it is not accelerating. Therefore, the net force on the particle is zero. According to **Stoke's law**, we can solve for the terminal velocity by equating the two preceding equations:

$$u = \frac{2\, g r^2 \left(\rho_{part} - \rho\right)}{9\eta} \qquad\qquad [9\text{-}1]$$

For details of Stoke's law and its derivation, see Chapter 30.

The following is an approximation of the terminal velocities for various particle sizes which can be calculated from Equation [9-1].

$r\,(\mu\text{m})$	u (cm/sec)
0.1	8×10^{-5}
1	4×10^{-3}
10	3×10^{-1}
100	25
1000	390

The larger the particle size, the faster the terminal velocity is. Customarily, **settling time** is defined as follows:

$$\text{settling time} = (\text{distance traveled})/(\text{terminal velocity}) \qquad [9\text{-}2]$$

For a particle 1 μm in radius, it will take 290 days to travel 1 km. Settling is a relatively minor mechanism (estimated to be 10–20% of the total deposition rate) for particle removal in the atmosphere. Impaction by wind is a significant mechanism, but the major removal processes are "washout" and "rainout" associated with rainfall. Figure 9-2 illustrates common collection devices for particulate matter. A detailed discussion of these collection devices will appear in Chapter 34, Vol. 4B.

9.2 SULFUR OXIDES

Sulfur can be considered as an impurity in most coals and oils, as shown in Table 9-4. Sulfur dioxide is largely associated with the burning of coal and some crude oils for electricity and heating. This gas has well-known effects on human beings. Most individuals show bronchial response to SO_2 at concentrations of 5 ppm, and more sensitive people at 1 ppm. The odor can be noticed at concentrations that are 10 times lower. However, it is **sulfuric acid aerosol** (which is 10 times more irritating), formed from the oxidation of sulfur dioxide, that causes the most damaging health effects in urban atmospheres. Sulfuric acid aerosol is a **secondary particle** because it is formed by a gas-to-particle conversion process in the atmosphere. In contrast, **primary particles** are emitted directly into the atmosphere without intermediate conversion steps. Sulfur dioxide could be oxidized in the atmosphere to sulfur trioxide, but the conversion is slow in the absence of catalysts. It was found that nitrogen oxide and some metal oxides work as catalysts in this conversion reaction. The reaction can also be greatly accelerated with the acid of the ozone. The ozone donates an oxygen atom to form sulfur trioxide, which, in turn, combines rapidly with water to form sulfuric acid. The sulfuric acid can condense to form aerosol droplets. Besides the adverse health effect, the aerosol is capable of greatly reducing visibility. Figure 9-3 illustrates the conversion process.

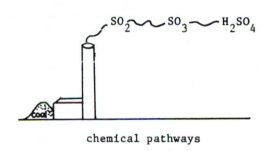

Figure 9-3. Formation of sulfuric acid aerosol from sulfur dioxide.

Table 9-4. Sulfur Content of Fossil Fuels

	API° Gravity	Carbon Residue (%)	Sulfur (wt %)	Asphaltene (%)
Qayarah (Iraq) heavy oil	15.3	15.6	8.4	20.4
Boscan (Venezuela) asphaltene	10.3	10.4	5.6	11.9
Athabasca (Canada) tar sand	5.9	18.5	4.9	16.9
Trinidad Lake bitumen	0.7	10.8	6.2	33.3
Mexico residua	7.9	28.9	6.4	23.2
Kuwait residua	5.5	23.1	5.5	11.1
Alberta crude oil	22	4.45	2.63	15.6
Bituminous goal	--	6.6	1.72^a	--

ᵃOrganic sulfur compounds only.

9.2.1   Desulfurization

There are many ways of reducing SO_2 concentrations. Burning low-sulfur fuel is one of the possibilities. Coal has a sulfur content ranging up to 3.4%, but in the Arizona strip mines some coal is found with a sulfur content of only 1%. Also, it is possible to extract the sulfur from the fuel. For oil, this is fairly simple and is currently being done at some refineries.

Sulfur exists as either organic or inorganic forms in coal, as shown in Table 9-5. The inorganic sulfur compound in coal is mainly pyrite (FeS_2). The pyrite can be removed fairly easily by screening powdered coal, that is pulverized for feeding, to large furnaces to improve its combustion characteristics. Also, both pyrite and organic sulfur compounds (such as RSR, RSH, or =CH—S—CH=) can be removed by one of the following reactions:

(1) Displacement

$$=N: + FeS_2 \rightarrow =NFe + S_2^{2-}$$

$$R_1S_xR_2 + Nu^- \rightarrow R_1S_xNu + R_2^-$$

$$\text{For example } RSSR + R_3P \rightarrow [\, R_3P^+ - SR, RS^- \,]$$

$$\downarrow$$

$$R_3P = S + RSR \qquad (Nu = \text{nucleophilic agent})$$

(2) Acid-Base Neutralization

$$4H^+ + FeS_2 + 2e \rightarrow 2H_2S + Fe^{2+}$$

$$RSH + OH^- \rightarrow RS^- + H_2O$$

(3) Oxidation

$$[O] + FeS_2 \rightarrow Fe^{2+} + 2S + O^{2-}$$

$$[O] + R_1S_xR_2 \rightarrow R_1SO_3H + R_2SO_3H$$

$$\downarrow H_2O, \Delta$$

$$R_1OH + R_2OH + 2H_2SO_4$$

(4) Reduction

$$FeS_2 + H_2 \rightarrow FeS + H_2S$$

$$FeS_2 + H_2 \rightarrow Fe + H_2S$$

$$R_1S_xR_2 + 4H \rightarrow R_1H + R_2H + H_2S_x$$

(5) Solvent Partition

$$R_1S_xR_2 + X \longrightarrow \begin{matrix} R_1 \\ \diagdown \\ \diagup \\ R_2 \end{matrix} S_x^+X^-$$

(6) Thermal decomposition

$$R_1S_xR_2 \xrightarrow{\Delta} R_1R_2 + S_x$$

$$RCH_2CH_2SH \xrightarrow{\Delta} RCH = CH_2 + H_2S$$

Table 9-5.   Sulfur Forms in Selected Bituminous Coal -- Worldwide

Region and Country	Location or Mine	Sulfur, Percent w/w[a]			Ration of Pyritic to Organic Sulfur
		Total	Pyritic	Organic	
ASIA					
USSR	Shakhtersky	0.38	0.09	0.29	0.031
China (mainland)	Taitung	1.19	0.87	0.32	2.7
India	Tipong	3.63	1.59	2.04	0.78
Japan	Miike	2.61	0.81	1.80	0.45
Malaysia	Sarawak	5.32	3.97	1.35	2.9
NORTH AMERICA					
U.S.	Eagle No. 2	4.29	2.68	1.61	1.7
Canada	Fernie	0.60	0.03	0.57	0.053
EUROPE					
Germany	—	1.78	0.92	0.76	1.2
United Kingdom	Derbyshire	2.61	1.55	0.87	1.8
Poland	—	0.81	0.30	0.51	0.59
AFRICA					
S. Africa	Transvaal	1.39	0.59	0.70	0.84
AUSTRALIA	Lower Newcastle	0.94	0.15	0.79	0.19
SOUTH AMERICA					
Brazil	Santa Caterina	1.32	0.80	0.53	1.5

[a] Moisture-free basis, pyrite + sulfate reported as pyrite.

Conjugated bonds alpha to sulfur atom tend to stabilize the structure. For example, thiophene and its derivatives such as benzothiophene or dibenzothiophene are quite difficult to have the sulfur bonds cleaved.

9.2.2   Removal of Sulfur Dioxide

Because fuel cannot be 100% desulfurized due to technical and economic reasons, the emission of sulfur dioxide from burning fuels is inevitable. To abate the air pollution, one alternative is to remove the sulfur dioxide from the stack gases by using chemical scrubbers. This process is often called **flue gas desulfurization (FGD)**. The most common process is the **limestone process**. The stack gas is passed through a slurry of limestone (calcium carbonate), which removes sulfur dioxide quite efficiently (it has also removed all the HCl coproduced). This reaction, as well as other SO_2 removal processes, are summarized here:

Control Technology — Flue Gas Desulfurization (FGD)

- Wet Lime — Limestone Process

$$CaCO_3 \xrightarrow{\Delta} CaO + CO_2 \uparrow$$

$$CaO + SO_2 \rightarrow CaSO_3$$

$$CaO + SO_2 + \frac{1}{2}O_2 \rightarrow CaSO_4$$

$$CaO + H_2O \rightarrow Ca(OH)_2$$

- MgO Scrubbing

$$MgO + SO_2 \rightarrow MgSO_3$$

$$MgSO_3 \xrightarrow{\Delta} MgO + SO_2 \uparrow$$

MgO can be easily recycled

- Sodium Citrate Scrubbing

$$NaH_2 Cit + SO_2 + H_2O \rightarrow NaH(HSO_3 \cdot H_2 Cit)$$

$$\downarrow H_2O$$

$$S + NaH_2 Cit + H_2O$$

- Catalytical Oxidation

$$SO_2 \xrightarrow{V_2O_5} SO_3 \xrightarrow{H_2O} H_2SO_4$$

Table 9-6. Summary of SO₂ Removal Processes

Process and Developer	Description	Chemistry
Sulfite absorption (Wellman-Power Gas)	A solution method for concentrating dilute SO_2 via bisulfite formation, crystallization, and thermal regeneration. No reduction or oxidation in the solution step.	$SO_2 \text{ (dil.)} + H_2O + Na_2SO_3 \rightarrow NaHSO_2$ $SO_2 \text{ (conc.)} + H_2O + Na_2SO_3 \xleftarrow{\text{Heat}}$
Magnesium oxide (Chemico/Basic)	Essentially a concentration process using MgO as a collecter, followed by regeneration and the production of an SO_2 stream.	$SO_2 \xrightarrow{200°-300°F} MgSO_3 \xrightarrow{1400°F} SO_2$ MgO regeneration
Molten salt (Atomics International)	Dilute SO_2 is concentrated by absorption in molten salt as sulfite, and then reduced to sulfide and hence H_2S. M stands for metal.	contact H_2SO_4 process $SO_2 + M_2CO_3 \xrightarrow{800°F} M_2SO_3 + CO_2$ $H_2S + M_2CO_3 \leftarrow M_2S + H_2O + CO_2$ claus $S + H_2O$ SO_2
Manganese dioxide (Mitsubishi)	SO_2 is initially concentrated and oxidized to metal sulfate, followed by regeneration of MnO_2 and production of ammonium sulfate.	$SO_2 \rightarrow MnSO_4 \xrightarrow{NH_4OH} (NH_4)_2SO_4 + H_2O$ MnO_2 Regeneration air

Table 9-6. continued

Process and Developer	Description	Chemistry
Limestone (TVA, Combustion Engineering, Chemico, others)	Simultaneous reaction of SO_2 with limestone and air oxidation of resulting sulfite to sulfate results in a slag that requires suitable disposal. Reaction may take place inside furnace or in flue-gas scrubber.	$CaCO_3 \xrightarrow{SO_2, SO_3, \text{air}} CaSO_4 + CO_2$
Catalytic (Monsanto)	Accepts hot dilute SO_2 gas stream rather than high-concentration SO_2 for acid-plant feed.	$\text{Air} + SO_2 \xrightarrow[V_2O_5]{900°F} SO_3 \xrightarrow{H_2O} H_2SO_4$
Activated carbon (Westvaco, Hitachi, Chemiebau, others)	All methods depend on adsorptive powers of various forms of active carbon to first concentrate and then catalyze oxidation of SO_2 to SO_3 for acid or sulfate production. Fluidized, fixed, and plugged-flow beds have all been employed.	$SO_2 \xrightarrow[\text{active carbon}]{\text{air}, H_2O} H_2SO_4$
Ammonia scrubbing (Showa Denko)	Adsorption and concentration of SO_2 and air in ammonia solution yields bisulfate and thiosulfate, which then forms sulfate, water, and sulfur.	$SO_2 + NH_4OH \xrightarrow{\text{air}} HN_4HSO_3 + (NH_4)_2S_2O_3 \longrightarrow (NH_4)_2SO_4 + H_2O + S$

A typical limestone is composed of 94% $CaCO_3$, 1.5% $MgCO_3$, and the remainder is inert material. Limestone is cheap and abundant, but the large quantities of calcium sulfate produced pose a major waste disposal problem. A process utilizing sulfate-reducing bacteria to regenerate the limestone has proven technically feasible, but large carbon sources are necessary for bacterial metabolism. Table 9-6 lists all the FGD processes.

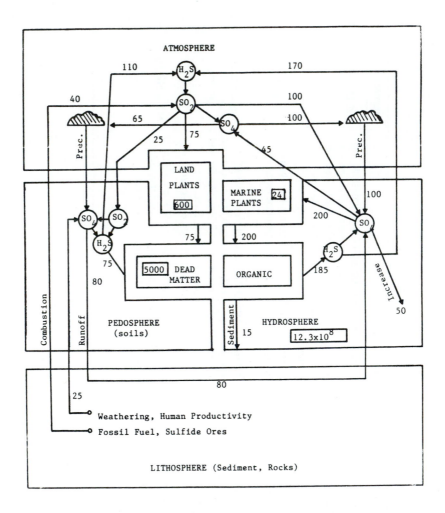

Figure 9-4.   Circulation of sulfur in nature. The units are millions of metric tons of sulfur. The enclosed figures are simply amounts; the other figures are amount per year.

9.2.3   Fate of Sulfur Dioxide

The ultimate fate of SO_2 will probably stay in the ocean, which can absorb much more than we are now producing. Figure 9-4 illustrates the sulfur cycle. The lifetime of SO_2 in the atmosphere is much shorter than that of CO_2, which is several years. The emissions of SO_2 are 20 times less than those of CO_2, and background air concentrations are a million times less. It is estimated that the lifetime for industrial SO_2 is 3 days, as shown in Table 9-7. Concerns about other species coproduced with SO_2 such as SO, SO_3, COS, CS and so on. They are in very low concentration. Therefore, these coproduced sulfur species are insignificant, as shown in Figure 9-5.

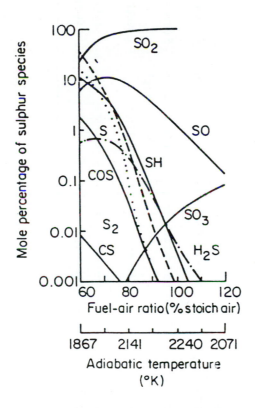

Figure 9-5.   Equilibrium distribution of sulfur-containing species in propane-air flames with unburnt gases initially containing 1% SO_2. (After G.M. Johnson, C.J. Mathews, M.Y. Smith and D.V. Williams, *Combust Flame*, 15:211 (1970).)

Table 9-7. Sources, Concentrations, and Major Reactions at Atmospheric Trace Gases

Gas	Anthropogenic Sources	Natural Sources	Background Concentration	Estimated Lifetime	Removal Mechanisms
SO_2	combustion of coal and oil	volcanoes	0.002-0.01 ppm	3 days	oxidation to sulfate photochemically or catalytically
H_2S	chemical processes	biological	0.002-0.02 ppm	1 day	oxidation to SO_2
CO	combustion	oxidation of CH_4, oceans	0.12-0.15 ppm	0.1 year	reaction with OH in troposphere and stratosphere. Soil removal
$NO-NO_2$	combustion	bacterial action in soil	NO: 0.2-2 ppb NO_2: 0.5-4 ppb	5 days	oxidation to nitrate by photochemical reactions or on aerosol particles
NH_3	waste treatment	biological decay	6-20 ppb	2 weeks	reaction with SO_2 to form $(NH_4)_2SO_4$. Oxidation to nitrate
N_2O	none	biological action in soil	0.25 ppm	4 years	photodissociation in stratosphere
CH_4	combustion, chemical processes	swamps, paddy fields	1.5 ppm	1.5 years	reaction with OH

9.3 AUTOMOTIVE EMISSIONS

The major pollutants for automobile driving is CO among many other pollutants such as particles, SO_x and NO_x. All these will cause health problem in the biosphere. For example, the formation of photochemical smog in Los Angeles is related to the pollutant's properties. Two more issues will be addressed here: additives to improve the performance of the engines such as oxgenators and antiknocking agents; and modification of the pollutant composition in automobile emissions with a catalytic converter.

Table 9-8.   Estimated Global Anthropogenic Carbon Monoxide Sources in 1970

Source	Emission, Tg
Motor vehicles	222
Other mobile sources	25
Coal combustion	11
Fuel oil combustion	40
Industrial processes	22
Petroleum refining	5
Solid waste disposal	23
Miscellaneous (agricultural burning, etc.)	23
TOTAL	371

9.3.1   Carbon Monoxide

More than 60% of the global anthropogenic carbon monoxide source is from automotive emissions as shown in Table 9-8. Carbon monoxide is an odorless, tasteless, and colorless gas. Upon entering the respiratory system, it combines in the lungs with the hemoglobin in the blood stream to form carboxyhemoglobin, COHb. This process reduces the capability of the hemoglobin to carry oxygen to the body tissues. Both oxygen and carbon monoxide are bound to the iron atoms in the hemoglobin molecules, but the binding of carbon monoxide is 320 times more effective than that of oxygen. Hence, low levels of carbon monoxide can still result in high levels of COHb.

At COHb levels of 2–5%, effects such as impairment of time interval discrimination and visual acuity are found in the central nervous system. At levels greater than 5%, there are cardiac and pulmonary functional changes. Figure 9-6 shows the physiological effects of carbon monoxide poisoning.

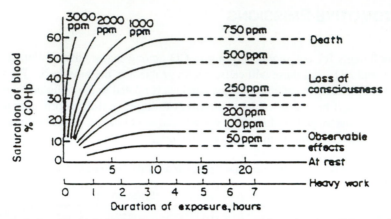

Figure 9-6. Physiological effects of carbon monoxide poisoning. (Source: Lower Diagram: P. C. Wolfe, *Environ. Sci. Technol.* 5:213 (1971))

The principle sources of CO is both from fossil fuel combustion and biomass in nature. There is a small fraction of ^{14}CO in the troposphere. The residence time of CO in the troposphere is about 0.1 year. This approximation is based on the following example:

[Example 9-1]   From fossil fuel combustion rate, estimate the residence time of CO. Also approximate the production rate of CO from biomass alone.

We will set up the production rate as Equations (a) and (b).

$$\frac{d(CO)}{dt} = P_1 + P_2 - k(CO) \tag{a}$$

P_1 = production rate of CO from biomass
P_2 = production rate of CO from fossil fuel combustion

$$\frac{d(^{14}CO)}{dt} = NP_1 + P_3 - k(^{14}CO) \tag{b}$$

P_3 = production rate of ^{14}CO in troposphere = 290 mole/yr
$N = 1.17 \times 10^{-12}$ = fraction of ^{14}C from biomass

Also, P_2 can be estimated
we burn 5.7 Pg of C of fossil fuel/yr or (÷ 12)   (from Section 8.2.1 in Chapter 8)

$$= 475 \text{ T mole of C/yr}$$

Using

$$\Phi = 1.4 \text{ (excess of } O_2 \text{ in atm), } \Phi \text{ here is equivalence ratio at } \Phi = 1.4$$

the ratio $CO_2/CO = 1 \times 10^{-1}/115 \times 10^3$ (from Fig. 9-12 by reading off from the graph) or $CO/(CO_2 + CO) \approx 0.015$
Therefore,

$$P_2 = 0.015 \times 475 \text{ T mole} = 7 \text{ T mole/yr}$$

Solving by assuming a state of equilibrium, and setting both Equations (a) and (b) equal to zero,

$$P_1 = 180 \text{ T mole/yr} = 5 \text{ Pg/yr}$$

$$k = 11 \text{ yr}^{-1}, \ 1/k = 0.09 \text{ yr} \approx 0.1 \text{ yr}$$

9.3.2   Nitrogen Oxides

In general, the symbol NO_x indicates a seven oxides mixture of nitrogen, which consists of NO, NO_2, NO_3, N_2O_3, N_2O_4, and N_2O_5. Of those seven oxides, the most important two are NO and NO_2. In the United States the mobile sources account for 40% of NO_x, the remainder is from the combustion of utility industry. The **thermal NO_x** is formed from reactions between nitrogen and oxygen in the air during combustion. NO_x produced by this manner is called the **Zeldovich's model**. Of course, if fuel contains nitrogeneous organics NO_x also can be produced.

$$N_2 + O = NO + N$$

$$N + O_2 = NO + O$$

$$N + OH = NO + H$$

During combustion the ratio of NO and NO_2 can be a useful indicator. Therefore, the following two reactions are essential:

$$N_2 + O_2 = 2NO$$

$$K_{P_1} = \frac{(P_{NO})^2}{P_{N_2} P_{O_2}} = \frac{(Y_{NO})^2}{Y_{N_2} Y_{O_2}} = 10^{-30} \ (300K) = 7.5 \times 10^{-9} \ (1000K) = 4 \times 10^{-4} \ (2000K)$$

$$NO + \frac{1}{2} O_2 = NO_2$$

$$K_{P_2} = \frac{P_{NO_2}}{P_{NO}(P_{O_2})^{\frac{1}{2}}} = \frac{P_T^{-\frac{1}{2}} Y_{NO_2}}{(Y_{NO})(Y_{O_2})^{\frac{1}{2}}} = 10^6 \ (300K) = 1.2 \times 10^2 \ (1000K) = 3.5 \times 10^{-3} \ (2000K)$$

Here

K_{Pi} = equilibrium constant of the ith reaction.

P_i = partial pressure of component i, atm.

Y_i = mole fraction of component i

P_T = total pressure, atm.

From the two previous equations, it can be seen that

- At flame zone temperature (3000–3600°F) the NO_x concentration can reach 6000–10,000 ppm. The ratio of NO/NO_2 may reach from 500:1–1000:1.
- At flue gas exit temperature (300–600°F) there will be very low NO_x concentration (<1ppm). Therefore, no effort is made for any FGD for the control of NO_x. The ratios of NO/NO_2 at this low temperature is from 1:10,000–1:10.

[Example 9-2]   Calculate the NO_x concentration and the NO/NO_2 ratio for a typical flue gas composition of 76% N_2, 4% O_2, 8% CO_2, and 12% H_2O. (After Cooper and Alley with permission).

We already have K_{P_1} at 2000°K, which is close to 3000°F.

$$K_{P_I}(2000K) = 4 \times 10^{-4} = \frac{(P_{NO})^2}{P_{N_2} P_{O_2}}$$

thus

$$(P_{NO})^2 = 4 \times 10^{-4} (0.76)(0.04)$$

or $\phi_{NO} = 3.49 \times 10^{-3}$ atm. or eqlm. conc. = 3490 ppm
also

$$K_{P_2}(2000K) = 3.5 \times 10^{-3} = \frac{P_{NO_2}}{P_{NO} P_{O_2}^{\frac{1}{2}}}$$

thus

$$P_{NO_2} = 3.5 \times 10^{-3} (P_{NO})(0.04)^{\frac{1}{2}} = 2.44 \times 10^{-6} \text{ atm. or eqlm. conc.} = 2.4 \text{ ppm}$$

or total NO_x concentration = 3490 + 2.4 = 3492.4 ppm

Now

$$\frac{P_{NO}}{P_{NO_2}} = \frac{(NO)}{(NO_2)} = 1.42 \times 10^3$$

which falls in the range of the previous statement.

It was found that production of NO is sensitive to temperature; for example, experiments indicated that below 1600°C, less than 200 ppm of NO are formed, but above 1800°C, several thousands ppm of NO are found. An empirical formula is developed.

$$C_{NO}(\text{ppm}) = 5.2 \times 10^{17} \left(\exp \frac{-72,300}{T} \right) Y_{N_2} Y_{O_2}^{\frac{1}{2}} t \qquad [9\text{-}3]$$

Here T is absolute temperature, (time in seconds) and Y_i is the mole fraction. In combustion, usually an equivalence ration, Φ, is used

$$\Phi = \frac{(A/F)\,\text{actual}}{(A/F)\,\text{stoichiometric}}$$

[9-4]

which is the quotient of air to fuel ratio; for example, the combustion of gasoline is

$$C_7H_{14} + 10\tfrac{1}{2}O_2 + 39\,N_2 + \tfrac{1}{2}Ar \rightarrow 7\,CO_2 + 7\,H_2O + 39\,N_2 + \tfrac{1}{2}Ar$$

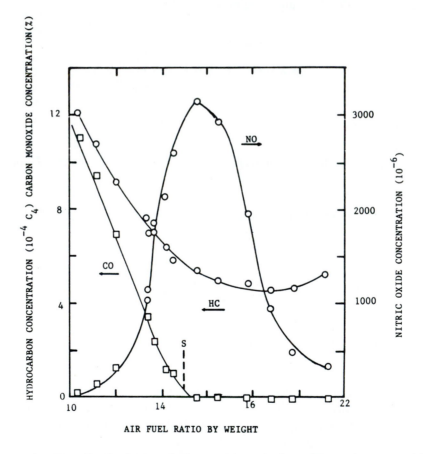

Figure 9-7.   The effects of the equivalence ratio on hydrocarbon, carbon monoxide, and nitricoxide exhaust emission. (Source: W.G. Agnew, Research Publication GMR-743 General Motors Corp., 1968)

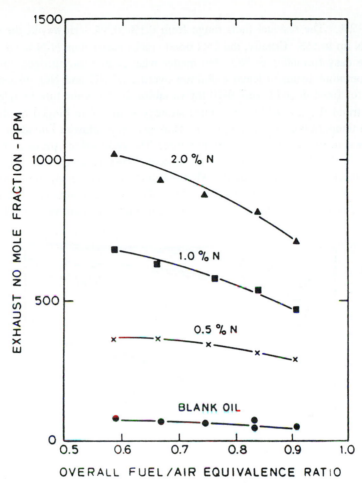

Figure 9-8.   Measured exhaust NO mole fractions (dry basis, corrected to stoichi-ometric) for an oil-fired furnace with various amounts of pyridine (C_5H_5N) added to the fuel.

Here, the stoichiometric ratio is for the combustion of 98g of fuel (C_7H_{14}). It requires 336g of oxygen, 1092g of nitrogen, 20g of argon, and 1478g of air. An approximation for the molar basis is n (1 + 79/21) 29. If 10.5 moles of oxygen is used, then the required air is 1450g (29 is the molecular weight of air). Therefore, the mass ratio of Φ_{mass} = 1450/ 98 = 14.8 and the molar ratio of Φ_{mol} = 1. In Figure 9-7, if $\Phi < 1$, and fuel is rich, then unburned fuel vapors and CO will be emitted. On the other hand, if $\Phi > 1$ and fuel is lean, then NO emission will be increased.

Another type of NO_x is termed **fuel** NO_x. When a fuel contains organically bond ni-trogen, such as coals or fuel oils, the contribution of fuel NO_x to total NO_x production is sig-nificant, as shown in Figure 9-8. Most the United States coals contains % N value ranging from 0.5%–2%. The residual fuels range from 0.1%–0.5%. However, the shale oil may contain % N up to 6%. Usually, the C-N bond cracks easier than N-N bond. This process explains the easy formation of NO. No matter what source the nitrogen comes from, the higher temperature seems to leave a definite overuse of NO and NO_2 concentration. See Figure 9-9 for fixed Φ and Figure 9-10 for variables Φ. Even the turbine inlet temperature shows this trend (Figure 9-11). A control strategy is therefore hinged on the decrease of combustion temperature. For example, the **flue gas recirculation** intends to reroute some of the flue gas to furnace at a lower temperature. The **reduced air preheat** lowers the peak temperature in the flame zone. Also, the **reduced firing rates** have been practiced to reduce the heat released per unit volume. **Water injection** or steam injection can also become effective means for reducing thermal NO_x. Also, the flue gas treatment such as the **selective catalytic reduction**, which have been operating in Japan, can convert the NO_x by NH_3 injection.

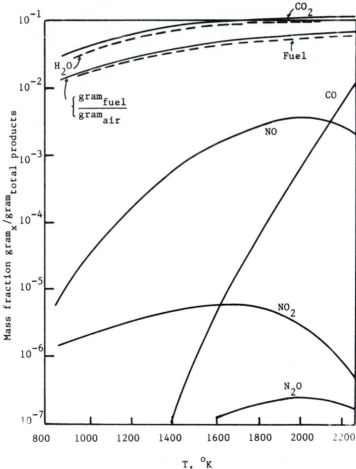

Figure 9-9.   Variation of NO_x and CO production with temperature.

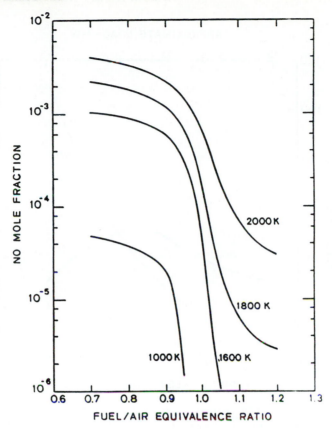

Figure 9-10. Equilibrium NO mole fractions for premixed methane-air combustion at pressure of 1 atm.

$$4\,NO + 4\,NH_3 + O_2 \rightarrow 4\,N_2 + 6\,H_2O$$

$$2\,NO_2 + 4\,NH_3 + O_2 \rightarrow 3\,N_2 + 6\,H_2O$$

Also, the wet absorption method has been used. For example, at high pH

$$NO + MnO_4^- + 2\,OH^- \rightarrow NO_2^- + MnO_4^{2-} + H_2O$$

and at low or neutral pH

$$NO + MnO_4^- \rightarrow NO_3^- + MnO_2$$

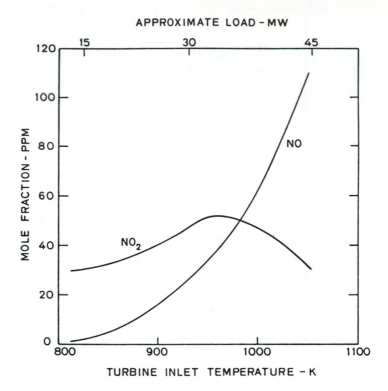

Figure 9-11.   NO and NO$_2$ exhaust mole fractions for a gas turbine operating on natural gas for various loads. (Permission from Gordon and Breach Publishers. Fig. 2 of G.M. Johnson and M.Y. Smith, *Combustion Sci. Technol.* 16:67 (1978))

Finally, the adiabatic flame temperature and equilibrium product distribution for the constant adiabatic combustion of n-octane is shown in Figure 9-12. The molar ratio of different products can be evaluated from different values of equivalence ratio. For more on combustion chemistry, see Chapter 23.

9.3.3   Photochemical Smog

Photochemical smog was first recognized as a problem in Los Angeles in 1943, and has since been detected in many cities of the world. It refers to the complex mixture of products formed from the interaction of sunlight with two major components of automobile exhaust, nitric oxide (NO), and hydrocarbon. Furthermore, stable meteorological conditions such as an inversion layer favor the creation of smog. The presence of smog, which is highly oxidizing in nature, is known by its effects—cracking of stressed rubber, eye and throat irritation, unpleasant odor, plant damage, and decreased visibility.

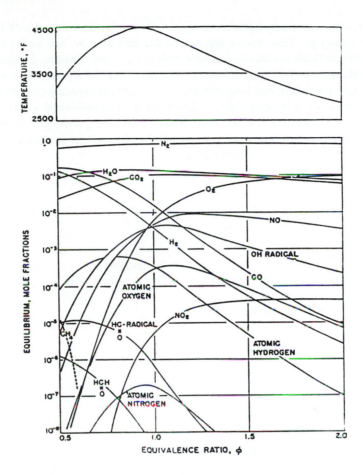

Figure 9-12. Relationship between equivalence ratio, adiabatic flame temperature and equilibrium product distribution for the constant volume adiabatic combustion of n-octane. Initial temperature 77°F and initial pressure 10 atm. (Source: R.J. Stefferson et. al. *Engineering Bull.* Purdue University, Engineering Extension St., No. 122, 1966)

The chemistry of photochemical smog is complex; a flow chart for the chemistry of smog formation is given in the figure on the next page. Basically, it involves a catalysis of the oxidation of hydrocarbons in air to form products that are themselves reactive and irritating to biological tissue. The catalysis requires sunlight and the key chemical ingredient, nitrogen dioxide. At the beginning of the smog formation reaction, however, there is only nitric oxide (NO). It is the combination of hydrocarbon with nitric oxide that forms nitrogen dioxide. The process is set in motion by a reaction with the ozone to produce hydrocarbon free radicals, highly reactive molecules with unpaired electrons. Because of the unpaired electron, the free radical combines readily with molecular oxygen to form a reactive oxygen species that can easily transfer an oxygen atom to nitric oxide, which in turn forms more nitrogen dioxide. This process regenerates the free radicals and works as a chain reaction. The free radicals eventually combine with oxygen and nitrogen dioxide to form the oxidation products (eye and lung irritants), and gradually the hydrocarbon supply is depleted. The most potent eye and lung irritants in smog are peroxyacetylnitrates (PAN).

Los Angeles smog is comparable to London fog as an industrial event. London fog requires smoke (combustion), fog (location), and coal volatile (industry); Los Angeles smog requires NO_x (combustion), sunlight (location), and hydrocarbons (industry—mostly transportation). The schematics are indicated here:

Industrial Events
London Fog

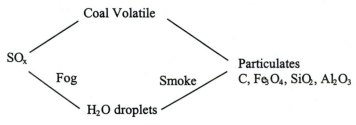

Los Angeles Smog

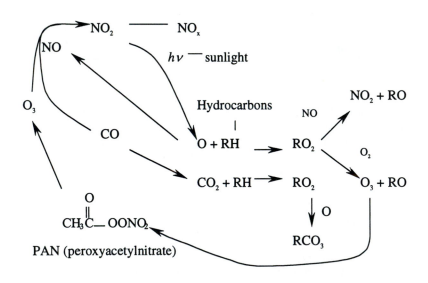

9.3.4   Antiknocking Agents

The **combustion reaction** in an internal combustion engine involves a series of radical reactions. Without suitable control, the air/fuel mixture tends to ignite spontaneously as it is heated during the compression stroke in the cylinder. This sets off a small explosion preceding the desired one, which is induced by the spark when the fuel is maximally compressed. This preignition, or knocking, decreases the efficiency of the engine and also sets up harmful stresses that increase engine wear. To correct this, an antiknocking agent is often added to control the radical reaction.

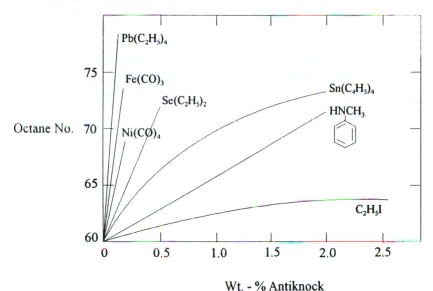

Figure 9-13.   Relative effects of several metallo-organic compounds as antiknock agents. [From Fig. 4, Livingston, *Ind. Eng. Chem.*, 43:663 (1951)]

Figure 9-13 gives the relative effects of several antiknocking agents. It shows tetraethyl lead to be the most effective. Even with such a dosage required, it results in a higher motor octane number. Due to the concern with inorganic lead acting as an agent to cause a variety of effects on human health, including liver and kidney damage, gastrointestinal damage, mental health effects in children, and abnormalities in fertility and pregnancy, the use of $Pb(C_2H_5)_4$ as an antiknocking agent is diminishing.

An alternative to using tetraethyl lead is to change the composition of gasoline so that it is less likely to generate the free radicals during preignition. Aromatic hydrocarbons such as BTX (benzene, toluene, and xylene), do not easily break down into radicals and could be added to upgrade the quality of gasoline, but they are more costly. Some other antiknocking agents such as MMT (methylcyclopentadienyl manganese tricarbonyl) have been chosen, but they are less effective and have a great potential to generate carbonyl radical, a very toxic by-product.

Following the phase out of lead alkyl additives, oxygenated gasoline program went into effect in 1992 requiring gasoline to contain 2.7% by weight of oxygen. To maintain required oxygen content, corresponding imports of oxygenators have to be blends. The most common one is methyl t-butyl ether (MTBE). MTBE is used as an oxygenater for reformulate gasoline. In many gasoline blends the MTBE content can reach 11–15% because gasoline needs an oxygen content of 2.0–2.7%; thus MTBE is not an additive. The production was 7.1 M tonnes in 1993 and anticipated to reach 15.6 M tonnes in 1998. MTBE is a suspected human carcinogen. During 1996, a jet ski event was held in Anaheim, California, and 15 M gal. of water from Orange County could not be recycled due to high contamination levels. Three drinking water wells in Santa Monica were found to contain up to 600 ppb of MTBE in 1996. Furthermore, many other ethers, such as dipropyl ether (DIPE), ethyl t-butyl ether (ETBE) and t-anyl methyl ether (TAME) are also used for some gasoline blends to substitute the use of MTBE. The fate of MTBE is that it can be oxidized into t-butyl formate (air) or hydrolized into t-butyl alcohol (water).

Antiknocking Agents

Tetraethyl Lead

$$Pb(CH_3CH_2)_4 \rightarrow Pb + 4CH_3CH_2$$

MMT (Methyl Cyclopentadienyl Manganese Tricarbonyl)

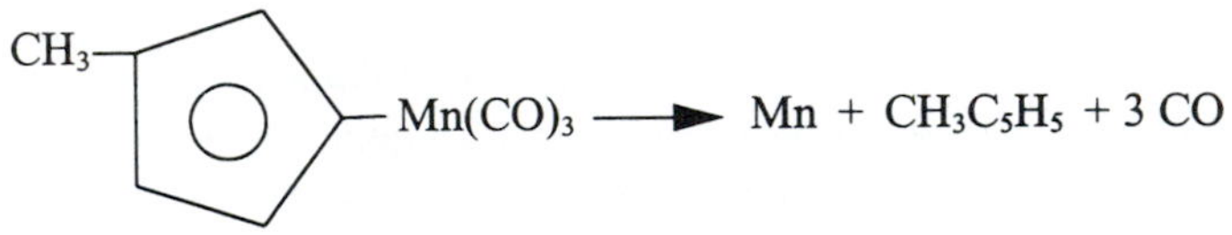

MTBE (Methyl Ter-Butyl Ether)

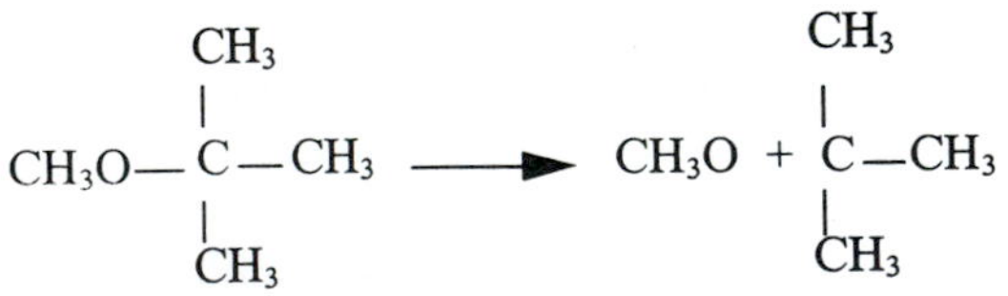

There is a considerable amount of additives introduced when using transportation fuel, as shown here:

Additives

Stabilizer
Prevention of gum formation (e.g., Ketimines)

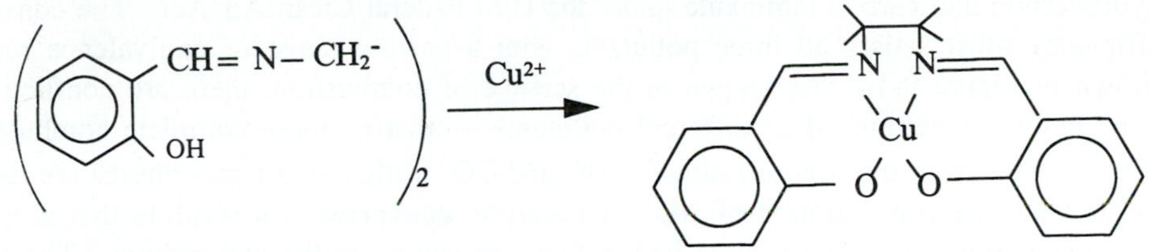

$$\left(\begin{array}{c} \text{C}_6\text{H}_4(\text{OH})\text{CH}=\text{N}-\text{CH}_2^- \end{array} \right)_2 \xrightarrow{\text{Cu}^{2+}} \text{Cu complex}$$

Pour Point Depressor

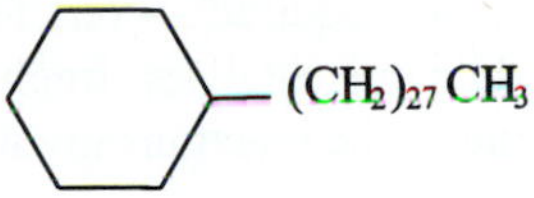

cyclohexyl$-(\text{CH}_2)_{27}\text{CH}_3$

Antioxidant

$R_2N-C_6H_4-CH_2-C_6H_4-NR_2$

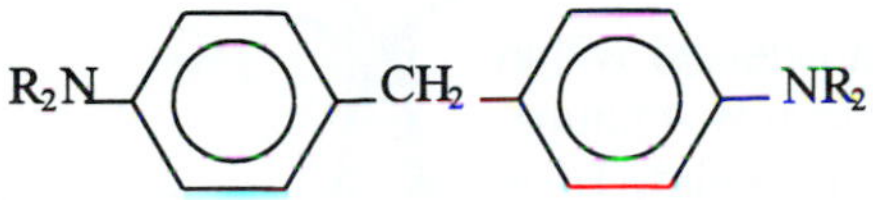

High Pressure Additive

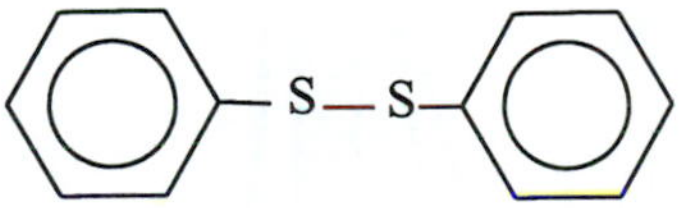

$C_6H_5-S-S-C_6H_5$

Corrosion Inhibitors

$$\left(\begin{array}{c} RO \\ RO \end{array} P\!\!\begin{array}{c} S \\ S^- \end{array} \right)_2 M$$

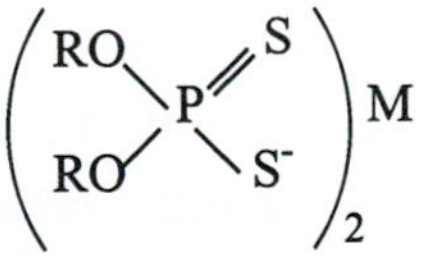

9.3.5 Catalytic Converters

As previously mentioned, it is obvious that automotive emissions cause air pollution problems. Stringent standards have been set for the concentrations of nitrogen oxides as well as hydrocarbon and carbon monoxide under the U.S. Federal Clean Air Act. The conversion efficiency must satisfy all three pollutants with a narrow range of equivalence ratio, as shown in Figure 9-14. As known in the science of combustion, there are conflicting requirements for getting rid of different pollutants — that is, more complete combustion is necessary to lower the concentrations of HC and CO, while lower temperatures are required to decrease the concentration of NO. A **catalytic converter** is a solution that eliminates pollutants from the exhaust gases before they are vented to the atmosphere. The overall chemistry of catalytic conversion is rather complicated. HC and CO are oxidized to carbon dioxide and water. However, the oxidation of NO would produce nitrogen dioxide, which is itself a pollutant. Instead, the nitric oxide must be reduced to molecular nitrogen, which is stable. So, two catalytic converters are required — one for reduction and the other for oxidation, as shown in Figure 9-15. In some catalysts, finely divided platinum is used in both converters. Figure 9-16 shows some of the reactions involved.

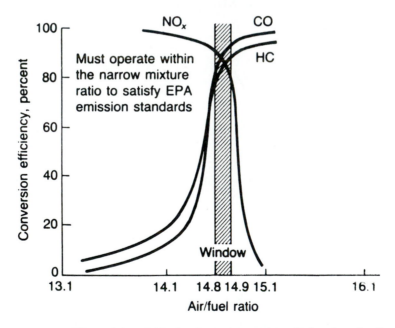

Figure 9-14.   Effect of the air/ fuel ratio on conversion efficiencies of a three-way catalyst. (Source: Niepoth, G.W., Gumbeton, J.J., and Haefner, D.R., *Closed Loop Carburetor Emission Control Systems*, 71st annual meeting, Air Pollution Control Association, June 1978.)

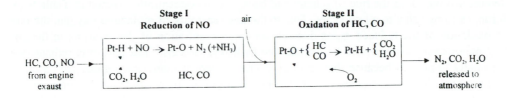

Figure 9-15.   Catalytic converter for treating auto emissions.

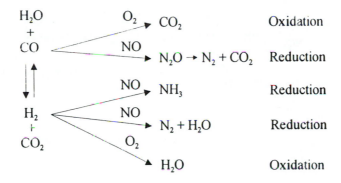

Figure 9-16.   Reactions in catalytic converters.

A fundamental requirement of the converter is that the gasoline is unleaded. If leaded gasoline were burned, the lead compounds would be expelled as small solid particles of lead sulfate and oxide. These compounds would deposit on the microscopic pores of the converter and cover the catalytic metals, thereby reducing the capability of the emission conversion.

9.4 TROPOSPHERIC CHEMISTRY

The troposphere contains the air we breathe; from it falls the water we drink. Its chemistry consists mainly of the oxidation of reduced molecules released by human and nonhuman activities on the Earth's surface. Apart from CO_2, N_2, and N_2O, which are unreactive, the major emissions are SO_2, H_2S, CO, NO and NO_2, NH_3, and hydrocarbons. It has been estimated that the amount of pollutants produced by the human race is 1 ton/yr per capita, which is about 5–6 pounds/day. The residence time for various atmospheric trace gases was determined based on the rate of release and background concentration (listed in Table 9-7). It ranges from 1 day to a few years. Due to the low reactivity of molecular oxygen, the rate of oxidation of the reduced gases depends on the concentration of the catalysts in the air. The major catalysts appear to be oxygen and hydroxyl radicals. The hydroxyl radicals are especially important because they control the rate at which many trace gases are oxidized and removed from the atmosphere. In the proceeding text, there are some reactions of hydroxyl and other radicals in the troposphere. Also, the reactions with CO, CH_4, and NO are summarized. For details, see Figure 9-17.

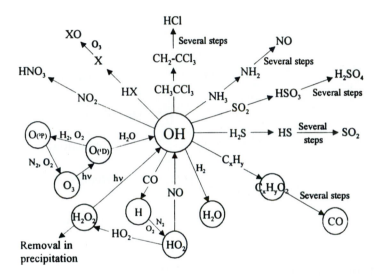

Figure 9-17.   Photochemistry of OH radical controls trace gas concentration.

Hydroxyl Radical in Troposphere

$$O_3 + h\nu\,(1200 > \lambda > 315 \text{ nm}) \rightarrow O(^3P) + O_2$$

$$O(^3P) + O_2 + M \rightarrow O_3 + M \qquad (M = N_2)$$

$$O_3 + h\nu\,(\lambda < 315 \text{ nm}) \rightarrow O(^1D) + O_2$$

$$O(^1D) + H_2O \rightarrow 2OH$$

Reaction with $CO + CH_4$

$$CO + OH \rightarrow CO_2 + H$$

$$CH_4 + OH \rightarrow CH_3 + H_2O$$

$$H + O_2 \rightarrow HO_2 \quad \text{(hydroperoxyl)}$$

$$CH_3 + O_2 \rightarrow CH_3O_2 \quad \text{(methylperoxyl)}$$

$$HO_2 + NO \rightarrow NO_2 + OH$$

$$HO_2 + O_3 \rightarrow 2O_2 + OH \quad \text{(Regenerate)}$$

$$HO_2 + OH \rightarrow H_2O + O_2 \quad \text{(terminate)}$$

$$HO_2 + HO_2 \rightarrow H_2O_2 + O_2 \quad \text{(rain out)}$$

Reaction with NO Supersonic Transport (SST)

$$HO_2 + NO \rightarrow NO_2 + OH$$

$$NO_2 + h\nu \rightarrow NO + O$$

$$NO + OH \rightarrow HNO_2$$

$$NO_2 + OH \rightarrow HNO_3 \quad \text{(rain out)}$$

In all cases except SO_2 and CO, the natural emissions of these trace gases greatly exceed the contribution from human activities, and in all cases the removal rates are fast enough that background concentrations are far less than the levels that might affect human health. However, these rates are not fast enough to cope with the high local concentrations that result from urban congestion and lead to serious air pollution.

We have already emphasized that photochemical smog is based on a free radical mechanism. However, free radical chemistry and inhibitors are also key elements of pollutant elimination.

Diethylhydroxyamine (DEHA), an inhibitor, is a clear, volatile liquid with only a mild odor. So far it has proven to be nontoxic and nonmutagenic. Some tests should be conducted on it by dispersing it into the atmosphere. The following is a summary of its functions as a smog inhibitor and a flame retardant:

- Inhibition of Photochemical Smog

DEHA (diethyl hydroxylamine)

$$(C_2H_5)_2NOH + OH \rightarrow (C_2H_5)_2NO + H_2O$$

- Flame Retardants (see Section 23.1.1)

Tris [tris (12,3—dibromipropyl)phosphate]

$$O=P—(O—CHBr—CH_2Br)_3$$

$$\downarrow$$

$$PO_4 + 3CHBr—CH_2Br$$

$$\downarrow$$

$$Br + CH = CH$$

A radical inhibitor is a stable radical. Asphaltene in asphalt is an example of such; it will inhibit even the radiation from cosmic rays. Thus asphalt roof shingles have certain advantages. Other radiation shields or aging retardants are as follows:

Radical Inhibitor

- Vitamin C

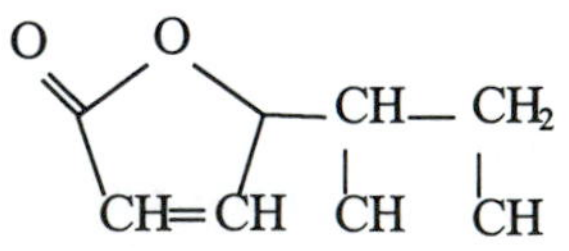

- BHT

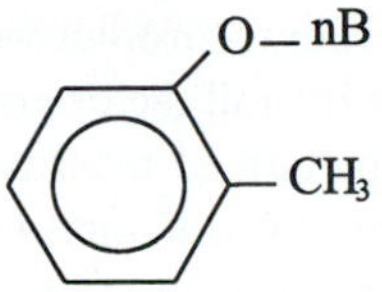

$O - nB$

CH_3

(benzene ring)

- MEA

$$NH_2CH_2CH_2SH$$

- WR 2721

$$NH_2 - (CH_2)_3 - NH(CH_2)_3 - S - \overset{\overset{\displaystyle O}{\|}}{\underset{\underset{\displaystyle OH}{|}}{P}} - OH$$

- AET

$$H_2N - (CH_2)_3 - S - C \overset{\nearrow NH_2}{\searrow NH}$$

- Cystein

$$HOOC - \underset{\underset{\displaystyle NH_2}{|}}{CH} - CH_2 - S$$

(Aging retardant)

9.5 METEOROLOGY INFLUENCED BY POLLUTION

Even though the total input and output of radiant energy to and from the Earth is essentially in balance, it is not in balance at every point on the Earth. The amount of energy reaching the Earth's surface depends, in part, on the nature of the surface (sea vs. land, for example) and the degree of cloudiness, as well as on the latitude of the location. The uneven distribution of energy resulting from latitudinal variation in insolation and from differences in absorptivity of the Earth's surface leads to the large scale air motions of the earth. In particular, the tendency to transport energy from the tropics to polar regions, thereby redistributing energy inequalities on the Earth, is the overall factor governing the general circulation of the atmosphere. To predict the general pattern of macroscale air circulation on the Earth, we must consider both the tendency for thermal circulation and the influence of **Coriolis forces**, as shown in Figure 9-17. Meteorology is of an environmental engineer's concern, because it is both related to the weather and pollution problems in the troposphere. Transport of the pollutants depends heavily on the meteorological conditions. The pattern of general circulation shown in Figure 9-18 does not represent the actual state of atmospheric circulation on a given day. The irregularities of land masses and their surface temperatures tend to disrupt the smooth global circulation patterns. Another influence that tends to break up zonal patterns is the Coriolis force. The boundary layers and the unevenness of land surfaces will be discussed in Chapter 10. Air that converges at low levels toward regions of low pressure must also execute a circular motion because of Coriolis forces. Low pressure systems are usually associated with warm fronts, giving steady rain and drizzle, and cold fronts, giving heavy local rain. The effect of friction at the surface is to direct the winds at low levels in part toward the region of low pressure, producing an inward spiraling motion.

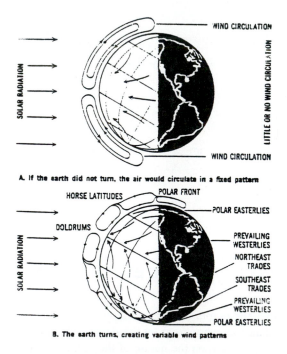

Figure 9-18.   Global wind patterns. (Source: American Lung Association)

This vortex-like motion is called a **cyclone**. The center of a cyclone is usually a rising column of warm air. Similarly, a low-level diverging flow from a high pressure region will spiral outward. No wave fronts and no wind and dispersion, which cause serious air pollution episodes, are associated with high pressure systems. Such a region is called an **anticyclone**.

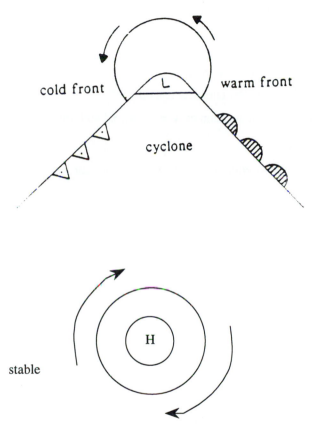

In the Northern Hemisphere, the motion of a cyclone is counterclockwise and that of an anticyclone, clockwise.

9.5.1 Dispersion of Pollutants

Turbulent diffusion has two approaches: **Eulerian** and **Lagrangian**.

For the Eulerian, approach the species are relative to a fixed coordination system; for the Lagrangian approach, concentration changes are relative to moving fluid. The following are descriptions for both approaches:

Eulerian Approach

For $i = 1, 2, \ldots, N$ species, then

$$\frac{\partial C_i}{\partial t} + \frac{\partial}{\partial x_j} U_j C_i = D_i \frac{\partial^2 C_i}{\partial x_j \partial x_j} + R_i (C_1 \cdots C_N, T) + S_i (\bar{x}, t) \qquad [9\text{-}5]$$

C_i = concentration of ith species

U_j = jth component of fluid velocity

D_i = molecular diffusivity of species i in fluid

R_i = rate of generation of species i by chemical reaction

S_i = rate of addition of species i at location of $\bar{x} = (x_1, x_2, x_3)$ and time t

Lagrangian Approach

Single particle at $(\bar{x}', t')$ for location and time. Considering subsequent motion at a later time t, the probability is

$$\psi (\bar{x}, t) \, d\bar{x} \qquad [9\text{-}6]$$

at time t, the element is

$$x_1 \rightarrow x_1 + d\,x_1$$

$$x_2 \rightarrow x_2 + d\,x_2 \qquad [9\text{-}7]$$

$$x_3 \rightarrow x_3 + d\,x_3$$

Probability density function is

$$\int_{-\infty}^{\infty} \int_{-\infty}^{\infty} \int_{-\infty}^{\infty} \psi (\bar{x}, t) \, d\bar{x} = 1$$

$$\psi (\bar{x}, t) = \int_{-\infty}^{\infty} \int_{-\infty}^{\infty} \int_{-\infty}^{\infty} Q(\bar{x}, t \,|\, \bar{x}', t') \psi (\bar{x}', t') \, d\bar{x}' \qquad [9\text{-}8]$$

We will now discuss how to determine the atmospheric concentration of pollutants emitted from single sources. We are usually concerned with horizontal dispersion (y-direction) and vertical dispersion (z-direction). **Horizontal dispersion** depends on the wind direction and speed. Meteorologists commonly use the **wind rose** to present wind direction and wind speed data. Figure 9-19 illustrates pollution rises in SO_2 concentration of 250 mg/m^3 in a chemical plant.

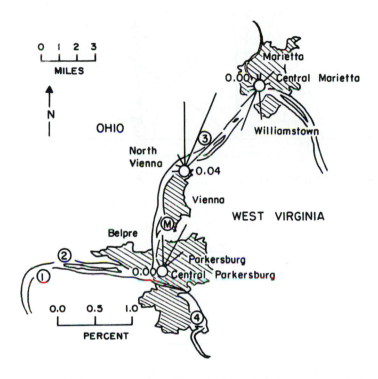

Figure 9-19.   Pollution roses, with SO_2 concentrations greater than $250\mu g/m^3$. The major suspected sources are the four chemical plants, but the data indicate that Plant 3 is the primary culprit.

Vertical dispersion depends on temperature profiles in the atmosphere. Figure 9-20 illustrates five possible **temperature profiles**. (1) **Adiabatic lapse rate**: T decreases with height such that any vertical movement imparted to an air parcel will result in the parcel maintaining the same T or density as the surrounding air (Neutral stable). (2) **Superadiabatic**: A rising air will be warmer than its environment so it becomes more buoyant (Unstable). (3) **Subadiabatic**: A rising air parcel is cooler than its surroundings so it becomes less buoyant and returns (Stable). (4) **Isothermal**: Temperature constant with height. (Stable). (5) **Inversion**: Temperature increases with height (Extremely stable).

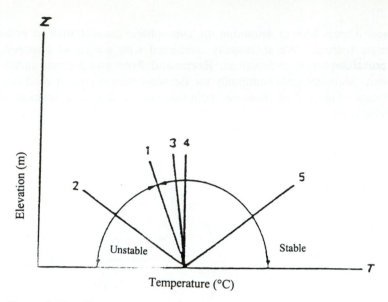

Figure 9-20.   Temperature profiles.

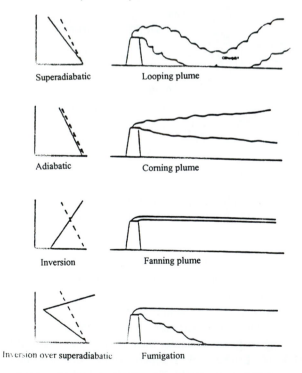

Figure 9-21.   Plume shapes and atmospheric stability.

The atmospheric stability can determine the plane shapes out of a stack, as shown in Figure 9-21. In the figure the broken lines represent the adiabatic lapse rate and the solid lines depict the prevailing conditions. At the theoretical adiabatic lapse rate, the atmosphere is uniform, and coning occurs. Under unstable conditions, looping is observed. The dispersion is greater, but associated fluctuations will cause segments of the plume to reach ground level close to the stack.

Under stable conditions, the plume will have little tendency to disperse — a condition known as fanning.

9.5.2 Gaussian Model

There are several models available for predicting the downwind concentrations of a single source. Attempts have been made to correlate the dispersion coefficients with atmospheric conditions. Table 9-9 notes the atmospheric conditions and Figure 9-22 gives the dispersion coefficients. The following example explains how to use these figures and the Gaussian model. By applying the **Gaussian function**, the solution for the plume concentration takes the form where

$$C(x, y, z, H) = \frac{Q}{2\pi\,\sigma_y \sigma_z U}\,\exp\left[-\frac{1}{2}\left(\frac{y}{\sigma_y}\right)^2\right]\left[\exp\left(-\frac{1}{2}\left(\frac{z-H}{\sigma_z}\right)^2\right)\right] + \exp\left[-\frac{1}{2}\left(\frac{z+H}{\sigma_z^2}\right)\right]\quad [9\text{-}9]$$

C = concentration in g/m^3

Q = source strength in g/sec

U = average wind speed in m/sec

σ_y, σ_z = dispersion coefficients in y and z direction in meters

H = effective height of source emission in meters

Table 9-9. Atmospheric Stability Key for Figure 9-22

Surface Wind Speed	Day Incoming Solar Radiation (Sunshine)			Night Thinly Overcast	
(at 10 m), m/sec	Strong	Moderate	Slight	4/8 Low Cloud	3/8 Cloud
2	A	A-B	B	—	—
2-3	A-B	B	C	E	F
3-5	B	B-C	C	D	E
5-6	C	C-D	D	D	D
6	C	D	D	D	D

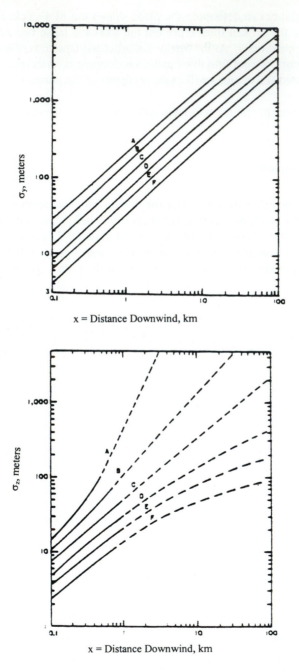

Figure 9-22.   Dispersion coefficients.

[Example 9-3] For a sunny summer afternoon, estimate the ground level concentration 200 meters downward from a stack if the wind speed is 4m/sec. The height of the stack is 20 m and the efficient concentration (Q) out of it is 0.01 kg/sec.

From Table 9-9 it is found that type B is most fitted to the conditions (sunny afternoon and $U = 4$m/sec). Then from Figure 9-22, $\sigma_y = 36$ and $\sigma_z = 20$ at $x = 200$ m.

At plane center line $\quad$ y = 0.

At ground level $\quad$ z = 0.

Thus $\quad$ C =

$$\frac{0.01}{2(3.14)(4)(100)(40)} \exp\left(-\frac{1}{2}\left(\frac{0}{100}\right)^2\right)\left[\exp\left(-\frac{1}{2}\left(\frac{0-20}{40}\right)^2\right) + \exp\left(-\frac{1}{2}\left(\frac{0+20}{40}\right)^2\right)\right]$$

$$= 9.95 \times 10^{-8}(1)(e^{-1/8} + e^{-1/8})$$

$$= 1.76 \times 10^{-7} \text{ kg/m}^3 = 176 \quad \text{g/m}^3$$

REFERENCES

9-1.   W. L. Chameides and D. D. Davis, "Chemistry in the Troposphere," C & E N, p. 39 (Oct. 1982).

9-2.   J. H. Seinfeld, *Air Pollution*, McGraw-Hill, New York, 1975.

9-3.   H. C. Perkino, *Air Pollution*, McGraw-Hill, New York, 1974.

9-4.   W. Strauss and S. J. Mainwaring, *Air Pollution*, Edward Arnold, London, 1984.

9-5.   T. G. Spiro and W. M. Stigliani, *Environmental Issues in Chemical Perspective*, State University of New York Press, Albany, New York, 1980.

9-6.   H. J. Sanders, "Flame Retardants," C & E N, p. 22 (Apr. 24, 1978).

9-7.   J. B. Edwards, *Combustion*, Ann Arbor Science, Ann Arbor, Michigan, 1974.

9-8.   I. Glassman, *Combustion*, Academic, New York, 1977.

9-9.   D. J. Patterson and N. A. Henein, *Emissions from Combustion Engines and Their Control*, Ann Arbor Science, Ann Arbor, Michigan, 1973.

9-10. A. W. Demmler, "Automotive Catalysis," Auto. Eng. 85, 29-32 (1977).

9-11. G. Baumbach, *Air Quality Control: Formation and Sources, Dispersion, Characteristics and Impact of Air Pollutants*, Springer-Verlag, Berlin, 1996.

9-12. R. M. Whitcomb, *Non-Lead Antiknock Agents for Motor Fuels*, Noyes, Porkridge, New Jersey, 1975.

9-13. N. Calder, *The Weather Machine*, Viking Press, New York, 1974.

PROBLEM SET

1. Assume that the concentration of suspended particulates in a polluted atmosphere is 170 μg/m. The particulates contain adsorbed sulfate and hydrocarbons comprising 14% and 9% of the weight, respectively. An average person respires 8,500 l of air daily and retains 50% of the particles smaller than 1 μm in diameter in the lungs. How much sulfate and hydrocarbon accumulate in the lungs in one year if 75% of the particulate mass is contained in particles smaller than 1 μm?

2. Using the figures of combustion product distribution versus equivalence ratio, and given a 10-gallon gasoline (isooctane) consumption in an automobile without emission control, approximate the following:

    a) The volume ratios of CO and CO_2 at $\phi = 1$, 0.7 and 1.3.

    b) The weight in lbs. of the CO and CO_2 produced at $\phi = 1$. (See Fig. 9-12.)

3. Estimate the concentration of SO_2 downwind of a 1,000 MW power plant burning 10,000 tons of 1% sulfur coal per day. The stack height is 250 meters. The wind speed has been measured on a clear day as 5 m/sec at the top of a 10 m tower. Find the pollutant concentration at a distance of 1 and 5 km away, if the meteorologists estimate the hourly mean value of diffusion coefficients in y and z directions as

x(km)	y(m)	z(m)
1	140	125
5	540	500

    Also, find the results if the stack height is doubled.

4. Consider the following atmospheric temperature soundings:

Elevation (ft)	Temperature (°F)
0	70.0
200	68.0
400	66.0
600	72.0
800	70.0
1000	68.0

a.   Indicate the type of lapse rate involved for:

0 – 400 ft

400 – 600 ft

600 – 1000 ft

b.   Determine the plume type if the stack were:

300 ft. tall

500 ft. tall

700 ft. tall

c.   What would be the ground-level concentration of the pollutant (negligible, moderate, high) if the stack were:

300 ft. tall

500 ft. tall

700 ft. tall

C H A P T E R **1 0**

HYDROSPHERE — WATER PROPERTIES AND GROUNDWATER

*I*n addition to sunlight and air, water is an indispensable element for most plant and animal life. A casual observation of the world map would suggest that the supply of water is endless, since it covers over 80% of the Earth's surface. Unfortunately, we cannot use it directly; over 95% is in the salty oceans, 2% is tied up in the polar ice caps, and most of the remainder is beneath the Earth's surface. Therefore, only a small fraction of the water in the world is available for human use. This chapter will focus on hydrology, the chemical properties of water, the chemistry of runoff, hardness and acid rain, groundwater movement, and contaminated aquifers. We especially emphasize the chemical aspects of underground water contamination and the chemical restoration of contaminated aquifers. The following two chapters will describe the hydrosphere in greater depth. The major topics of the upcoming chapters will be pollution in natural water and the chemical treatment of wastewater.

10.1 WATER CYCLE

Water is not present merely in seas and lakes. Table 10-1 gives a picture of the total hydrosphere. All water is locked into a recycling process called the **hydrologic cycle**. One third of the solar energy absorbed by the Earth's surface goes into the hydrologic cycle. Solar energy, especially in the tropics, evaporates water from the ocean surface, filling the air mass above with large quantities of water vapor. When these warm, moist, maritime masses conflict with cool, dry air over large land areas, some of the water vapors precipitate out. Seventy percent of the annual precipitation evaporates or is transpired by plants, while the remaining 30% goes into the streamflow. About a quarter of this streamflow is used for various purposes that can be broadly divided into irrigation, municipal water supplies, industrial uses, and electric utilities. Some of the water is evaporated during use, but most of it eventually finds its way into the ocean. Figure 10-1 illustrates the water cycle.

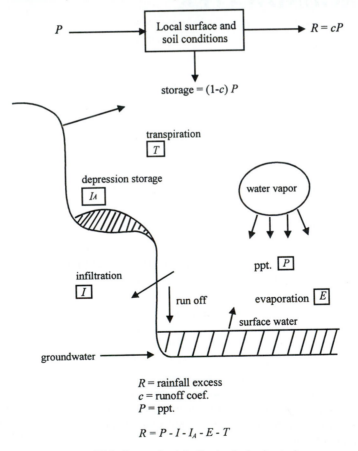

$$R = P - I - I_A - E - T$$

This figure depicts the hydrologic cycle.

Table 10-1. The Total Hydrosphere

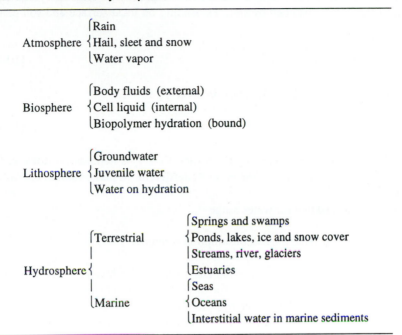

Atmosphere { Rain / Hail, sleet and snow / Water vapor

Biosphere { Body fluids (external) / Cell liquid (internal) / Biopolymer hydration (bound)

Lithosphere { Groundwater / Juvenile water / Water on hydration

Hydrosphere {
Terrestrial { Springs and swamps / Ponds, lakes, ice and snow cover / Streams, river, glaciers / Estuaries
Marine { Seas / Oceans / Interstitial water in marine sediments

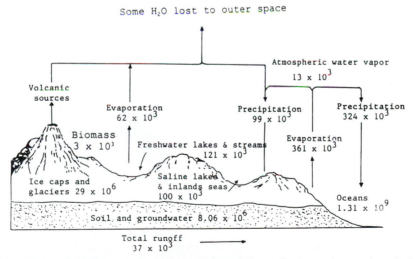

Some H₂O lost to outer space

Atmospheric water vapor
13×10^3

Volcanic sources

Evaporation 62×10^3

Precipitation 99×10^3

Precipitation 324×10^3

Biomass 3×10^3

Freshwater lakes & streams 121×10^3

Evaporation 361×10^3

Ice caps and glaciers 29×10^6

Saline lakes & inlands seas 100×10^3

Oceans 1.31×10^9

Soil and groundwater 8.06×10^6

Total runoff 37×10^3

Figure 10-1. The water cycle. Volumes of water in each reservoir are given in km³. Flows from one reservoir to another are in km³/year. Data from L. Hodges. "Environmental Pollution," pp. 126-127. Holt, New York, 1973. Also from J. Harte, "Consider a Spherical Cone, a Course in Environmental Problem Solving", William Kauffman, Los Altos, CA, 1985.

One definition for **runoff**, also called **rainfall excess** in the hydrological cycle shown here, is the rainfall that is not absorbed by soil. Depending on local surface and soil conditions,

$$R = cP \qquad\qquad [10\text{-}1]$$

and the storage is $(1 - c)P$. From the mass balance

$$R = P - I - I_A - E - T \qquad\qquad [10\text{-}2]$$

where R is rainfall excess, P is **precipitation**, I is **infiltration**, I_A is **depression storage**, E is **evaporation**, T is **transpiration**, and c is the **runoff coefficient**. Usually rainfall excess is a function of time.

It should be emphasized that for water usage

$$\text{withdrawals} = \text{consumption} + \text{returns}$$

For example, with regards to irrigation the United States freshwater usage consists of 50% consumption and 50% return; however, for thermal electric power, there is 2% consumption and 98% return. The U.S.G.S., giving examples of withdrawals that serve a variety of ends, concludes that there are nearly 2000 gal of water withdrawn per person per day. Out of the 2000 gal. of water, the domestic use accounts for only 100 gal of personal use in the home, while the bulk is industrial (e.g., 60% or 1200 gal—it takes 100,000 gal to make one automobile) and agricultural (e.g., 35% or 700 gal for irrigation).

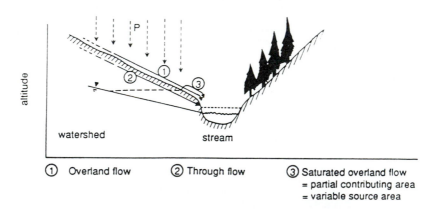

Figure 10-2.   Conceptual models of peak runoff generation.

10.1.1 Chemistry of Runoff

Direct runoff or overland flow (also called the Hortonian overland flow) is the runoff of precipitation without infiltration. This is important in understanding the water quality as unaltered by discharge, bad land, or urban runoffs with disturbances of the soil structure. A cross-section view is illustrated in Figure 10-2.

The mixing models have been developed to express this type of rapid flow generation. The samples may be two-component systems, as in the following:

$$C_t Q_t = C_g Q_g + C_s Q_s \qquad\qquad [10\text{-}3]$$

and

$$Q_t = Q_g + Q_s \qquad\qquad [10\text{-}4]$$

where C is the concentration of a given solute in mm/L, Q is the discharge in L/s, and the subscripts g, s, and t indicate respectively groundwater, surface (direct rapid), and total runoff components. From Equations [10-3] and [10-4],

$$\frac{Q_s}{Q_g} = \frac{C_g - C_t}{C_t - C_s} \qquad\qquad [10\text{-}5]$$

or

$$C_t = \frac{C_g + C_s \left(\dfrac{Q_s}{Q_g} \right)}{1 + \dfrac{Q_s}{Q_g}} \qquad\qquad [10\text{-}6]$$

Assuming,

$$\frac{Q_s}{Q_g} = \beta\, Q_t \qquad\qquad [10\text{-}7]$$

Here Q_t actually is the stream discharge. If we define the difference between groundwater and rapid runoff concentration as

$$C_d = C_g - C_s \qquad\qquad [10\text{-}8]$$

then

$$C_t = \left(\frac{C_d}{1 + \beta \, Q_t}\right) + C_s \qquad\qquad [10\text{-}9]$$

Johnson has plotted the **concentration in stream discharge** for the Hubbard Brook catchments against $1/(1 + \beta Q_t)$ to obtain a slope of $C_d = C_g - C_s$ and an intercept of C_s. The plots are expressed in Figure 10-3. The decreasing current actions with discharges such as Na^+, Mg^{2+}, and Ca^{2+} can be explained as dilution of the high current action in deep soil water as a result of the weathering of silicate rock. The increase in Al concentration is due to the high concentration in the acid topsoil. The seasonal fluctuation of NO_3^- and K^+ is due to biological activities of uptaking.

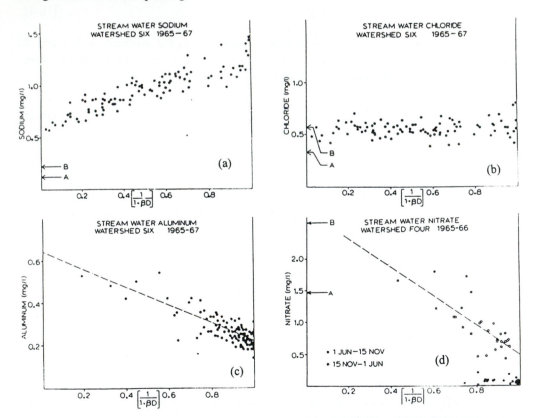

Figure 10-3.   Variation of concentrations in Hubbard Brook streamflow with the reciprocal of discharge (note that D stands for total discharge = Q_t). Reprinted with permission from Johnson et. al., 1969. Copyright by the American Geophysical Union.

Other models are summarized here:

$$C_t = aQ_t^{-1/n}$$

$$C_t = aQ_t^{-1/n} + C_s$$

$$C_t = b - a \log Q_t$$

$$C_t = a \exp(-bQ_t + 1/n)$$

$$C_t = b - aQ_t^{1/n}$$

$$C_t = (C_g - C_s)/(1 + aQ_t^{1/n}) + C_s$$

$$C_t = a(Q_t - Q_b)^{-1/n} + C_s$$

$$C_t = C_g/(1+aQ_t)^{1/n} \qquad \text{[10-10]}$$

where the subscripts t, b, s, and g are respectively total runoff, base flow (before peak flow), surface runoff, and groundwater; and a, b, and n are arbitrary parameters used for fitting.

10.2 CHEMICAL PROPERTIES OF NATURAL WATERS

Most water molecules have a molecular weight of 18. In the water molecule, both hydrogen atoms are located on the same side of the oxygen atom, and their bonds with the oxygen atom are 105° apart. The hydrogen atoms carry a positive charge while the oxygen atom is negatively charged. Because of this distribution of charge, H_2O is a strongly dipolar molecule. The water molecule dipoles attract each other and form aggregates through bonds that are known as hydrogen bonds, as shown in Figure 10-4. It is thought that these aggregates in water at room temperature can reach sizes of up to about 100 H_2O molecules.

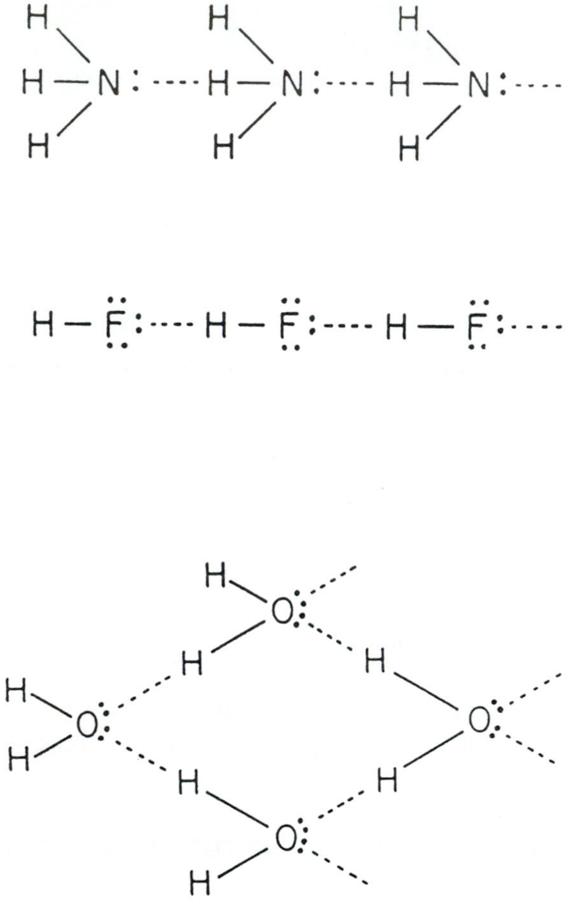

Figure 10-4. Hydrogen bonding in water as compared to ammonia and hydrogen fluoride.

Water is by far the most abundant liquid on the surface of the Earth, and it is essential to all known forms of life. Its properties in the liquid state are, however, highly anomalous. Hydrogen bonding in water is responsible for many of its unusual properties. Water is a dihydride of oxygen; dihydrides of other elements in the same family of the periodic table as oxygen are H_2S, H_2Se, and H_2Te. These heavier molecules are all gases at atmospheric pressure and room temperature (25°C). Water is a liquid that becomes a gas only when the temperature is increased to 100°C and above. This can also be seen from a comparison of melting and boiling points for the hydrides of the elements in the first row of the periodic table, as shown here:

Melting Point and Boiling Point of First Row Elements

	CH_4	NH_3	H_2O	HF
Melting point (°C)	-182	-33	0	-83
Boiling point (°C)	-164	-78	100	20

Not only does water melt and boil at a higher temperature than any of its neighboring hydrides, but it also has a larger range of temperature over which it is a liquid. One characteristic that makes the planet Earth uniquely suitable for the evolution of life is that its surface temperature, over most of its extent, lies within the liquid range of water.

Water is far denser than its related species at any given temperature; the maximum density occurs at 4°C. That means it expands upon freezing, whereas almost all other substances contract upon solidification. The reason for this is that ice is an open-structured substance that is less dense than the liquid water from which it forms. This property has far-reaching ramifications. If solid H_2O were denser than liquid H_2O, ice would form at the bottom of natural bodies of water rather than at the top, and lakes would freeze from the bottom upward. Consequently, life in its present form in aquatic systems would not exist, because natural bodies of water would freeze solidly whenever the temperature fell below the freezing point of water.

The polarity of water is an important factor in determining its solvent properties. The minerals that make up the Earth's crust are largely inorganic solids in which positively and negatively charged ions exist in a lattice structure held together by very strong electrostatic forces. These forces must be overcome upon dissolution. Water greatly assists this process by reducing the magnitude of these forces by a factor of about 80 (relative to air). This is the value of its dielectric constant (D). The large value of the dielectric constant stems from the large value of the dipole moment resulting from the partial charges in the hydrogen and oxygen atoms. Water, with this dipolar character, has the power to surround a positively charged ion with the negatively charged part of its molecule (or the reverse), thereby isolating the ions from their surrounding ions. The ion, surrounded by water molecules, can then leave the crystal ions and move out into solution.

Besides these characteristics, water possesses a high surface tension (70 dyne/cm), which is important in surface phenomena, droplet formation in the atmosphere, and many physiological processes including transport through biomembranes; a large heat capacity (75.5 KJ/mole K); a high heat of fusion (44.1 KJ/mole); and a large thermal conductivity that provides an important heat transfer mechanism in stagnant systems such as cells. The large latent heat produces a stable liquid state. Water itself is quite inert; the dissociation is small. Water is also highly transparent, which thickens the biologically productive euphatic zone. Because it is such a large body, water often serves as a sink for many substances. For example, DDT can be found in ice caps. A summary of the chemical properties of water is shown in the following table:

Property	Comparison with Normal Liquids	Significance
State	Liquid rather than gas, like H_2S, H_2Se, and H_2Te	Provides life media
Heat capacity	Very high	Moderates environmental temperatures, good heat transport medium
Latent Heat of Fusion	Very high	Moderating effect, tends to stabilize liquid state
Latent Heat of Vaporization	Very high	Moderation effect, important in atmospheric physics and in precipitation-evaporation balance
Density	Anomalous maximum of 4°C (for pure water)	Freezing from the surface and controls temperature distribution and circulation in bodies of water
Surface Tension	Very high	Important in surface phenomena, droplet formation in the atmosphere, and many physiological processes including transport through biomembranes
Dielectric Constant	Very high	Good solvent
Hydration	Very extensive	Good solvent and mobilizer of environmental pollutants, alters the biochemistry of solutes
Dissociation	Very small	Provides a neutral medium but with some availability of both H^+ and OH^- ions
Transparency	High	Thickens biologically productive euphatic zone
Heat Conduction	Very high	Can provide an important heat transfer mechanism in stagnant systems such as cells

10.3 ACIDITY AND HARDNESS

In Chapter 3 we were introduced to some concepts about pH, acidity, and alkalinity. Here, we will spend some time discussing hardness and some environmental aspects related to acid rain.

10.3.1 Hardness

Calcium, magnesium, and other divalent cations in water can combine with organic radicals in soaps to form undesirable precipitates; for example

$$2\,C_{17}H_{35}COO^{-} + Ca^{++} = Ca(C_{17}H_{35}COO)_2$$

Hard waters, or waters containing these divalent ions, also produce scales in hot-water pipes, heaters, boilers, and other units in which the temperature of the water is increased materially. The hardness of waters varies considerably from place to place. In general, surface waters are softer than groundwaters. The hardness of water reflects the nature of the geological formations with which it has been in contact.

The hardness of water is derived largely from contact with soil and rock formations. Rain water as it falls upon the Earth is incapable of dissolving the tremendous amounts of solids found in many natural waters. The ability to dissolve is gained in the soil when carbon dioxide is released by bacterial action. The soil water then becomes highly charged with carbon dioxide, which exists in equilibrium with carbonic acid. Under the low pH conditions that develop, basic materials, particularly limestone formations, are dissolved.

$$H_2CO_3 + CaCO_3 = Ca^{++} + 2HCO_3$$

Because limestone is not pure carbonate but includes impurities such as sulfates, chlorides, and silicates, these materials become exposed to the solvent action of the water as the carbonates are dissolved, and they pass into the solution too.

Calcium and magnesium cause by far the greatest portion of the hardness occurring in natural waters. Usually, hardness is classified into carbonate and noncarbonate hardness with respect to anions associated with the metallic ions. The part of the total hardness that is chemically equivalent to the bicarbonate plus carbonate alkalinities present in a water is called **carbonate hardness** (formerly called temporary hardness because through prolonged boiling it can be caused to precipitate). The amount of hardness in excess of the carbonate hardness is called **noncarbonate hardness** (formerly called permanent hardness because it cannot be removed or precipitated by boiling). Noncarbonate hardness cations are associated with sulfate, chloride, and nitrate anions.

Lime $Ca(OH)_2$ and soda ash Na_2CO_3 are two convenient and economical materials used in industry to remove excess hardness.

$$Ca(OH)_2 + Ca^{++} + 2\ HCO_3^- = 2CaCO_3(s) + 2H_2O$$

Ammonia can be used to remove scales in the bathtub due to hard water.

$$Ca^{++} + 2HCO_3^- + 2NH_3 = CaCO_3 + 2NH_4^+ + CO_3^-$$

In industry, ion exchange resins or zeolites are also used to exchange sodium ions with divalent ions to produce soft water.

In addition to surfactants, detergent formulation contains other agents called **builders**, which are intended to eliminate precipitation by the positive ions. They can do this by tying the ions up, either in a soluble form or in a precipitate that can settle easily. Chemicals that tie up the ions in a soluble form are called **chelating agents**. Sodium tripolyphosphate (STP) is a commonly used chelating agent because it is cheap and has the advantage of rapidly breaking down in the environment to sodium phosphate. Phosphate ions can also serve as nutrients for plants and buffers in aqueous systems. Nevertheless, consumption of phosphate in detergents has decreased by 67% over the past 10 years in the United States because the natural bodies of water are being overfertilized as a result of using STP.

Sodium nitrilotriacetate (NTA), $N(C_2H_2O_2)_3Na_3$, is another chelating agent that has considerable promise; But there is concern that, in addition to binding to calcium, NTA could bind to heavy metals and could mobilize these toxic elements in the environment. NTA is also suspected to be related to some birth defects. Sodium silicates and sodium borate are two alternatives. A famous household softener, Borax, contains $Na_2B_4O_7\ 10H_2O$. Incidentally, detergents are sometimes called **soft detergents** if they are biodegradable. Details of chelation and chelating agents will be discussed in Chapter 19. Water softening and calcium carbonate will be detailed in Chapter 19.

10.3.2 Acid Rain

The acidity of the rain and snow (**acid rain**) falling on widespread areas of the world has been rising during the past three decades or so. This may be a result of the combustion of tremendous quantities of fossil fuels. The United States itself annually discharges approximately 50 million metric tons of sulfur and nitrogen oxides into the atmosphere. Through a series of complex chemical reactions, these pollutants can be converted to acids (see Table 10-2).

The Hubbard Brooks Experimental Forest in the White Mountains of New Hampshire provides the longest known record for pH of precipitation in the United States (see Figure 10-5). It was found that in Norway, where the acidity of rain and snow is the highest, the acidity of lake water is likewise high (see Figure 10-6).

Table 10-2.   Sulfuric and Nitric Acids Are Major Sources of Acidity in Precipitation

Substance	Concentration In Precipitation (mg per liter)	Contribution to Free Acidity[a] (microequivalents per liter)	Contribution to Total Acidity[a] (microequivalents per liter)
H_2CO_3	0.62[b]	0	20
NH_4^+	0.92	0	51
Al, dissolved	0.05[c]	0	5
Fe, dissolved	0.04[c]	0	2
Mn, dissolved	0.005[c]	0	0.1
Total organic acids	0.34	2.4	4.7
HNO_3	4.40	39	39
H_2SO_4	5.10	57	57
Total[d]:		98	179

a at pH 4.01

b equilibrium concentration

c average value for several dates

d Data from a sample of rain collected at Ithaca, NY, on Oct. 23, 1975.

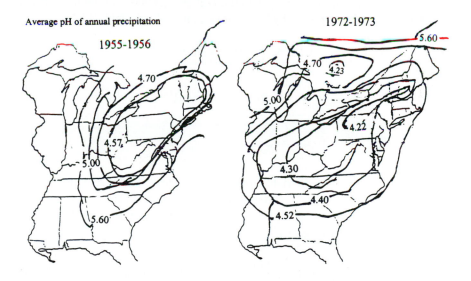

Figure 10-5.   Acidity of precipitation has increased markedly in the Eastern United States (Sources: C.V. Cogbill and G.E. Likens; C.V. Cogbill, Thomas Burton, Patrick Brezonik, and Gray Henderson)

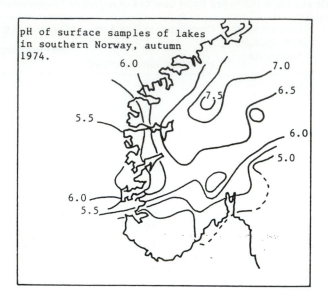

Figure 10-6.   pH of surface samples of lakes in southern Norway, autumn 1974.

Pure water is known to be in equilibrium with atmospheric carbon dioxide and results in a pH of 5.6 due to the release of hydrogen ions from carbonic acid, H_2CO_3.

$$CO_2 + H_2O = H_2CO_3$$

$$H_2CO_3 = HCO_3^- + H^+$$

$$HCO_3^- = CO_3^{2-} + H^+$$

Potentially strong acid will yield a pH of 4 and below. Sulfur dioxide can be acidized in the atmosphere (ca. 1-5% hr^{-1}). It has two absorption bands for troposphere wavelength: one at ca. 384 nm, giving rise to triplet state SO_2, and the other at ca. 294 nm, causing formation at a higher energy excited singlet state.

$$SO_2 + h\nu = \bullet SO_2$$

$$\bullet SO_2 + O_2 = SO_3 + O$$

$$SO_2 + O = SO_3$$

$$SO_3 + H_2O = H_2SO_4$$

The reaction in cloud-droplets appears to yield the bisulfite and sulfite.

$$SO_2(g) + H_2O = SO_2(aq)$$

$$SO_2(aq) + H_2O = H_3O^+ + HSO_3^-$$

$$HSO_3^- + H_2O = H_3O^+ + SO_3^{2-}$$

The sulfate can be oxidized by atmospheric oxygen, and this process is catalyzed by metal ions such as Cu^{2+} and Fe^{3+}.

$$2SO_3^{2-} + O_2 = 2SO_4^{2-}$$

Other oxidizing agents are also present; for example, O_3 and H_2O_2.

$$HSO_3^- + O_3 = HSO_4^- + O_2$$

$$SO_3^{2-} + H_2O_2 = SO_4^{2-} + H_2O$$

Oxidation of NO_2 to nitric acid is quite fast (ca. 10% h^{-1}). Reactions with an OH radical or with ozone are as follows:

$$NO_2 + OH\cdot = HNO_3$$

$$NO_2 + O_3 = NO_3 + O_2$$

$$NO_3 + NO_2 = N_2O_5$$

$$N_2O_5 + H_2O = 2HNO_3$$

HCl can be directly released from coal combustion ions. Through incineration all these chemical species have been modified by NH_3 in the atmosphere.

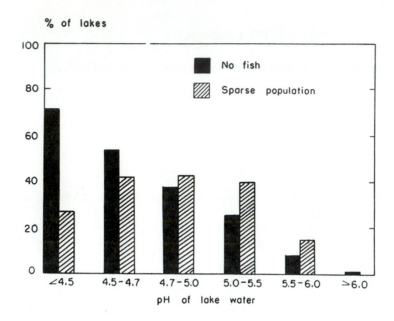

Figure 10-7.   Fish population declines as the acidity of lake water increases.

Hundreds of lakes in North America and Scandinavia have become so acidic that they can no longer support fish life. Figure 10-7 illustrates the relationship between the fish population and the acidity of lake water. Besides the aquatic effects of acid precipitation, the yield from agricultural crops can be reduced as a result of both the direct effects of acids on foliage and the indirect effects resulting from the leaching of minerals from soils. The productivity of forests may be affected in a similar manner. The leachate of heavy metals (e.g., Al) to lakes or rivers is one of the causes of fish being unable to survive. In this case, the presence of Al^{+3} in water is toxic to fish due to the reaction of minerals therein with low pH level.

10.4 GROUNDWATER

Groundwater is water that has percolated downward from ground surface through the soil pores. Formations of soil and rock (porous media) that have become saturated with water are known as groundwater reservoirs or aquifers. Water is withdrawn from aquifers by wells. One of the giant aquifers in the United States is called Ogallalo aquifer which underlies parts of 8 states. In some parts the rate of water use is 2 to 3 order of magnitude greater than rate of water discharge. In some parts of this aquifer, contamination has been found of salts that have been exploited from agriculture production.

10.4.1 Aquifer

Subsurface water occurs in two different zones: the upper zone has both air and water filling the cracks and pores between particles of soil and rock, whereas the lower zone is filled with water only. As indicated in Figure 10-8, the upper zone is termed the **unsaturated zone (vadose zone)**, which contains vadose water, while the lower zone is called the **saturated zone**, which contains groundwater. The vadose water is not available for use; on the contrary, the groundwater supplies most of our drinking water. Between the two layers there is a transition region called the capillary fringe, and just above the groundwater is the water table. Usually, an unconfined aquifer is only restricted in the bottom by the presence of a confining bed or layer. If the aquifer is restricted in both the top and bottom with the confining layers, then it is termed a **confined aquifer**, as shown in Figure 10-9. The confining layers can be referred to as **aquitards** or **aquicludes**. Sometimes water can also be located in the unsaturated zone; this is trapped water and it is usually referred to as a **perched water table**. The water level in an artesian well, which is levelled to the recharge area, is termed the **piezometric surface** or the **potentiometric surface**.

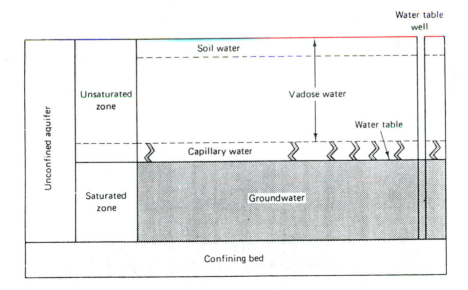

Figure 10-8. An unconfined aquifer is made up of saturated and unsaturated zones. A well penetrating the saturated zone would have water at the level of water table.

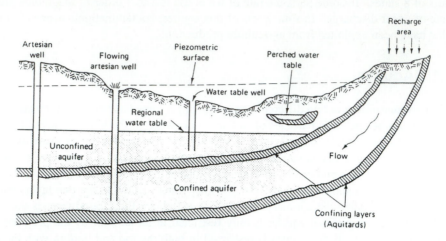

Figure 10-9.   A confined aquifer and artesian wells.

Porosity is defined as the ratio of the volume of voids to the total volume of the aquifer rock. The specific yield or the specific porosity is a true measure of the amount of water that can be drained out from the aquifer rock. In an unconfined aquifer, the **specific yield** is the volume of water available per unit area per unit decline in water table. This value is equivalent to the storage coefficient of a confined reservoir.

The **hydraulic gradient** for an unconfined aquifer is defined as the slope of the water table or the piezometric surface. In a microscopic sense, it is the change in head divided by the change in horizontal distance, or

$$dh/dL \qquad\qquad\qquad [10\text{-}10]$$

If one knows the difference in the heads of the two wells, one can predict the direction of flow.

10.4.2   Darcy's Law and Groundwater Movement

Darcy's law states that the flow rate is proportional to the cross sectional area times the hydraulic gradient

$$Q = KA \frac{dh}{dL} \qquad\qquad\qquad [10\text{-}11]$$

where

Q = the flow or the gross discharge and

$$Q = qA \quad (L^3/T) \qquad \text{[10-11A]}$$

and
q = Darcy velocity (L^3/L^2T)
A = cross-sectional area (L^2)
K = hydraulic conductivity (L/T)

Sometimes,

$$dh/dL = (\phi_1 - \phi_2)/L = \text{hydraulic gradient} \qquad \text{[10-11B]}$$

and

ϕ = hydraulic potential (L)
L = length (L)

The hydraulic potential (ϕ) can be expressed as

$$\phi = z + P/\rho g \qquad \text{[10-12]}$$

(see Bernoulli equation in Equation [10-65] in Section 10.4.3)
where

z = depth (L)
P = hydrostatic pressure $(M/L^{-1}T^{-2})$
ρ = density of fluid (M^3/L)

Thus

$$q = K(P_1 - P_2)/\rho g L \quad \text{for } z_1 = z_2 \qquad \text{[10-13]}$$

Often Darcy's law is used to measure the **permeability** of the medium (either soil or rock). In this case, the equation is written as

$$q = \frac{k}{\eta} \frac{dP}{L} \qquad \text{[10-14]}$$

where

k = intrinsic permeability of the medium (L^2)

η = viscosity of the fluid (M/LT)

v = kinetic viscosity of the fluid (L^2/T)

Thus

$$K = \frac{\rho g L q}{(P_1 - P_2)} = \frac{\rho g k}{\eta} = \frac{kg}{v}$$
[10-15]

For example, the viscosity of water at 20°C is 1 cp (0.01 g/cm sec)

$$g = 980 \text{ cm/sec}^2$$

$$k/K = 10^{-5} \text{ (cm sec)}$$
[10-16]

A confirmation of hydraulic conductivity (K) and permeability (k) can be found in Figure 10-10.

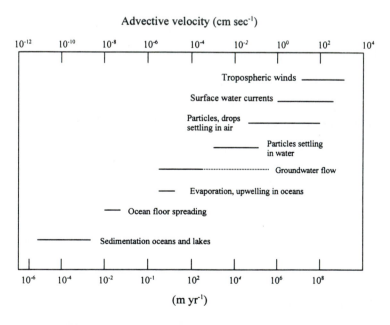

Figure 10-10.   Characteristic velocities associated with major transport processes near the Earth's surface.

In fluid mechanics a well-known equation for tube flow called the **Poiseuille equation** is

$$u = \frac{1}{8} \frac{d\rho}{\eta dz} a^2$$

[10-17]

where a is the tube radius, z is the streamwise direction, and m is the **hydraulic radius,** which is

$$m = \frac{\text{cross - sectional area of tube}}{\text{wetted perimeter of tube}}$$

[10-18]

For cylindrical tube of radius a, $m = \pi a^2 / 2\pi a = a/2$. Assuming $k_0 = 2$ the generalized Poiseuille equation becomes

$$u = \frac{m^2}{k_0 \eta} \frac{\Delta P}{L_e}$$

[10-19]

In Equation [10-19], because $\Delta P / L_e = dp/dz$, $\Delta P / L_e$ can be expressed as pressure gradient. In a real aquifer for porous media, the flow is random and the m value can be estimated as

$$m = \frac{\text{void volume}}{\text{wetted surface of porous medium}} = \frac{\phi V}{V(1-\phi)S_o}$$

[10-20]

Here ϕ is **porosity** (ratio of voids/total volume), V is volume of porous medium, and S_0 is specific surface of the porous medium.

$$S_o = \frac{\text{porous medium surface area}}{\text{unit volume of porous medium solids}}$$

[10-21]

Furthermore, Darcy velocity is assuming the media have 100% porosity. The actual velocity often is higher due to the solid portion in the medium. Thus the actual velocity, u (cm/ sec), is

$$u = \frac{q}{\phi}$$

[10-22]

Substituting this equation and the equation for the definition of m [Eq. 10-18] into the generalized Poiseuille equation [Eq. 10-19], then

$$q = \frac{1}{k_o \eta} \frac{d^3}{S_0^2 (1-\phi)^2} \frac{\Delta P}{L_e}$$

[10-23]

L here is the length of one of the average twisted flow tubes in aquifer. We would prefer to consider overall thickness of the sections of porous medium. Thus we add a constant

$$K' = \frac{L_e}{L} k$$

[10-24]

where L is the length of porous medium section and K' is Kozeny constant. After substitution

$$q = \frac{\phi^3}{K' \eta S_0^2 (1-\phi)^2} \frac{\Delta P}{L}$$

[10-25]

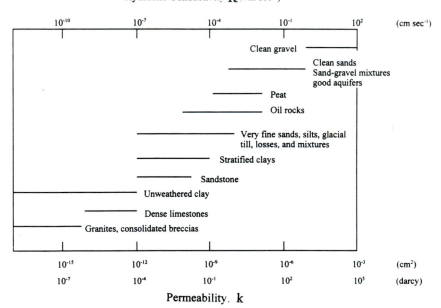

Figure 10-11.   The coefficients of hydraulic conductivity and permeability of sediments and rocks.

This is called the **Carman-Kozeny equation**. Finally, if we compare this equation with Darcy's law equation, then we have an equation for the permeability

$$k = \frac{\phi^3}{K'S_0^2 (1-\phi)^2}$$

[10-26]

Thus the Poiseuille equation and the Darcy's equation are connected through the definition of permeability.

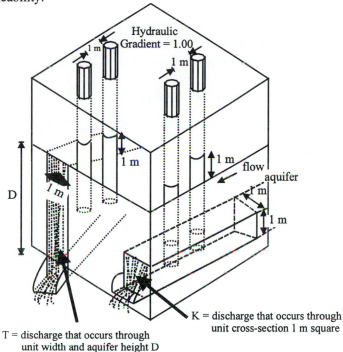

Figure 10-12. Illustration of definition of permeability (K) and transmissibility (T). (Source: Johnson Division. UOP. *Ground Water and Wells.*)

Figure 10-10 gives the characteristic velocities associated with major transport processes near the earth's surface. The advective velocity of groundwater flow ranges from 10^{-6} to 10^{-1} cm/sec. Figure 10-11 illustrates some of the coefficients of the hydraulic conductivity and permeability of sediments and rock. It can easily be found that the ratio of the permeability to the hydraulic conductivity is about 10^{-5} cm/sec as previously mentioned. **Transmissibility** (*T*) is also a convenient parameter to use. The detailed definitions of hydraulic conductivity (*K*) and *T* are illustrated in Figure 10-12. The mathematical relationship between *K* and *T* is

$$T = KD \qquad\qquad [10\text{-}27]$$

where D is the saturated thickness of the aquifer.

[Example 10-1]   For an artesian aquifer in the coastal region of Florida, the vertical drop is 10 m over a distance of 100 Km. Find the residence time of the water in this 100 Km long aquifer where the average porosity of the medium is 30%.

The hydraulic gradient $= \Delta\phi/L = 10$ m/100 km $= 10^{-4}$
For a good aquifer, from Figure 10-5, $K = 10^{-1}$ cm/sec
Then $q = K\Delta\phi/L = (10^{-1}$ cm sec$^{-1})(3 \times 10^{7}$ sec yr$^{-1})(10^{-4}) = 300$ cm yr$^{-1} = 3$m yr^{-1}
$u = 3$m yr$^{-1}/30 = 10$m yr^{-1}
The residence time $= 10^{5}/10$m yr$^{-1} = 10{,}000$ yr.

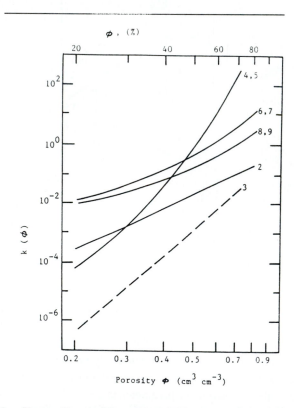

Figure 10-13.   Dependence of the permeability k on sediment porosity ϕ, according to the models listed in Table 10-3.

Permeability depends greatly on

- the grain size of the sediment, r,
- the sediment porosity (ratio of voids/ total volume), ϕ, and
- the packing arrangement of particles.

Table 10-3. Coefficient of Hydraulic Permeability k (cm^2 or Approximately 10^8 Darcy) as a Function of Sediment Porosity ϕ (Fraction) and Particle Radius r (cm)

Equation	Explanatory notes
1. $2.47 \times 10^{-19}\, r^2$	Krumbein and Monk (1942), sands, $0.005 < r < 0.1\,\text{cm}$.
2. $k = \text{constant} \times \phi^5$	Terzaghi (1925) in Rieke and Chilingarian (1974, p. 148), $0.2 < \phi < 0.8$.
3. $k \propto \phi^3 r^2$	Sands, from data of Bear and Weyl (1973); proportionality factor depends on ϕ $0.25 < \phi < 0.4$.
4. $k = 10^{-9} \left(\dfrac{\phi}{1-\phi} \right)^7$	Marine clayey sediments (Bryant et al., 1974).
5. $k = 7.25 \times 10^{-11} \left(\dfrac{\phi}{1-\phi} \right)^7$	Aragonitic sediment, $0.2 < \phi < 0.7$, from data of Robertson (1967). Original data also obey $\log K = 17.0 + 13.6$.
6. $k = \dfrac{\phi^3}{(1-\phi)^2} \times \dfrac{c_k}{S_s^2}$	The Carmen-Kozeny equation, where c_k is the Kozeny constant and S_s is the surface area of the pore space per unit volume of solid (Bear, 1972, p. 166). For beds made of spherical and cylindrical particles, see Equations 7, 8, and 9.
7. $k = \dfrac{\phi^3}{(1-\phi)^2} \times \dfrac{r^2}{45}$	Spherical particles, $c_k = 1/5$ and $S_s = 3/r$ (cm^{-1}) in Equation 6.
8. $k = \dfrac{-2\ln(1-\phi) + 4(1-\phi) - (1-\phi)^2 - 3}{1-\phi} \times \dfrac{r^2}{8}$	Circular cylinders, flow parallel to cylinder axis. R is cylinder radius. The Kozeny constant c_k given by Happel and Brenner (1973, p. 393). For straight circular cylinders, $S_s = 2/r$ (cm^{-1}) in Equation 6.
9. $k = \dfrac{-\ln(1-\phi) - \dfrac{1-(1-\phi)^2}{1+(1-\phi)^2}}{1-\phi} \times \dfrac{r^2}{8}$	Circular cylinders, flow perpendicular to cylinder axis, parameters as in Equations 8 and 6. For a random network of cylinders, Happel and Brenner (1973) recommend a weighted sum of k from Equations 8 and 9, in proportions of 2/3 and 1/3.

Many models have been proposed to correlate permeability with these parameters. Table 10-3 lists some of them, and Figure 10-13 shows the dependence of permeability k on sediment ϕ. Generally, the higher the porosity, the higher the permeability.

When a well is pumped, the water table (unconfined aquifer) or the piezometric surface (confined aquifer) forms a cone of depression in the vicinity of the well. Assuming the drawdown is small in comparison to the depth of the aquifer, and the flow to the well is horizontal and radial, then

$$Q = KA\frac{dh}{dr} = K2\pi rh\frac{dh}{dr} \qquad [10\text{-}28]$$

because the cross-sectional area is cylindrical around the well, then

$$\int_{r}^{r_1} Q\frac{dr}{r} = 2\pi K\int_{h}^{h_1} h\,dh$$

or

$$Q\ln\frac{r_1}{r} = \pi K\left(h_1^{\,2} - h^2\right)$$

or

$$Q = \frac{\pi K\left(h_1^{\,2} - h^2\right)}{\ln\left(\dfrac{r_1}{r}\right)} \qquad [10\text{-}29]$$

If $h = h_w$, which is the drawdown, then the drawdown can be calculated if the pumping rate, Q, is known.

10.4.3   Stream Function and Turbulent Flow

Some basic concepts of hydraulics and hydrodynamics are introduced here. A **path line** is the trace made by a single particle over a period of time in the flow of a liquid. The path line shows the direction of the particle's velocity. **Streamlines** show the mean direction of a number of particles at the instant of time. A series of curves being tangent to the means of the velocity vectors are streamlines. Path lines and streamlines are identical in the steady flow of a liquid in which there are no fluctuating velocity components. Such flow is either that of an ideal functionless fluid or of one so viscous that no eddies are formed. This is a

laminar type of flow. In contrast, another type of flow is a **turbulent** flow in which the path lines and streamlines are not coincident. The path lines are irregular while the stream-lines are everywhere tangent to the local mean temporal velocity. When a dye or a tracer is frequently injected into the flow to trace the motion of fluid particles, it is termed a **streak line** or a **filament line**.

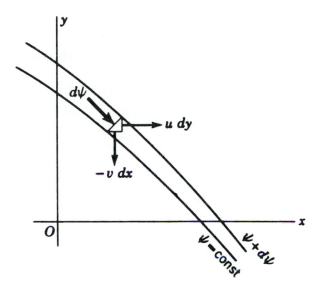

Figure 10-14.   Stream function.

A **stream function** Ψ, bored on the continuity prime cycle, is a mathematic expression of the **flow field**. In a two-dimensional case, let $\psi(x,y)$ be the streamline near the origin then $\psi + d\psi$ represents the second streamline. In Figure 10-14, $d\Psi$ will be the flow carried out between the two streamlines. For continuity, referring to the triangular fluid element, an incompressible fluid is

$$dy = -vdx + udy \qquad\qquad [10\text{-}30]$$

Also for $d\psi$

$$d\psi = \frac{\partial \psi}{\partial x}\,dx + \frac{\partial \psi}{\partial y}\,dy \qquad\qquad [10\text{-}31]$$

From these two equations, we note

$$u = \frac{\partial \psi}{\partial y}$$

$$v = -\frac{\partial \psi}{\partial x} \qquad \text{[10-32]}$$

Here u and v are velocity components at any point of a two-dimensional flow field. The equation of continuity may be expressed in terms of ψ

$$\frac{\partial u}{\partial x} + \frac{\partial v}{\partial z} = 0 \qquad \text{[10-33]}$$

then

$$\frac{\partial}{\partial x}\frac{\partial \psi}{\partial y} - \frac{\partial}{\partial z}\frac{\partial \psi}{\partial x} = 0 \qquad \text{[10-34]}$$

or

$$\frac{\partial^2 \psi}{\partial x \partial y} = \frac{\partial^2 \psi}{\partial z \partial x} \qquad \text{[10-35]}$$

There is also a velocity potential, ϕ, for the velocity vector

$$\nabla \phi = u \qquad \text{[10-36]}$$

or

$$u_i + v_j + w_k = \frac{\partial \phi}{\partial x} i + \frac{\partial \phi}{\partial y} j + \frac{\partial \phi}{\partial z} k$$

in two-dimensional space

$$u = \frac{\partial \phi}{\partial x}$$

$$v = \frac{\partial \phi}{\partial y}$$ [10-37]

For substituting the continuity equation into the preceding equation, we get the following:

$$\frac{\partial^2 \phi}{\partial x^2} + \frac{\partial^2 \phi}{\partial z^2} = 0$$ [10-38]

Also, there is a **vorticity** defined as the curl of velocity.

$$w = \nabla \times u$$ [10-39]

The solution of the preceding equation is by a determinant.

$$\nabla \times u = \begin{vmatrix} i & j & k \\ \frac{\partial}{\partial x} & \frac{\partial}{\partial y} & \frac{\partial}{\partial z} \\ u & v & w \end{vmatrix}$$ [10-40]

The solution for a two-dimension case is

$$d\omega = \left(\frac{\partial v}{\partial x} - \frac{\partial u}{\partial y} \right) dx dy$$ [10-41]

Substituting the velocity potential into the vorticity equation

$$\omega = \frac{\partial v}{\partial x} - \frac{\partial u}{\partial y} = \frac{\partial}{\partial x}\left(-\frac{\partial \phi}{\partial y} \right) - \frac{\partial}{\partial y}\left(-\frac{\partial \phi}{\partial x} \right)$$

$$= -\frac{\partial^2 \phi}{\partial x \partial y} + \frac{\partial^2 \phi}{\partial y \partial x} = 0$$ [10-42]

There is no vorticity, and flow is irrotational. This type of flow is termed **potential flow**.

The **streamline function** is

$$d\psi = \frac{\partial \psi}{\partial x} dx + \frac{\partial \psi}{\partial y} dy \qquad [10\text{-}43]$$

and the velocity potential is

$$d\phi = \frac{\partial \phi}{\partial x} dx + \frac{\partial \phi}{\partial y} dy \qquad [10\text{-}44]$$

Using velocity components u and v

$$d\psi = -vdx + udy \qquad [10\text{-}45]$$

$$d\phi = -udx - vdy \qquad [10\text{-}46]$$

Along a streamline ψ = constant and $d\psi = 0$

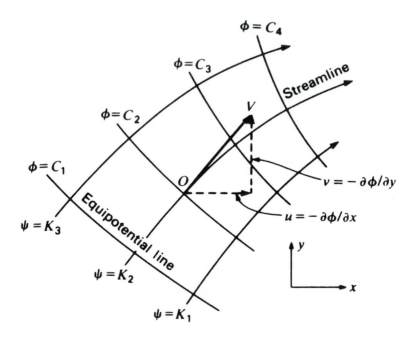

Figure 10-15.   Flow net.

$$\frac{dy}{dx} = \frac{v}{u} \qquad\qquad [10\text{-}47]$$

and along an **equipotential line**, shown in Figure 10-15, ϕ = constant and $d\phi = 0$.

$$\frac{dy}{dx} = -\frac{u}{v} \qquad\qquad [10\text{-}48]$$

The streamlines and equipotential lines are orthogonal, which are perpendicular to each other. In this manner, ϕ and ψ are required to form an orthogonal network for forming a **flow net** provided irrotationality (condition for ϕ) and continuity (condition for ψ) are satisfied.

[Example 10-2]   A flow is defined as $u = 2x$ and $v = -2y$. Find the stream function and potential function for this flow and plot the flow net.

Check for continuity.

$$\frac{\partial u}{\partial x} + \frac{\partial v}{\partial y} = 2 - 2 = 0$$

It is now possible to have a stream function

$$d\psi = -v\,dx + u\,dz = 2y\,dx + 2x\,dy$$

$$\psi = 2xz + c_1$$

Check for irrotationality.

$$\frac{\partial v}{\partial x} - \frac{\partial u}{\partial y} = 0 - 0 = 0$$

Therefore a potential function exists

$$d\phi = -u\,dx - v\,dy = -2x\,dx + 2y\,dy$$

$$\phi = -\left(x^2 - y^2\right) + c_2$$

Given numerical values of ψ and ϕ curves can be drawn as depicted by Figure 10-16. (Only one quadrant is shown.)

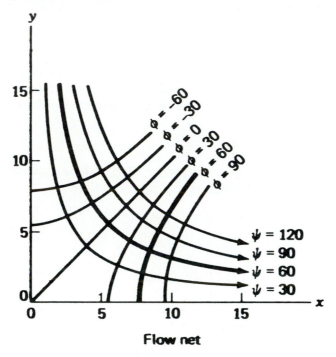

Flow net

Figure 10-16.   Graph for the Example 10-2. (Only one quadrant is shown here).

We now can summarize some relations as follows:

$$\nabla \cdot u = 0 \qquad\qquad [10\text{-}49]$$

The preceding equation represents the **continuity** equation

$$\nabla \times u = \omega = 0 \qquad\qquad [10\text{-}50]$$

which represents no vorticity, and its flow is **irrotational**

$$\nabla \phi = u \qquad\qquad [10\text{-}51]$$

which represents the **velocity potential**. It can be seen from the preceding equations that

$$\nabla \cdot u = \nabla \cdot \nabla \phi = \nabla^2 \phi = 0 \qquad [10\text{-}52]$$

which represents the **Laplace equation**. Now, if we take the steady state of the Euler equation

$$u \cdot \nabla u = -\frac{1}{P} \nabla P + g \qquad [10\text{-}53]$$

Using a scalar field of g

$$g = \nabla G$$

and

$$G = -gZ \qquad [10\text{-}54]$$

Thus

$$u \cdot \nabla u = -\frac{1}{\rho} \nabla P + \nabla G \qquad [10\text{-}55]$$

From vector algebra identity

$$u \cdot \nabla u = \nabla(\frac{1}{2} u \cdot u) - u \times (\nabla \times u) \qquad [10\text{-}56]$$

Therefore, from the righthand side

$$\nabla(\frac{1}{2} u \cdot u) - u \times \omega = -\frac{1}{\rho} \nabla P + \nabla G \qquad [10\text{-}57]$$

When evaluating along a streamline in the flow, the pressure gradient term can be expressed as

$$\frac{1}{\rho} \nabla p = \nabla \left(\int \frac{dP}{\rho} \right) \qquad [10\text{-}58]$$

or

$$\nabla\left(\int\frac{dP}{\rho}+\frac{1}{2}u\cdot u-G\right)=u\times\omega \qquad\qquad [10\text{-}59]$$

To form a dot product of both sides

$$u\cdot\nabla\left(\int\frac{dP}{\rho}+\frac{1}{2}u\cdot u-G\right)=u\cdot\left(u\times\omega\right) \qquad\qquad [10\text{-}60]$$

Therefore

$$u\cdot\nabla\left(\int\frac{dP}{\rho}+\frac{1}{2}u\cdot u-G\right)=0 \qquad\qquad [10\text{-}61]$$

and it follows that

$$\int\frac{dP}{\rho}+\frac{1}{2}u\cdot u-G=\text{constant along a streamline} \qquad\qquad [10\text{-}62]$$

or

$$\frac{P}{\rho}+\frac{U^2}{2}+gZ=\text{constant along a streamline} \qquad\qquad [10\text{-}63]$$

This equation is the **Bernoulli equation** for the irrotational flow where P, U, and Z are the variables. Alternatively the Bernoulli equation can be expressed as

$$\frac{P}{\delta}+\frac{U^2}{2g}+Z=\text{constant} \qquad\qquad [10\text{-}64]$$

because $\delta=\rho g$
Another way to express the Bermoulli equation is

$$H=\frac{P}{\gamma}+Z+\frac{U^2}{2g} \qquad\qquad [10\text{-}65]$$

P/γ is **pressure head**, representing the energy per unit weight stored in the fluid by virtue of the pressure; Z is **elevation head**, representing the potential energy per unit weight of fluid; and, $u^2/2g$ is the **velocity head**, representing the kinetic energy per unit weight of fluid. The sum of the three terms, which all have the dimension of (L), is termed the **total head**, H. For a frictionless incompressible fluid with no machine between 1 and 2.

$$H_1 = H_2 \qquad [10\text{-}66]$$

For a real fluid

$$H_1 = H_2 + h_L \qquad [10\text{-}67]$$

where h_L is called the **head loss**. If there is a machine between 1 and 2, then

$$H_1 + h_m = H_2 + h_L \qquad [10\text{-}68]$$

where h_m is the energy head portion, contributed by a machine. If the machine is a pump, then $h_m = h_p$; if the machine is a turbine then $h_m = -h_t$, and the energy head has to be extracted.

Flow is not limited to a laminar flow, induct, or conduit and even along a flat plate. If there is a viscous sublayer, which will transfer a negative momentum to the overlying fluid, a nonuniformity in the x-direction will be developed, and eventually the flow will transform into a turbulent. This transformation from a laminar boundary layer, through a transition zone, to a turbulent boundary layer is depicted in Figure 10-17. Clark analyzed the turbulence problem and we will follow his presentation for the boundary layer. He begins with the x-component of Navier-Stokes equation of a two-dimensional flow.

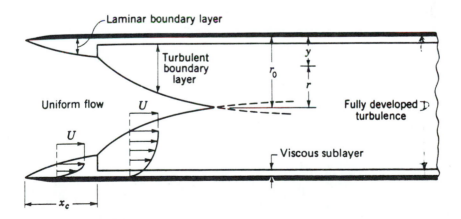

Figure 10-17.   Development of boundary layer in a pipe.

$$u\frac{\partial u}{\partial x} + v\frac{\partial u}{\partial y} = -\frac{\partial p}{\partial x} + v\left(\frac{\partial^2 u}{\partial x^2} + \frac{\partial^2 u}{\partial y^2}\right)$$ [10-69]

If the **boundary layer thickness**, δ, is thin, then the outside edge of the boundary layer, Δy, is small. And, accordingly, due to Bernoulli equation, $\Delta p = 0$; thus, one can drop the first term on the righthand side. Let us proceed with the component of the viscous terms. First, one wants to estimate the magnitude of individual relatives, u, when compared with the overall velocity, U. From Boolean algebra

$$u \subset (U)$$ [10-70]

which is along the x-direction. For along the y-direction

$$\frac{\partial u}{\partial y} \subset \left(\frac{U}{\delta}\right)$$ [10-71]

or the estimation of

$$\frac{\partial^2 u}{\partial y^2} \subset \left(\frac{U}{\delta^2}\right)$$ [10-72]

Also, for the x-direction

$$\frac{\partial u}{\partial x} \subset \left(\frac{U}{x}\right)$$ [10-71]

$$\frac{\partial^2 u}{\partial x^2} \subset \left(\frac{U}{x^2}\right)$$ [10-72]

Therefore

$$\frac{\dfrac{\partial^2 u}{\partial y^2}}{\dfrac{\partial^2 u}{\partial x^2}} \subset \frac{\dfrac{U}{\delta^2}}{\dfrac{U}{x^2}} \subset \left(\frac{x}{\delta}\right)^2$$ [10-73]

because x $\gg \delta$, for the majority of the boundary layers. Thus, the term $\partial^2 u / \partial x^2$ of the Navier-Stokes equation (Eq. 10-69) can be dropped. Hence, it becomes

$$u \frac{\partial u}{\partial x} + v \frac{\partial u}{\partial y} = v \frac{\partial^2 u}{\partial y^2} \qquad [10\text{-}74]$$

Also, the two-dimensional continuity equation

$$\frac{\partial u}{\partial x} + \frac{\partial v}{\partial y} = 0 \qquad [10\text{-}75]$$

which is the boundary-layer equation and the boundary conditions are

$$u = v = 0 \ at \ y = 0$$
$$u = U \ at \ y = \infty$$

Using the stream function, Equation [10-32], to substitute to Equation [10-74] we obtain

$$\frac{\partial \psi}{\partial \psi} \frac{\partial^2 \psi}{\partial x \partial y} - \frac{\partial \psi}{\partial x} \frac{\partial^2 \psi}{\partial y^2} = v \frac{\partial^3 \psi}{\partial y^3} \qquad [10\text{-}76]$$

A solution of Equation [10-76] can be obtained by transformation of variables.

$$\psi(x, y) = (v U x)^{\frac{1}{2}} g(\eta) \qquad [10\text{-}77]$$

and η, an independent variable, is

$$\eta = \frac{y}{2 \left(\dfrac{vx}{U} \right)^{\frac{1}{2}}} \qquad [10\text{-}78]$$

Now the following transforming relations (Eqs. 10-79 to 10-83) successively derived:

$$u = \frac{\partial \psi}{\partial y} = \frac{U}{2} g'(\eta) = \frac{U}{2} g' \qquad [10\text{-}79]$$

$$-v = \frac{\partial \psi}{\partial x} = \frac{1}{2}\left(\frac{vU}{x}\right)^{\frac{1}{2}}(g - \eta g')$$

[10-80]

$$\frac{\partial^2 \psi}{\partial x \partial y} = -\frac{U\eta}{4x}g''$$

[10-81]

$$\frac{\partial^2 \psi}{\partial y^2} = \frac{U}{4}\left(\frac{U}{vx}\right)^{\frac{1}{2}}g''$$

[10-82]

$$\frac{\partial \psi^3}{\partial y^3} = \frac{U^2}{8vx}g'''$$

[10-83]

Substituting the preceding relations into the differential equation, Equation [10-76],

$$g''' + gg'' = 0$$

[10-84]

This differential equation, Equation [10-84], can be solved with

$$g = g' = 0 \ \ at \ \ \eta = 0$$
$$g' = 2 \ \ \ at \ \ \eta = \infty$$

The numerical solutions are listed in Table 10-4. From the table $u < U$, initial $u \to U$, and $u/U = 1$. Now we can find boundary thickness layer $y = \delta$ and from Equation [10-78] we can derive the following

$$\frac{y}{x} = \frac{2\eta}{\left(\dfrac{Ux}{v}\right)^{\frac{1}{2}}} = \frac{2\eta}{(\text{Re}_x)^{\frac{1}{2}}} = \frac{\delta}{x}$$

[10-85]

Here, Re_x is **boundary layer Reynold number**

$$\text{Re}_x = \frac{Ux}{v}$$

[10-86]

We can calculate that as the boundary layer thickness decreases, the boundary layer Reynold number increases.

Another approach to turbulence flow is from the consideration of stress tension, τ_{ij}. The **shear stress** acting normal to the y-axis and in planes parallel to the x-axis is

$$\tau_{yx} = \mu\left(\frac{\partial Uy}{\partial x} + \frac{\partial Ux}{\partial y}\right) \qquad\qquad [10\text{-}87]$$

Table 10-4. Solution of Laminar Boundary Layer Problem

$\eta = \dfrac{y}{2}\sqrt{\dfrac{U}{vx}}$	g'	$\dfrac{u}{U}$	g''
0	0	0	1.32824
0.2	0.2655	0.1328	1.3260
0.4	0.5294	0.2647	1.3096
0.6	0.7876	0.3938	1.2664
0.8	1.0336	0.5168	1.1867
1.0	1.2596	0.6298	1.9670
1.2	1.4580	0.7290	0.9124
1.4	1.6230	0.8115	0.7360
1.6	1.7522	0.8761	0.5565
1.8	1.8466	0.9233	0.3924
2.0	1.9110	0.9555	0.2570
2.2	1.9518	0.9759	0.1558
2.4	1.9756	0.9878	0.0875
2.6	1.9885	0.9943	0.0454
2.8	1.9950	0.9962	0.0217
3.0	1.9980	0.9990	0.0096
3.2	1.9992	0.9996	0.0039
3.4	1.9998	0.9999	0.0015
3.6	1.9999	1.0000	0.0005
3.8	2.0000	1.0000	0.0002
4.0	2.0000	1.0000	0.0000
5.0	2.0000	1.0000	0.0000

Source: Modified from Welty, Wicks, and Wilson, *Fundamentals of Momentum, Heat, and Mass Transport*, p. 173, 1976.

Because there is velocity in the y-direction

$$\tau_{yx}|_{y=0} = \mu \frac{\partial Ux}{\partial y}|_{y=0} \qquad \text{[10-88]}$$

From Equation [10-79],

$$\frac{\partial u}{\partial y} = \frac{U}{4}\left(\frac{U}{vx}\right)^{\frac{1}{2}} g'' \qquad \text{[10-89]}$$

or

$$\tau_{yx}|_{y=0} = \frac{\mu U}{4}\left(\frac{U}{vx}\right)^{\frac{1}{2}} g''|_{y=0} = \frac{\mu U}{4}\left(\frac{U}{vx}\right)^{\frac{1}{2}} g''(0)$$

Now $g''(0)$ can be obtained from Table 10-4 as $g''(0) = 1.32824$, or

$$\tau_{yx}|_{y=0} = 0.322 \mu U\left(\frac{U}{vx}\right)^{\frac{1}{2}}$$

$$= 0.332\rho\, U^2\left(\frac{v}{Ux}\right)^{\frac{1}{2}}$$

$$= 0.332\rho\, U^2 \text{Re}_x^{-\frac{1}{2}} \qquad \text{[10-90]}$$

The **skin-friction drag coefficient** for the flat plate is

$$f_f = \frac{\tau_{yx}|_{y=0}}{\frac{1}{2}\rho U^2} = 0.664\, \text{Re}_x^{-\frac{1}{2}} \qquad \text{[10-91]}$$

This is also referred to as the **Fanning friction factor** or **pipe-function factor** if flow is in cylindrical conduits. The shear stress at the boundary as expressed in Equation [10-89] is a function of U^2 and, hence, it is possible to adopt a **shear velocity,** $U*$

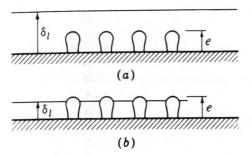

Figure 10-18. Turbulent flow near boundary. (a) Relatively low R, $\delta_l > e$. If $\delta_l > 6e$ pipe behaves as a smooth pipe. (b) Relatively high R, $\delta_l < e$. If $\delta_l < 0.3e$ pipe behaves as a wholly rough pipe.

$$U* = \left(\frac{\tau_0}{\rho}\right)^{\frac{1}{2}}$$ [10-92]

The shear velocity is related to the eddy diffusity of momentum ν_t by

$$\nu_t = \kappa U * Z$$ [10-93]

Here, κ is the von Kámán constant. Large eddies and swirls are responsible for disturbed flow that typifies turbulent flow. Roughness in a pipe usually is defined by a **roughness height**, e, which can be illustrated as in Figure 10-18. If the boundary thickness is lower than e, then the pipe is rough; on the other hand, if the boundary thickness is much higher than e, then it is a smooth pipe. A **friction factor**, f, is generally used, in practice.

$$f = 4 f_f$$ [10-94]

For the three regions in relation of roughness

- Smooth-pipe flow, $\delta > 6e$

$$f^{-1/2} = 2 \log \mathrm{Re}\ f^{1/2} - 0.8$$

- Transitional flow, $6e > \delta > 0.3e$

$$f^{-1/2} = -2 \log \left(\frac{e/D}{3.7} + \frac{2.51}{\mathrm{Re}}\ f^{-1/2}\right)$$

- Rough-pipe flow, $\delta < 0.3e$

$$f^{-1/2} = 2 \log \frac{D}{e} + 1.14$$

[10-95]

(D is diameter of the pipe)

A **Moody diagram**, as Figure 10-19, is useful for the estimation of e, and one can use Table 10-5. The shear velocity also can separate the three regions.

- Hydraulically smooth regime

$$0 \leq \frac{eu_*}{\nu} \leq 5$$

- Transition regime

$$5 \leq \frac{eu_*}{\nu} \leq 70$$

Table 10-5. Values of Absolute Roughness e for New Pipes

	Feet	Millimeters
Drawn tubing, brass, lead, glass, centrifugally spun cement, bituminous lining, transite	0.000005	0.0015
Commercial steel or wrought iron	0.00015	0.046
Welded-steel pipe	0.00015	0.046
Asphalt-dipped cast iron	0.0004	0.12
Galvanized iron	0.0005	0.15
Cast iron, average	0.00085	0.25
Wood stave	0.0006 to 0.003	0.18 to 0.9
Concrete	0.001 to 0.01	0.3 to 3
Riveted steel	0.003 to 0.03	0.9 to 9

Note: $\dfrac{e}{D} = \dfrac{e\ in\ feet}{D\ in\ feet} = \dfrac{e\ in\ mm}{D\ in\ mm} = 10^{-1} \times \dfrac{e\ in\ mm}{D\ in\ cm}$

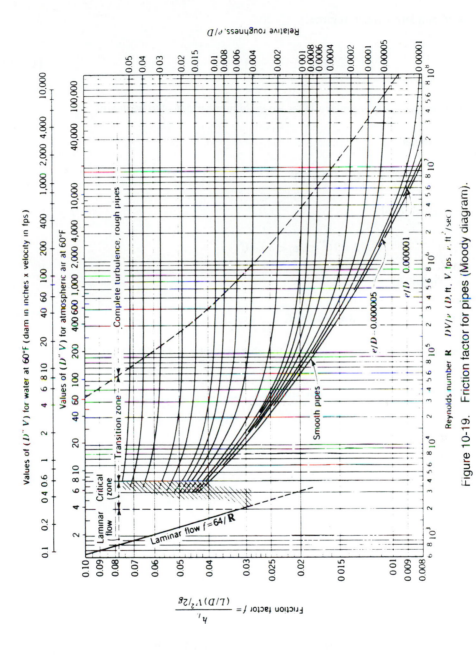

Figure 10-19. Friction factor for pipes (Moody diagram).

- Completely rough regime

$$\frac{eu_*}{v} \geq 70 \qquad\qquad\qquad\qquad [10\text{-}96]$$

Furthermore, the boundary-layer Reynold number can also be useful

- Laminar

$$\mathrm{Re}_x < 2 \times 10^5$$

- Transitional

$$2 \times 10^5 < \mathrm{Re}_x < 3 \times 10^6$$

- Turbulent

$$\mathrm{Re}_x > 3 \times 10^6 \qquad\qquad\qquad\qquad [10\text{-}97]$$

Another way for differentiating the three regions is shown in Figure 10-20. In this case,

$$U^+ = \frac{U_z}{U_*}$$

$$Y^+ = \frac{YU_*}{v}$$

- Viscous sublayer

$$U^+ = Y^+ \text{ for } Y^+ \leq 5$$

- Generation region

$$U^+ = 5.0 \ln Y^+ - 3.05 \text{ for } 5 < Y^+ < 30$$

- Turbulent region

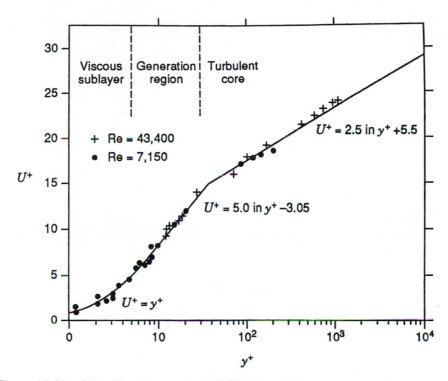

Figure 10-20.   Velocities above a smooth flat plate showing universal velocity laws. High and low Re data are used from M.M. Clark, *Transport Modeling for Environmental Engineers and Scientists*, Wiley-Interscience, 1996. Permission obtained from John Wiley.

$$U^+ = \kappa^{-1}\ln Y^+ + 5.5 \text{ for } Y^+ > 30 \qquad\qquad [10\text{-}98]$$

These **logarithmic laws** also can be modified for applications to a number of environmental problems, such as rivers, streams, ocean bottom surfaces, and various Earth surfaces. We define a roughness length, Z_0, for the surfaces, as shown in Table 10-6.

$$Z_0 = \frac{e}{30} \qquad\qquad [10\text{-}99]$$

The velocity distribution in turbulent regions can be given by a **universal logarithmic law.**

Table 10-6.   Roughness Lengths for Various Surfaces

Surface	Z_o (m)
Very smooth (e.g., ice)	10^{-5}
Snow	10^{-3}
Smooth sea	10^{-3}
Level desert	10^{-3}
Lawn	10^{-2}
Uncut grass	0.05
Fully grown root crops	0.1
Tree covered	1
Low-density residential	2
Central business district	5-10

Source: Seinfeld, Atmospheric Chemistry and Physics of Air Pollution, p. 495, 1986. Reprinted with permission of John Wiley & Sons, Inc.

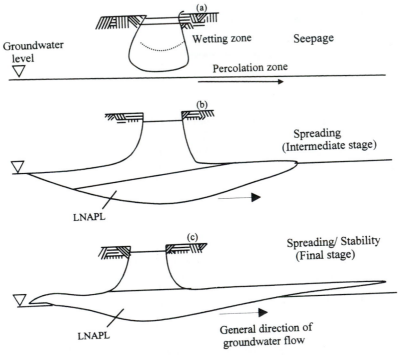

Figure 10-21.   Stages of subsurface hydrocarbon migration (as approved in Proc. Nat. Water Well Assn. 2nd Canadian/American Conf. on Hydrogeology, Bauff, Alberta, 1985, pp. 31-35).

$$U^+ = \frac{1}{\kappa}\ln\frac{y}{z_0} \quad \text{for } y \geq z_0 \qquad [10\text{-}100]$$

Real laminar and turbulent flow always evolve boundary layers. The universal logarithmic law will be suitable for data obtained regardless by pipes or flat plates. Furthermore both velocity and distance are dimensionless. For low Reynolds number flows, environmental problems such as drag on a place or transport through porous media will have applications.

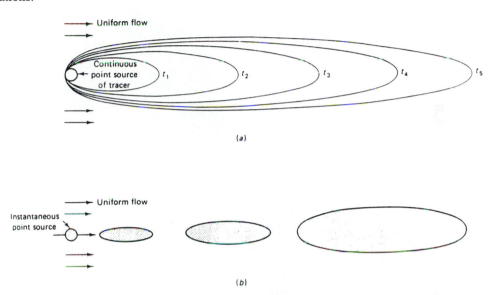

(a)

(b)

Figure 10-22. Spreading of a tracer in two-dimensional uniform flow field in an isotropic sand: (a) continuous tracer feed with step function initial condition; (b) instantaneous point source. (Source: Freeze/Cherry, *Groundwater*, 1979, p. 394. Reprinted by permission of Prentice Hall, Inc., Englewood Cliffs, New Jersey.)

10.4.4 Hydrodynamic Control for Contaminant Plume

When a toxic substance enters the groundwater, a complex situation exists. Even taking the simple case, the toxicant can be in the suspended particulates or in the dissolved form. As shown in Figure 10-21, both can also be in the sediments, either as sediment particulates or in the form of entering interstitial water. Often the organic liquid will create multiphase flow problems. Often the **nonaqueous phase liquid** (NAPL) can be separated into two different classes: one is light in density, the **light nonaqueous phase liquid** (LNAPL) such as petroleum hydrocarbons; the other is heavy, called the **dense nonaqueous phase liquid**

(DNAPL) such as chlorine-containing hydrocarbons. The spreading of a tracer in a two-dimensional uniform flow filled in an isotopic sand will tend to give plumes that are elliptical in shape, because longitudinal dispersion is stronger than the transverse dispersion, as shown in Figure 10-22. In an actual field experiment, when a chloride tracer (Cl⁻) is co-injected with carbon tetrachloride (CTET) and perchloroethylene (PCE) into an aquifer, there are separations into different zones after 21 months as shown in Figure 10-23.

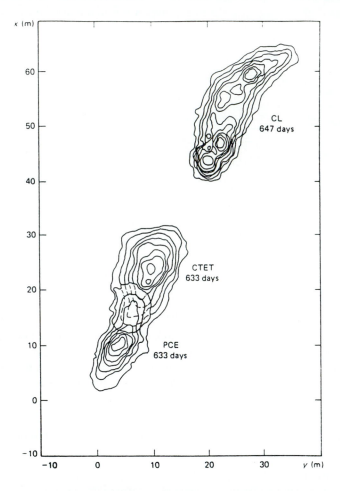

Figure 10-23.   Plume separation for chloride (Cl), carbon tetrachloride (CTET), and tetrachloroethylene (PCE) 21 months after injection into an actual aquifer. (Source: Roberts, Goltz, and MacKay, 1986. "A Natural Grade Experiment on Solute Transport in a Sand Aquifer, 3, Retardation Estimates and Mass Balances for Organic Solutes." *Water Resources Research* 22(13):2047-2058, The American Geophysical Union.)

Table 10-7. **(a)** Partition Coefficients for Octonol-Water (k_{ow}) and Organic Carbon-Water (K_{oc}). Estimation of K_{oc} from K_{ow} (After Karickhoff S. W., *Chemosphere*, 10, p. 833-846, 1981)

Compound	Log K_{ow}	Log K_{oc}	Compound	Log K_{ow}	Log K_{oc}
Hydrocarbons and chlorinated hydrocarbons			*Carbamates*		
3-methyl cholanthrene	6.42	6.09	Carbaryl	2.81	2.36
Dibenz(a,h) anthracene	6.50	6.22	Carboturan	2.07	1.46
7,12-dimethylbenz(a) anthracene	5.98	5.35	Chloropropham	3.06	2.77
Tetracene	5.90	5.81	*Organophosphates*		
9-methylanthracene	5.07	4.71			
Pyrene	5.18	4.83	Malathion	2.89	3.25
Phenathrene	4.57	4.08	Parathion	3.81	3.68
Anthracene	4.54	4.20	Methylparathion	3.32	3.71
Naphthalene	3.36	2.94	Chlorpyrifos	3.31	4.13
Benzene	2.11	1.78			
1,2-dichloroethane	1.45	1.51	*Phenyl ureas*		
1,1,2,2-tetracholroethane	2.39	1.90	Diuron	1.97	2.60
1,1,1-trichloroethane	2.47	2.25	Fenuron	1.00	1.43
Tetrachloroethylene	2.53	2.56	Linuron	2.19	2.91
γ HCH (lindane)	3.72	3.30	Monolinuron	1.60	2.30
α HCH	3.81	3.30	Monuron	1.46	2.00
β HCH	3.80	3.30	Fluometuron	4.34	2.24
1,2-dichlorobenzene	3.39	2.54	*Miscellaneous Compounds*		
pp'DDT	6.19	5.38			
Methoxychlor	5.08	4.90	13Hdibenzo(a,i) carbazole	6.40	6.02

Table 10-7.   **(a)** continued

22', 44', 66' PCB	6.34	6.08	2,2'biquinoline	4.31	4.02
22', 44', 55' PCB	6.72	5.62	Dibenzothiophene	4.38	4.05
			Acetophenone	1.59	1.54
Chloro-s-triazines					
			Terbacil	1.89	1.71
Atrazine	2.33	2.33	Bromacil	2.02	1.86
Propazine	2.94	2.56			
Simazine	2.16	2.13			
Trietazine	3.35	2.74			
Ipazine	3.94	3.22			
Cyanazine	2.24	2.26			

(b) Estimation of K_{oc} from K_{ow} by the Expression $\log K_{ow} = a\,\log K_{oc} + b$ (After Schwartzenbach R. P. and J. Westall, *Environ. Sci. Technol. 15*, p. 1360-1367, 1981)

Regression Coefficient		Correlation Coefficient	Number of Compounds	Type of chemical
a	b			
0.544	1.337	0.74	45	Agricultural chemicals
1.00	-0.21	1.00	10	Polycylic aromatic hydrocarbons
0.937	-0.006	0.95	19	Triazines, nitroanilines
1.029	-0.18	0.91	13	Herbicides, insecticides
1.00	-0.317	0.98	13	Heterocylic aromatic compounds
0.72	0.49	0.95	13	Chlorinated hydrocarbons and alkylbenzenes
0.52	0.64	0.84	30	Substituted phenyl ureas and alkyl-N-phenyl carbamates

This retardation of the transport of most organic compounds in aquifers is actually due to their solubility in water which can be predicted from the partition coefficients for octanol-water, K_{ow}, as shown in Figure 10-24 and Table 10-7. Generally, if the fraction of organic carbon in water is known (such as fulvic acids, humic acids, or humin), the distribution coefficient for the sediments can be evaluated.

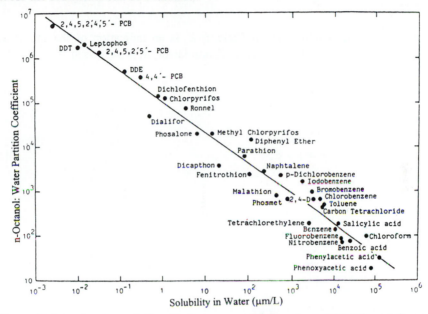

Figure 10-24.   Log-log relationship between solubility of a number of organic compounds and their octonol/water distribution (or partition) coefficient. (After G. Gambolati and G. Verri, *Advanced Methods of Groundwater Pollution Control*, Springer Verlag, Berlin, 1995.)

$$K_d' = K_{oc} f_{oc} \qquad\qquad [10\text{-}102]$$

where K_d' is the distribution coefficient, and

$$K_d' = s/C \qquad\qquad [10\text{-}103]$$

where s is adsorbed concentration in mg/kg dry soil or ppm, and C is the concentration in water in mg/L. A scaled expression of K_d' is

$$K_d = \frac{q}{C} = \frac{\rho_b s}{\phi C} = \frac{\rho_b}{\phi} K_d' \qquad\qquad [10\text{-}104]$$

where ρ_b is the bulk density of the sediments, ϕ is the porosity of the sediment here, and q is the adsorbed concentration expressed in mg/L of the porewater. The conversion factor is

$$\frac{\rho_b}{\phi} = 6 \text{ kg/L} \qquad [10\text{-}105]$$

This **corrected distribution coefficient**, K_d is an indication of the movement of a given compound in aquifer. Usually a retardation factor, R, is expressed as

$$K_d = 6K_d'$$

and

$$R = 1 + K_d \qquad [10\text{-}106]$$

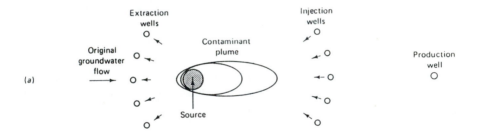

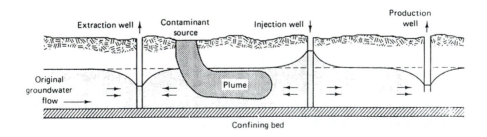

Figure 10-25.   Hydrodynamic control with injection wells and extraction wells to protect a production well. (a) plan view; (b) cross-section. (After Masters)

[Example 10-3] Calculate the retardation of lindane and of PCB in groundwater flow in a sediment containing 0.3% organic matter.

In Table 10-7, the K_{oc} of lindane = $10^{3.3}$
or

$$\log K_d' = 3.3 + \log 0.003 = 0.8$$

$$K_d' = 6.3 \text{ mL/g}$$

$$K_d = (6.3)(6) \cong 38$$

Similarly, for PCB

$$\log K_d' = 5.6 + \log 0.003 = 3.1$$

$$K_d' = 1200 \text{ mL/g and } K_d = 7200$$

Thus, lindane moves 40 times slower and PCB moves 7,200 times slower than water velocity.

The manipulation of hydraulic gradients for the control and removal of a groundwater plume is termed **hydrodynamic control**. A method to protect a production well (for drinking water use) from the approaching of a moving plume is to place a row of injection wells between the plume and the production well, as shown in Figure 10-25. The extraction well is used to remove the contaminants in the plume (which usually have to go through a treatment facility), and then use the purified water to reinject through the rows of injection wells.

Extraction wells should be placed closer to the head of the plume within the capture zone. The **capture zone** is the region within which all the flow lines converge on the extraction well (flow net). As shown in Figure 10-26, the envelope surrounding the capture zone can be calculated out as

$$y = \pm \frac{Q}{2Bq} - \frac{Q}{2\pi Bq} \tan^{-1}\left(\frac{y}{x}\right) \qquad \qquad [10\text{-}107]$$

where B is aquifer thickness and

$$\tan\phi = \frac{y}{x}$$

Hence, for $0 \le \phi \le 2\pi$,

$$y = \frac{Q}{2Bq}\left(1 - \frac{\phi}{\pi}\right) \qquad [10\text{-}108]$$

For $x \rightarrow \infty$, $\phi = 0$, $y = Q/2Bq$; thus the maximum total width of the capture zone = $2(Q/2Bq) = Q/Bq$. For $\phi = \pi/2$, $x = 0$, $y = Q/4Bq$; thus, the width of the capture zone to the y-axis = $Q/2Bq$.

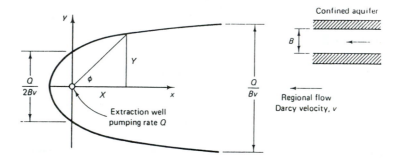

Figure 10-26. Capture-zone-type curve for a single extraction well located at the origin in an aquifer with regional flow velocity v and thickness B, and pumping at the rate Q. (Based on Javandel and Tsang, 1986.)

10.4.5   Chemical Restoration of Contaminated Aquifers

The conventional method for containment of contaminant plumes is to construct a wall of impermeable material surrounding the plume from the surface to the aquitord. The slurring cutoff wall or grout curtain is constructed with backfilled material consisting of a mixture of soil and bentonite. Such material is relatively impermeable, but cannot serve as a foolproof guarantee for impermeability by toxic substances. For all the geotechnical fabric material, Yen has used a biopolymer of the polyester type, poly β-hydroxybutyrate (PHB) and poly β-hydroxyvelerate (PHV) derived from common bacteria such as *Alcaligenes eutrophus*, which can be grown under anaerobic conditions in soil. According to laboratory experiments, the relative permeability has reduced down to 1 million fold. In this manner the source of pollution can be cut off by the biobarrier technique. Furthermore, zones that are relatively contaminated can be also isolated from the more concentrated ones if bioremediation is applied to the aquifer. This is termed **zonal bioremediation**. (For details please also see Chapter 29).

Besides pump-and-treat, **flushing** is considered a good method for aquifer cleanup. The method is based on the fact that the sediment can adsorb the molecules from the solution,

$$q = K_d C \qquad \text{[10-109]}$$

where

q = sorbed concentration (mass/L pore water)

K_d = distribution coefficient

C = solute concentration (mass/L pore water)

The overall change in concentration due to transport, dispersion, and sorption can be written as the following expression that

$$\left(\frac{\partial C}{\partial t}\right)_x = -u\left(\frac{\partial C}{\partial x}\right)_t + D_L\left(\frac{\partial^2 C}{\partial x^2}\right)_t - \left(\frac{\partial q}{\partial t}\right)_x \qquad \text{[10-110]}$$

Neglecting the term of dispersion of Equation [10-110]

$$\left(\frac{\partial C}{\partial t}\right)_x = -u\left(\frac{\partial C}{\partial x}\right)_t - \left(\frac{\partial q}{\partial t}\right)_x \qquad \text{[10-111]}$$

The second term of Equation [10-111] can be expressed as

$$\left(\frac{\partial q}{\partial t}\right)_x = \left(\frac{dq}{dC}\right)\left(\frac{\partial C}{\partial t}\right)_x \qquad \text{[10-112]}$$

After substitution into Equation [10-111], which can be written

$$\left(1 + \frac{dq}{dC}\right)\left(\frac{\partial C}{\partial t}\right)_x = -u\left(\frac{\partial C}{\partial x}\right)_t \qquad \text{[10-113]}$$

Now for $C(x,t)$ = constant, we have by definition

$$dC(x,t) = 0 = \frac{\partial C}{\partial x} dx + \frac{\partial C}{\partial t} dt$$

or

$$\left(\frac{\partial C}{\partial t} \right)_x = -\left(\frac{\partial C}{\partial x} \right)_t \left(\frac{\partial x}{\partial t} \right)_C \qquad \text{[10-114]}$$

Substitute Equation [10-114] to Equation [10-113], then

$$u = \left(\frac{\partial x}{\partial t} \right)_c \left(1 + \frac{\partial q}{\partial C} \right) \qquad \text{[10-115]}$$

then allow

$$u_{c_i} = \left(\frac{\partial x}{\partial t} \right)_C \qquad \text{[10-116]}$$

as the concentration of i's species, and then we obtain from Equation [10-115]

$$u_{c_i} = \frac{u}{1 + \left(\dfrac{dq}{dC} \right)} \qquad \text{[10-117]}$$

The pore-water flow velocity is inversely related to the pore volume of fixed length L from an aquifer to the flushed, or

$$\frac{u}{u_{c_i}} = \frac{V_{c_i}}{V_0} \qquad \text{[10-118]}$$

where

V_0 = pore volume of column with length L (m^3)
V_{c_i} = pore volume required to flush the column for C_i to arrive at L

Therefore, using Equation [10-117] we obtain

$$\frac{dq}{dC} = \frac{V_{C_i}}{V_0} - 1 \equiv V_{c_i}^*$$ [10-119]

There is a simple relationship between the slope of adsorption isotherm at C_i and the number of pore volumes that must flush the column to arrive at that concentration. Thus, $V_{c_i}^*$ is termed the **flushing factor**, as shown in Figure 10-27.

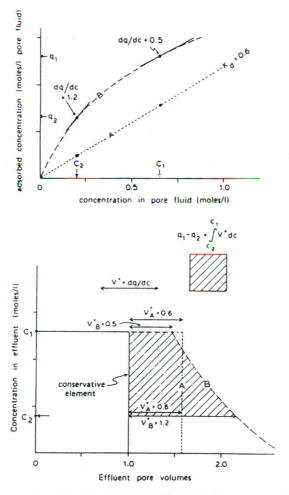

Figure 10-27.   Elution of chemicals with different desorption isotherms from a column: substance A with linear desorption isotherm, B with convex desorption isotherm (left), Isotherm effects on breakthrough curves. Desorption isotherm can be obtained by graphical integration as shown for B (right).

[**Example 10-4**]   Concentration of trichloroethylene (TCE) in groundwater is 10 mg/L in an aquifer. How many pore volumes need to be flushed in order that TCE concentration is below 1 mg/L? Assume that an approximate sorption isotherm is $q = 6 + 6 \ln C$.

Differentiation of the isotherm yields

$$\frac{dq}{dC} = \frac{6}{C_{TCE}} = V^*$$

and

$$V^*_{(c=1)} = 6$$

Thus, in order to meet the condition $V_t/V_0 = 1 + 6 = 7$, the pore volume of 7 times of the original has to be pumped out from the area to lower TCE. Also, $K_d = \frac{q}{C} \approx 1.4$ will give a much lower estimate. (See Equation 10-104)

REFERENCES

10-1.   T. G. Spiro, and W. M. Stigliani, *Environmental Issues in Chemical Perspective*, State University of New York Press, Albany, New York 1980.

10-2.   V. L. Snoeyink, and D. Jenkins, *Water Chemistry*, Wiley, New York, 1980.

10-3.   C. N. Sawyer, and P. L. McCarty, *Chemistry for Environmental Engineering*, McGraw-Hill, New York, 1978.

10-4.   W. Stumm, and J. J. Morgan, *Aquatic Chemistry*, Wiley, New York, 1981.

10-5.   G. E. Likens, "Acid Precipitation," C & EN, 22, 29 (1976).

10-6.   L. R. Ember, "Acid Pollutants: Hitchhiker Ride the Wind," C & EN, 20, Sept. 14 (1981).

10-7.   U.S. Environmental Protection Agency, "Acid Rain," EPA- 600/8-79-028, October (1979).

10-8.   A. Lerman, *Geochemical Process: Water and Sediment Environments*, Wiley, New York, 1979.

10-9.   G. Gambolati and G. Verri, *Advanced Methods for Groundwater Pollution Control*, Springer-Verlag, Berlin, 1995.

10-10. R. L. Daugherty, J. B. Franzini, and E. J. Finnemore, *Fluid Mechanics with Engineering Applications*, 8th ed., McGraw-Hill, New York, 1985.

10-11. M. M. Clark, *Transport Moderling for Environmental Engineers and Scientists*, Wiley, New York, 1996.

10-12. G. M. Fair, J. C. Geyer, and D. A. Okun, *Water and Wastemaker Engineering*, Vol. 1, *Water Supply and Wastewater Removal*, Wiley, New York, 1966.

10-13. G. M. Masters, *Introduction to Environmental Engineering and Science*, Prentice-Hall, Englewood Cliffs, New Jersey, 1991.

10-14. G. K. Batchelaor, *An Introduction to Fluid Mechanics*, Cambridge University Press, 1967.

10-15. L. H. Keith, *Energy and Environmental Chemistry, Acid Rain*, Vol. 2, Ann Arbor Science, Ann Arbor, Michigan, 1982.

10-16. J. A. Roberson and C. T. Crowe, *Engineering Fluid Mechanics*, 6th ed. Wiley, New York, 1997.

10-17. R. K. Linsely and J. B. Franzini, *Water Resources Engineering*, 3rd ed., McGraw-Hill, New York, 1978.

10-18. I. J. Higgins and R. G. Burns, *The Chemistry and Microbiology of Pollution*, Academic Press, London, 1975.

PROBLEM SET

1. Five hundred kilograms of n-propanol ($CH_3CH_2CH_2OH$) is accidentally discharged into a body of water containing 10^8 l. By how much is the BOD (in milligrams per liter) of this water increased? Assume the following reaction:

$$C_3H_8O + \frac{9}{2} O_2 \rightarrow 3 CO_2 + 4 H_2O$$

2. a) A lake with a cross-sectional area of 1 km$_2$ and a depth of 50 m has a euphatic zone that extends 15 m below the surface. What is the maximum weight of the biomass (in grams of carbon) that can be decomposed by aerobic bacteria in the region of the lake below the euphatic zone during the summer when there is no circulation with the upper layer? The reaction is

$$(CH_2O)_n + nO_2 \xrightarrow{\text{bacteria}} nCO_2 + nH_2O$$

The solubility of oxygen in pure water saturated with air is 8.9 mg/L; $m^3 = 1.0001$.

b) Sugarcane, one of the most efficient converters of photosynthetic energy, yields about 3,600 g carbon/m^2 per year. If the lake had the same level of productivity, how deep would it have to be to completely digest the biomass aerobically?

● ● ● ●

Ici venu, l'avenir est paresse.
L'insecte net gratte la sécheresse;
Tout est brûlé, défait, reçu dans l'air
À je ne sais quelle sévère essence...
La vie est vaste, étant ivre d'absence,
Et l'amertume est douce, et l'esprit clair.

Les morts cachés sont bien dans cette terre
Qui les réchauffe et sèche leur mystère.
Midi là-haut, Midi sans mouvement
En soi se pense et convient à soi-même...
Tête complète et parfait diadème,
Je suis en toi le secret changement.

● ● ● ●

These are two stanzas (lines 67–68) of Paul Valéry's celebrated poem "The Graveyard by the Sea." On the shores of the Mediterranean, Valéry lamented the dead and rejoiced in the transformation of the living by "Nirvana."

● ● ● ●

Now that I have come here, the future stretches out in idleness.
The sharp insect scrapes at the dryness of the ground;
All is burned, decomposed, resolved in the air
Into I know not what rarified essence...
Life is vast, being drunk with nothingness,
And bitterness is sweet, and the mind clear.

The hidden dead lie easy in this earth
Which warms them again and dries up their mystery.
Noon high above, motionless Noon
Within itself thinks itself and unto itself suffices...
O complete head and perfect diadem,
I am the secret change taking place in you.

● ● ● ●

CHAPTER 11

HYDROSPHERE — NATURAL WATER AND POLLUTION

*I*n this chapter, we will discuss various natural water systems; for example, oceans, estuaries and fjords, rivers and streams, and lakes. For the ocean, it is important to understand that it acts as the sink for weathered salts, the buffer for CO_2 and the Sillen's brake for atmospheric oxygen. The forms of estuaries and fjords are perfect examples of sediment traps in which minerals and petroleum are formed. Next, the self-purification of rivers and streams with the understanding of stream management or zoning is emphasized. The principle is guided by Gibb's diagram. Finally, the formation and life cycles of lakes are explored especially in reference to the eutrophication of nutrients, fertilizers, sewage, and industrial tailings. In general, the principles of marine and fresh water chemistry are the theme of this chapter. For the pollution of natural water systems, we will use the oil pollution in open waters and the tributyltin pollution in marine environments as examples.

11.1 CHEMICAL OCEANOGRAPHY

The Oceans represent a chemical system covering 71% of the Earth's surface and accounting for 77% of the water in the hydrogeological cycle, as discussed in Chapter 10. The massive body has an average depth of 33.7 km, whereas in deep sea this value will exceed 10 km. Seawater is a solution of gas and solids containing both organic and inorganic compounds. It is a well oxygenated solution and is buffered at pH = 8 containing almost all elements. It is considered as a sink for all the salts that are present in sediments from the weathering process of the lithosphere.

Thermodynamically, oceans form an open system where both energy and mass can be exchanged across the boundaries. They may be considered as a homogenous equilibrated system, yet this is an over-simplification. At best, oceans may be treated as a steady-state system. The major soluble elements in seawater are summarized in Table 11-1. Traditionally, those elements exhibiting concentrations greater than 1 mg/kg, with the exclusion of silicon are major soluble elements. When the ratios of the concentrations are found invariant with time and locations, the term **nonconservative** is employed, because concentration is governed by chemical and biological process only. **Salinity, S,** is defined as the total salt content; that is, the mass of the total dissolved solid expressed in g/kg or 0/00. The factor termed **chlorinity** (Cl 0/00) is determined by silver nitrate titration and cannot differentiate the halides present. The relationships can be expressed by

Table 11-1. The Major Elements in Seawater

Element	Chemical Species	Concentration for S = 35‰ (mol dm^{-3})	(g kg^{-1})	Ratio to Chlorinity (Cl = 19.374‰)
Na	Na$^+$	4.79×10^{-1}	10.77	5.56×10^{-1}
Mg	Mg^{2+}	5.44×10^{-2}	1.29	6.66×10^{-2}
Ca	Ca^{2+}	1.05×10^{-2}	0.4123	2.13×10^{-2}
K	K$^+$	1.05×10^{-2}	0.3991	2.06×10^{-2}
Sr	Sr^{2+}	9.51×10^{-5}	0.00814	4.20×10^{-4}
Cl	Cl$^-$	5.59×10^{-1}	19.353	9.99×10^{-1}
S	SO$_4^{2-}$, NaSO$_4^-$	2.89×10^{-2}	0.905	4.67×10^{-2}
C (inorganic)	HCO$_3^-$, CO$_3^{2-}$	2.35×10^{-3}	0.276	1.42×10^{-2}
Br	Br$^-$	8.62×10^{-4}	0.673	3.47×10^{-3}
B	B(OH)$_3$, B(OH)$_4^-$	4.21×10^{-4}	0.0445	2.30×10^{-3}
F	F$^-$, MgF$^+$	7.51×10^{-5}	0.00139	7.17×10^{-5}

Based on Dyrssen & Wedborg (1974).

Table 11-2. The Major Components in the Model Ocean Relative to 1 Liter of Water

Substance	Amount (moles)	Comments
H_2O	54.9	(1 liter)
Si	6.06	mostly solid silicates and SiO_2
Al	1.85	mostly solids
Na	0.76	0.48 moles in solution
Ca	0.56	0.01 moles in solution
Cl	0.55	mostly in solution
C	0.55	see C cycle
Fe	0.55	mostly solids
Mg	0.53	0.05 moles in solution
K	0.41	0.01 moles in solution

After Sillen, 1961.

$$S\ 0/00 = 1.80655\ Cl\ 0/00 \qquad [11\text{-}1]$$

Because the dissolved species in the ocean are controlled by the mineral solids and atmosphere present in the boundaries of the ocean, different physicochemical models have been set up to account for the behaviors of some of the major elements. **Sillen's model** will be explored here. The model is based on using 1 liter of water as indicated by Table 11-2. In this model where silicon is most abundant, the solution process is

$$SiO_2(crystal) + 2H_2O = Si(OH)_4\ (aq),\ k = 2 \times 10^{-4}$$

$Si(OH)_4$ is a weak acid; for example,

$$Si(OH)_4\ (aq) + H_2O = Si(OH)_4^-\ (aq) + H_3O^+,\ k = 3.5 \times 10^{-10}$$

$$Si(OH)_4\ (aq) = Si_4O_6(OH)_6^{2-}\ (aq) + 2H_3O^+ + 2H_2O$$

$$Al(OH)_3\ (s) + OH^- = Al(OH)^{4-}\ (aq),\ K = 10^{-1}$$

This weak acid aluminum dissolved species can interact with $Si(OH)_4$ to form a basic solution.

$$Al(OH)^{4-}\ (aq) + Si(OH)_4\ (aq) = \frac{1}{2}\ Al_2Si_2O_5(OH)_4\ (s) + OH^- + 2\frac{1}{2}\ H_2O,$$

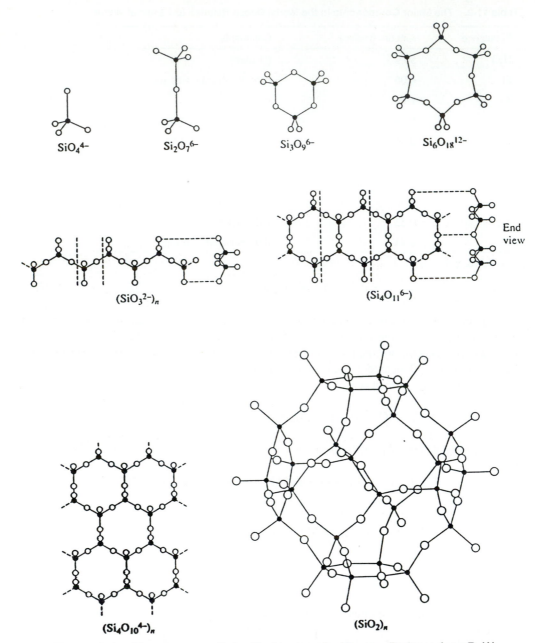

Figure 11-1.   The common units in silicate minerals. (Source: Redrawn from R. W. Raisewell, P. Brimblecombe, D. L. Dent, and P. S. Liss. *Environmental Chemistry*. London: Edward Arnold Publishers. 1980)

$$K = 10^{-6}$$

Because there are more cations than anions written in Table 11-2, some of these must form oxides or hydroxides.

$$3Al_2Si_2O_5(OH)_4 \text{ (s)} + 4SiO_2 \text{ (s)} + 2K^+ + 2Ca^{2+} + 15H_2O = 2KCaAl_3SiO_6(H_2O)_6 \text{ (s)} + 6H_3O^+$$

The H_3O^+ is the controlling reaction for pH because Al and Si are large. In sediments, K^+ is more abundant than Na^+, Ca^{2+} is more abundant than Mg^{2+}, and $K^+/Na^+ = 1.4$; whereas in seawater, $K^+/Na^+ = 0.0026$. Thus for the previous equation

$$K_{eq} = (H_3O^+)/(K^+)^2(Ca^{2+})^2$$

and pH of seawater is influenced by cationic concentration.

Other species (such as carbonate) will also enter the Sillen's model; for example, 0.46 moles of $CaCO_3$ and 0.09 moles of $MgCO_3$. The carbonate will enter into the pH-controlling reactions, but the amount is small compared to the proton capacity available from aluminosilicates. When all minerals are considered, the buffering capacity approaches 1 mole/L; therefore, the CO_2 in the atmosphere does not effect the pH of seawater much. Nevertheless, the seawater still maintains the balance of atmospheric CO_2 and the carbonate in sediments.

Oxygen and iron are important for the model. Most oxygen is in the atmosphere, but some is in the ocean according to Henry's law. Goethite may be the "brake" for an atmospheric increase of oxygen for global photosynthesis activity.

In natural water, both iron and manganese control the phosphorous and sulfur in a redox system. A good illustration can be summarized in Figure 11-2, where manganese nodules and pyrite are formed. Furthermore, it seems that iron can regulate the partial pressure of oxygen in this planet's atmosphere as a **Sillen's brake** for global photosynthesis activity.

$$12FeOOH(s) = 4Fe_2O_3(s) + 6H_2O + O_2 \text{ (g)}$$

Assuming a steady state condition, the input from weathering products brought in by rivers, volcanic activity, atmospheric phenomena, and so on, is balanced by removal through sedimentation, ion exchange, biological production of inert materials, and so on.

$$\left(\frac{dC}{dt}\right)_{in} = \left(\frac{dC}{dt}\right)_{out} \qquad [11\text{-}2]$$

$\left(\dfrac{dC}{dt}\right)$ is rate of change of concentrations. The residence time, τ, is defined as

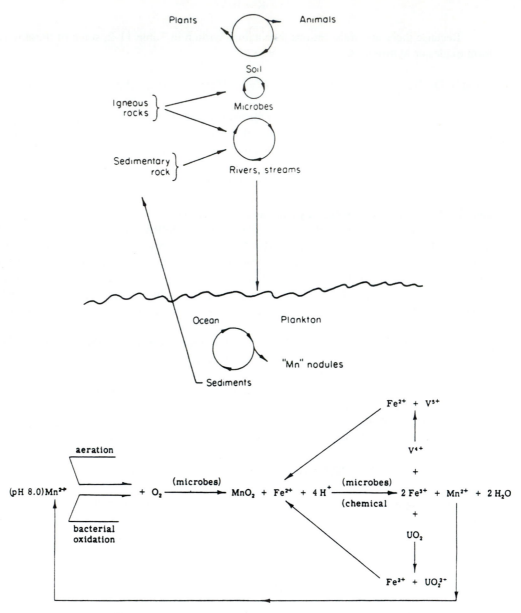

Figure 11-2.   Biogeochemical manganese cycle and possible role of manganese in the oxidation of uranium and vanadium.

Table 11-3. The Residence Times of Some Elements in Seawater

Element	Principal Species	Concentration (mol dm^{-3})	Residence Time (y)
Li	Li$^+$	2.6×10^{-5}	2.3×10^6
B	B(OH)$_3$, B(OH)$^-_4$	4.1×10^{-4}	1.3×10^7
F	F$^-$, MgF$^+$	6.8×10^{-5}	5.2×10^5
Na	Na$^+$	4.68×10^{-1}	6.8×10^7
Mg	Mg^{2+}	5.32×10^{-2}	1.2×10^7
Al	Al(OH)$^-_4$	7.4×10^{-8}	1.0×10^2
Si	Si(OH)$_4$	7.1×10^{-5}	1.8×10^4
P	HPO$^{2-}_4$, PO$^{3-}_4$	2×10^{-6}	1.8×10^5
Cl	Cl$^-$	5.46×10^{-1}	1×10^8
K	K$^+$	1.02×10^{-2}	7×10^6
Ca	Ca^{2+}	1.02×10^{-2}	1×10^6
Sc	Sc(OH)$_4$	1.3×10^{-11}	4×10^4
Ti	Ti(OH)$_4$	2×10^{-8}	1.3×10^4
V	H$_2$VO$^-_4$, HVO$^{2-}_4$	5×10^{-8}	8×10^4
Cr	Cr(OH)$_3$, CrO$^{2-}_4$	5.7×10^{-9}	6×10^3
Mn	Mn^{2+} , MnCl$^+$	3.6×10^{-9}	1×10^4
Fe	Fe(OH)$^+_2$, Fe(OH)$^-_4$	3.5×10^{-8}	2×10^2
Co	Co^{2+}	8×10^{-10}	3×10^4
Ni	Ni^{2+}	2.8×10^{-8}	9×10^4
Cu	CuCO$_3$, CuOH$^+$	8×10^{-9}	2×10^4
Zn	ZnOH$^+$, Zn^{2+} , ZnCO$_3$	7.6×10^{-8}	2×10^4
Br	Br$^-$	8.4×10^{-4}	1×10^8
Sr	Sr^{2+}	9.1×10^{-5}	4×10^6
Ba	Ba^{2+}	1.5×10^{-7}	4×10^4
La	La(OH)$_3$	2×10^{-11}	6×10^2
Hg	HgCl$^{2-}_4$, HgCl$_2$	1.5×10^{-10}	8×10^4
Pb	PbCO$_3$, PbOH$^-$	2×10^{-10}	4×10^2
Th	Th(OH)$_4$	4×10^{-11}	2×10^2
U	UO$_2$(CO$_3$)$^{4-}_2$	1.4×10^{-8}	3×10^6

Based on Brewer (1975).

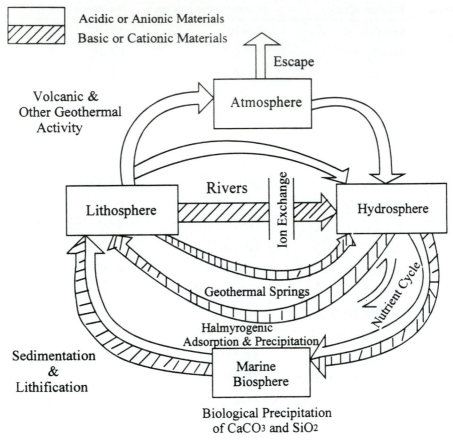

Figure 11-3.   The cycle of cationic and anionic species in seawater.

$$\tau = \frac{C}{(dC/dt)}$$

[11-3]

where C is total dissolved concentration. The residence time calculated out is in Table 11-3.

It is a common hypothesis that the seawater is from the earth's crust while the inorganic ions may be derived by the interaction of major spheres, as shown in Figure 11-3. The seawater can also be lost by **evaporite** formation. Deposits of evaporites generally consist of gypsum, rock salt, or a mixture of NaCl and KCl. If a narrow channel (such as a strait) is connected by oceans or semiclosed oceans, evaporite formation will take place. For example, the salinity of the Red Sea is 4.1%, whereas the average salinity is 3.5%.

A few words on oceans should be clarified here. The word **neritic** versus **ocenaic** pertains to the closeness to shore. Also **enphotic** zone (epipalagic) is shallow in depth; after that is **disphotic** zone (mesopelagic); still deeper is the **aphotic** zone (bathypelagic); usually the bottom of the ocean is called the **benthic** zone.

11.1.1   Oil Pollution

One aspect of ocean pollution is contamination by petroleum. In 1975, the U.S. National Academy of Science workshop estimated that circa 6 million tons of petroleum hydrocarbons enter the ocean yearly. This flux is composed of natural seeps (10%), inputs from the atmosphere (10%), urban and river runoff and coastal industrial wastes (40%), and tanker operations (especially wasting of cargo tankers) (40%). It is clear that the last two sources cause 80% of the total flux to the ocean. Tanker operation is the major single source of oil pollution in the ocean. Figure 11-4 gives the world shipping lanes and major ocean currents.

As early as 1922, the resulting oil pollution of British shores was harmful enough to prompt a law to prohibit the discharge of oil or oily waste in territorial waters. The present position in international law recognizes the absolute prohibition of visible oil discharge at sea for new ships over 20,000 tons.

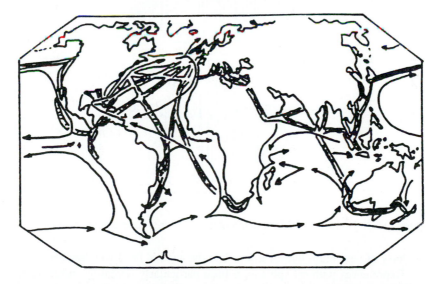

Figure 11-4.   World shipping lanes before the closure of the Suez Canal (Stippled) and major ocean currents (arrows). (After A. Nelson-Smith, 1973.)

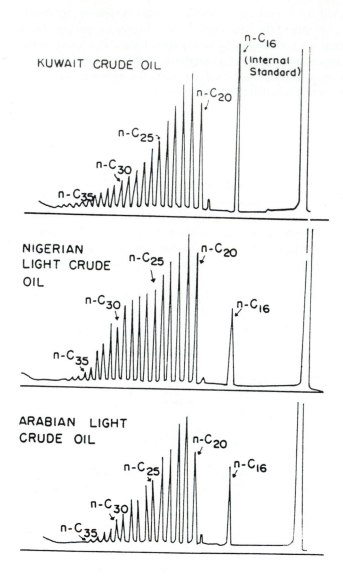

Figure 11-5.   Normal paraffin profiles of crude oil residues above 343°C.

The entry of petroleum hydrocarbons into the aquatic food web has been clearly demonstrated. Experiences with oil spills have been particularly revealing in regard to the vulnerability of the marine environment to petroleum. Certain petroleum hydrocarbons have been shown to interfere with the processes of chemoreception through the blocking of receptive organs. Reproductive processes also may become impaired as a result.

When oil spills occur, the oil spreads on the water. At the same time, components of low boiling points ("light ends") evaporate rapidly, entraining successively higher-boiling fractions. Significant amounts of compounds up to C_8 are carried off in this way. Figure 11-5 gives normal paraffin profiles of crude oil residues above 343°C. In the case of the Kuwait crude oil spill at sea, the crude soon lost most of its fractions of boiling point up to 300°C, diminishing by more than one-third of its mass or about 43% of the total volume.

A model has been proposed to estimate the rate of oil slicking on water:

$$\frac{\pi\left(r_t^3 - r_o^3\right)\rho_\omega}{3V\left(\rho_\omega - \rho_o\right)\rho_o} = k_r t \qquad [11\text{-}4]$$

where

r_0 = slick radius at $t = 0$ (cm)

r_t = slick radius at $t = t$ (cm)

V = volume of oil spilled (cm^3)

k_r = Blokker's constant (rate constant)

ρ_o = density of oil (g/cm^3)

ρ_w = density of water (g/cm^3)

t = time of spreading (sec)

Slick thickness

$$h_t = \frac{k}{t^{\frac{2}{3}}} \quad \text{(cm)} \qquad [11\text{-}5]$$

$$k = \left(\frac{V}{\pi}\right)^{\frac{1}{3}} \left[\frac{\rho_w}{3\rho_o\left(\rho_w - \rho_o\right)k_r}\right]^{\frac{2}{3}} \qquad [11\text{-}6]$$

The following is a table of some of the Blokker's constants for petroleum k_r (at 9°C).

Libyan	1085
Iranian heavy	750
Kuwait	1480
Iraq	975
Venezuela	1340

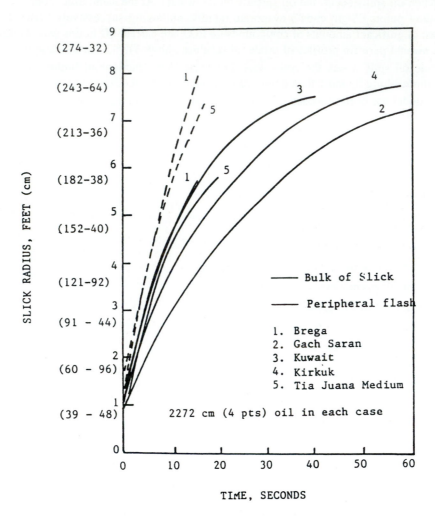

Figure 11-6.   Oil slick spreading on water. (After Berride et al., 1965, Institute of Petroleum, London.)

Figure 11-6 gives the slick radius as a function of time for various crudes. Within 30 seconds, the slick radius can reach 7 feet for Kuwait crude. Figure 11-7 shows the variation of $(r_t^3 - r_0^3)$ with time, as an oil slick spreads.

Although spectacular oil spills have been highly publicized over the years, the smaller day-to-day inputs in the coastal waters and harbors of the world produce chronic pollution that is much larger in total volume. Municipal and industrial effluents, as well as runoff from the land and rivers, all contribute significantly. Offshore oil drilling will be increasingly important as the search for oil in the continental shelf area intensifies, adding more pollution to the ocean. Preventive measures of oil spills are with examples as follows:

- Dispersant   —$(CH_2OCH_2)n$— amines
- Sinking agent   siliconized sand
- Sorbent   polyurethane vs. straw for g. oil adsorped/g. medium is 72.7 vs. 5.8 (Bunker C)
- Combustion promoter   silane treated silica
- Biodegradation   using prepackaged bacterial inoculate with organic
  inoculate   soluble N and P compounds as nutrients
- Gelling agent   organic Ca salts
- Magnetic liquid   ferromagnetic properties of Fe_3O_4
- Beach cleaners   powdered enzymes and oxidizers

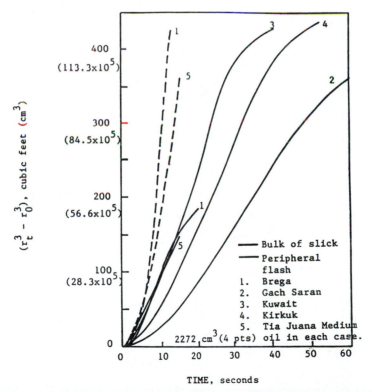

Figure 11-7.   Variation of $(r_t^3 - r_0^3)$ with time as oil slick spreads. (Ref. Berride et al., 1965.)

11.1.2   Tributyltin in a Marine Environment

The anthropogenic addition of a number of chemical species in water (or the contamination) can be best illustrated with a metal such as lead. Suppose a soluble lead Pb^{2+} is present in water (this could originate from lead-based solder joints or scales). There are many soluble species whose formations depend on pH. (See Figure 11-8.)

Tributyltin (TBT) is used as an antifouling marine paint for large ships as well as recreation crafts. Although it is effective in preventing the attachment of barnacles to the surface of a vessel in such a manner as not to increase the dead weight of that vessel while travelling, TBT paint will slowly be hydrolyzed in marine water and is toxic to various nontarget organisms including native mollusks. The following is a list of derivations commonly used in the literature.

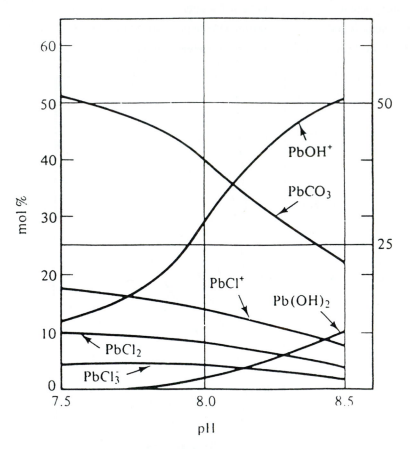

Figure 11-8.   The calculated distribution of Pb (II) in seawater at 25°C and 1 atm.
(From Bilinsky & Stumm, 1973.)

$$R'COOSnR_3 + H_2O \rightarrow R_3SnOH + R'COOH$$

$$\uparrow \qquad\qquad\qquad \uparrow$$

Paint (copolymer)   TBE salt

$$R_3SnOH \xrightarrow[TBT]{} R_3Sn^+ + OH^-$$

(degradation scheme)

$$R_3SnX \rightarrow R_2SnX_2 \rightarrow RSnX_3 \rightarrow SnX_4$$

TBT   DBT   MBT   T

When these tributyltin ions transport across mitochondrial membranes for eukaryotic organisms, they will preferentially bind the imidazole system of the histidine residue from heme proteins. Because imidazole is essential in coordination for binding oxygen hemoglobin, their interference will reflect on the sequence of electron carriers for mitochondria and consequently inhibit phosphorylation interrupting the basic energy process. This will mechanistically explain the toxicity of the biocide activity of TBT. The scheme of oxygen transport is illustrated in Figure 11-9.

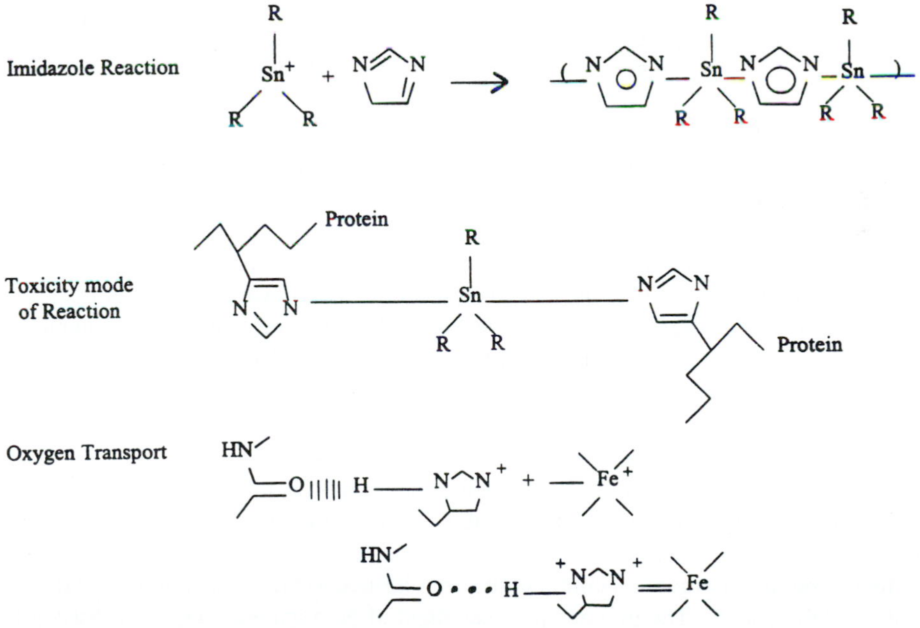

Figure 11-9.   Imidazole for oxygen transport and blockage.

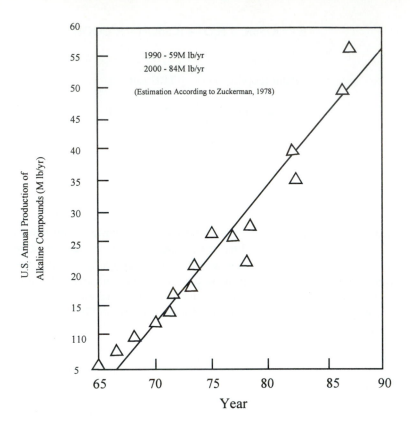

Figure 11-10.   Projected annual vs. production of alkaline compounds. (Permission by American Chemical Society, Zuckerman et al. in ACS symposium series #82, 1978.)

In 1976, the annual world consumption of organotin was 55 million lbs. Of this, the United States used almost half. The trend of consumption is upward, with an annual growth rate of 12% for the last decade, as shown in Figure 11-10. The United States annual production of alkyltin compounds is projected to be 84 million lbs/yr by the year 2000. Of the total amount, about 30% ends up in the marine environment. No one knows what will be the consequence of the increase in potential loading and its impact on assimilative capacity. At this time, there is no simulated modeling for TBT in existence. Even submodels, such as hydrographic input of diffusive leaching, cannot be integrated into a sequestration because degradation, detoxification, and so on, are taking place simultaneously, as shown in Figure 11-11.

Increased use of organotin compounds is not limited to biocides. Another major use is for polyps stabilization. The tin content in sediment of Narragansett Bay is increasing logarithmically, as shown in Figure 11-12. Environmental stresses both in magnitude and duration are certainly real. The description or resuspension in water has to be considered, as shown in Figure 11-13.

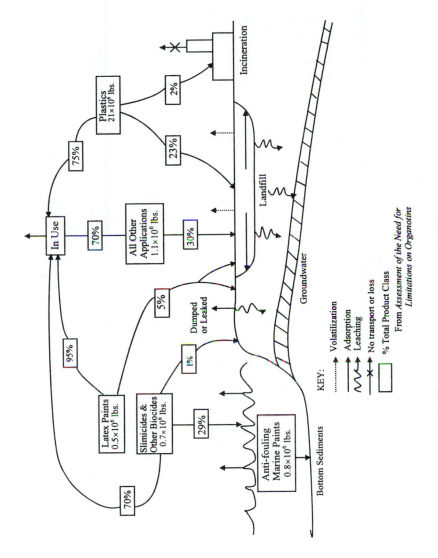

Figure 11-11.   Geochemical cycle of TBT in the environment (After EPA-OTS Draft Report).

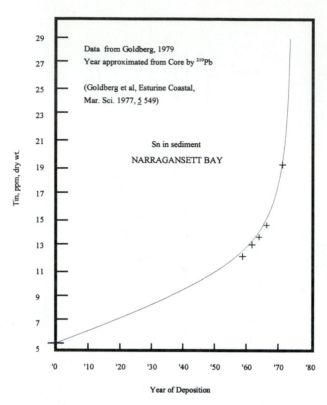

Figure 11-12.   Environmental accumulation of tin in sediments is exponential.

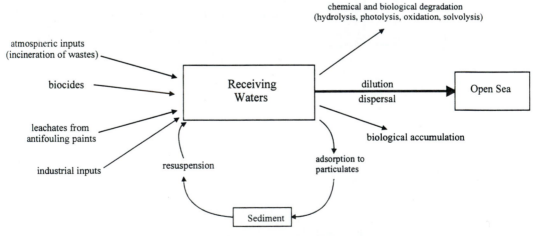

Figure 11-13.   Input and uptake by TBT (After Stebbing, 1985).

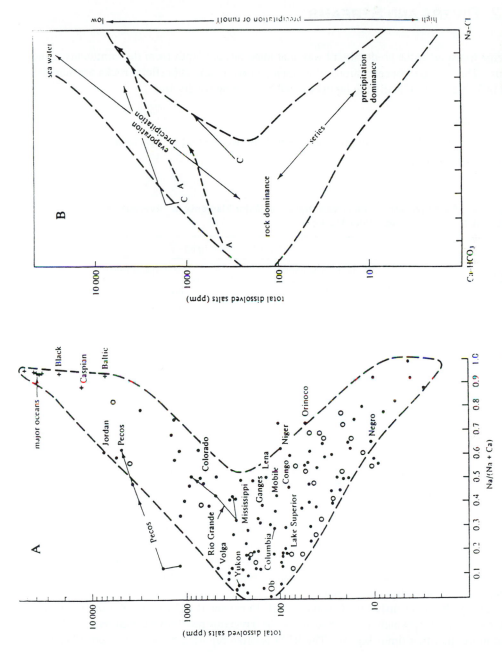

Figure 11-14. (A) A variation of the weight ratio Na/(Na + Ca) as a function of the total dissolved salts for several surface waters. (B) Diagrammatic representation of processes controlling the chemistry of the world surface waters. (From Gibbs, 1970.)

11.2 RIVERS AND STREAMS

Riverine transport is the predominant way that materials are input from the continents to the oceans. The average concentrations of elements in rivers and superficial rocks are summarized in Table 11-4. Usually the inputs carried by riverine waters are:

- salts in rain water
- continental material in drainage basins from weathering and erosion
- anthropogenic in origin

Table 11-4. A Comparison of the Concentration of Major Elements in "Average" Riverine Particulate Material and Superficial Rocks

Element	Concentrations (g kg $^{-1}$)	
	Riverine Particulate Material	Superficial Rocks
Al	94.0	69.3
Ca	21.5	45.0
Fe	48.0	35.9
K	20.0	24.4
Mg	11.8	16.4
Mn	1.1	0.7
Na	7.1	14.2
P	1.2	0.6
Si	285.0	275.0
Ti	5.6	3.8

From Martin & Meybeck (1979).

Some rivers are linked with oceans, the important indicator for world surface water is Na^+ (for seawater) and Ca^{2+} (freshwater). A diagram expressing this is developed by Gibbs and can be located in Figure 11-14. A number of rivers are located. The **Gibbs' river diagram** can be further separated into precipitation dominance, rock dominance, and evaporation/crystallization dominance regions.

The global river influx of dissolved solids to oceans is 4.2 Pg/yr. Yet the particulate matter contribution, which is referred to as the **riverine particulate material** (RPM), is about more than four times higher. The RPM is often reported by a 0.4-0.5 μm filter from the dissolved solid. Chemical fractionation has been used to sort out the anthropogenic inputs in RPM. A chemical extraction method has been developed to separate the anthropogenic elements from the natural weathering elements. By successive extraction with four different reagents, the following four different fractions are obtained:

- NH_4OAC — exchangeable
- NH_2OH/HCl — associated with Mn-Fe oxide surface coatings
- H_2O_2/HCl — organically associated
- $HF/HClO_4$ — resistant

The first two types are associated with anthropogenic sources; the latter two types are associated with natural weathering sources. The distribution of the four fractions will be an indication of the degree of pollution of a river. In Figure 11-15, the copper speciation of some rivers can illustrate this point.

Chemically, if there is an increase in the concentration or mass transport of certain chemical species, this is pollution. Reversely, if there is a decrease then it is termed **self-purification**. The self-purification of streams involve the following:

- transport and incorporation into deposits
- reaction within the water mass or suspended matter
- exchange reaction of volatiles with the atmosphere
- chemical and biochemical oxidation within the sediments

Amount of self-purification of rivers, S_m in mole/sec can be expressed as

$$S_m = Q(C_o - C_u) \qquad\qquad [11\text{-}7]$$

where Q is flow in m^3/s and C_0 and C_u is respectively the concentrations in the upstream and downstream in mole/m^3. The rate of self-purification can be expressed as

$$S_r = \frac{dC}{dt} = \frac{(C_0 - C_u)}{t} \qquad\qquad [11\text{-}8]$$

For ecological models, the rate can be expressed in terms of biomass in the river (mole/g/s)

$$S_e = \frac{S_m}{G} = \frac{Q(C_0 - C_u)}{t(g'Pv + g''Q)} \qquad\qquad [11\text{-}9]$$

where G is the total biomass in g, g' and g'' are respectively attached and suspended biomass in g/m^2 and g/m^3, P is the length of wetted cross-profile in m, and v is flow velocity in m/s. or

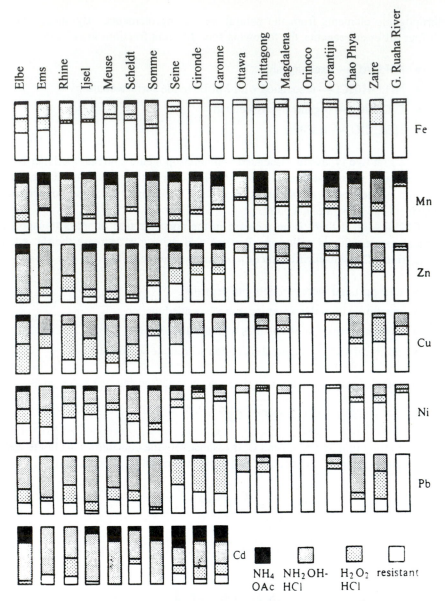

Figure 11-15.   The speciation of trace metals in 18 different river sediments, arranged according to their approximate geographic position from north to south. Most tropical contained low cadmium levels, and no reliable data were obtained. For the Rio Magdalena and Orinoco River, insufficient material was available for determination of the 'Exchangeable' (NH$_4$OAc) fraction, and this is contained in the hydroxylamine extract. (From Salomons and Forstner, 1980.)

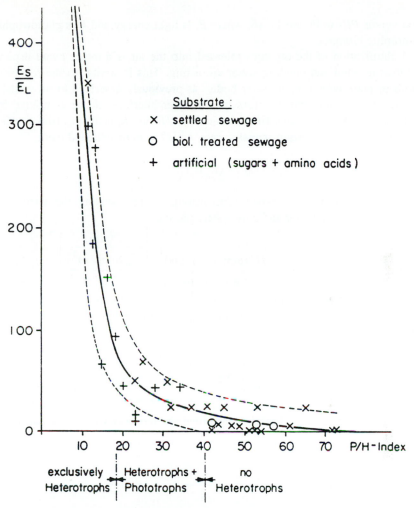

Figure 11-16. P/H Index of phytocenoses in model rivers at comparable hydraulic conditions as a function of the ratio E_s/E_L. River water: groundwater with the addition of various pollutants. E_s and E_L in kcal/(dm^2) (day). (Data compiled from numerous independent model river studies from 1965-1970 by K. Wuhrmann.)

$$S_r = S_\varepsilon \left(\frac{g'}{R} + g'' \right) \quad \text{mol/m}^3\text{/s} \qquad [11\text{-}10]$$

where R is hydraulic radius in m. Different substrates added to model rivers confirm that the imported energy from substrate organics, E_s, is important because it is correlable with heterotroph or prototroph to compete for dominance of growth space. The ratio of E_s/E_L is plotted versus P/H in Figure 11-16, where E_L is light energy and P is phototrophic and H is heterotrophic biomass.

Volatilization of the organics released into the air is a major event especially when both blowing wind and howling water are acting. This is similar to the release of volatile organics or petroleum to open water bodies as previously described in oil spills. The mass exchange of a given chemical across the air-water interface can be computed by the "two film" theory. If K_l is the liquid film coefficient (L/T) and K_g is the gas film coefficient (L/T), then the **overall volatilization transfer rate**, k_l (L/T) can be obtained from

$$(k_l)^{-1} = (K_l)^{-1} + (K_g H_e)^{-1}$$ [11-11]

where H_e is the Henry's constant (dimensionless), representing the partitioning of the chemicals between the water and atmosphere phases.

$$H_e = \frac{H'_e\,(\text{atm}\cdot\text{m}^3/\text{mole})}{RT\,(\text{atm}\cdot\text{m}^3/\text{mole})} = \frac{\left[\dfrac{P(\text{atm})}{C_w\,(\text{mole/m}^3)}\right]}{RT}$$ [11-12]

where P is partial pressure and C_w is water solubility concentration.

Furthermore, the liquid film coefficient, K_l, can be estimated from the oxygen transfer coefficient, K_L, by

$$K_l = \left(\frac{32}{M}\right)^{\frac{1}{4}} K_L$$ 11-13]

where M is the molecular weights of the spilled chemicals and K_L can be approximated from reaeration coefficient

$$K_a = \frac{K_L}{H} = \frac{(D_L U)^{\frac{1}{2}}}{H^{\frac{3}{2}}}$$ [11-14]

or

$$K_L = \left(\frac{D_L U}{H}\right)^{\frac{1}{2}}$$

where D_L is the oxygen diffusivity at 20°C (8.1×10^{-5} ft^2/ hr), U is average stream velocity, and H is average depth. On the other hand, the gas film coefficient can be estimated empirically from

$$K_g = 168\left(\frac{18}{M}\right)^{\frac{1}{4}} U_w \qquad\qquad [11\text{-}15]$$

where U_w is the wind speed in m/s.

[Example 12-1]   Chlorobenzene is discharged into a stream where the wind speed is 5 m/s and water temperature is 20°C. The depth of the stream is 0.4 m and the water velocity is 0.60 m/s. Compute the volatilization rate of chlorobenzene.

Oxygen transfer coefficient can be estimated by

$$K_L = \left(\frac{D_L U}{H}\right)^{\frac{1}{2}}$$

$$= (1.81 \times 10^4 \ \text{m}^2/\ \text{day})^{1/2} \ (0.60 \ \text{m/s})^{1/2} \ (8.64 \times 10^4 \ \text{s/day})^{1/2}/ \ (0.4 \ \text{m/s})^{1/2}$$

$$= 4.84 \ \text{m/day}$$

Liquid film coefficient

$$K_l = (32/113)^{1/4} \ (4.84 \ \text{m/day}) = 3.53 \ \text{m/day}$$

Gas film coefficient

$$K_g = 168 \ (18/113)^{1/4} \ (5) = 531 \ \text{m/day}$$

Dimensionless Henry's constant

$$H_e = \frac{H'_e}{RT} = \frac{0.0037 \ \text{atm-m}^3/\text{mole}}{8.206 \times 10^{-3} \ \text{atm-m}^3/\text{mole} \ °\text{K} \times 293°\text{K}} = 0.154$$

$$\frac{l}{k_l} = \frac{1}{K_l} + \frac{1}{K_g \, H_e} = \frac{1}{3.53} + \frac{1}{531(0.154)} = 0.283 + 0.0122$$

or

$$k_l = 3.38 \ \text{m/day}$$

11.3 CHEMICAL LIMNOLOGY

The study of the physical, chemical, and biological characteristics of rivers and lakes are in the domain of **limnology**. For the counterpart, the effort toward the water in the ocean is termed **oceanography**. For rivers, because the turbulent flow causes mixing, there will be no temperature gradients developing. However, for lakes, due to the nonmixing, the top layer is heated up more than the bottom layer. In this manner there is vertical stratification. As shown in Figure 11-17, the upper layer is called **epilimnion** and the bottom layer is called **hypolimnion**. The middle layer is called **thermocline** (or metalimnion), wherein the transition zone and the temperature changes rapidly over a short distance of depth. Chemical factors affect the pattern within the limnolocal domain vastly including all the biological communities. For example, the phosphorous will affect both algae and fish as shown in Figure 11-18. The properties of lakes will be modified accordingly, including nutrients, as shown in Figure 11-19.

As an ecological unit, often the lake and river will also include the drainage basin, which is also known as catchment area or watershed. Because vegetation and soil will be surrounding the body of water, organic peat will be formed with bog vegetation as a sponge. It should be remembered that the peat will eventually become coal via the coalification process; for example, via lignite.

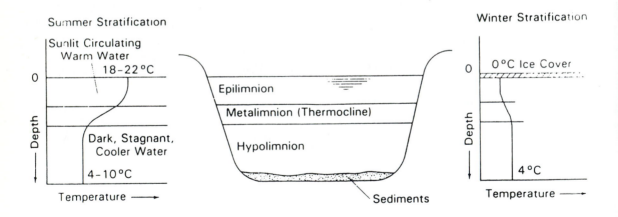

Figure 11-17.   Thermal stratification of a deep lake.

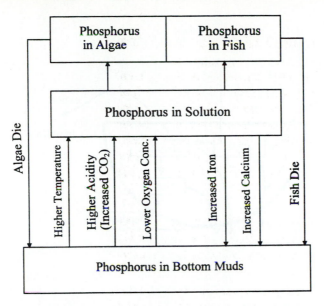

Figure 11-18.   Chemical factors that effect phosphorus equilibria in lakes. (Redrawn after H.R. Jones, *Detergents and Pollution, Problems and Technical Solutions,* Park Ridge, NJ, Noyes Data Corporation, 1972, p. 8.)

Heavy metals can settle from receiving waters (such as tributaries) together with biogenic and other particles as transport carriers. Actually, many sediment depth profiles serve as indicators of heavy metal pollution. For lakes, the residence time of heavy ions is drastically reduced due to the scavenging actions by sedimentation. For example, in Lake Greiffensee, the sedimentation rate is 0.37 Tg/yr. The computation of the soluble metals is best to be performed by the mass balance model, assuming steady state is attainable. For example, the lake can be comparable to a reactor as indicated by Figure 11-20. Let the input and output fluxes be J_i (i=4), then

$$V \frac{dC}{dt} = J_1 + J_2 - J_3 - J_4 \qquad\qquad [11\text{-}16]$$

This equation is also used for the total phosphorous concentration calculation as seen in Equation [11-25].

Here J_1 is the annual input from rivers and streams, J_2 is the annual rainfalls to the lake, J_3 is the annual sedimentation amount and J_4 is the annual outflow to other water body systems. Because precipitation is approximately equal to evaporation, the lake is a closed system.

Now the influx concentration of any metal sphere, C_i, is carried in by

$$J_1 = QC_1 \qquad\qquad [11\text{-}17]$$

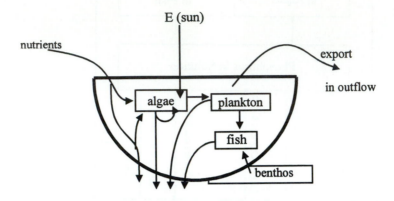

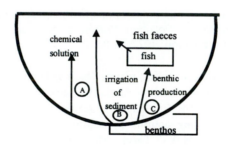

Figure 11-19.   (top) Common view of nutrient pathways. (bottom) Potential sources of return from sediment.

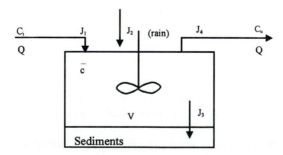

Figure 11-20.   Mass balance model of a lake at steady state.

assuming the rain does not affect C_i. The final ultimate concentration is the exit concentration, C_u, and can be effected as

$$J_3 = SP = K_d C_u P \tag{11-18}$$

Here, P is the sedimentation rate and S is the concentration of metal species in suspended matter. Because the distribution coefficient, k_d, is defined as

$$k_d = \frac{S}{C_u} \tag{11-19}$$

Finally, the exit flux is

$$J_4 = QC_u \tag{11-20}$$

For steady state
$$C_u = C = \underline{C} \tag{11-21}$$
Substituting Equations [11-17], [11-18], and [11-20] into Equation [11-16] for differentiation

$$\frac{dC}{dt} = \frac{QC_i + J_2}{V} - C\left(\frac{Q + k_d P}{V}\right) \tag{11-22}$$

or after integration

$$C(t) = C_0 \exp\left(\frac{Q + k_d P}{V}t\right) + \frac{QC_i + J_2}{Q + k_d P}\left[1 - \exp\left(\frac{-Q + k_d P}{V}t\right)\right] \tag{11-23}$$

At $t=\infty$ and $C(t)=\underline{C}$, Equation [11-23] becomes

$$\underline{C} = \frac{QC_i + J_2}{Q + k_d P} \tag{11-24}$$

Stumm and Morgan used Equation [11-24] to calculate the heavy metal concentration in the water leaving the lake. For example, in Greiffensee, assuming the volume is 0.125 Gm^3, Q is 89 M m^3/yr, P is 0.37 Tg/yr, and J_2 (rain) = 1300 kg/ yr. For metal ions $C_i(Zn)$ = 1908 mg/m^3, $C_i(Pb)$ = 3.2 mg/m^3, $k_d(Zn)$ = 25 m^3/kg, and $k_d(Pb)$ = 120m^3/kg. After using Equation [11-24], the results are $\underline{C}(Zn)$ = 3.1 mg/m^3 and $\underline{C}(Pb)$ = 0.4 mg/m^3. The field data collected are Zn = 4.1 mg/m^3 and Pb = 0.6 mg/m^3. The critical field data are close to the calculated values.

11.4 EUTROPHICATION

Natural waters acquire their chemical characteristics by dissolution and by chemical reactions with solids, liquids, and gases with which they have come into contact during the various parts of the hydrological cycle. In some instances, biological activities also play a role.

The water carried in streams is considered to consist of two fractions: one which is made up of subsurface water and groundwater that reenters the surface water, and the other which is a surface runoff fraction that enters the drainage system during and soon after the precipitation period. The relative proportions of those components and the concentration of dissolved species in each, as influenced by the interactions of rainwater with minerals and vegetation and by the evaporation and transpiration from plants, largely determine the composition of river waters. Figure 11-21 gives the dissolved solids of rivers as a function of runoff. In the modeling work, streams are usually assumed to be fixed-length plug flow chemical reactors with the superimposition of the influences of pollution and waste disposal. Rivers are also considered to possess the ability of self-purification.

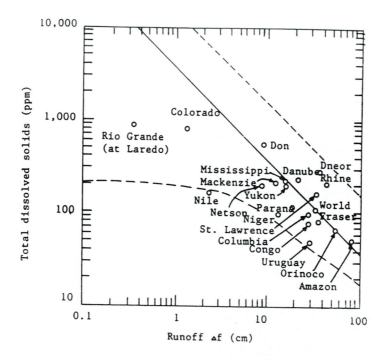

Figure 11-21.   Dissolved solids of rivers as a function of runoff (After H. D. Holland).

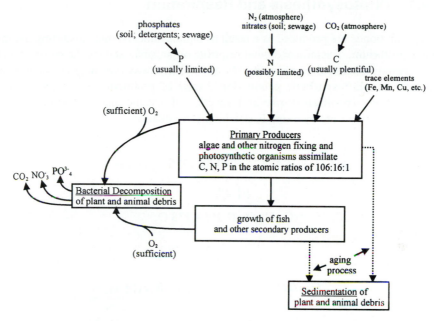

Figure 11-22. Factors that affect aquatic production, decomposition, and sedimentation.

As discussed before, the sea is an open, dynamic system with variable inputs and outputs of mass and energy for which the state of equilibrium is a constraint. Because the sea has remained constant during the recent geological past, it may be well-justified to interpret the ocean as a **steady-state model**. Input is balanced by output in a steady-state system. The system considered is a single box model of the sea; that is, an ocean of constant volume, temperature, pressure, and uniform composition.

The situation in lakes, as mentioned before, is more complicated than that of sea in many regards. Most substances entering lakes are **nonconservative** (i.e., have a residence time different from that of water). In most lakes, the input rates of many substances has increased, and consequently, concentrations of many constituents are not time-variant. If the input rates of nutrients are too high, lakes may also have some of the eutrophication problems that are discussed in Section 11.4.2.

The aquatic environments are further complicated by the interaction with the biosphere. There is a constant production, decomposition, and sedimentation of biomass, as illustrated by Figure 11-22. Another factor that should be pointed out is that agricultural irrigation will not only add dissolved solids to the rivers or lakes, but put a burden on underground aquifers. For example, one of the largest aquifers in North America, the Ogallala aquifer, which crosses eight states in the United States, suffers from this; even the rate of use is three orders of magnitude greater than the rate of recharge.

11.4.1   Photosynthesis and Respiration

Energy-rich bonds are produced as a result of photosynthesis; thus, distorting the thermodynamic equilibrium. Bacteria and other respiring organisms catalyze the redox processes that tend to restore chemical equilibrium. In a simplified way, we may consider a stationary state between **photosynthetic production** P (rate of production of organic material) and **heterotrophic respiration** R (rate of destruction of organic material) and chemically characterize this steady state by a simple stoichiometry equation.

$$106\ CO_2 + 16\ NO_3^- + HPO_4^- + 122H_2O + 18H$$

$$P\downarrow\ R\uparrow$$

$$(C_{106}H_{263}O_{110}N_{16}P_1) + 138\ O_2$$

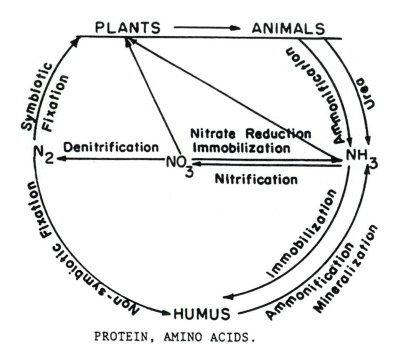

Figure 11-23.   The nitrogen cycle.

Algal protoplasm may also be conveniently expressed as $(CH_2O)_{106}(NH_3)_{16}(H_3PO_4)$. The stoichiometric formulation of the equation reflects, in a simple way, **Liebig's law of minimum**, which states that plant growth is controlled by the availability of a single nutrient, the **limiting nutrient**, meaning in this case, phosphorous.

Figure 11-23 shows the nitrogen cycle. Nitrifying bacteria have evolved to use reduced nitrogen as a fuel source in a process called **nitrification**. Some of them (organisms of the genus *Nitrosomonas*) oxidize ammonia to nitrite, as shown here:

$$NH_4^+ + OH^- + 1.5\ O_2 \rightarrow NO_2^- + H^+ + 2H_2O$$

While others (*Nitrobacter*) oxidize nitrite further to nitrate

$$NO_2^- + 0.5\ O_2 \rightarrow NO_3^-$$

The nitrogen cycle is completed by denitrifying bacteria in the nitrification process, which converts nitrate back to N_2.

$$NO_3^- \rightarrow NO_2^- \rightarrow NO \rightarrow N_2O \rightarrow N_2$$

Nitrate, which has converted to nitrite, will cause methemoglobieumia (blue blood) problems. Table 11-5 tabulates nitrate concentration in some vegetables, and it shows that the nitrate concentration in spinach is the highest.

Elemental sulfur is chemically stable in the presence of oxygen in most environments but is readily oxidized by sulfur-oxidizing bacteria; for example, *Thiobacilles thiooxidans* resulting in the formation of sulfate and hydrogen ions. The energy generated can be used for building up the biomass.

Table 11-5. Average ppm Nitrate in a Variety of Foods

	Average ppm of Nitrate	Number Samples Analyzed
Mixed vegetables	88	2
Carrots	101	8
Green beans	163	3
Garden vegetables	180	5
Graham crackers	211	1
Squash	282	5
Wax beans	444	2
Beets	977	6
Spinach	1373	5

$$S + 3/2\ O_2 + H_2O \rightarrow H_2SO_4$$

$$CO_2 + H_2O \rightarrow (CH_2O) + O_2$$

A wide variety of organisms can use sulfate as a sulfur source and carry out assimilatory sulfate reduction; for example, *Desulovibrio desulfuricans*.

$$CaSO_4 + 2\ (CH_2O) \rightarrow CaS + 2H_2O + 2CO_2$$

or

$$CaSO_4 + 2(CH_2O) \rightarrow CaCO_3 + H_2S + CO_2 + H_2O$$

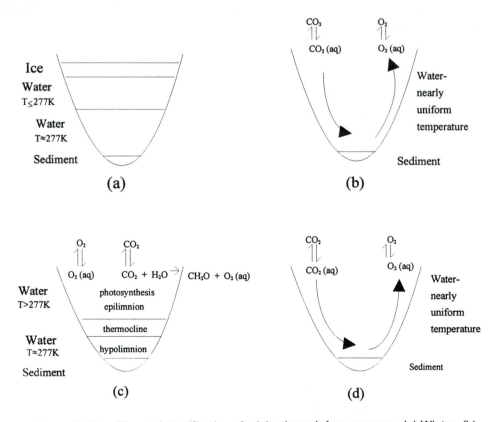

Figure 11-24.   Thermal stratification of a lake through four seasons: (a) Winter, (b) Spring (turnover), (c) Summer, and (d) Fall (turnover).

11.4.2 Eutrophication and Its Control

Figure 11-24 illustrates the thermal stratification of a lake through four seasons. In a stratified lake, excessive production of algae and oxygen in the upper layers (P>>R) may be paralleled by anaerobic conditions at the bottom (R>>P). This is because most of the photosynthetic oxygen escapes into the atmosphere and does not become available to the deeper water layers, and eventually the algae sink to the bottom of the lake.

Overnutrition of bodies of water caused by inputs of phosphates, nitrogen compounds, or other nutrients is commonly called **eutrophication**. Technically, eutrophication is simply the natural process of providing a body of water with the nutrients for the aquatic life it supports. A lake starts its life cycle as a clear body of water, which is described as **oligotrophic**. As nutrients enter the lake through land runoff, and as aquatic life grows and dies, the water acquires a high content of organic debris. At this stage the lake is considered **mesotrophic**. Eventually it fills in completely, forming a marsh and then dry land. The Green River basin in Utah and Colorado was a lake basin (Lake Uinta) that lasted 4 million years and then dried out to be replaced by the Colorado River, which has already lasted for 40 million years. Lake Gosiate in Wyoming eventually also dried out. This basin is rich in oil shale deposits.

Table 11-6. Summary of Estimated Nitrogen and Phosphorus Reaching Wisconsin Surface Waters

Source	N	P	N	P
	Lbs. per year		(% of total)	
Municipal treatment facilities	20,000,000	7,000,000	24.5	55.7
Private sewage system	4,800,000	280,000	5.9	2.2
Industrial wastes[a]	1,500,000	100,000	1.8	0.8
Rural sources				
manured lands	8,110,000	2,700,000	9.9	21.5
other cropland	576,000	384,000	0.7	3.1
forest land	435,000	43,500	0.5	0.3
pasture, woodlot and other lands	540,000	360,000	0.7	2.9
groundwater	34,300,000	285,000	42.0	2.3
Urban runoff	4,450,000	1,250,000	5.5	10.0
Precipitation on water areas	6,950,000	155,000	8.5	1.2
Total	81,661,000	12,557,500	100.0	100.0

a excludes industrial wastes that discharge to municipal systems. Table does not include contributions from aquatic nitrogen fixation, waterfowl, chemical deicers, and wetland drainage.

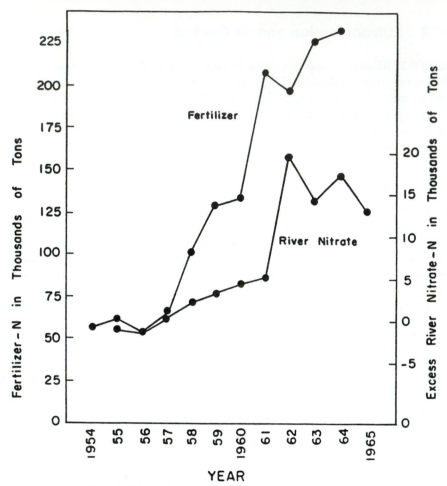

Figure 11-25.   Trend of river nitrate to fertilizer use.

The rate of eutrophication establishes the balance between the production of aquatic life and its destruction by bacterial decomposition. Under natural conditions, the rate of decomposition is nearly equal to the rate of production, and little sedimentation occurs. Where there are large inputs of nutrients from human sources, bacterial decomposition cannot keep the pace with productivity, and sedimentation increases. Table 11-6, which summarizes amounts of nitrogen and phosphorus reaching surface water, may serve as an example of the ratio of natural and man-made sources of loading. Figure 11-25 illustrates that there is a close relationship between the fertilizer used and the excess riverine nitrate concentration.

To remedy the problem, people have applied methods to control the input of nutrients to lakes; for example, by restricting the usage of phosphate detergents and removing phosphate at sewage treatment plants. Phosphate removal can be done fairly simply by adding lime, calcium oxide, aluminum sulfate, or ferric chloride to the sewage. Figure 11-26 predicts promising results for the application of phosphate control. Some of the control methods are as follows:

- diverting nutrients from lakes — especially diverting of sewage
- removing nutrients from sewage
- controlling availability of nutrients within lakes — for example, flocculation of nutrients from euphoric zone, prevention of thermocline formation in summer
- removing nutrients from lakes — for example, removing macrophytes and large quantity of fish, and so on
- relieving symptoms of eutrophication — for example, using algicide such as copper sulfate and mechanical harvesting
- improving agricultural practices — for example, using barrier for groundwater flow, grafting fertilizer molecules of biomass on humin on structure in soil.

The level of eutrophication is directly related to water quality variables such as T_p ($\mu g/L$), which is the total **phosphorous concentration** in a lake. Chlorophyll a concentration ($\mu g/L$), the **Secchi depth** (m), and hypolimnetic oxygen (DO) in % saturation are shown in Table 11-7. The Secchi depth usually employs a disk by lowering it in the water and recording the depth at which the disappearance of the disk by eye occurs. This empirical measurement, however, is correlable to the extinction coefficient by solar radiation at the lake. The depth at which 1% of the surface still remains is of use in eutrophication studies; for example, $z_1 = 4.61/ K_e$ where $I/ I_o = \exp(-K_e z)$.

Table 11-7. Trophic Status of Lakes

Water Quality Variable	Oligotrophic	Mesotrophic	Eutrophic	Reference
Tp ($\mu g/1$)	<10	10-20	>20	a
Chlorophyll ($\mu g/1$)	< 4	4-10	>10	b
Secchi depth (m)	> 4	2-4	<2	a
Hypolimnetic oxygen (% saturation)	>80	10-80	<10	a

a. USEPA (1974). National Eutrophication Survey Working Paper, No. 23.

b. NAS, NAE (1972). Water Quality Criteria, A Report of the Committee on Water Quality.

Source: R.V. Thomann and J.A. Mueller, 1987.

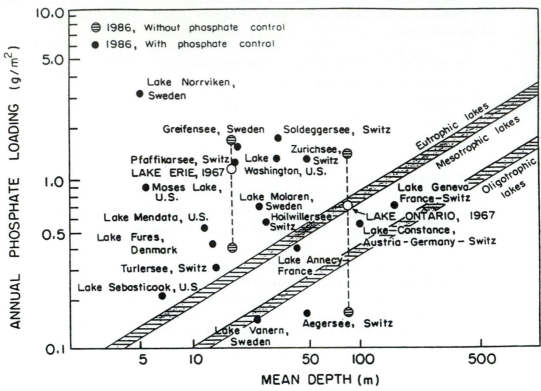

Figure 11-26.   Critical phosphorus loading as a function of depth (After R. Vollen Weider).

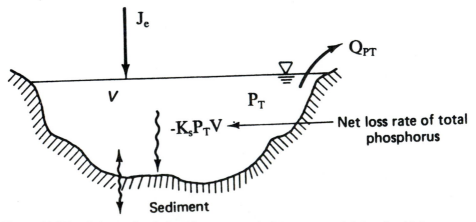

Figure 11-27.   Schematic of phosphorus mass balance—completely mixed lake. (Modified after Thomann and Mueller, 1987.)

Total phosphorous concentration still remains an important factor related to the eutro-phication problem. Usually, the phosphorous mass balance for a completely mixed lake (assumption) with steady-state conditions, representing a seasonal/annual average, is used. As indicated by Equation [11-16] and Figure 11-27.

$$V \frac{dP_T}{dt} = J_e - u_s A_s P_T - Q P_T \qquad\qquad [11\text{-}25]$$

or

$$V \frac{dP_T}{dt} = J_e - k_s P_T V - Q P_T \qquad\qquad [11\text{-}26]$$

for $k_s = u_s/H$ where

V = volume of lake (L^3)

P_T = total phosphorous concentration in lake (M/L^3); for example, $\mu g/L$

Q = outflow

A_s = lake surface area (L^2)

J_e = external flux of phosphorous, (M/T); for example, g/s

k_s = overall loss rate of total phosphorous ($1/T$)

H = depth of lake (L)

at a steady state

$$P_T = \frac{J_e}{Q + u_s A_s} \qquad\qquad [11\text{-}27]$$

If an area loading rate is used

$$J_e' = J_e/A_s \qquad [M/L^2 \times T; \text{ for example, g/m}^2 \times \text{yr}] \qquad\qquad [11\text{-}28]$$

then

$$P_T = J_e'/(q + u_s) \qquad\qquad [11\text{-}29]$$

$$q = Q/A_s = \text{hydraulic overflow rate } (L/T)$$

or

$$P_T = J_e'/\, H(t_d^{-1} + k_s)$$ [11-30]

where $t_d = \dfrac{V}{Q}$ = detention/time of the lake

k_s is difficult to determine, an estimation has been used,

$$k_s = \frac{10}{H}$$ [11-31]

[Example 11-2]   A lake in Pennsylvania has a surface area of 7.77×10^7 m^2 and an average depth of 8m. This lake receives 30 in/yr of rainfall. (a) There is a sewage treatment plant close to the city, which serves a population of 50,000. The water usage is 150 gcd, the influent phosphate for the plant is 6 mg/L, and the plant can only remove 20% of the phosphorous. (b) The combined sewers, which serve 6 mi^2, have a runoff coefficient of 0.45. The overflow of phosphorous concentration is 4 mg/L and is captured by the sewage treatment plant of 5%. (c) The storm drains have a runoff coefficient of 0.27 in a service area of 4 mi^2. The concentration of phosphorous from the storm drain is 0.7 mg/L. (d) At the hillside of the lake, there is an upstream gage that measures the annual average flow of 500 cfs coming from virgin land and contains a phosphorous concentration of 20 ppb. (e) To the north of the lake, there is agricultural land with a drainage area of 60 mi^2, which has a phosphorous loading of 0.5 1b/mi^2 day and the runoff is 30% of rainfall. (f) To the south of the lake, there is a forest with 80 mi^2 of drainage area, which carries a phosphorous loading of 0.15 lb/mi^2 day, and the runoff is 30% rainfall.

     Calculate the total phosphorous concentration of the lake. What is the trophic state of this lake? (after Thomann and Mereller)

In analysis, the lake geometry is as follows:

$$A = 7.77 \times 10^7 \text{ m}^2$$

$$H = 8 \text{ m}$$

$$V = AH = 6.22 \times 10^7 \text{ m}^3$$

     The upstream flow plus the sum of the instrumental flow from the drainage areas equals the outflow.

Q_a (sewage treatment plant)

$$= 50{,}000 \text{ cap} \times 150 \text{ gcd} \times \text{MGD}/10^6 \text{ gal} \times 1.548 \text{ cfs/ MGD} = 11.6 \text{ cfs}$$

Q_b (combine sewers)

$$= C \text{ (runoff coefficient) } I \text{ (rainfall rate in/hr) } A \text{ (acres) } (1 - \text{capture})$$

$$= 0.45 \,(30 \text{ in/yr} \times 1 \text{ yr/365 days} \times 1 \text{ day/24 hr}) \,(6 \text{ mi}^2 \times 640 \text{ acre/mi}^2) \,(1 - 0.05)$$

$$= 5.61 \text{ cfs}$$

$$Q_c = 0.27 \,(\frac{30}{3.64 \times 24}) \,(4 \times 640) = 2.36 \text{ cfs}$$

$$Q_d = 500 \text{ cfs}$$

$$Q_e = (30 \times 0.3) \text{ in/yr} \,(\frac{0.07367 \text{ cfs/ mi}^2}{\text{in/yr}}) \,(60 \text{ mi}^2) = 39.8 \text{ cfs}$$

$$Q_f = (30 \times 0.3) \,(0.7367) \, 80 = 53.0 \text{ cfs}$$

$$\sum Q = Q_a + Q_b + Q_c + Q_d + Q_e + Q_f = 612 \text{ cfs} = 612 \text{ cfs} \,(\frac{1 \text{ m}^3/\text{s}}{35.4 \text{ cfs}}) = 17.3 \text{ m}^3/\text{s}$$

For the lake total phosphorous loading ($J = QC$)

$$J_a = 11.6 \text{ cfs} \,[\, 6 \,(1 - 0.20) \text{ mg/L} \,] \,(5.39 \frac{\text{lb/day}}{\text{mg/L - cfs}}) = 301 \text{ lb/day}$$

$J_b = 5.61 \times 4 \times 5.39 = 121$ lb/day

$J_c = 2.36 \times 0.7 \times 5.39 = 9$ lb/day

$J_d = 500 \times 0.02 \times 5.39 = 54$ lb/day

$J_e = 0.5$ lb/mi^2 day $\times 60$ mi$^2 = 30$ lb/day

$J_f = 0.15 \times 80 = 12$ lb/day

$$\sum J = J_a + J_b + J_c + J_d + J_e + J_f = 527 \text{ lb/day}$$

This is similar to Equation [11-16]. Thus, the area loading is

$$J = 527 \text{ lb/day} \times 365 \text{ day/yr} \times 454 \text{ g/lb} = 8.73 \times 10^7 \text{ g/yr}$$

or

$$J' = J/A = 8.73 \times 10^7 / 7.77 \times 10^7 = 1.12 \text{ g/ m}^2 \text{ yr}$$

The hydraulic detention time is

$$t_d = V/Q = 6.22 \times 10^8 \text{ m}^3/ 17.3 \text{ m}^3/\text{s} \times 1 \text{ yr}/ 3.154 \times 10^7 \text{s} = 1.14 \text{ yr}$$

$$q = \text{overflow rate} = Q/A = (V/H \times 1/Q)^{-1} = H/t_d = 8\text{m}/ 1.14 \text{ yr} = 7.02 \text{ m/yr}$$

Assuming $K_s = 1.55$ or $U_s = 12.4$ m/yr $(K_s = U_s/H)$
or

$$P_t = J'/ (q + U_s) = \left(\frac{1.12 q/ \text{ m}^2 \text{ yr}}{7.02 \text{ m/yr} + 12.4 \text{ m/yr}} \right) = 0.058 \text{ g/ m}^3 = 58 \ \mu\text{g/L}$$

The lake is in eutrophic status.

_____

An important note should be made here. For hydraulic and water-related calculation, the concentration expressed in English system is MGD, cfs, or lb/day but for the metric systems, the concentration is always expressed in mg/L, ppm, and so on. There are two formulae shown in Equations [11-32] and [11-33] which are commonly used to accommodate both systems in practice.

$$J = 8.34\, QC \qquad\qquad [11\text{-}32]$$

$$lb/day = (\frac{lb}{MG - mg/L})\,(MGD)\,(mg/L)$$

or

$$J = 5.39\, QC \qquad\qquad [11\text{-}33]$$

$$lb/day = (\frac{lb/day}{cfs - mg/L})\,(cfs)\,(mg/L)$$

In actual case for metric system, the flow is expressed in m³/s. Also the approximation can be made

$$1\ mg/L = 1\ g/m^3 = 10^{-3}\ kg/m^3$$

Thus

$$J = QC$$

where J is in g/s, Q is m³/s and C is mg/L.
The preceding Equations [11-32] and [11-33] can be simplified as

$$8.34\ lb/day = MGD - mg/L \qquad\qquad [11\text{-}32]$$

$$5.39\ lb/day = cfs - mg/L \qquad\qquad [11\text{-}33]$$

The formulaes in Equations [11-32] and [11-33] are essential to the calculation of problems in later chapters, especially for the accompanying Volume 4B of *Environmental Chemistry*.

REFERENCES

11-1.   J. P. Riley and G. Skirrow, *Chemical Oceanography*, Academic Press, London, 1975.

11-2.   G. Sillen, "The Physical Chemistry of Seawater" in *Oceanography* (M. Sears, ed.), American Association of Science, Publication No. 67, Washington, DC, 1961.

11-3.   H. Brichert, J. P. Riley, and G. Skirrow, *Chemical Oceanography*, Academic Press, London, 1965.

11-4.   A. Lerman, *Geochemical Processes: Water and Sediment Environments*, Wiley-Interscience, New York, 1979.

11-5.   A. Nelson-Smith, *Oil Pollution and Marine Ecology*, Plenum Press, New York, 1973.

11-6.   H. D. Holland, *The Chemistry of the Atmosphere and Oceans*, Wiley-Interscience, New York, 1978.

11-7.   S. A. Berridge, R. A. Dean, R. G. Fellows, and A. Fish, "The Properties of Persistent Oil at Sea" in *Proceedings of the Symposium Scientific Aspects of Pollution of the Sea by Oil* (P. Hepple, ed), Institute of Petroleum, London, 1965.

11-8.   R.M. Harrison, S.J. deMora, S. Radsomanikis, and W.R. Johnston, *Introductory Chemistry for the Environmental Sciences*, Cambridge University Press, Cambridge, 1991.

11-9.   R.V. Thomann and J.A. Mueller, *Principles of Surface Water Quality Modeling and Control*, Harper and Row, New York, 1987.

11-10. R. M. Harrison, *Understanding Our Environment: An Introduction to Environmental Chemistry and Pollution*, 2nd ed., Royal Society of Chemistry, Cambridge, 1995.

11-12. W. Stumm and J. J. Morgan, *Aquatic Chemistry*, 2nd ed., Wiley-Interscience, 1981.

11-13. R. V. Thomann and J. A. Maeller, *Principles of Surface Water Quality Modeling and Control*, Harper and Row, New York, 1987.

11-14. E. J. Middlebrooks, D. H. Falkenborg, and T. E. Maloney, *Modeling the Eutrophication in Process*, Ann Arbor Science, Ann Arbor, Michigan, 1974.

11-15. A. V. Kaffka, *Sea-Dumped Chemical Weapons: Aspects, Problems and Solutions*, Kluwer Academic, Dororecht, 1996.

11-16. S. J. deMora, *Tributylin, Core Study of an Environmental Contaminant*, Cambridge University Press, Cambridge, 1996.

11-17. L. C. Wrobel, *Water Pollution, 2. Modeling, Measuring and Prediction, Computational Mechanics*, Southampton, 1993.

11-18. G. Tchohanogloeus and T. G. Schroeder, *Water Quality*, Addison Wesley, 1985.

PROBLEM SET

1. If 100,00 gal quantity Venezuelan oil was spilled offshore 2 miles to Long Beach Harbor, what time would the first oil slick reach the shore? What is the thickness of the slick?

2. The Cu^{2+} concentrations of a river upstream and downstream is respectively 4 and 2 m/m^3/day. If the attached and suspended biomass is about 0.5 g/m^3 respectively and the hydraulic radius is 50 m, find the rate of self-purification and the amount of ecological self-purification of the river.

CHAPTER **12**

HYDROSPHERE — WATER TREATMENT

The chemicals present in water affect the water quality for its end use. We must learn that not only the key parameters for describing the water quality are essential, but the chemistry of various spheres including the interactions thereof are equally important. Prior to even developing a treatment technology, the constituents (as well as the amount of chemical species in a given wastewater) must be identified. In general, the development of various combinations of schematics from chemical unit processes and observations is essential for development of a useful, multi-stage treatment.

This chapter consists of four sections. The first section will exemplify pollution and how it affects water quality. We will review the chemistry of DO, BOD, and COD and their role in water quality criterion. In the second section, we will review why staged water treatment is necessary. In the third section, odor and taste in water will be addressed. Then, in the fourth section, industrial wastewater will be discussed, with regard to its characteristics and treatments.

12.1 WATER QUALITY CRITERIA

The ratio of pollutant fluxes to natural fluxes increases with the increasing activity of civilization. The quality of water bodies thus generally reflects the range of human activity within the catchment area. In a broad sense, the potential perturbation of lakes, rivers, estuaries, and coastal areas may be related to population density and energy dissipation in the drainage area of these water bodies. Figure 12-1 shows the relationships among per capita energy consumption, population density, and energy consumption per unit area for various countries. As Figure 12-1 shows, in most countries of the Northern hemisphere the energy flux by civilization markedly exceeds the biotic energy flux.

Pollutional loading may be related to the population density and to the per capita waste production in a drainage area. The potential loading, J, of various rivers and estuaries may be estimated by

$$J = \frac{\text{inhibitants}}{\text{drainage area}} \times \frac{\text{drainage areas}}{\text{runoff}} \times \frac{\text{waste production}}{\text{capita}} \times (1-\eta) \qquad [12\text{-}1]$$

where η is the **effectiveness of environmental protection measures** such as recycling, waste retention, and waste treatment. The higher the effectiveness, the lower the loading factor, J, is. Similarly, the loading of a lake can be formulated as

$$J = \frac{\text{inhabitants}}{\text{drainage area}} \times \frac{\text{drainage areas}}{\text{lake area}} \times \frac{1}{\text{lake depth}} \times \frac{\text{waste production}}{\text{capita}} \times (1-\eta) \qquad [12\text{-}2]$$

The gross national product per time within the drainage area may be used to estimate the potential waste production because it measures economic production — that is, the value of material goods and services for private and public consumption. Table 12-1 illustrates the comparison of some loading parameters of some lakes. The six lakes at the top of the list in the table are or have been eutrophied prior to treatment or waste diversion.

Water pollution consists of a variety of material flows that depend on population density, lifestyle, and cultural activities. The resulting water composition is determined by the entity of interacting chemical, physical, and biological factors which are **intensity factors** (activity, concentration, redox potential, temperature, and velocity gradient). These intensive variables, above all the activities of the chemical constituents, primarily determine the type of community of organisms present in the water.

Water quality criteria are scientifically established requirements concerning intensity factors. These criteria form the basis for judgements with respect to the compatibility of a water composition with ecological objectives or designated water uses. Standards are tolerance levels established by governmental authorities in programs for water pollution abatement. Table 12-2 lists criteria ranges for raw water sources of domestic water supplies in California.

For drinking water quality, there is the maximum contaminant level (MCL). To reach the MCL goal, the U.S. EPA established the primary standard concerning the synthetic organic chemicals (SOSs), the trihalomethanes (THMs), the volatile organic chemicals (VOCs), and the microbiological contaminant of coliform ranges from $10^6/100$ mL to 1/100 mL, as shown in Table 12-3. The 1994 MCL goal from the EPA also includes the elimination of *Giardia*, *Legionella*, and viruses.

The preservation of fresh water as a supply of potable water and the maintenance of most natural waters as life preservation systems such as production of aquatic food and reservoirs for genetic diversity) are among the most important goals of water pollution control. It is difficult to evaluate objectively and codify water quality because (1) the effects of water composition on the various ecological consequences are not well understood and are difficult to quantify, and (2) it is difficult to define a reference state (a hypothetical pristine state) of the water.

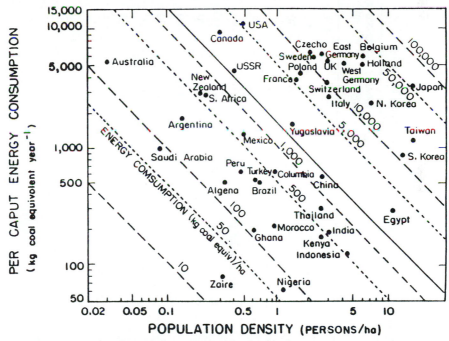

Figure 12-1. The relationships among per-person energy consumption, population density, and energy consumption per unit area (or population potential) for different countries in 1972. [Note: the area of each country includes only FAO-defined agricultural areas. For comparison, solar input at the Earth's surface is ca. 10^6 kg coal eq year^{-1} ha^{-1}. (1 kg coal ea year^{-1} = 1.1 × 10^{-4} Wm^{-2})] (After Y. H. Li, Ref 12-9.)

Table 12-1. Comparison of Some Loading Parameters of Some Lakes

Lake	Country	Surrounding Factor [a]	Mean Depth (m)	Inhabitants Per km^{-2}	Inhabitants Per m^3 Lake Volume	Energy consumption Per Lake Volume (W m^{-3})
Greifensee	Switzerland	15	19	441	348	1.81
Plattensee	Hungary	10	3	~60	200	0.97
Lake Washington	United States	~15	18	~50	42	0.48
Lake Constance	Switzerland-Germany-Austria	19	90	114	24	0.12
Lake Lugano	Switzerland-Italy	11	130	264	22.3	0.11
Lake Biwa	Japan	4.5	41	~150	16	0.07
Lake Winnipeg	Canada	35	13	~3	8.1	0.07
Lake Titicaca	South America	14	~100	~40	5.6	0.001
Lake Victoria	Africa	3	40	~70	5.1	0.002
Lake Baikal	USSR	17	730	~5	0.6	0.0005
Lake Tanganiika	Africa	4	572	~50	0.3	0.0001
Lake Inari	Lapland	12	~50	0.5	0.1	0.0005
Lake Superior	Canada-United States	1.5	145	~5	0.05	0.0005

[a] Drainage area/ lake area

Two water quality criteria have been used most commonly in previous decades: (1) the concentration of **dissolved oxygen** as a pollution and the biochemical oxygen demand as a loading parameter; and (2) **indicator organisms** that are indicative of the existence of certain pollution conditions. This concept which is referred to as **biotic index** is illustrated in Figure 12-2.

There are some collective parameters, such as **chemical oxygen demand** (COD), **biological oxygen demand** (BOD), and **total organic carbon** (TOC). One or more are often used to estimate the quantity of organic matter present in water bodies. COD is obtained by measuring the equivalent quantity of an oxidizing agent (usually permanganate or dichromate in acid solution), necessary for oxidation of the organic constituents. The amount of oxidant consumed is customarily expressed in equivalents of oxygen. The BOD test measures the oxygen uptake in the microbiologically mediated oxidation of organic matter directly. In both tests, not all the organic matter reacts with the oxidants. In determinations of TOC, the carbon oxide produced in the oxidation or combustion of a water sample is measured.

Table 12-2. Criteria Ranges for Raw Water Sources of Domestic Water Supply in California

Constituent	Excellent Source of Water Supply, Requiring Disinfection Only As Treatment	Good Source of Water Supply, Requiring Usual Treatment Such As Filtration and Disinfection	Poor Source of Water Supply, Requiring Special or Auxiliary Treatment and Disinfection
BOD (5-day), mg/L			
Monthly average:	0.75-1.5	1.5-2.5	over 2.5
Maximum day, or sample:	1.0-3.0	3.0-4.0	over 4.0
Codiform MPN per 100 ml			
Monthly average:	50-100	50-5,000	over 5,000
Maximum day, or sample:	Less than 5% over 100	Less than 20% over 5.000	Less than 5% over 20,000
Dissolved oxygen			
mg/L average:	4.0-7.5	4.0-6.5	4.0
% saturation:	75% or better	60% or better	—
pH (average)	6.0-6.5	5.0-9.0	3.8-10.5
Chlorides, max. mg/L	50 or less	50-250	over 250
Fluorides, mg/L	Less than 1.5	1.5-3.0	over 3.0
Phenolic compounds, max, mg/L	None	0.005	over 0.005
Color, units	0-20	20-150	over 150
Turbidity, units	0-10	10-250	over 250

Groups (families)	Score
Mayfly larvae (e.g. Euphemeridae, Ecdyonuridae) **Stone-fly larvae** (e.g. Leuctridae, Perlidae) Cased-caddis larvae (with stones and sand)	10
Damselfly and dragonfly larvae Caseless (free-living) caddis larvae (e.g. philopotamidae)	8
Mayfly larvae (Caenidae) Cased-caddis larvae (with plant debris)	7
Large freshwater mussels (60 × 100 mm) (Unionidae) Freshwater shrimp (Gammaridae)	6
Water bugs (e.g. Corixidae) Water beetles (e.g. Halipidae, Elminthidae) Caseless caddis larvae (e.g. Hydropsychidae) Fly larvae (e.g. Tipulidae, Simulidae) Flatworms (e.g. Planariidae)	5
Mayfly larvae (Baetidae) Alderfly larvae (Sialidae) Water mites	4
Snails (e.g. Lymnaeidae, Planorbidae, Physidae) Small freshwater bivalves (e.g. Sphaeriidae) Leeches (e.g. Glossiphoniidae) Water hog louse (Asellidae)	3
Fly larvae (midge) (Chironomidae)	2
Worms (e.g. Tubificidae) Fly larvae (rat-tailed maggot)	1

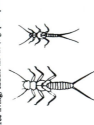

Figure 12-2.   Simplified ranking of a typical biotic index.

Table 12-3.   Drinking Water Standards

Contaminant	United States EPA	Canada NHW	International WHO
PRIMARY STANDARDS (Health) MCL			
Total Coliforms (Membrane Filter)	Avg 1/100 mL	2/100 mL	0
	Max 4/100 mL	3/100 mL	—
Turbidity	1-5 TU	1-5 TU	<1
Inorganic Chemicals (mg/ L)			
Arsenic (As)	0.05	0.05	0.05
Barium (Ba)	1.0	1.0	—
Cadmium (Cd)	0.010	0.005	0.005
Chromium (Cr)	0.05	0.05	0.05
Fluoride (F)	1-2 (15°C)	1.5	1.5
Lead (Pb)	0.05	0.05	0.05
Mercury (Hg)	0.002	0.001	0.001
Nitrate (N)	10.0	10.0	10.0
Selenium (Se)	0.01	0.01	0.01
Silver (Ag)	0.05	0.05	—
Organic Chemicals (mg/ L)			
Endrin	0.0002	0.0002	—
Lindane	0.004	0.004	0.003
Methoxychlor	0.1	0.01	0.030
Toxaphene	0.005	0.005	—
2-4-D	0.1	0.1	0.1
2,4,5 TP	0.01	0.01	—
Trihalomehanes	0.10	0.35	—
SECONDARY STANDARDS (Aesthetics) RCL			
Chloride (Cl)	250 mg/ L	250 mg/ L	250 mg/ L
Color	15 color units	15 color units	15 color units
Copper (Cu)	1.0 mg/ L	1.0 mg/ L	1.0 mg/ L
Iron (Fe)	0.3 mg/ L	0.3 mg/ L	0.3 mg/ L
Manganese (Mn)	0.05 mg/ L	0.05 mg/ L	0.1 mg/ L

Table 12-3.   (continued)

Contaminant	Unites States	Canada	International
	EPA	NHW	WHO
Odor	3 (Threshold)	Nil	Nil
pH	7.5 ± 1	7.5 ± 1	7.5 ± 1
Sulfate (SO_4)	250 mg/ L	500 mg/ L	400 mg/ L
Total Diss. Solids	500 mg/ L	500 mg/ L	1000 mg/ L
Zinc (Zn)	5.0 mg/ L	5.0 mg/ L	5.0 mg/ L

Where two values are noted (turbidity, fluorides), the lower one indicates the recommended contaminant level (RCL); the higher one indicates the maximum contaminant level (MCL) acceptable.

Sources: U.S. Environmental Protection Agency (EPA), *National Interim Primary Drinking Water Regulations*, EPA 570/9-76-003, 1976; Dept. of National Health and Welfare Canada (NWH), *Guidelines for Canadian Drinking Water Quality*, 1978; World Health Organization (WHO), *International Standards for Drinking Water*, 1983.

12.1.1   Chemistry of Dissolved Oxygen (DO)

Any gas equilibrated with water is governed by the so-called Henry's law. This law states that the amount of gas which dissolves is proportional to the partial pressure of the gas. If X is any gas, then

$$X_{(aq)} = \text{const.} \, P_{X(g)}$$

or

$$K_H = \frac{X_{(aq)}}{P_{X(g)}} \qquad \text{[12-3]}$$

The proportional constant is Henry's law constant. Some common values are listed following this paragraph, all expressed in units of mole/L/atm. Henry's law will be discussed in detail in Chapter 26.

N_2	6.5×10^{-4}
CO_2	3.4×10^{-2}
CO	9×10^{-4}
O_2	1.3×10^{-3}
O_3	1.3×10^{-2}

In the case of oxygen, the atmosphere contains 0.21 atm O_2, so the solubility of oxygen in water can be evaluated

$$O_{2(aq)} = K_H \, P_{O_2 \, (g)}$$

$$= (1.3 \times 10^{-3} \text{ mole L}^{-1} \text{ atm})(0.21 \text{ atm})$$

$$= 2.7 \times 10^{-4} \text{ mole L}^{-1}$$

or

$$= (2.7 \times 10^{-4} \text{ mole L}^{-1})(32 \text{ g mole}^{-1})(1000 \text{ mg/g})$$

$$= 8.7 \text{ mg L}^{-1} = 8.7 \text{ ppm}$$

(Notice that the difference of ppm in air is only by volume basis. In dissolved species in water, the unit can be expressed on weight basis.)

Dissolved oxygen (DO) is essential for aquatic life, and this value can be altered by thermal pollution, and decomposition of biomass; for example, algal blooms and any oxidizable substances in water such as sewage, and so on. The measurements of DO can be carried out as follows:

Winkler's Method of Titration
The sample is treated with manganese sulfate in an alkaline solution. The precipitated manganese dioxide is used to oxidize I^- to I_2, which is back-titrated with standard sodium thiosulfate solution until no I_2 end point can be seen.

$$Mn^{2+} + OH^- + \tfrac{1}{2}O_2 \rightarrow MnO_2(s) + H_2O$$

$$MnO_2(s) + 4H^+ + 2I^- \rightarrow I_2 + Mn^{2+} + 2H_2O$$

$$I_2 + 2Na_2S_2O_3 \rightarrow Na_2S_4O_6 + 2NaI$$

Spectrophotometry
Methyltene blue and indigo carmine, which are dyes, can be oxidized by O_2 to the forms leaving different colors.

Makareth Oxygen Electrode
Oxygen can diffuse in the cell through a thin, disposable polyethylene membrane.
    Cathode (made of Ag)

$$O_2(g) + 2H_2O(e) + 4e^- \rightarrow 4OH^-(aq)$$

Anode (made of Pb)

$$4OH^-(aq) + 2Pb(s) \rightarrow 2Pb(OH)_2(s) + 4e^-$$

Overall

$$O_2(g) + 2H_2O(l) + 2Pb(s) \rightarrow 2Pb(OH)_2(s)$$

The potential across this, cell which depends on P_{O_2}, can be measured as follows:

$$E_{cell} = E^0 - \frac{RT}{nF} \ln\left(\frac{1}{P_{O_2}}\right) \qquad [12\text{-}4]$$

This voltametric device is calibrated with constant potential, and the current flow is directed proportional to DO.

12.1.2   Biochemical Oxygen Demand (BOD)

In a water solution, the organics can be utilized by microorganisms. The amount of oxygen consumed during microbial utilization of the organics is termed **BOD**. Laboratory determination is based on the DO concentrations initially and finally. Most natural and municipal wastewaters contain a population of microorganisms that will consume the organics. In sterile waters, microorganisms must be added and the material containing the organisms determined and subtracted from total BOD of the mixture. Usually, the BOD_5 represents the oxygen consumed in five days. The total BOD or DOD at any given time period can be determined.
    The rate at which organics are utilized by microorganisms is assumed to be first-order reaction. Mathematically, they can be expressed as

$$\frac{dL_t}{dt} = -kL_t \qquad [12\text{-}5]$$

where L_t is the oxygen equivalent of organics at time t and k is reaction rate constant usually the units of L_t are mg per liter, and k are day^{-1} or

$$\frac{d\,L_t}{L_t} = -kdt$$

$$\int_{L_0}^{L} \frac{dL_t}{L_t} = -k \int_{0}^{t} dt \qquad \text{[12-6]}$$

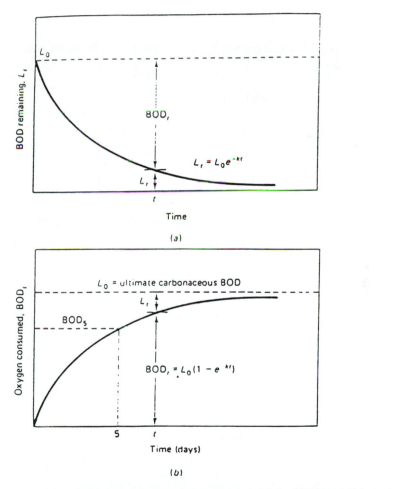

Figure 12-3.   Idealized carbonaceous oxygen demand: (a) the BOD remaining as a function of time, and (b) the oxygen consumed.

$$\ln\left(\frac{L_t}{L_0}\right) = -kt \qquad\qquad [12\text{-}7]$$

$$L_t = L_0 e^{-kt}$$

Here, L_0 represents total oxygen equivalent of organics at time zero. Graphically, the oxygen equivalent, L, and BOD, mg/L of O_2 can be seen in Figure 12-3. We define

$$y_t = L_0 - L_t = L_0 - L_0 e^{-kt} = L_0\left(1 - e^{-kt}\right) \qquad\qquad [12\text{-}8]$$

where y_t represents BOD$_t$ of the water. As y_t approach L_0, the BOD$_t$ becomes BOD$_u$, the ultimate BOD. So

$$BOD_u = L_0 \qquad\qquad [12\text{-}9]$$

Usually, the common logarithm of base 10 is used.

$$\frac{L_t}{L_0} = e^{-kt} = 10^{-k't} \qquad\qquad [12\text{-}10]$$

where $k' = k/2.3$. To evaluate k and L_0, Thomas has developed a graphical method, from

$$y_t = L_0\left(1 - 10^{-k't}\right) \qquad\qquad [12\text{-}11]$$

rearrange to read

$$\left(\frac{t}{y_t}\right)^{\frac{1}{3}} = \left(2.30 k' L_0\right)^{-\frac{1}{3}} + \left(\frac{k'^{\frac{2}{3}}}{3.43 L_0^{\frac{1}{3}}}\right) t \qquad\qquad [12\text{-}12]$$

If one plots $(t/y_t)^{1/3}$ versus t, a straight line will result with slope b and intercept a, and

$$k' = 2.61 \frac{b}{a} \qquad\qquad [12\text{-}13]$$

$$L_0 = \frac{1}{\left(2.3\, k' a^3\right)} \qquad\qquad [12\text{-}14]$$

and

$$k = 2.3\,k' \qquad\qquad [12\text{-}15]$$

12.1.3 Chemical Oxygen Demand (COD)

This test employs potassium dichromate in boiling sulfuric acid (150°C) in the presence of a silver catalyst to oxidize the organics into CO_2 and H_2O. The hexavalent chromate is reduced to trivalent chromium ion. Taking monopotassium salt of phthalate as an example, the balanced equation is

$$2KC_8H_5O_4 + 10K_2Cr_2O_7 + 41H_2SO_4 = 16CO_2 + 46H_2O + 10Cr_2(SO_4)_3 + 11K_2SO_4$$

In the preceding equation, each molecule of potassium dichromate has the same oxidizing power as 1.5 molecules of oxygen. The reason is that Cr^{6+} to Cr^{3+} requires three electrons, but oxygen only requires two electrons. Therefore, two moles of potassium phthalate consume 15 moles of oxygen, which is in this case, equivalent to 10 moles of dichornate. The COD of the sample is determined by titrating the remaining dichromate with ferrous sulfate

$$6Fe^{2+} + Cr_2O_7^{2-} + 14H^+ = 6Fe^{3+} + 2Cr^{3+} + 7H_2O$$

In general, the balance of equation of organic molecules to have the chromate can be simplified by the following:

$$C_nH_aO_b + cCr_2O_7^{2-} + 8cH^+ = nCO_2 + \frac{(a+8c)}{2}H_2O + 2cCr^{3+}$$

and

$$c = \frac{2n}{3} + \frac{a}{6} - \frac{b}{3}$$

Using this equation to figure out the ratio of dichromate to phthalate, the ratio is still 5 to 1 because $c = 5$.

An oxidation-reduction indicator such as ferroin (ferrous 1,10-phenonithroline sulfate) can indicate when all the dichromate can be reduced by ferrous ions. It gives sharp color changes in spite of the green color produced by Cr^{3+} ion.

12.1.4   Theoretical Oxygen Demand (ThOD) and Other Tests

Similar to potassium dichromate oxidation as mentioned in Section 12.1.3, potassium permanganate has been selected to obtain similar results. This is termed **permanganate value (PV)**. A rapid automated test has been developed to oxidize the sample in presence of catalyst at 900°C with a stream of air. This is termed **total oxygen demand (TOD)**. A total carbon analyzer can also determine the total organic carbon (TOC) by removing the inorganic carbon through acidification or through dual combustion tube in the analyzer. The TOC can correlate well with COD result. Stumm and Morgan have provided a chart (see Figure 12-4) that the oxidation state of organic compound can be estimated by

$$\frac{4(TOC - COD)}{TOC} = \text{oxidation state} \qquad [12\text{-}15]$$

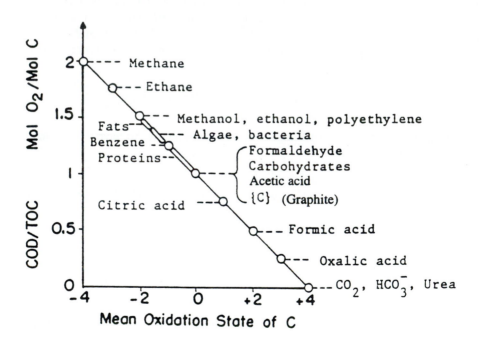

Figure 12-4.   Oxygen demand and mean oxidation state of organic C. (Stumm and Morgan, 1981. Ref. 12-1.)

Linear relationships also are generally found to exist between each of four assays, with relative strength being in the following order:

$$PV < BOD < COD < COD < TOD$$

ThOD can be approximated from simple calculation. For urea, CH_4N_2O, oxygen is still needed.

$$CH_4 N_2 O + \frac{9}{2} O_2 = CO_2 + 2 H_2 O + 2 NO_3$$

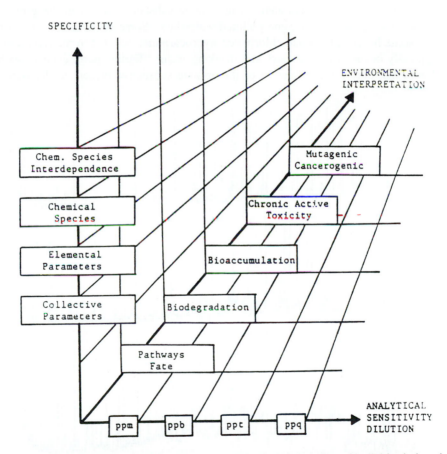

Figure 12-5. Sensitive analytical techniques and a knowledge of individual chemical species and their interdependence are prerequisites for water quality interpretations. (Stemm and Morgan, 1981, Ref. 12-1.)

Thus 1 g urea requires 1.2 mg of O_2 or in solution the ThOD value is 1200 mg O_2/L.

Implicit in water quality criteria is a chemical model. With the help of the model, tolerance levels compatible with designated water uses can be rationalized and quantified. In measuring and quantifying the diverse chemical variables (including pollutants), one first encounters the analytical problems of sensitivity and specificity. Analytical chemistry has made remarkable progress in improving the sensitivity of detection. The environmental effects of a substance, such as the toxicological effects and chemical and geochemical reactivity, is structure specific, as shown in Figure 12-5. The other factor making the environmental interpretation more complicated is its dependence on the knowledge of pathways and of biogeochemical parity.

Remember that even the water we drink is not pollutant-free. Figure 12-6 gives gas chromatographic results for the analysis of volatile substances found in the ground, river and drinking water within the same polluted watershed. Some of the more refractory substances (some hydrocarbons and chlorinated hydrocarbons) detected in the river water may also typically occur in groundwater and drinking water. Furthermore, even in such a detailed analysis, only a small fraction of the organic substances present in the water is detected.

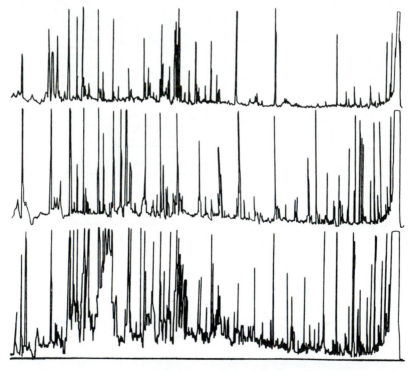

Figure 12-6.   Specific detection of organic contaminants in river water (top), groundwater (middle), and drinking water (bottom). Each peak represents (at least) one compound.

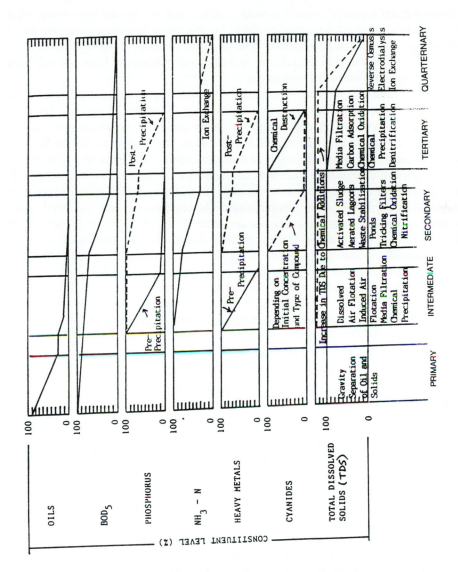

Figure 12-7.   Fate of industrial wastewater constituents in treatment processes.

12.2 STAGED WASTEWATER TREATMENT

To the environmental engineer's concern, water treatment can be divided into sewage treatment of wastewater and drinking water supplies. Potable water treatment plants are generally simpler than sewage treatment plants. The unit operations in the potable water treatment plants can also be found in the practice of wastewater treatment. Here, we will focus on sewage and industrial wastewater treatment.

Figure 12-7 illustrates the fate of industrial wastewater constituents in treatment processes. One can also see from the figure that various operations can be applied. The processes selected in a treatment plant depend heavily on the quality of the source water and the quality of the effluent required. Economic consideration and regulation standards of the effluents are usually the controlling factors of water treatment. The main objective of conventional wastewater treatment processes is the reduction of the biochemical oxygen demand, suspended solids, and pathogenic organisms. In addition, it may be necessary to remove nutrients, toxic components, nonbiodegradable compounds, and dissolved solids. Conventional wastewater treatment processes are often classified as primary treatment, intermediate treatment, secondary treatment, tertiary treatment, and quaternary treatment. Most of the common operations are shown in Figure 12-7. Because many different combinations of these operations are possible, each situation must be evaluated in order to select the best combination. Remember that in each of the treatments, there are at least a half dozen unit operations that have evolved. Each unit operation again depends on a particular contaminant (chemicals) in the water. The order of the unit process may be discharged according to (1) the original chemical composition (2) the by-product formed during the treatment, and (3) the precursors for potential and anticipated products.

12.2.1 Primary and Intermediate Treatment

Primary treatment processes are used to screen out coarse solids, to reduce the size of solids, to eliminate floating oil and grease, and to equalize fluctuations in flow or concentration through short-term storage. **Intermediate treatment processes** include dissolved air flotation (DAF), induced air flotation, media filtration, and chemical precipitation.

Impurities in water vary in size by about six orders of magnitude, from a few angstroms for soluble substances to a few hundred microns for suspended materials. The removal of a large proportion of these impurities in wastewater treatment is accomplished by sedimentation. In a sedimentation unit, solid particles are allowed to settle to the bottom of the tank under quiescent conditions. However, because many of the impurities are too small for gravitational settling alone, to be an effective removal process, the aggregation of these particles into large, more readily settleable aggregates is essential for successful separation by sedimentation. This process of aggregation is termed **"coagulation"** (discussed in Chapter 21). Chemicals are often used in the coagulation process to destabilize the colloidal particles and thus to increase the rate of aggregation. Common chemicals used are alum,

Table 12-4. Chemical Compounds Used in Coagulation Processes

Compounds	Formula	Commercial Strength	Grades Available	Weight (lbs/ft)	Remarks
Coagulants:					
Aluminum sulfate	$Al_2(SO_4)_3 \cdot 18H_2O$	17 % Al_2O_3	lump powder granules	Powder: 38-45 Other: 57-67	Coagulation and sedimentation systems; prior to pressure, filters for removal of suspended matter and oil
Sodium aluminate	$Na_2Al_2O_3$	55 % Al_2O_3	crystals	50-60	Usually added with soda ash to softeners
Ammonium alum	$Al_2(SO_4)_3(NH_3)_2SO_4 \cdot 24N_2O$	11 % Al_2O_3	lump powder	60-68	Coagulation system — not widely used
Potash alum	$Al_2(SO_4)_3 \cdot K_2SO_4 \cdot 24N_2O$	11 % Al_2O_3	lump powder	64-68	Coagulation system — not widely used
Copperas	$FeSO_4 \cdot 7H_2O$	55 % $FeSO_4$	crystals granules	63-66	Suitable coagulant only in pH range of 8.5-11.0
Chlorinated copperas	$FeSO_4 \cdot 7H_2O + 1/2CO_2$	48 % $FeSO_4$	—	—	Ferrous sulfate and chlorine are fed separately
Ferric sulfate	$Fe_2(SO_4)_3$	90 % $Fe_2(SO_4)_3$	powder granules	60-70	Coagulation — effective over wide range of pH, 4.0-11.0
Ferric chloride hydrate	$FeCl_3 \cdot 6H_2O$	60 % $FeCl_3$	crystals	—	Coagulation — effective over wide range of pH, 4.0-11.0
Magnesium oxide	MgO	90 % MgO	powder	25-35	Essentially insoluble — fed in slurry form

Table 12-4. Continued

Compounds	Formula	Commercial Strength	Grades Available	Weight (lbs/ft)	Remarks
Coagulant Aids:					
Bentonite	—	—	powder	60	Essentially insoluble — fed in slurry form
Sodium silicate	$Na_2O(SiO_2)_{3.25}$	40 Be solution	solution	86	—
pH Adjusters:					
Lime, hydrated	$Ca(OH)_2$	93 % $Ca(OH)_2$	powder	25-50	pH adjustment and softener
Soda ash	Na_2CO_3	99 % Na_2CO_3	powder	34-52	pH adjustment and softener
Caustic soda	$NaOH$	98 % $NaOH$	flake, solid, ground, solution	—	pH adjustment, softening, oil-removal systems
Sulfuric acid	H_2SO_4	200 % H_2SO_4	liquid	—	pH adjustment

ferric chloride, or lime. Table 12-4 summarizes the chemical compounds used in the coagulation process.

The reduction of solids in these stages reduces oxygen requirements in a subsequent biological step and also reduces the solids loading into the secondary sedimentation tank.

12.2.2 Secondary Treatment

Secondary treatment generally involves a **biological process** to remove organic matter through biochemical oxidation. The operations include activated sludge, aerated lagoons, waste stabilization ponds, trickling filters, chemical oxidation, and nitrification. The particular process selected depends upon such factors as quantity of wastewater, biodegradability of waste, and availability of land. Activated sludge reactors and trickling filters are the most commonly used biological processes.

In the activated sludge process (see Chapters 28 and 29 for details), wastewater is fed to an aerated tank where microorganisms consume organic wastes for maintenance and for generation of new cells. The resulting microbial floc (activated sludge) is settled in a sedimentation vessel called a clarifier, or thickener. A portion of the thickened biomass is usually recycled to the reactor to improve the performance through higher cell concentrations. Trickling filters are beds packed with rocks, plastic structures, or other media. Microbial films grow on the surface of the packing and remove soluble organics from the wastewater flowing over the packing.

12.2.3 Tertiary Treatment

Many effluent standards require wastewater treatment to remove particular contaminants or to prepare water for reuse. **Tertiary treatment** is also called the **polishing step**. Some common tertiary operations are removal of phosphorous compounds by coagulations with chemicals, removal of nitrogen compounds by ammonia stripping with air or by nitrification — denitrification in biological reactors, and removal of residual organic and color compounds by adsorption on activated carbon (see Chapter 32 for more details). The effluent water is often treated with chlorine or ozone to destroy pathogenic organisms before discharge into the receiving waters.

12.2.4 Quaternary Treatment

In cases where softer water is desired, **quaternary treatment** is necessary, and an ion exchange column is added to the process. Also, reverse osmosis or electrodialysis are commonly used if the removal of dissolved solids is required (see both Chapters 20 and 33 for more details).

12.3 OLFACTION AND TASTE IN WATER

Both taste and odor are important perceptions of an aesthetic quality. The primary test qualities are sour (e.g., HCl), salty (e.g., NaCl), sweet (e.g., sucrose), and bitter (e.g., caffeine). The primary olfactory qualities are camphoraceous (moth repellent), peppermint (mint candy), floral (roses), ethereal (dry-cleaning fluid), pungent (vinegar), and putrid (H_2S). There is a **threshold concentration** for various substances that cause taste and odor. It should be pointed out that the substances in water causing olfaction (Table 12-6) are different from those in air (Table 12-5).

Table 12-5.   Odor Thresholds of Various Substances in Air

Substance	Description	Concentration Causing Faint Odor (mg/L)
Allyl sulfide	Garlic odor	0.00005
Amyl acetate (iso)	Banana odor	0.0006
Benzaldehyde	Odor of bitter almonds	0.003
Chlorine	Pungent and irritating odor	0.010
Coumarine	Vanilla odor, pleasant	0.00034
Crotyl mercaptan	Skunk odor	0.000029
Diphenylchlorarsine	Shoe polish odor	0.0003
Hydrogen sulfide	Odor of rotten eggs, nauseating	0.0011
Ozone	Slightly pungent, irritating odor	0.001
Phenyl isothiocyanate	Cinnamon odor, pleasant	0.0024
Phosgene	Odor of ensilage or fresh-cut hay	0.0044

Source: Adapted from J. Olishifski, *Fundamentals of Industrial Hygene*, National Safety Council, Chicago, (1971)

A technique for detecting taste- and odor-producing organic compounds in water or sediments has been developed. This is called **close-loop stripping** analysis (CLSA), which strips semi-volatile organics from water for identification by GC-MS. The odor thresholds and detection limits are summarized in Tables 12-6 and 12-7.

It is widely known that odor, taste, and tongue sensations in water are caused by various **algae** and **actinomycetes** present in groundwater and surface water (Tables 12-6 and 12-8). The associated biochemical transformations including decaying and putrefaction can be important. Chlorination of water, which produces all types of chlorophenols, will give bitter tastes. Various organic compounds isolated from odor-causing aquatic organisms are identified in Table 12-9. The taste thresholds are listed in Table 12-10.

Table 12-6.   Odor Thresholds of Various Substances in Water

Compound	Threshold Odor Concentration (mg/ L)
2 – Octanol	0.13
Styrene	0.05
Ethylbenzene	0.1
Nathalene	0.007
p – Dichlorobenzene	0.15
Chloroform	20.0
Nonanal	0.001
Methyl sulfide	0.003
Geosmin	0.000005
Methylisoborneol (MIB)	0.000005
Trichloroethene	2.6
Tetrachloroethene	2.8
Dichloromethane	24.0
Toluene	0.14

Table 12-7.   Odor Thresholds and CLSA Detection

Compounds	CLSA Detection Limit (ng/ L)	Lowest Reported Threshold Odor Concentration (ng/ L)
Geosmin	2	10
2 – Methylisoborneol	2	29
2 – Isopropyl – 3 – methoxy pyrazine	2	2
2 – Isobutyl – 3 – methoxy pyrazine	2	2
2,3,6 – Trichloranisole	5	7

Source: M.J. *JAWWA 73*, 530-537, McGuire et al. (1981).

Table 12-8.   Odors, Tastes, and Tongue Sensations Association with Various Algae

Algal Genus	Algal Group	Odor When Algae Are:		Taste	Tongue Sensation
		Moderate	Abundant		
Anabaena	Blue-green	Grassy, nasturtium, musty	Septic	—	—
Anacystis	Blue-green	Grassy	Septic	Sweet	—
Aphanizomenon	Blue-green	Grassy, nasturtium, musty	Septic	Sweet	Dry
Asterionella	Diatom	Geranium, spicy	Fishy	—	—
Ceratium	Flagellate	Fishy	Septic	Bitter	—
Dinobryon	Flagellate	Violet	Fishy	—	Slick
Oscillatoria	Blue-green	Grassy	Musty, spicy	—	—
Scenedesmus	Green	—	Grassy	—	—
Spirogyra	Green	—	Grassy	—	—
Synura	Flagellate	Cucumber, muskmelon, spicy	Fishy	Bitter	Dry, metallic slick
Tabellaria	Diatom	Geranium	Fishy	—	—
Ulothrix	Green	—	Grassy	—	—
Volvox	Flagellate	Fishy	Fishy	—	—

Source: Adapted from C.M. Palmer, *Algae in Water Supplies*, U.S. Dept HEW, Washington D.C., (1962).

Table 12-9.   Structure of Various Compounds Isolated from Odor-Causing Aquatic Organisms

Compound	Structure	Associated Organisms
Methylisoborneol (MIB)		*Actinomycetes* *Oscillatoria curviceps* *Oscillatoria tenuis*
Geosmin		*Actinomycetes* *Sympioca muscoum* *Oscillatoria tenuis* *Oscillatoria simplicissima* *Oscillatoria scheremetievi*
Mucidone		*Actinomycetes*
Isobutyl mercaptan	CH_3\ $>CHCH_2 — SH$ CH_3/	*Microcystis flos-aquae*
n–Butyl mercaptan	$CH_3(CH_2)_3–SH$	*Microcystis flos-aquae* *Oscillatoria chalybea*
Isopropyl mercaptan	CH_3\ $>CHSH$ CH_3/	*Microcystis flos-aquae*
Dimethyl disulfide	$CH_3–S–S–CH_3$	*Microcystis flos-aquae* *Oscillatoria chalybea*
Dimethyl sulfide	$CH_3–S–CH_3$	*Oscillatoria chalybea* *Anabaena*
Methyl mercaptan	CH_3SH	*Microcystis flos-aquae* *Oscillatoria chalybea*

Table 12-10.   Taste Thresholds for Selected Materials

Material	Taste Threshold (mg/L)
Zn^{2+}	4-9[b]
Cu^{2+}	2-5[b]
Fe^{2+}	0.04-0.1[b]
Mn^{2+}	4-30[b]
2 – Chlorophenol[a]	0.004
2,4 – Chlorophenol[a]	0.008
2,6 – Chlorophenol[a]	0.002
Phenol	>1.0
Fluoride	10[b]

[a] Created by the action of chlorine on phenol.

[b] Threshold detected by 5 percent of panel.

Source: J. Cohen, et al., JAWWA 52,660 (1960).

Both odor and taste thresholds do not have individual Gaussian distributions. Individuals may be different and there are anosmic defects (less sensitive). The results of screening for specific anosmics are in Table 12-11. The acceptability of olfactometric results obtained have to be agreed on by different panels, as shown in Figure 12-8.

Table 12-11.   Results of Screening for Specific Anosmics

Compounds	Odor Character	Percent (%)	Anosmic Defect Factor Between Mean Anosmic Threshold and Mean Threshold for Normal Observers
Isovaleric acid	Sweaty	3	42
1 – Pyrroline	Spermous	16	39
Trimethylamine	Fishy	6	830
Isobutyraldehyde	Malty	36	340
5α-Androst–16–en–3–one	Urinuous	47	770
ω - pentadecalactone	Musky	12	13
4 - chloroaniline	Mixed	41	Not reported

Modified after H. Van Langenhore and N. Schamp in Encyclopedia of Environmental Control Technology, Vol.2, by P.N. Cheremisinoff, editor.

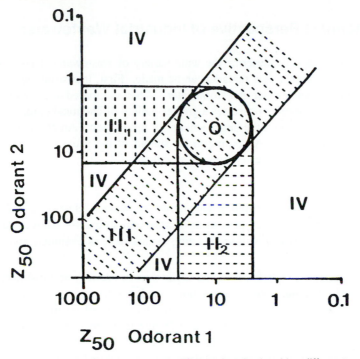

Figure 12-8.   Evaluation of olfactometric results obtained by different panels with different olfactometers. (I) Both measurements are acceptable. (II) One or both measurements are unacceptable. (III) Systematic errors have been made. (IV) Both results are unacceptable. (V. Thiele and H. Bahnmuller, *Staub, Reinhalt Luft*, *45*, 200, 1985.)

Prevention and control is always done at the source. The use of algicides (such as copper sulfate) together with citric acid as a complexing agent is often the practice. The use of chlorine and the destratification of reservoirs by mechanical mixing is also possible. The use of biological control is more efficient; for example, the use of *Bacillus subtilis* and *B. cereus* for the oxidation of the many metabolites of actinomycetes. For water supply, activated carbon and ozonation are the practice.

12.4 INDUSTRIAL WASTEWATER

Domestic wastewater contain primarily human excreta which can be easily decomposed. Even so-called **Graywater** (excluding toilet waste) can be easily treated. On the contrary, industry wastewater contains largely xenobiotics (not from nature) which are often resistant to treatment.

12.4.1 Chemical Perspective of Industrial Wastewater

It is difficult to meaningfully describe the wide variety of wastewater derived from every industrial sector. However, a few remarks can be made. First, industrial wastewater is different from municipal wastewater and stormwater. When compared with municipal wastewater, the industrial wastewater possesses a greater variety of chemical compositions due to various industrial processes and the larger amount of production. An attempt at a comparison is shown in Table 12-12. According to the output of the gross chemical species, the general breakdown of the major categories are as follows:

- Metal plating wastes, painting and derusting wastes, electronic and printing wastes, mining and metal processing wastes, and so on. — These wastes have high metal contents as well as chelating agents such as cyanides, and citric acids.

- Dairy and canning wastes, fruit and sugar wastes, brewery and distillery wastes, stockyard, slaughterhouse, packinghouse and poultry-plant wastes, agriculture wastes, and so on. — These wastes are characterized by the high protein or carbohydrate content. One remarkable feature is the recoverable fraction of the relatively nontoxic wastes that can be reused in the food industry. The principle of recovery of whey or casin from dairy wastes is no different from the recovery of albumin from modern abattoirs. So is the recovery of valuable amino acids or specific saccharides from cane-sugar manufacturers.

- Paper and pulp wastes, textile waste, leather wastes, and dyeing and painting wastes. — Various chemicals are used, including the vat dyes. The recoverable material includes lignin sulfonate, tannic acid, and so on.

- Energy and power producing wastes, including nuclear and geothermal plants, refinery wastes, oilfield wastes, heavy chemical industry wastes, steel mill, metal recovery, and finishing wastes. — Any high-temperature operation will generate a number of toxic materials. The bulk of water is used in cooling operations, ballast water blowdowns and miscellaneous discharges.

- Various fine chemical industry wastes, munitions and weaponry wastes, etc. — These wastes generally are hazardous in nature.

Regarding the wastewaters from the industry sectors, there are also some inherent problems with them. The following list is a survey of these wastewaters. In general, they are more difficulties to cope with. In many instances they are described as "alive," meaning that the water quality parameters (such as BOD and COD) change from day to day. This is due to either the photochemical change, air oxidation, or microorganism content.

Table 12-12. Representative Values of Contaminants in Wastewater

Waste Parameter	Municipal (R + C + I)			Industrial (Process)				Stormwater (Annual Runoff)
	Small	Medium	Large	Food	Meat	Plating	Textile	Small/ Medium/ Large
Volume (L)								
/capita/ day	400	500	600	—	—	—	—	—
/tonne prod.	—	—	—	10,000	12,000	—	100,000	—
% runoff	—	—	—	—	—	—	—	30/35/45
MPN (10^6/100/mL)	100	80	70	0	—	0	0	0.008
BOD_5	190	240	300	1,200	640	0	400	14
COD	320	400	500	—	—	0	—	100
TOC	135	170	215	—	—	—	—	—
Susp. Solids	225	300	350	700	300	0	100	170
Diss. Solids	450	600	700	—	200	—	1,900	170
Total N	40	30	25	0	3	0	0	3.5
Total P	10	8	7	0	—	0	0	0.35
pH	7.0	7.0	7.0	—	7.0	4 or 10	10	—
Copper	0.14	0.17	0.21	0.29	0.09	6	0.31	0.46
Cadmium	0.003	0.010	0.016	0.006	0.011	1	0.03	0.025
Chromium	0.04	0.08	0.16	0.15	0.15	11	0.82	0.16
Nickel	0.01	0.06	0.11	0.11	0.07	12	0.25	0.15
Lead	0.05	0.1	0.2	—	—	—	—	—
Zinc	0.19	0.29	0.38	1.08	0.43	9	0.47	1.6

Note: Concentrations of constituents are in mg/ L. Values for all parameters may vary widely from those noted.

Small   Small residential (R) community

Medium   Medium-size diversified municipality, residential (R), commercial (C), and industrial (I) areas with separate sewers

Large   Large industrialized city (R + C + I) with combined sewers

Food   Food waste (canning factory: pickles, beets, tomatoes, pears)

Meat   Meat processing (poultry plant with no manure or blood recovery)

Plating Plating shop (wastes are acidic with chromate baths, alkaline with cyanide baths, and are less than 2,000 m³/d for most plants)

Textile Textile mill (spun cotton yarn processed into cotton goods, sized with starch)

Adapted in part from P. G. Collins, and J. W. Ridgeway, Journal Environmental Engineering Division, American Society of Civil Engineers, Vol. 106, Reading, Mass: EE-1, 1980; L. A. Klein et al., Journal, Water Pollution Control Federation, Vol. 46:12, 1974; N. L. Nemerow, *Industrial Water Pollution*, Addison-Wesley, 1978; I. Polls and R. Lanyon, Journal, Environmental Engineering Division, American Society of Civil Engineers, Vol. 106, EE-1, 1980; and D. H. Waller, and Novak, Z., Journal of Water Pollution Control Federation, Vol. 53:3, 1981.

Problems of Industrial Wastewater

High concentration loading > 1,000–100,000 TOC when compared with domestic wastes

Complexes and chelates

Unstable

May contain biodegradable components

Colloidal state

Highly colored

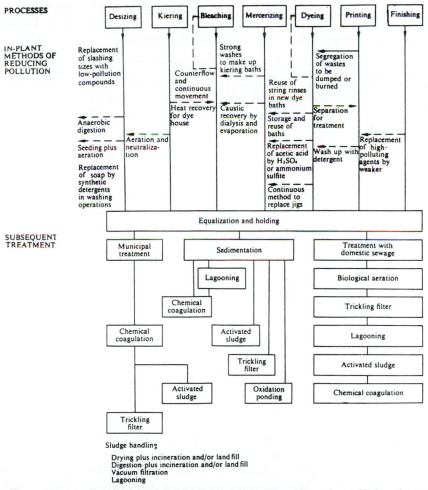

Figure 12-9.   Cotton-textile finishing waste-treatment flow chart. (Taken from the chart prepared for the F.W.P.C.A.)

One of the characteristics of industry wastewater treatment is that all the available methods can be applied. Usually, a given process will include 10-20 stages of different unit processes and operations. If one intends to treat a given wastewater, one should be prepared to understand the entire chemical process. After that, the potential value and compatibility for a given stage or course can be realized, and the wastewater can be more effectively treated. Figure 12-9, a flow chart of cotton-textile finishing waste treatment, illustrates this point.

Furthermore, for a particular type of wastewater one must know what the exact chemical composition is. The sample indication of COD, BOD, and so on is not sufficient. Unless the targeted compound which one has to eliminate is known, one cannot develop an antidote for it. Thus in the screening test, exact chemical analysis will be conducted to discover exactly what is an average chemical composition in a given wastewater. The following table lists some treatment plans for certain types of wastewater.

Type of Wastewater	Chemical Composition	Treatment Methods
Geothermal brine	H_3BO_3, HF, H_2S, Hydrocarbons	Stripping - GAC
Retort water	NH_4HCO_3, RCOOH, Nitrogen bases	Electro-oxidation
Coal conversion water	Phenol, NH_3, PAH	Pre-separation treatment, Biofilter
Postchlorination water	$CHCl_3$, THM	Ultrasound
Derusting water	Citric acid, Triethanolamine	AOP (UV-H_2O_2)
Pink water	TNT, RDX, NG, DOP, Polyacrylic acid	Anaerobic treatment

The first item in the preceding table illustrates the problem of boron in geothermal plant wastewater or geothermal brine. Boron is toxic to plant and vegetation because it interrupts the transportation metabolism of micronutrients. Therefore, efforts have been targeted towards removing boron in wastewater. An efficient way of removal is to employ a highly selective boron resin, Amberlite IRA-743, to take up the borate from waste brine, followed by using strong acid for the removal of boron from exhausted resin and subsequently regenerating the resin by an alkali. The mechanism of the reaction is illustrated in Figure 12-10. An efficient process in most cases is economically unsound and is not practical. For example, in the Kizilidere geothermal field in Turkey, the maximum permissible discharge to the nearby Büyük Menderes River is below 1 ppm. This river water is used for irrigation and because the process to control the boron is costly (not even F and S), electricity production would increase by 7¢ (US)/ kWh^{-1}. This is not ideal because utilities for most places is only 10¢ / kWh^{-1}. Both the retort wastes and coal conversion water will be discussed in synfuel wastewater.

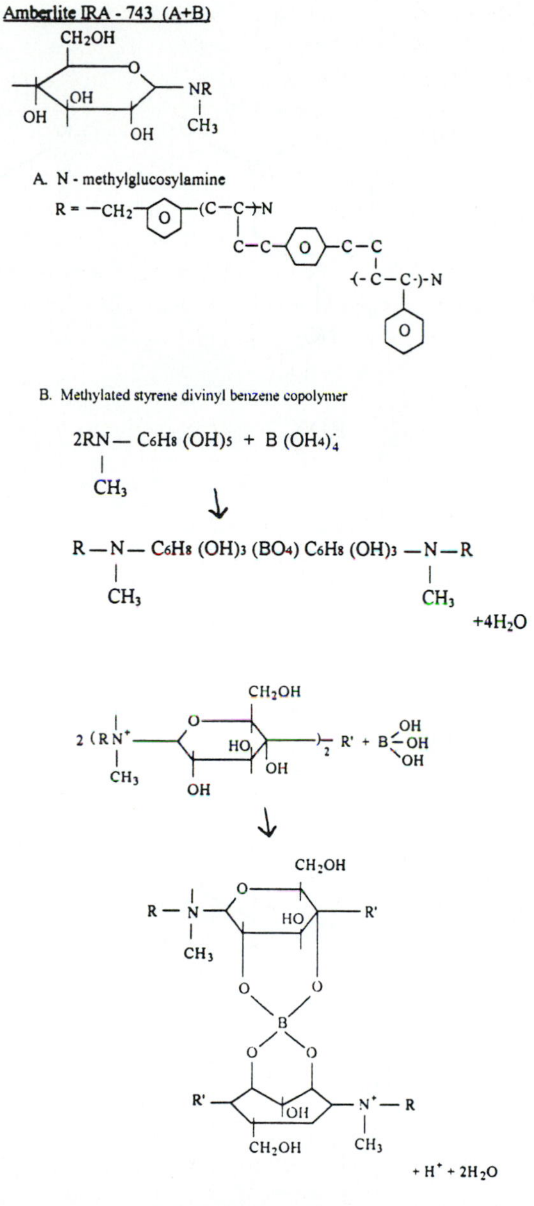

Amberlite IRA - 743 (A+B)

CH_2OH

OH

OH

OH

NR

CH_3

A. N - methylglucosylamine

$R = -CH_2-$ ⟨O⟩ $-(C-C-)N$

$C-C-$ ⟨O⟩ $-C-C$

$\{-C-C-\}-N$

⟨O⟩

B. Methylated styrene divinyl benzene copolymer

$2RN - C_6H_8 (OH)_5 + B (OH)_4^-$

CH_3

↓

$R - N - C_6H_8 (OH)_3 (BO_4) C_6H_8 (OH)_3 - N - R$

CH_3 CH_3

$+4H_2O$

$2 (RN^+ -$ ... HO ... CH_2OH ... OH $)_2 R' + B-OH$ ... OH

CH_3 OH

↓

CH_2OH

$R - N -$ ... HO ... R'

CH_3

O   O

B

O   O

$R' -$ ... OH ... $N^+ - R$

CH_2OH CH_3

$+ H^+ + 2H_2O$

Figure 12-10.   Reaction mechanism for remediation of boron.

Current Exploxives

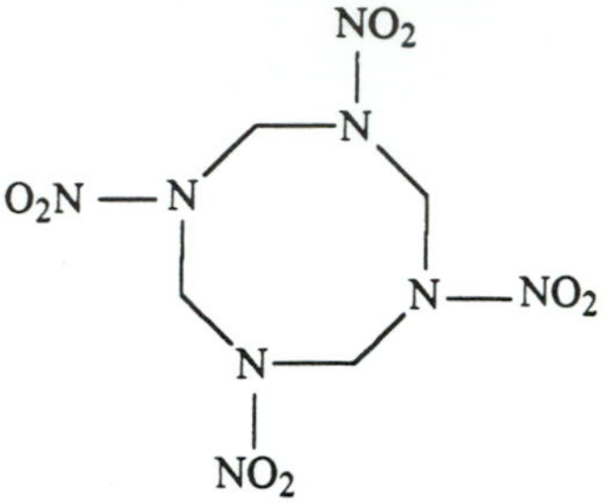

HMX 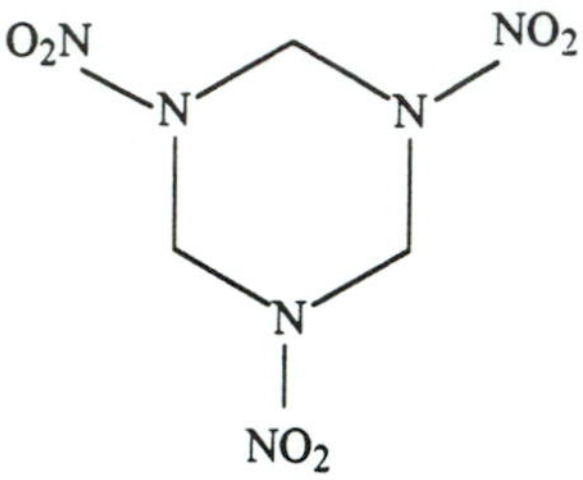   RDX 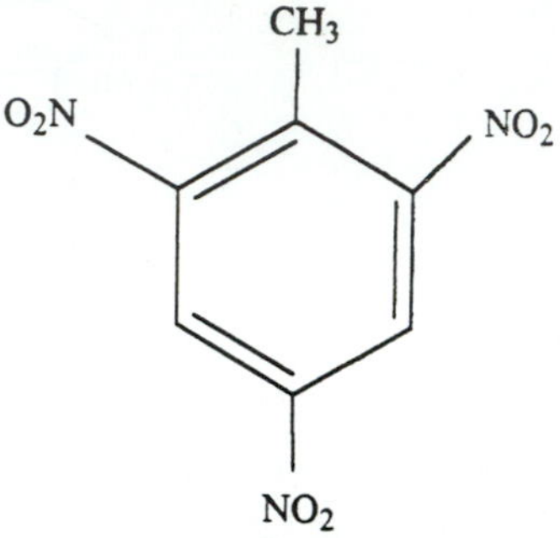   TNT

New Exploxives

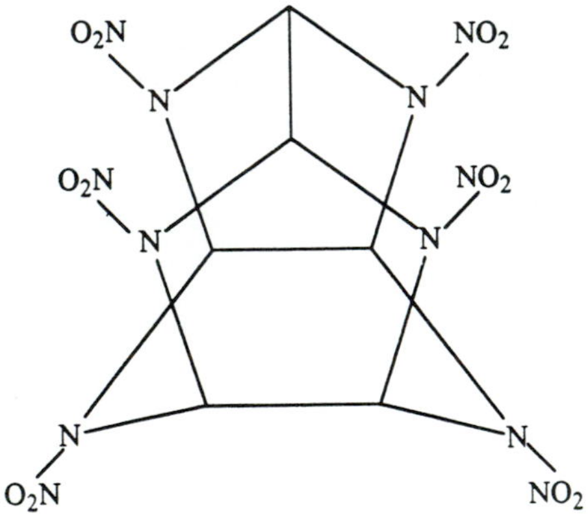

CL-20 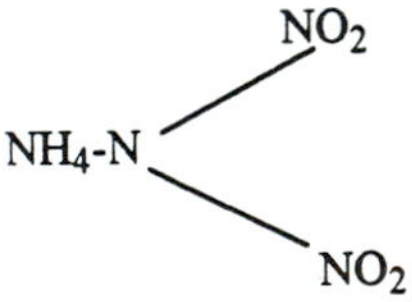   ADN 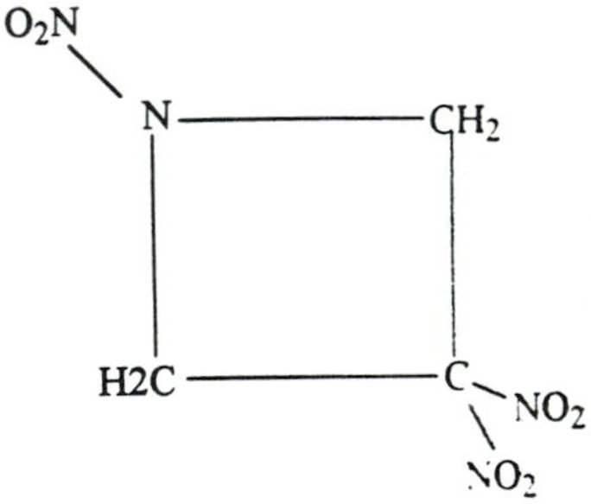   TNAZ

Figure 12-11. Common energetics available.

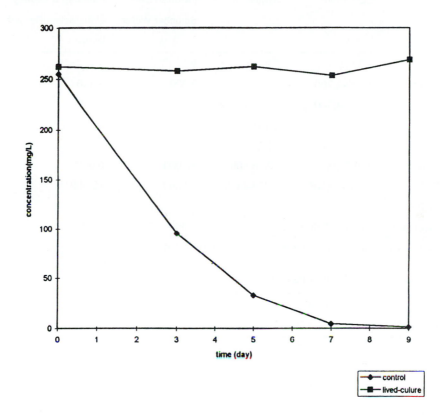

Figure 12-12.   ADN degradation by digested sewage sludge. (Kwon et al. North Am. Water and Environmental Congress, Anaheim, CA, 1996.)

Pink water usually refers to military or munitions wastewater, which contains explosives or energetics. Most energetics or explosives are nitro compounds that can be produced by C-nitration (such as TNT and TNB); the N-nitration, which includes nitramines (such as RDX, HMX and ADN) and; the O-nitration, which includes nitroglycerin, nitrocellulose, and so on. Figure 12-11 illustrates some of the current energetics available, which may be possible components of the pink water. At the moment, using mixed anerobic bacteria of digested sewage is the most effective treatment of pink water, as shown in Figure 12-12. The principle is based on the bacteria for the dentrification process, shown in Figures 12-13 and 12-14. Pesticides of nitroso amine functions can also be subjected to this treatment, as shown in Figure 12-15.

Table 12-13.   Comparison of Coal Wastewaters

	Coke Plant	Synthane	Fluidized Bed Scrubber Water	Pittsberg & Midway Liquefaction Recycle Water
pH	8.3-9.1	7.9-9.3	9.1	9.1
Alkalinity	1,200-2,700	—	3,200	3,360
NH_3	1,800-4,300	2,500-11,000	3,000	5,000
CN	10-37	0.1-0.6	—	—
SCN	100-1,500	21-200	—	—
Phenols	410-2,400	200-6,600	10,000	6,000
COD	2,500-10,000	1,700-43,000	18,000	12,000
Specific Conductance	11,000-32,000	—	5,300	4,700

Concentrations are expressed in ppm; conductivities are in μmhos/cm.

Table 12-14.   Typical Retort Water Analyses

Parameter	Concentration (mg/L, Except pH)
pH	8.5-8.7
Alkalinity	15,000-32,900
$NH_3 - N$	4,800-16,800
Organic $-$ N	733-17,000
Phenols	8.5-170
COD	11,000-18,000
BOD	350-12,000

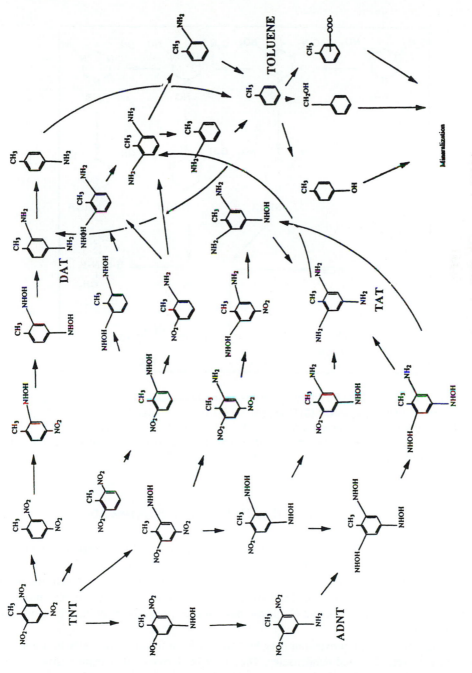

Figure 12-13.   Plausable biopathway for TNT. (Kwon et al. 1996.)

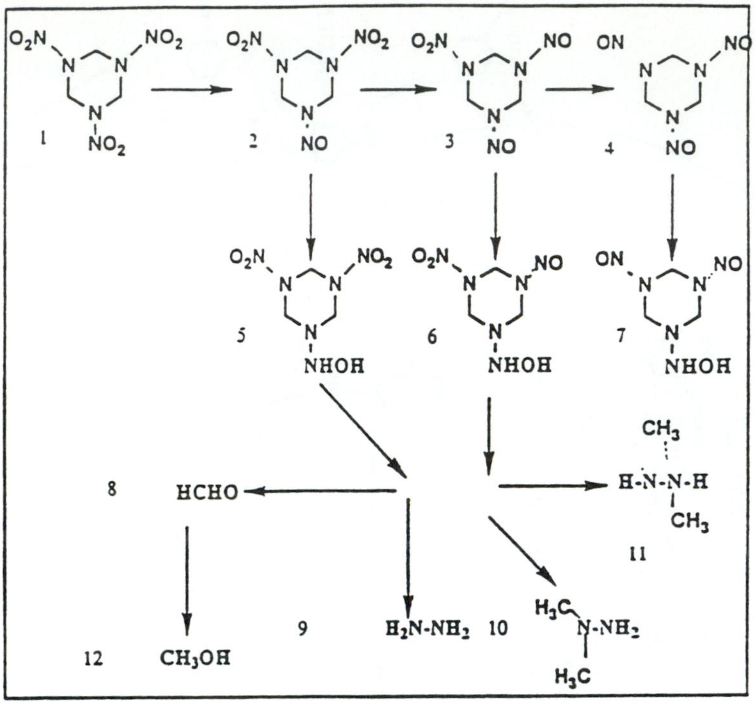

Figure 12-14.   Proposed pathway for the anaerobic biodegradation of RDX. Compounds: (1) RDX; (2) MNX; (3) DNX; (4) TNX; (5) 1-hydroxlamino-3,5-dinitro-1,3,5-triazine;(6) 1-hydroxylamino-3-nitroso-5-1,3,5-triazine; (7) 1-hydroxylamino-3,5-dinitroso-1,3,5-triazine;(8) formaldehyde;(9) hydrazine; (10) 1,1-dimethyhyrazine; (11) 1,2-dimethylhydrazine; (12) methanol. (McCormick, 1981.)

12.4.2 Chemistry Associated with Synfuel Wastewaters

In order for the synfuel industry to produce alternative liquid fuels for transportation as well as pumpable (portable) fuels, chemical conversion of the raw fuel and the subsequent refining and upgrading methods must involve high-temperature treatment. As a result, the weak linkages in the fuel molecules will be dissociated in many instances, producing products with heteroatoms such as N, S, and O. These new species produced may have a significant influence on our health.

The sources of coal conversion may be various, from the cooling water to the actual scrubber water, recycles, and condensates. They may be derived either from gasification or liquefaction processes. For oil shale retort water, this is most interesting, because water is usually coproduced with the oil in the amount of equal quantities. The loading of chemical constituents of these waters is extraordinarily high; and, in many cases, they appear as black syrups. The typical composition of coal wastewater is shown in Table 12-13 and retort water is shown in Table 12-14. The trace elements in the in-situ retort water are shown in Tables 12-15 and 12-16. Similarly, the trace elements in coal process waters are listed in Table 12-17. It has been found that arsenic appeared in many organic species in retort water. Furthermore, uranium has also been identified in retort water.

Perhaps one of the major properties of these waters is the appearance of a large variety of polycyclic aromatic hydrocarbons (PAH). Because the process waters are intimately in contact with coal liquid, the processing waters will have large numbers of PAH, as shown in Figure 12-16. No matter how oil shale is retorted, the coproduced waters also contain PAH, as shown in Figure 12-17. The detection can be easily obtained by capillary gas chromatography, shown in Figure 12-17, or reversed-phase liquid chromatography, shown in Figure 12-18. Both benz(a)- and benz(e)- pyrens are found in these waters, as shown in Figure 12-19.

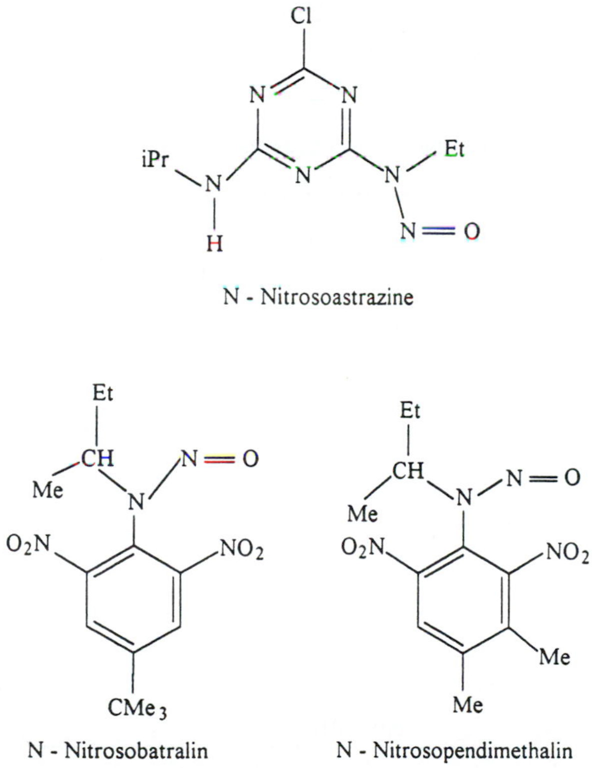

N - Nitrosoastrazine

N - Nitrosobatralin   N - Nitrosopendimethalin

Figure 12-15.   Example of nitrosated agrochemicals.

Table 12-15.   Trace Elements in Oil Shale Retort Water

Species	Concentration (mg/ L)	Land Application Limit for Irrigation Water
Boron	30 – 46	2 – 10
Fluorine	16 – 33	6 – 15
Lead	.04 – .19	4 – 10
Molybdenum	1 – 4	.02 – .05
Mercury	.001	—
Uranium	.064 – 1.08	—
Vanadium	.05 – .08	—

Table 12-16.   Trace Elements in Water Extracted from an Experimental In-Situ Retort

Species	Concentration (mg/L)	Est. Safe Concentration (mg/L)
Arsenic	.02 - .26	.05
Cadmium	.002 - .0035	.001
Copper	.042 - .087	.004
Manganese	.05 - .15	.10
Nickel	.10 - .30	.03
Selenium	.35 - .56	.01
Zinc	.09 - .77	.001 - .010

Source: From Washburne and Yen, 1981.

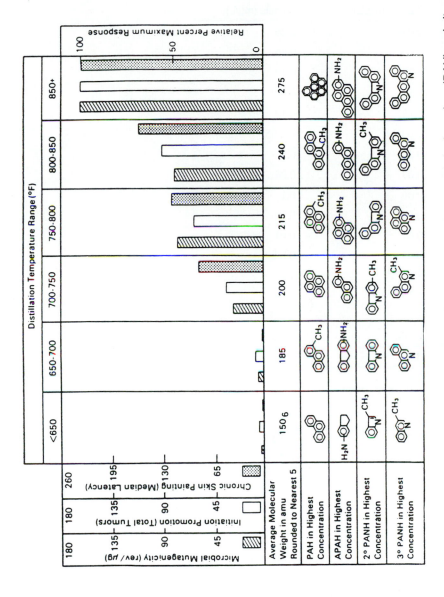

Figure 12-16.   Compounds found in the highest concentrations in polycyclic aromatic hydrocarbon (PAH) and nitrogen-containing polycyclic aromatic compound (N-PAC) fractions of solvent-refined coal II (SRC-II) 50°F boiling-point cuts shown below a histogram depicting response of those fractions in three different bioassays. A-PAHs = Amino-PAHs; 2° PANHs = secondary polycyclic aromatic nitrogen heterocycles; 3° PANHs = tertiary PANHs. Average molecule weight of the crude distillate fractions determined by low-voltage probe–inlet mass spectrometric analysis. (from Wilson et al., 1986.)

Table 12-17. Trace Elements in Coal Process Waters

Species	Gasification Sample (mg/L)	Liquefication Sample (mg/L)
Ni	< 0.6	0.26
Pb	< 0.1	0.36
Fe	0.27	0.12
Mn	0.18	0.005
Cr	0.12	0.12
As	< 0.05	< 0.05
Be	0.2	0.2
Cd	0.07	0.06
Co	0.06	0.1
Cu	0.05	0.02
Hg	0.01	0.01
Zn	0.05	0.03
Se	1.3	1.2
Ag	0.75	0.08
Mo	0.6	< 0.5
V	< 100	< 100
Sn	3.5	5.0
Mg	3.4	0.03
Ca	3.3	0.4
B	0.8	8.0
Al	< 10	< 10
Ba	< 5	< 5

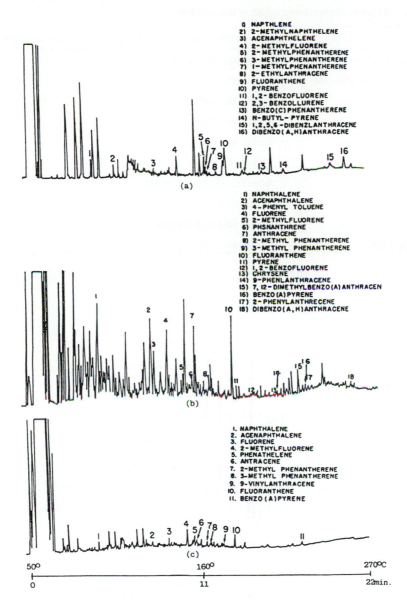

Figure 12-17.   GC analysis of (a) coal wastewater (No. 3), (b) oil shale retort water (Omega-9), and (c) oil shale retort water (No. 16). [From K.M. Sadeghi, H.C.G. de Nascinmento, M.A. Sadeghi, L.S. Wang, Y. Wang and T.F. Yen, *Fuel Sci. Tech. International*, *13*, 1393-1412,(1994)].

Table 12-18.   Nitrogen Systems Identified in Retort Water

Skeleton	Functionality (Compared to Known Carcinogenic Compound)
1,2-Benzene dicarbonitrile	Conjugated dicyanide
4-Diethylamino benzaldehyde	Conjugated carbonyl amine
2,5-Pyrrolidinedione	Conjugated carbonyl amine
Aziridine	Small aza-arene
2H-Quinolizine	Bridge head amine
Pyramidinedione	Linked diamide
2-Aminoisoxazole	Aza-(O)-substituted amide
2-Pyridiamine	α,α-diamine
Octahdrotetrazocine	Cyclic poly α,α-diamine
2-Methyl pyrazine	Conjugated Diamine

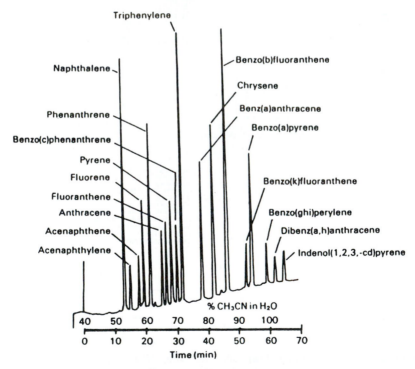

Figure 12-18.   Reverse-phase liquid chromatographic separation of polycyclic aromatic hydrocarbons. Column: Vydac 201TP reverse phase; Detection: ultraviolet absorbance at 254 NM; Conditions: linear gradient from 40–100% acetonitrile in water at 1 mL/min. (Adapted from Wise et al., 1980.)

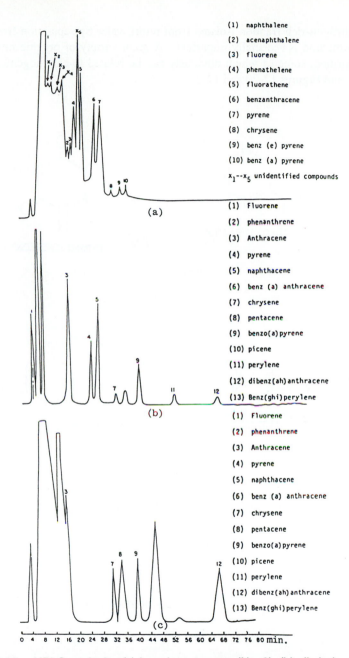

(1) naphthalene
(2) acenaphthalene
(3) fluorene
(4) phenathelene
(5) fluorathene
(6) benzanthracene
(7) pyrene
(8) chrysene
(9) benz (e) pyrene
(10) benz (a) pyrene
x_1--x_5 unidentified compounds

(1) Fluorene
(2) phenanthrene
(3) Anthracene
(4) pyrene
(5) naphthacene
(6) benz (a) anthracene
(7) chrysene
(8) pentacene
(9) benzo(a)pyrene
(10) picene
(11) perylene
(12) dibenz(ah)anthracene
(13) Benz(ghi)perylene

(1) Fluorene
(2) phenanthrene
(3) Anthracene
(4) pyrene
(5) naphthacene
(6) benz (a) anthracene
(7) chrysene
(8) pentacene
(9) benzo(a)pyrene
(10) picene
(11) perylene
(12) dibenz(ah)anthracene
(13) Benz(ghi)perylene

Figure 12-19.   HPLC analysis of (a) coal wastewater (No. 3), (b) oil shale retort water (Omega-9), and (c) oil shale retort water (No. 16). [From sadeghi et al. (1994). (Yen et al. ref 12-5.)]

The nitrogen-rich fraction isolated from retort water by separation from the macroreticular resin method is especially important. A great variety of organic nitrogen-skeletons have been formed, some of which obviously can be related to carcinogenicity as shown in Table 12-18 and Figures 12-20 and 12-21.

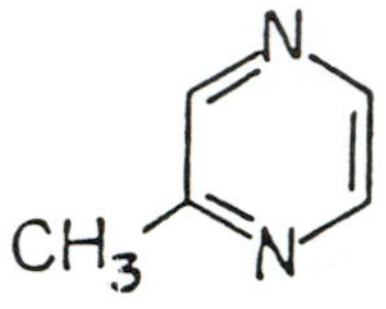

2-METHYL PYRAZINE

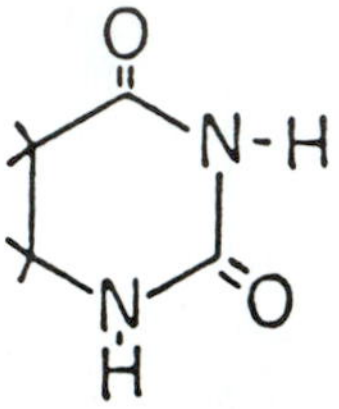

PYRAMIDINEDIONE

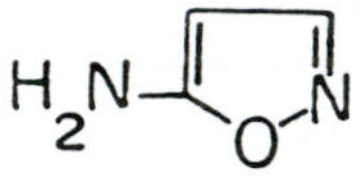

5-AMINOISOXAZOLE

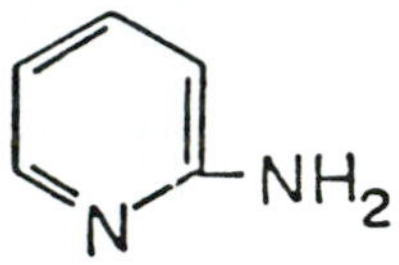

2-PYRIDINAMINE

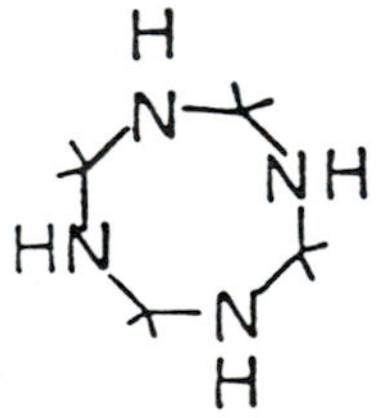

OCTAHYDROTETRAZOCINE

Figure 12-20.   Some diazine and polyazine compounds identified from retort water. (Yen, ref. 12-10.)

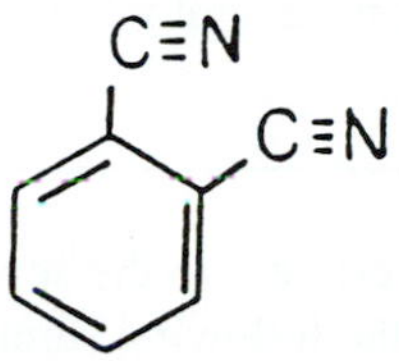

C≡N
C≡N

1,2-BENZENE DICARBONITRILE

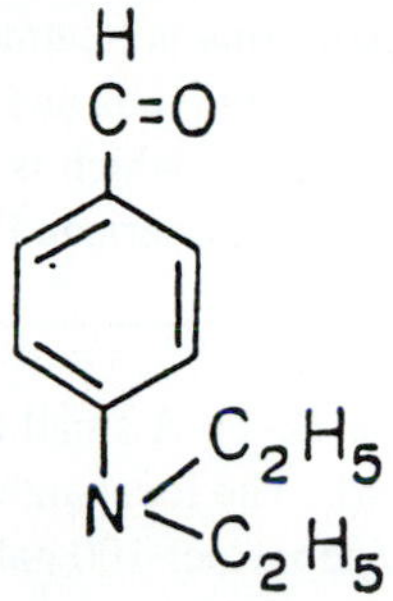

H
C=O

N C₂H₅ C₂H₅

4-DIETHYLAMINO BENZALDEHYDE

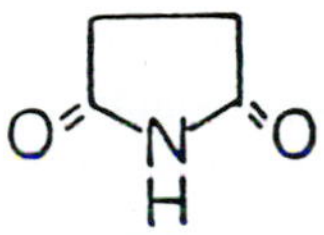

O N O
H

2,5-PYRROLIDINEDIONE

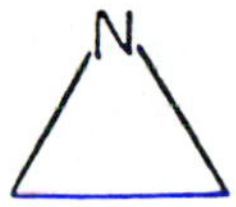

AZIRIDINE

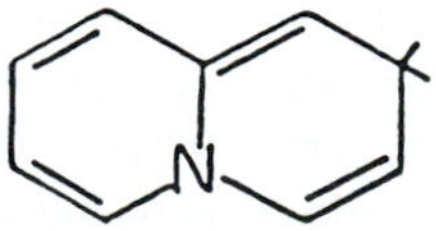

2H-QUINOLIZINE

Figure 12-21. Some nitrogen systems identified in retort water. (Yen, ref 12-10.)

All industrial wastewaters are termed as **trade effluents**. For larger companies, specific treatment plant in place will be used to process the effluents to meet the requirement of water quality standard. However, in many regions of the world, a small business can discharge the effluent to city sewer with certain requirement of the authority. One of the requirements is to pay a surcharge according to the quality of the effluent. One of the most costly operations is treatment of trade effluents involves screening, gut removal, separation of grease and oil suds and sedimentation. Conjunction to this is the design of weir-launder for the clarifiers, which is discussed in Chapter 30. For oil separation, several manuals are available from American Petroleum Institute.

[Example 12-1] A small textile manufacture in England discharges effluent to the sewer at 12000 gpd. The local authority that regulates the trade effluents has the following surcharge ranking (pence per 100 gal.)

Brewers, dairies, engineering shops	1
Dyeing and textile processes	2
Dyestuffs and manufacture	5
Bleach liquors	7
Spent gas liquors	25
Paint and varnish	45

Further, based on 1000 gal. discharge, the sedimentation charge is 12.3 p.; the McGovan strength exceeding the sewage energy 10 units is charged with 2.8 p.; also for S.S. there is a charge of 2.5 p. per 100 ppm over the sewage value. If the trade effluents contain S.S. at 1400 ppm over the sewage, which is 400 ppm, and the McGovan strength of its effluent (obtained by PV of Section 12.1.4) is 100 units versus the sewages which has 50 units, one can summarize costs as follows:

$$\text{Cost} = T + G + \left(M_t - M_s\right)\frac{M}{10} + \left(S_t - S_s\right)\frac{S}{100} + Q$$

There is the surcharge of effluent ranking types. G is the charge for pretreatment most for mechanical screening, settlements and such. M is the charge for the McGovan strength if beyond the sludge value. In 100 units, where strength = (ammoniacal N + organic N) 4.5 + (pV)6.5 (results of this is expressed in parts per 100,000), Q is the charge for color and others. The subscripts, t and s, are for trade effluent and sewages respectively.

$$\text{Cost (pence per 1000 gallon)} = 5 \times 10 + 12.3 + \frac{(100 - 50)}{10}2.8 + \frac{(1400 - 400)}{100}2.5 + 0 = 101.3p$$

Monthly cost = $101.3 \times 12 \times 30 = 36$ pounds 47pence

---

REFERENCES

12-1.   W. Stumm and J. J. Morgan, *Aquatic Chemistry*, Wiley, New York, 1981.

12-2.   D. W. Sundstrom and H. E. Klei, *Wastewater Treatment*, Prentice-Hall, Englewood Cliff, New Jersey, 1980.

12-3.   W. J. Weber Jr., *Physicochemical Processes for Water Quality Control*, Wiley, New York, 1972.

12-4.   R. L. Sanks, *Water Treatment Plant Design*, Ann Arbor Science, Ann Arbor, Michigan, 1980.

12-5.   T. F. Yen, J. I. S. Tang, M. Washburne, and S. Cohanim, *Analysis of Hazardous Organics Present in Liquid Wastes from Coal Conversion Processes*, EPA-R806 167-01-0, (NTIS), 1981.

12-6.   T. W. Schultz and J. N. Dumont, "Cytotoxicity of Untreated Coal Liquefaction Process Water (And a Comparison with Gasification Process Water)," *J. Env. Sci. Health*, Al3(9), pp. 641–651, (1978).

12-7.   T. F. Yen and G. C. Slawson Jr., *Compendium Reports on Coal Oil Shale Technology*, PB 293, 279, EPA-600/7-79-039 (NTIS), 1979.

12-8.   R. H. Gray, H. Drucker and, M. J. Massey, *Toxicology of Coal Conversion Processing*, Wiley, New York, 1988.

12-9.   Y. H. Li, *Environmental Conservation.*, 3, 171 (1976).

12-10. T. F. Yen, "Nature of Pollutants in Oil Shale and Coal Conversion Wastewaters," in *Environmental Engineering* (American Society of Civil Engineers, 1984 Specialty Conference) pp. 460–471, 1984.

12-11. H. Van Langenhore and N. Schamp, "Olfactometric Odor Measurement," in *Encyclopedia of Environmental Control Technology 2, Air Pollution Control* (P. N. Cheremisinoff, ed.), Gulf Pub., Houston, 1989, pp. 935–964.

12-12. P. C. G. Isaac, *Waste Treatment*, Pergamon, Oxford, 1960.

12-13. J. M. Montgomery, *Wastewater Treatment Principles and Design*, JMM, Pasadena, California, 1985.

12-14. S. D. Faust and O. M. Aly, *Chemistry of Water Treatment*, Butterworth, Boston, 1983.

12-15. I. J. Tinsley, *Chemical Concepts in Pollution Behavior*, Wiley, New York, 1979.

12-16. American Wastewater Association, *Water Quality and Treatment*, 4th ed., McGraw-Hill, New York, 1990.

12-17. D. L. Macalady, *Prospectives in Environmental Chemistry*, Oxford University Press, New York, 1998.

PROBLEM SET

1. A water sample whose BOD versus time data for the first five days has the following data

Time (days)	BOD (Y, mg/ L)
2	10
4	16
6	21

   Calculate the kinetic constants k, k', and L_0.

2. Determine the ThOD for glycine ($CH_2(NH_2)COOH$) using the following assumptions:

   a.) In the first step, the carbon is converted to CO_2 and the nitrogen is converted to ammonia.
   b.) In the second and third steps, the ammonia is oxidized to nitrite and nitrate.
   c.) The ThOD is the sum of the oxygen required for all three steps in grams of O_2 per mole.

3. Given the following results determined for a wastewater sample at 20°C, determine the ultimate carbonaceous oxygen demand, the ultimate nitrogenous oxygen demand (NOD), the carbonaceous BOD reaction-rate constant (K), and the nitrogenous NOD reaction-rate constant (K_n). Determine K ($\theta = 1.05$) and K_n ($\theta = 1.08$) at 25°C. (Courtesy of Edward Foree.)

Time, d	BOD, mg/ L	Time, d	BOD, mg/ L
0	0	11	63
1	10	12	69
2	18	13	74
3	23	14	77
4	26	16	82
5	29	18	85
6	31	30	87
7	32	25	89
8	33	20	90
9	46	40	90
10	56		

4. The following BOD results were obtained on a sample of untreated wastewater at 20°C:

t, d	0	1	2	3	4	5
y, mg/ L	0	65	109	138	158	172

   Compute the reaction constant K and ultimate first-stage BOD using both the least-squares and the Thomas methods. (Courtesy of Metcalf and Eddy, Inc.)

CHAPTER 13

PEDOSPHERE — SOIL CHEMISTRY

*T*he realm of soils and their inhabitants is the pedosphere. Soil is the medium in which crops grow, and it is the basis for nearly all forms of life on the solid earth. In addition, it acts as a buffer to control the water flow between sky, land, and sea. As the world becomes more industrialized, the role of soils becomes more important because they are a major sink for many of the xenobiotics. As with other natural, nonrenewable resources, it is important to ensure that soils are used conservatively so that the advantages we enjoy from soils now can still be with us in the future. To achieve this goal, it is necessary for us to understand soils and all the associated phenomena.

This chapter is composed of four sections. The first section is an introduction to soil, followed by a description of soil chemistry and its related erosion and weathering problems in the second section. These subjects are related to both agricultural and geotechnical applications. The third section deals with the contamination problems of soils. Current soil contamination regarding PCBs and related compounds is fully explored as well as DDT and other chloro-organics in use. The fourth section of the chapter gives a discussion on recent advances in the insecticide industry, including an in-depth investigation of the nature of the third generation of insecticides. It also focuses on it is our duty to learn more about the chemical warfare stockpile in different locations worldwide.

13.1 INTRODUCTION TO SOIL

Soil is the end-product of physical-chemical weathering and erosion in combination with biological actions on igneous rock. Soil is the interface, a thin layer mantle of the lithosphere that supports life. Soil is where the interactions between the lithosphere and the hydrosphere, atmosphere, and biosphere occur. Physically, soil is a porous mixture of inorganic particles, organic matter, air, and water. The three dominant inorganic particles in soil are **sand**, **silt**, and **clay**. They are usually classified according to their sizes, as shown in Table 13-1. Clays are the finest particles, with an equivalent diameter smaller than 0.002 mm, and they have a large specific surface area.

Component	Sand	Silt	Clay
Particle Size (mm)	2	.05	.002
Surface Area (cm²/g)	10	500	80×10^6

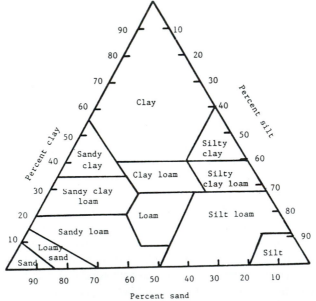

Figure 13-1.   The textural triangle from which the names of textural classes are obtained. There are a total of 12 classes of soil. (Source: U.S. Department of Agriculture.)

Table 13-1. Size and Surface Area of Soil Particles

Particle Type	Diameter (mm)	No. of Particles/ g	Surface area (cm²/ g)
Very coarse sand	2.00 - 1.00	90	11
Coarse sand	1.00 - 0.50	720	25
Medium sand	0.50 - 0.25	5,700	45
Fine sand	0.25 - 0.10	46,000	91
Very fine sand	0.10 - 0.05	722,000	227
Silt	0.05 - 0.002	5,780,000	454
Clay	0.002	90, 500,000,000	80,000,000

Assumed to have spherical shapes. Calculated on the basis of maximum diameters of the particle type.
Source: Foth and Turk (1972).

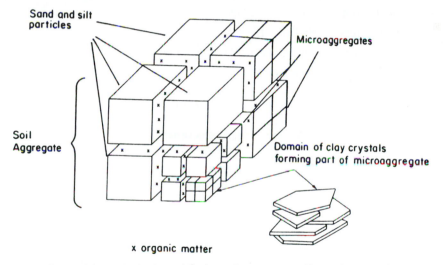

Figure 13-2.   A hypothetical model of a soil aggregate, illustrating the clustering of clay crystals to form domains, of domains to form microaggregates, and of microaggregates to form aggregates. Molecules of soil organic matter act as bonding agents between silt particles. [Source: Williams, Greenland and Quirk, *Aust. J. Soil Research* 5 77-83 (1967).]

Particle size distribution is most often called **soil texture** and is probably the most important physical property of soil. The U.S. Department of Agriculture has developed a method for naming soils based on particle size distribution. The relationship between textural analysis and class names is shown in Figure 13-1; it is often called a **textural triangle.** Soil classification system differs from country to country. The U.S. system is very comprehensive; for example, there are 10 orders, 47 suborders, and then greatgroups, subgroups, and series. The frequently used 10 orders are listed in Table 13-2. A common system for soil types is based on the **unified soil classification** system, shown in Table 13-3, which is based on the **group symbols** shown in Table 13-4. This is a widely used approximate method for different types of coursely-grained and finely-grained soils. In most soils, the particles tend to be grouped into aggregates or peds. Figure 13-2 illustrates a hypothetical model of a soil aggregate. Building and maintaining a good structure depends on (1) the influence of organic matter, (2) the shrink-swell processes associated with wetting and drying or freezing and thawing, (3) the action of plant roots and soil microorganisms, and (4) the modifying effects of adsorbed cations. If the aggregates so formed are stable, various forms of pores such as transmission pores, storage pores, residual pores, and bonding space will exist in the interstices between them, as shown in Table 13-5. Within these pore spaces, soil water can move freely, and the exchange of gases between soil and the atmosphere can proceed. Table 13-6 gives a simple classification of soil aggregates by size. In summary, there exist the following:

- **Transmission pores** — air, seepage
- **Storage pores** — capillary effect
- **Residual pores** — ion exchange
- Bonding spaces — strength

Clod → aggregate → microaggregate → domain

Table 13-2.   Soil Classification System —Key to Soil Orders

If soil has	Order
> 30% clay to 1 meter (40 in) or to lithic/ paralithic contact gilgai or slickensides or wedge-shaped aggregates	Vertisols
No diagnostic horizon other than ochric, anthropic, albic, argic	Entisols
No spodic, argillic, natric, oxic, petrocalcic, plinthite; but has cambic or histic	Inceptisols
Ochric or argillic but no oxic or spodic and usually dry	Aridisols
Spodic	Spodosols
Mean annual soil temperature > 8°C (47°F), properties not placing it in one of above, percentage base saturation < 35 @ 1.25 m (50 in) below top of argillic or 1.8 m (72 in) below surface	Ultisols
Mollic but no oxic	Mollisols
All other mineral soils without oxic	Alfisols
Oxic horizon	Oxisols
> 30% organic matter to a depth of 40 cm (16 in)	Histosols

Table 13-3. Unified Soil Classification Chart

Group symbols	Typical names	Information required for describing soils
GW	Well-graded gravels, gravel-sand mixtures; little or no fines	Given typical name; indicate approximate percentages of sand and gravel, maximum size, angularity, surface condition, and hardness of the coarse grains; local or geologic name and other pertinent descriptive information; and symbol in parentheses
GP	Poorly graded gravels, gravel-sand mixtures; little or no fines	
GM	Silty gravels, poorly graded gravel-sand-silt mixtures	
GC	Clayey gravels, poorly graded gravel-sand-clay mixtures	For undisturbed soils add information on stratification, degree of compactness, and drainage characteristics
SW	Well-graded sands, gravelly sands; little or no fines	
SP	Poorly graded sands, gravelly sands; little or no fines	Example: Silty sand, gravelly; about 20 % hard, angular gravel particles 12 mm maximum size; rounded and subangular sand grains coarse to fine; about 15 % nonplastic fines with low dry strength; well compacted and moist in place; alluvial sand; (SM)
SM	Silty sands, poorly graded sand-silt mixtures	
SC	Clayey sands, poorly graded sand-clay mixtures	
ML	Inorganic silts and very fine sands, rock flour, silty or clayey fine sands with slight plasticity	Give typical name; indicate degree and character of plasticity, amount and maximum size of coarse grains; color in wet condition, odor if any, local or geologic name, and other pertinent descriptive information; and symbol in parentheses
CL	Inorganic clays of low to medium plasticity, gravelly clays, sandy clays, silty clays, lean clays	
OL	Organic silts and organic silt-clays of low plasticity	
MH	Inorganic silts, micaceous or diatomaceous fine sandy or silty soils, elastic silts	For undisturbed soils add information on structure, stratification, consistency in undisturbed and remolded states, moisture and drainage conditions
CH	Inorganic clays of high plasticity, fat clays	Example: Clayey silt, brown; slightly plastic; small percentage of fine sand; numerous vertical root holes; firm and dry in place; loess; (ML)
Pt	Peat, muck, peat-bog, and so on	

Table 13-4.   Group Symbols of Soils

Soil type	Prefix	Subgroup	Suffix
Gravel	G	Well graded	W
Sand	S	Poorly graded	P
		Silty	M
		Clay	C
Silt	M	$W_L < 50\%$	L
Clay	C	$W_L > 50\%$	H
Organic	O		
Peat	Pt		

The coarse-grained soil is:

GW, GP or SW, SP	≤ 5% passes No. 200 sieve
GW-GM, GP-GM, GW-GC, GP-GC or SW-SM, SP-SM, SW-SC, SP-SC	5% < passing No. 200 sieve ≤ 12%
GM, GC or SM, SC	> 12% passes No. 200 sieve

Table 13-5.   A Functional Classification of Soil Pores

Name	Function	Equivalent, Cylindrical Diameter, μm
Transmission pores	Air movement and drainage of excess water	50
Storage pores	Retention of water against gravity, and release to plant roots	0.5-50
Residual pores	Retention and diffusion ions in solution	0.5
Bonding spaces	Support major forces between soil particles	0.005

Source: D.J. Greenland, Phil Trans. Roy. Soc. (London) *B281* 193-208 (1977)

Table 13-6.   A Simple Classification of Soil Aggregates by Size

Name	Description	Size Range
Clod	Clusters of aggregates	> 5 mm
Aggregate	Clusters of microaggregates and sand particles	0.5 - 5 mm
Microaggregate	Domains, silt and fine sand particles bonded by organic polymers	5 - 500 μm
Domain	Oriented clusters of clay crystals	< 5 μm

Source: Greenland, Soil and Fertilizers, *34*, 237-251, 1971

13.2 SOIL FORMATION AND SOIL PROPERTIES

The origin of most soils can be ultimately traced back to the alteration of igneous rocks from disintegration and decomposition processes. There are five major factors involved in soil formation: parental material (p), climate (cl), geological time (t), relief pressure (r), and natural organisms (o). This statement can be expressed as

$$\text{Soil formation} = f(p,cl,t,r,o)$$

which is called the **Dokuchaiev soil formation function**.

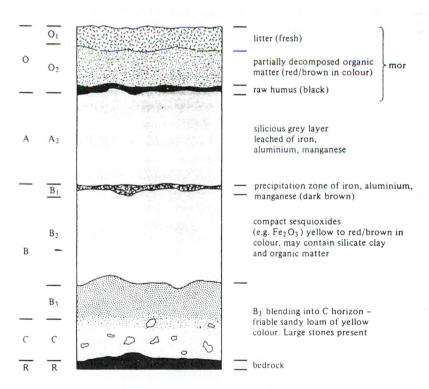

Figure 13-3.   Representation of a podsol profile. The boundaries between O and A and A and B horizons are quite distinct, and good examples of podsols lack A_1 and A_3 zones which, in other soils, represent transitional areas between O and B horizons, respectively.

Soils are sometimes described in terms of their profile morphology. The differences in readily observable profile characteristics are reflections of chemical, mineralogical, physical, and biological differences in the soils. Figure 13-3 shows a typical **soil profile** in which the O,A,B,C horizon nomenclature is commonly used.

OM↓

Igneous rock → Soil C Horizon C → Horizon B subsoil → Horizon A topsoil
↓ loss of Ca, Mg, K, Na

Silicon is one of the most abundant elements in the lithosphere (see Chapter 15) and, because the pedosphere originates from the lithosphere, it is the main element in soil. Silicate minerals are the basis of igneous rocks, which result from the solidification of the earth's molten magma. Sedimentary rocks, such as sandstone, form igneous ones by the action of weathering (including water erosion), which will be discussed further in Section 12.2.2. Another type of rock, the metamorphic, is created from the former two by heat, pressure, or solvent action (e.g., serpentine). The most abundant igneous rock is granite — a mixture of feldspar, mica, and quartz. Next to granite, the most important of the igneous rocks are ferromagnesium silicates, pyroxenes, and amphipoles. The continents appear to be slabs of granite about 20 miles thick, floating on the heavy basaltic material of the lithosphere.

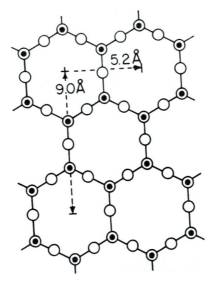

Figure 13-4.   Diagram of phyllosilicate sheet (top view). The black circles represent silicon atoms and the open circles represent oxygen atoms. Each silicon atom is tetrahedrally bound to four oxygen atoms. The oxygen atoms shown superimposed on the silicons are directed upward and bound to a second parallel layer.

Silicon dioxide, or silica, is a polymeric solid with a network consisting of silicon atoms bound tetrahedrally to four oxygen atoms. The oxygen atoms are each in turn bound to two silicon atoms. In this manner, the tetrahedron structure can become leaflike if the fourth bond of silicon sticks up out of the sheet, as shown in Figure 13-4. If the bond center is an aluminum ion, then the formation of a phillosilicate sheet such as kaolinite, shown in Figure 13-5, takes place. Aluminum prefers to have an octahedral coordination resulting in the formation of clay sheets, which we will discuss further in the section on weathering.

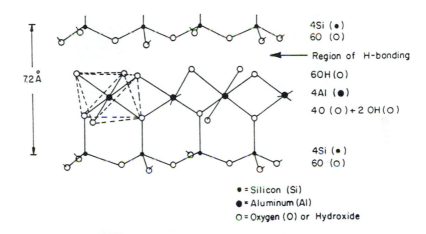

Figure 13-5. Structure of kaolinite, $Al_4Si_4O_{10}(OH)_8$. Figure shows phyllosilicate and octahedral layers. The distance between two successive plates is 7.2Å. Dashed line shows sixfold coordinate positions in octahedral layer. Note that six oxygen atoms are associated with four silicon atoms in the phyllosilicate layer because silicon shares each of its three oxygens with another silicon. Hence, each Si is bonded to 3/2 oxygen atoms.

Due to the nature of the sheet type of stacking, a number of structures can be created from the many possible ways of three-dimensional tessellation. The regular spacing remaining can be a variety of regular cavities or canals acting as either residue or storage pores. This is the basis of heterogenous catalysis in petro-chemical engineering that involves a number of faujasite structures such as zeolite or perovskite. Due to the interlayer polar characteristics within the clay layers, hydrogen bonding and interchelation molecules such as water, alcohol, and glycerine can expand or swell the clay minerals. This absorption capacity can allow the organic molecules (such as humin) to be bound within the soil.

The structure of the clay soil, as observed by scanning electron microscopy, is quite complex, as shown in Figures 13-6 to 13-7. Usually, if the soil is under stress, such as overburden, the clay soil assumes a more-or-less compact structure. Because joints, fissures, root holes, vorves, silt or sand lenses, and other discontinuities will effect the total mechanical properties of soil, the orientation of various structures in an undisturbed soil is important.

For example, the water content relating to different degrees of dispersion can effect the properties of cohesive soil, as shown in Figures 13-8 and 13-9.

There is oxygen and nitrogen in different locations of the pedosphere, and it is especially necessary for the **rhizosphere**. The rhizosphere is defined as the local soil environment greatly influenced by plant roots, as shown in Figure 13-10. The storage and transmission pores also greatly enhance the microbial growth, which is very common for any garden soil possessing different types of enzyme activists. The deterioration and biodegradation properties will be discussed later in detail.

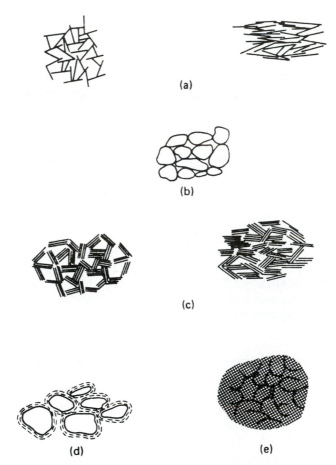

Figure 13-6.   Schematic representations of elementary particle arrangements: (a) individual clay platelet interaction; (b) individual silt or sand particle interaction; (c) clay platelet group interaction; (d) clothed silt or sand particle interaction; (e) partly discernible particle interaction. [After K. Collins and A. McGown, "The Form and Function of Microfabric Features in a Variety of Natural Soils," *Geotechnique,* 24 (2), 223-254, 1974.]

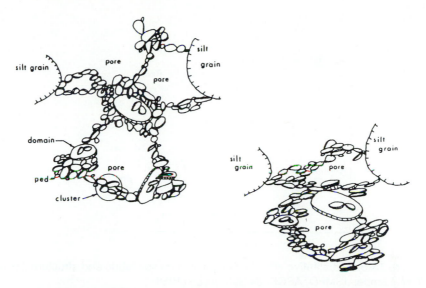

Figure 13-7.   Structure of a clay soil: (left) a porous, flocculated sediment interspersed with silt grains; (right) the sediment after it has been subjected to overburden or other stresses that have resulted in a reorientation of the domains, clusters, and peds into a more parallel (dispersed) state.

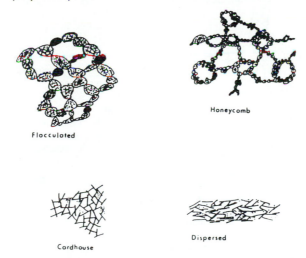

Figure 13-8.   Structure of clay soil using earlier terms of structure orientation. The flocculent structure might be obtained from sedimentation in water with a low salt content. The honeycomb structure could be obtained from sedimentation in a marine (high-salt-content) environment. The cardhouse description was highly used prior to SEM studies. The dispersed state is a convenient description for reorientation from compaction.

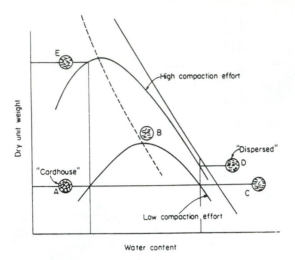

Figure 13-9.   Qualitative effect of compaction on soil fabric and structure. [Source: T.W. Lambe, JSMFD, ASCE, *84* SM2, 1655 (1958).]

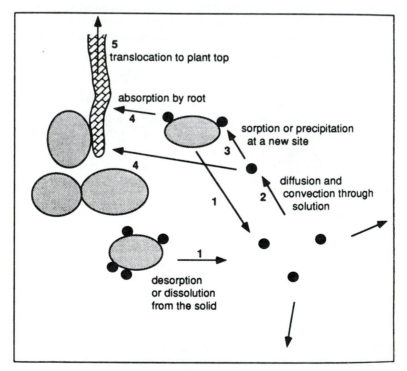

Figure 13-10.   Rhizosphere — the space used by plant roots to transport soil solid to plant top. There are 5 steps necessary for this. (Modified from McBride)

13.2.1   Soil Organic Matter

Although the organic components in soil only account for at most 5% by weight, they are essential in many aspects. Among all the organic components, humus is the most important. **Humus** (or the insoluble portion referred as **humin**) is the result, or residue, of the final degradation from biomass by microbiological actions, and as such is resistant to biodegradation. Thus it is a recalcitrant. Some major classes of organic compounds in soils are listed in Table 13-7. Soil humus consists of a base soluble fraction composed of humic acid and fulvic acid, which are naturally occurring high molecular weighted macromolecules. A hypothetical formula can be seen with the presence of aryl, carboxylic, hydroxyl, aldehyde, ketone, and so on, as shown in Figure 13-11. The insoluble fraction from soil humus is called **humin**, which in general contains nitrogen and sulfur. Young and Yen speculated that the formation of humin may have originated from melanoidin, which is a complex reaction product between amino acids and glucose. The electron spin resonance spectra of soil may be directly related to those of humus, as shown in Table 13-8.

There are various organics in soil (see a later discussion with Figure 13-22). Some are based on the metabolites of microorganisms; for example, rocks can be weathered through fungi interacting and the oxalic acid, and citric acid both of which can be good complexing agents. It ought to be emphasized here that the $\equiv$SiOH function not only can link with humus, which can extend its ability of bonding or complexing with a number of chemical agents, as shown in Figure 13-12, but the ion exchange of soil can also be achieved.

Table 13-7.   Major Classes of Organic Compounds in Soil

Compound Type	Composition	Significance
Humus	Degradation-resistant residue from plant decay, largely, C, H, and O	Most abundant organic component, improves soil physical properties and exchanges nutrients, is a reservoir of fixed N
Fats, resins, and waxes	Lipids extractable by organic solvents	Generally, they are only 1-5% soil organic matter may adversely affect soil physical properties by repelling water, and they may be phytotoxic
Saccharides	Cellulose, starches, hemicellulose, gums	Major food source for soil microorganisms, helps stabilize soil aggregates
N-containing organics	Nitrogen bound to humus, amino acids, amino sugars, and other compounds	Provides nitrogen for soil fertility
Phosphorous compounds	Phosphate esters, inositol phosphates (phytic acid), and phospholipids	Source of plant phosphate

Table 13-8. EPR Data of Some Naturally Occurring Materials

Sample	g-Value	Width (gauss)	Shape
Chlorophyll	7.81	420	+
	5.15	500	d*
	3.26	940	+
	2.43	520	d
	2.19	60	d
Humic acid	7.99	420	−
	5.09	570	d
	2.76	1040	+
	2.15	60	d
	2.08	620	+
Browning products	7.72	440	−
	5.00	540	d
	2.90	1300	−
	2.15	60	d
	1.94	1080	+
Hemoglobin	14.95	550	d
	4.18	1750	+
	2.98	30	d
Acetone extract of sediment	7.99	360	+
	5.08	560	d
	2.73	1800	+
	2.15	20	d

*
  d, derivative, + and − represent upward and downward features, respectively.

Source: T.F. Yen, *Chemistry of Marine Sediments*, Ann Arbor Sci. Pub., 1977, p. 16.

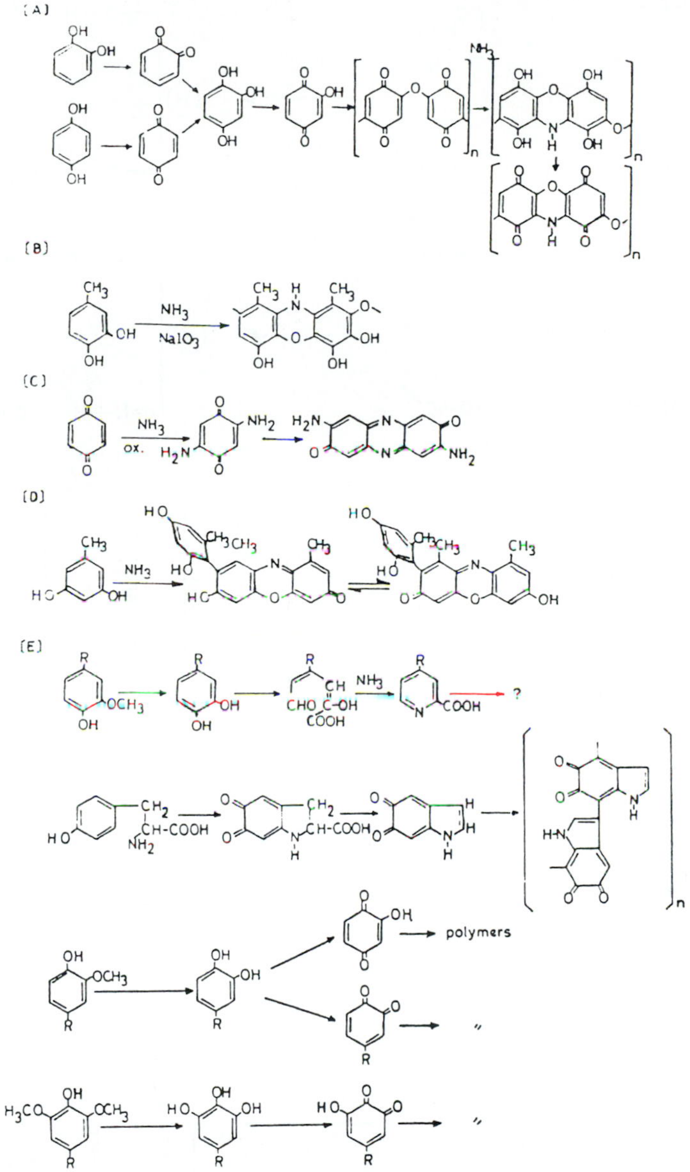

Figure 13-11.   Precursors of soil humin (Sources: Bremner, Flaig, Manskaya, and Drosdova, Yen etc.)

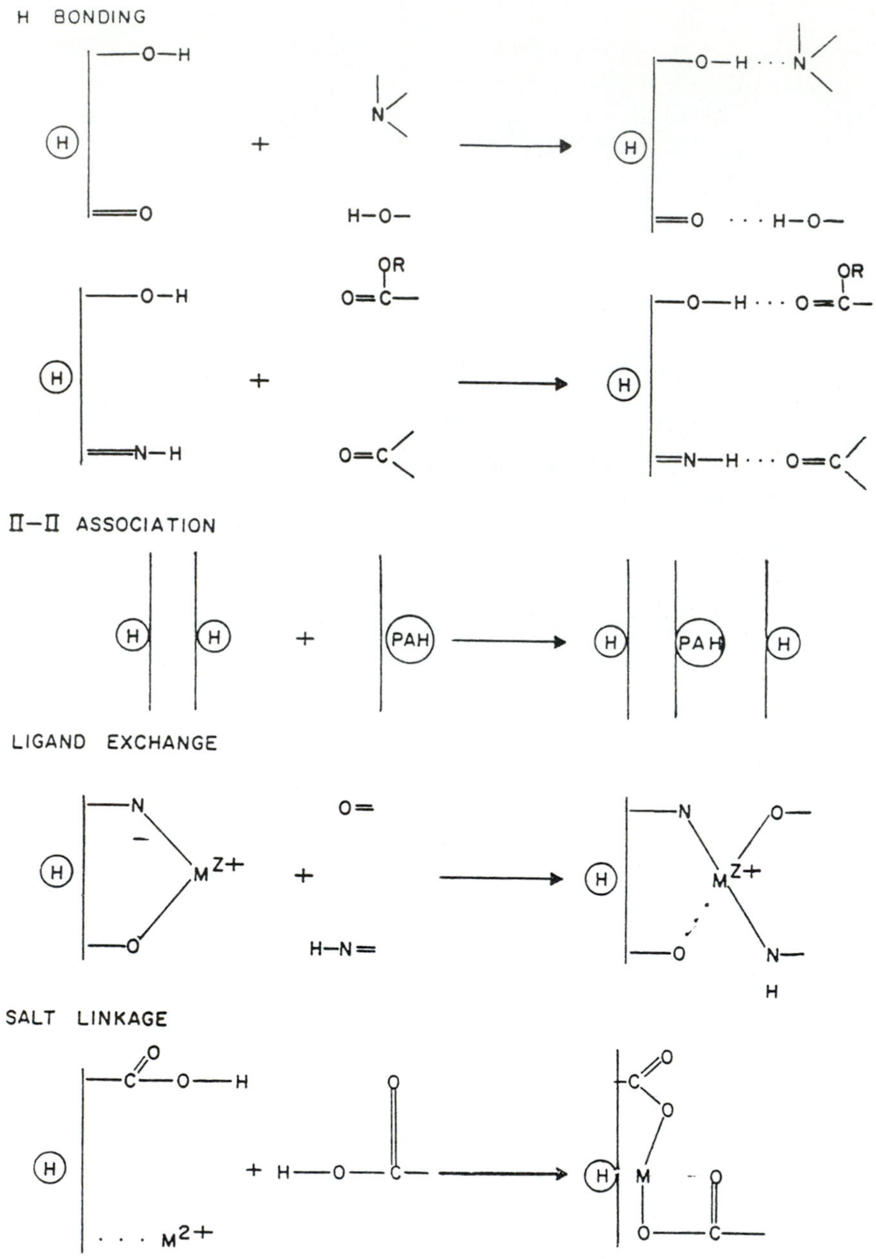

Figure 13-12.   Bonding mechanisms.

13.2.2   Chemical and Physical Weathering

Disintegration and **decomposition** are the two major weathering processes. Disintegration results from physical processes such as differential expansion of rock materials, expansion of water due to formation of ice in rock fissures, and abrasion and grinding action from hydrological flow. Decomposition is due to chemical processes such as hydrolysis, hydration, oxidation, reduction, carbonation, and solution effects. In addition to the physical and chemical processes, biological activity is also important in the weathering of rocks. For example, when moisture is present, lichens can grow on bedrock which, in turn, can produce acids such as citric acid and acetic acid through their metabolism. These acids can erode the rock away.

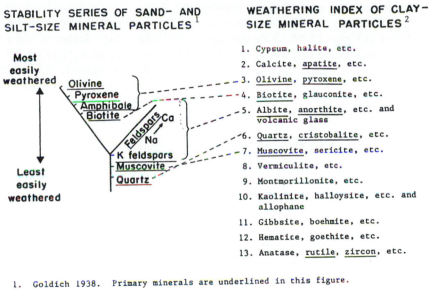

STABILITY SERIES OF SAND- AND
SILT-SIZE MINERAL PARTICLES [1]

WEATHERING INDEX OF CLAY-
SIZE MINERAL PARTICLES [2]

Most easily weathered

Olivine
Pyroxene
Amphibole
Biotite
Feldspars Ca
Na
K feldspars
Muscovite
Quartz

Least easily weathered

1. Cypsum, halite, etc.
2. Calcite, apatite, etc.
3. Olivine, pyroxene, etc.
4. Biotite, glauconite, etc.
5. Albite, anorthite, etc. and volcanic glass
6. Quartz, cristobalite, etc.
7. Muscovite, sericite, etc.
8. Vermiculite, etc.
9. Montmorillonite, etc.
10. Kaolinite, halloysite, etc. and allophane
11. Gibbsite, boehmite, etc.
12. Hematite, goethite, etc.
13. Anatase, rutile, zircon, etc.

1. Goldich 1938. Primary minerals are underlined in this figure.
2. Jackson 1968.

Figure 13-13.   The relative stability of coarsely and finely grained minerals in soils. The first series consists of primary minerals arranged from top to bottom, in the order of their crystallization from molten material, and also in the order of decreasing ease of weathering. The second series consists of a condensed version of the first in which the positions of muscovite and quartz have been interchanged because of the greater stability of soils of clay-sized mica. At the top and in most of the lower part of this series are secondary minerals. (Source: S. W. Buol, F. D. Hole and R. J. McCracken, *Soil Genesis and Classification*, p. 82, Iowa State University Press, 1973 and with the permission of Iowa State University Press.)

The chemical weathering schemes are shown here:

$$\xrightarrow{\text{(hydrolysis)}} H^+, Mg^{2+}, Fe^{2+}, H_4SiO_4$$

$$\text{Hypersthene (Mg, Fe)}SiO_3 \text{ (s)} \xrightarrow{\text{H}_2\text{O(hydration)}} Mg^{2+}, OH^-, Fe_2SiO_4, H_4SiO_4$$

$$\xrightarrow{\text{O}_2\,\text{(oxidation)}} Fe_2O_3 \cdot 3H_2O, Mg_2SiO_4, H_4SiO_4$$

Certain minerals in the parent rock in the soil are more resistant than others. The more chemically acidic minerals (such as quartz, muscovite mica, and some feldspars) are, the more stable they are as they become predominant in soil. On the other hand, the more basic minerals (such as pyroxenes) are, the more they are readily altered by chemical weathering, as shown in Figure 13-13. Although quartz (SiO_2) has a high degree of resistance to weathering, it does dissolve slightly in natural water to form silicic acid (H_4SiO_4). This slow dissolution process, as well as the chemical weathering of other minerals, follows the Arrhenius relationship,

$$k = A \, \exp(-E_d/RT)$$

Therefore, the reaction is temperature dependent, with the weathering of rocks faster in tropical than in temperate areas. Incidentally, quartz is not stable under strong basic conditions. At high temperatures it will dissolve in quinoline at 360°C. Minerals formed at high temperatures and pressures also weather more rapidly than those formed at low temperatures.

Silicon chemistry is very complex; silica can be hydrolysed into many species and some of them can be polymeric. If the aluminum ion can participate, layered materials termed **phyllosilicates** can be obtained.

$$SiO_2 \xrightarrow{2\,\text{H}_2\text{O}} H_4SiO_4 \rightarrow 4H^+ + (SiO_4)^{4-} \xrightarrow{H^+} Si(OH)_4 \xrightarrow{Al^{3+}} \text{Octahedral layers}$$

$$\xrightarrow{3\,\text{H}_2\text{O}} H_6Si_2O_7 \qquad\qquad\qquad\qquad \text{(phyllosilicates)}$$

$$\xrightarrow{4\,\text{H}_2\text{O}} H_8Si_3O_{10}$$

When hydrous oxide species of aluminum and silicon are present in appropriate concentrations in solution or are simultaneously released during weathering, the formation of silicoaluminum copolymers is thermodynamically favorable. Hence, clay minerals are formed. Clay minerals (phyllosilicates) are primarily crystalline alumina or magnesium silicates with stacked-layer structures. Each unit layer is, in turn, a sandwich of tetrahedral and octahedral sheets. In the tetrahedral sheets, each silicon atom is surrounded by four oxygen atoms in a tetrahedral arrangement. The octahedral sheet consists of the planes of oxygen in a hexagonal closest-packed arrangement, with alumina or magnesium atoms at the octahedral sites. Some clay minerals (e.g., kaolinite), which contain one tetrahedral sheet and one octahedral sheet in each of their layers, are termed **1:1 layer silicates**. Some three-sheet layer clays containing two outer tetrahedral sheets and one inner octahedral sheet are termed **2:1 layer silicates**. Both type of layered silicates are illustrated in Figure 13-14. Some common phyllosilicates with their interlay and composition are summerized in Table 13-9. The details of the crystal structures of clays were not elucidated until Pauling in l930 proposed using X-ray diffraction analysis on these minerals.

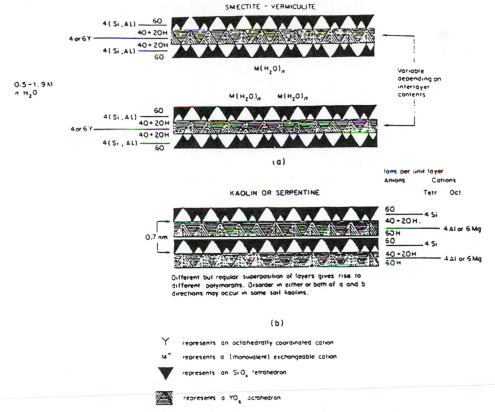

Figure 13-14.   Schematic representation of structures of principle phyllosilicate minerals: (a) 2:1 minerals, and (b) 1:1 minerals. Pyrophyllite and talc are similar to the micas, except that the tetrahedral occupancy is 4 Si, so that the layer change is zero and there are no interlayer cations.

Table 13-9. Classification and Genralized Structural Formulae of Phylosilicates

Layer type	Group	Octahedral occupancy	Negative charge per unit[a]	Unit formula Cations[b] Oct.	Tet.	Anions	Layer thickness nm	Interlayer composition Cations[c]	Hydroxide sheet[d]	Water	Occurrence in soils
1:1	Kaolinite	Di	0	Y_4	Z_4	$O_{10}(OH)_8$	0.7	None			Common
	(Halloysite)	Di	0	Y_4	Z_4	$O_{10}(OH)_8$	1.0-0.7	None		0.6-$4H_2O$	Common
	Serpentine	Tri	0	Y_6	Z_4	$O_{10}(OH)_8$	0.7	None			Rare
2:1	Pyrophyllite	Di	0	Y_4	Z_8	$O_{20}(OH)_4$	0.92	None			Rare
	Talc	Tri	0	Y_6	Z_8	$O_{20}(OH)_4$	0.9	None			Rare
	Micas	Di		Y_4	Z_8	$O_{20}(OH)_4$	1.00	X'_2			Common
		Tri	2	Y_6	Z_8	$O_{20}(OH)_4$	1.00	X'_2			
	Brittle Micas	Di		Y_4	Z_8	$O_{20}(OH)_4$	1.00	X''_2			Rare
		Tri	4	Y_6	Z_8	$O_{20}(OH)_4$	1.00	X''_2			
		Di		Y_4	Z_8	$O_{20}(OH)_4$	1.40		$A'''_4(OH)_{12}$		
	Chlorites	Di, tri	Variable	Y_4	Z_8	$O_{20}(OH)_4$	1.40		$A''_6(OH)_{12}$		Common
		Tri		Y_6	Z_8	$O_{20}(OH)_4$	1.40		$A''_6(OH)_{12}$		
	(Swelling chlorite)		Variable				≥ 1.40		$\sim A'''_4(OH)_{12}$	$n\,H_2O$	Common

Table 13-9. continued

Layer type	Group	Octahedral occupancy	Negative charge per unit [a]	Unit formula Cations[b] Oct.	Tet.	Anions	Layer thickness nm	Interlayer composition Cations[c]	Hydroxide sheet[d]	Water	Occurrence in soils
Smectites		Di	0.5-1.2	Y_4	Z_8	$O_{20}(OH)_4$	≥0.96	$X'_{0.5-1.2}$		$n\,H_2O$	Common
		Tri	0.5-1.2	Y_6	Z_8	$O_{20}(OH)_4$	≥0.96	$X'_{0.5-1.2}$			
Vermiculites		Di	1.2-1.9	Y_4	Z_8	$O_{20}(OH)_4$	≥0.94	$X'_{1.2-1.9}$		$n\,H_2O$	Common
Palygorskite		Tri	1.2-1.9	Y_6	Z_8	$O_{20}(OH)_4$	≥0.94	$X'_{1.2-1.9}$			
			?	Y_4	Z_8	$O_{20}(OH)_2(OH_2)_4$[c]		$X?$		$4\,H_2O$	Uncommon
Sepiolite			?	Y_8	Z_{12}	$O_{30}(OH)_4(OH_2)_4$		$X?$		$8\,H_2O$	Uncommon

[a] Negative charge per formula unit is twice that given by Bailey et al. (1071a) because the formula unit used here applies to the contents of a volume defined by the a × b unit cell base area that is one layer thick. For example, for chlorites this volume approximately $0.5 \times 0.9 \times 1.4\,nm^3$, and for palygorskite it is $1.8 \times 0.5 \times 0.65\,nm^3$.

[b] Y represents cations in octahedral coordination, most commonly Al but many others of similar dimensions can substitute for it isomorphically. Z represents cations in tetrahedral coordination, most commonly Si, but Al frequently replaces some Si in a regular or random manner; e.g., replacement of one in four occurs in the micas and gives rise to the negative charge of two per formula unit; in the brittle micas 2 Al replace two of each four Si.

[c] X' represents a monovalent cations, and X'' a divalent cation.

[d] A''' is an irrelevant cation (usually Al) and A'' is a divalent cation (usually Mg) but extensive isomorphous substitution may occur.

[e] Following Bradley (1940); according to Gard and Follett (1968) the anions are $O_{20}(OH)_2(OH_2)_3$.

Table 13-10.   Jackson- Sherman Weathering Stages

Characteristic minerals in soil clay fraction	Characteristic soil chemical and physical conditions
	Early stage
Gypsum	Very low content of water and organic matter,
Carbonates	very limited leaching
Olivine/ pyroxene/ amphibole	Reducing environments
Fe(II)-bearing micas	Limited amount of time for weathering
Feldspars	
	Intermediate stage
Quartz	Retention of Na, K, Ca, Mg, Fe(II), and silica:
Dioctahedral mica/ illite	Ineffective leaching and alkalinity
Vermiculite/ chlorite	Igneous rock rich in Ca, Mg, Fe(II), but no
	Fe(II) oxides
Smectites	Silicates easily hydrolyzed
	Flocculation of silica, transport of silica
	into the weathering zone
	Advanced stage
Kaolinite	Removal of Na, K, Ca, Mg, Fe(II), and silica:
Gibbsite	Effective leaching, fresh water
Iron oxides	Oxidation of Fe(II)
(goethite, hematite)	Acidic compounds, low pH
Titanium oxides	Dispersion of silica
(anatase, rutile, ilmenite)	Al-hydroxy polymers

Source: M.L. Jackson and G.D. Sherman, Adv. Agran 5, 219-318 (1953). M.L. Jackson, Soil Sci. 99, 15-22 (1965).

The dissolution of CO_2 from plant and microbial respiration processes also has an influence on the formation of clays. The following shows the alteration of calcium feldspar to phyllosilicates kaolinite with the aid of CO_2:

$$CaAl_2Si_2O_8 + 3H_2O + 2CO_2 \leftrightarrow Al_2Si_2O_5(OH)_4 + Ca^{++} + 2HCO_3^-$$

plagioclase   kaolinite

The changes in clay fraction mineralogy during the coverage of soil profile development are especially clear. The clay fraction differences at different weathering stages are evident in the 3 **Jackson-Sherman weathering stages,** as shown in Table 13-10.

13.2.3 Agricultural Applications

Many valuable minerals useful for plant life can be obtained in soil due to the complexing property in soil. These minerals are termed **micronutrients**. The oxidation of pyrite in soil causes the formation of acid-sulfate soils or cat clays.

$$FeS_2 + \frac{7}{2}O_2 + H_2O \rightarrow Fe^{2+} + 2H^+ + 2SO_4^{2-}$$

Soils containing marine sediments (such as those from Florida, New Jersey, and North Carolina) are likely to have **acid soils**. A useful test for acid soils is the peroxide test.

$$FeS_2 + \frac{15}{2}H_2O_2 \rightarrow Fe^{2+} + H^+ + 2SO_4^{2-} + 7H_2O$$

The level of sulfate and pH released will indicate the potential of acid soils. The adjustment is by adding lime to neutralize the soil.

In case of **alkaline soil** due to the presence of Na_2CO_3, then aluminum or iron sulfate can be added

$$2Fe^{3+} + 3SO_4^{2-} + 6H_2O \rightarrow 2Fe(OH)_3 + 6H^+ + 3SO_4^{2-}$$

Sulfur also can be added in such a manner that sulfur-oxidizers in soil can convert it into sulfuric acid for neutralization.

Fertilizers consisting of N, P, and K are designated by numbers (e.g., 6-12-8) showing that N is 6%, P_2O_5 is 12%, and K_2O is 8%. Liquid NH_3 obtained by the Haber process can be directly added to soil, or to inject in water. Ammonium nitrate, NH_4NO_3, is also a common fertilizer but can cause explosion. Super phosphate is more soluble than the parent mineral fluorapatite.

$$\text{Fluorapatite} \left(CaH_4(PO_4)_2 \cdot H_2O\right)$$

In general, the fertilizers are all soluble in water; therefore, the runoff from land became a problem for subsequent eutrophication. The best is to have the fertilizers either graft or bond to soil humus for prevention of leaching capability by water.   Alternatively, organic compounds containing N, P, and K can be made to minimize this potential. These are termed **hard fertilizer** in contrast to the water-soluble fertilizer, the **soft fertilizer**.

An important property of soil is ion exchange. Evidently, the transport of many metal ions is essential for plant life, not to mention the storage and distribution of water. It has been documented that about 4.5 tonnes of calcium ion can be stored in 1 hectare of land. The need for common fertilizer composed of potassium, nitrogen, and phosphorus is based on the slightly poor transport ability of soil due to the bulkiness of potassium ion and the weak coordination bond between soil grains and nitrate or phosphate group, usually larger ions are not readily ion-exchangeable.

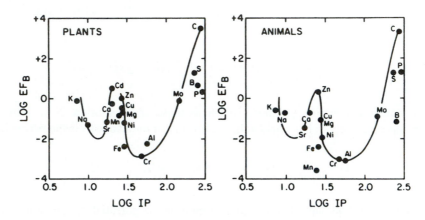

Figure 13-15.   Banin-Navrot plots for terrestrial plants and animals. [Based on enrichment factor data compiled by A. Banin and J. Navrot, Origin of life: Clues from relations between chemical compositions of living organisms and natural environments, *Science* 189: 550-551 (1975).]

The 16 elements that are essential to plant growth in soil are H, B, C, N, O, Mg, P, S, Cl, K, Ca, Mn, Fe, Cu, Zn, and Mo. Of these, B, Cl, Mn, Fe, Cu, Zn, and Mo are micronutrients (absorbed in trace amount) and Mg, Ca, and S are secondary nutrients. The remaining six elements are macronutrients. Usually, the **enrichment factor in biomass** (EF_B) can be correlated by a log-log plot of EF_B versus the ionic potential (IP) for the metals. These plots are termed **Banin-Navrot plots** and they are similar regardless of plant or animal origin. An example is illustrated by Figure 13-15. Both Ef_B and IP are defined as follows:

$$EF_B = \frac{\text{concentration of elements in organism}}{\text{concentration of elements in crustal rock}} \qquad [13\text{-}1]$$

$$IP = \frac{\text{valence of free cation of the elements}}{\text{radius of free cation of the elements}} \qquad [13\text{-}2]$$

Other elements can be toxic to plants. The mechanism of phytotoxicity is still not understood. Potential toxic metals can act in the following possibilities: for example, displacement of essential metal and complexation or reacting by modification to the metal. Strong complex forming metals usually have covalent characters. This approach can be qualified with a **Misono softness parameter** (Y) as follows:

$$Y = 10 \; \frac{I_z R}{Z^{\frac{1}{2}}} \; I_{z+1} \qquad\qquad [13\text{-}3]$$

when R is the ionic radius of metal ions whose valence is Z and whose ionization potential is I_z. A classification of metals by plotting the ionic potential to Misono softness is seen in Figure 13-16. Therefore, the toxicity sequence in general is in line with the direction, the softest Lewis acid being the most toxic, as shown in Table 13-11. Some commonly used parameters for nutrient uptake for plants are listed in Table 13-12. C_s is the nutrient bulk concentration in soil (mol m^{-3} soil) and C_l is the nutrient soil solution concentration (mol m^{-3} solution).

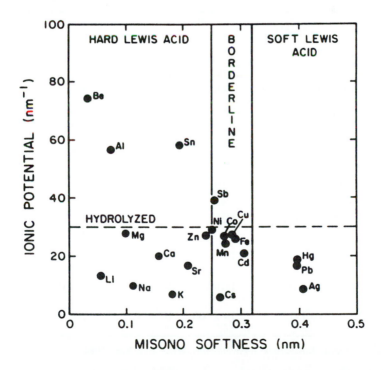

Figure 13-16.   Classification of metals according to ionic potential and Misono softness. (From G. Sposito, Ref. 13-8).

Table 13-11.   Representation Metal Toxicity Sequence

Organisms	Toxicity sequence[a]
Algae	$Hg > Cu > Cd > Fe > Cr > Zn > Co > Mn$
Flowering plants	$Hg > Pb > Cu > Cd > Cr > Ni > Zn$
Fungi	$Ag > Hg > Cu > Cd > Cr > Ni > Pb > Co > Zn > Fe$
Phytoplankton (freshwater)	$Hg > Cu > Cd > Zn > Pb$

Source: Based on data compiled by E. Nieboer and D.H.S. Richardson, the replacement of the nondescript term 'heavy metals' by a biologically and chemically significant classification of metal ions, Environ. Pollution B1:3-26 (1980), and by E. Eichenberger, the interrelation between essentiality and toxicity of metals in the aquatic ecosystem, Metal Ions Biol. Systems 20: 67-100 (1986).

[a] $Hg=Hg(II)$, $Fe=Fe(II)$, $Cr=Cr(III)$, $Co=Co(II)$, $Mn=Mn(II)$, $Pb=Pb(II)$.

Table 13-12.   Representative Values of the Soil Parameters[a]

Nutrient species	c_i (mmol m^{-3})	β_e/θ	D_e (10^{-10} m^2 s^{-1})	τ_D^b (days)
NO_3^-	3,000-11,000	1.0	2.5	1
$H_2PO_4^-$, HPO_4^{2-}	0.6-5.0	10-10^3	10^{-4}–10^{-2}	2×10^4
K^+	100-2,500	1-50	10^{-2}–10^{-1}	200
Ca^{2+}	500-5,000	10-100	10^{-3}–10^{-2}	2×10^3
Mg^{2+}	500-5,000	1-60	10^{-2}	200
SO_4^{2-}	700-1,500	2-10	1	1
$H_3BO_3^0$	10-3,500	1-3	2-4	1
Fe^{2+}	0.1-1.0	10^3	10^{-4}	2×10^4
Mn^{2+}	0.1-100	1-100	10^{-3}–10^{-1}	2×10^3
MoO_4^{2-}	0.01-0.2	10-2,000	10^{-2}–1.0	200

[a] Compiled from S.A. Barber, *Soil Nutrient Bioavailability*, Wiley, New York, 1984.

[b] $\tau_D = 2\delta^2/D_e$, $\delta = 3$ mm, D_e = lower value in column 4.

$$\beta_e = \frac{dC_s}{dC_l} \qquad \text{[13-4]}$$

the ratios of the two quantities is termed the **nutrient buffer power**, β_e, usually measured by the slope of nutrient adsorption isotherm. If D_l is the nutrient diffusion coefficient in soil solution and

$$D_e = \frac{\theta D_l}{\beta_e} \qquad \text{[13-5]}$$

where θ is the volumetric water content of the soil, f is an impedance factor (tortuosity) and D_e is called the **Nye diffusivity parameter**. Furthermore, if q is the surface excess of the nutrient and ρ_b is the dry bulk density of the soil, then β_e is related to the slope of nutrient adsorption isotherm.

$$\beta_e = \theta \left(1 + \frac{\rho_b \, dq}{dC_l} \right) \qquad \text{[13-6]}$$

A diffusion time constant, τ_D, is defined as

$$\tau_D = 2 \frac{\delta^2}{D_l} \qquad \text{[13-7]}$$

where δ is rhizosphere distance in μm.

13.2.4 Geotechnical Applications

Soil stabilization and soil erosion will be addressed here. **Soil erosion** is the removal of surface layers of soil by the agencies of wind, water, and ice. Erosion involves a process of both particles and transport by these agencies and is initiated by drag impact, or tractor forces acting on individual particles of soil at the surface. Erosion may also occur along the stream bank where the velocity of the flowing water is high and the resistance of the bank materials is low. Piping or spring sapping is another type of erosion caused by seepage and emergence of water from the face of an unprotected slope.

The susceptibility of a soil to erosion is known as its **erodibility**. Some soils (e.g., silts) are inherently more erodible than others (e.g., well-graded sands and gravel). In general, increasing the organic content and clay size fraction of a soil decreases erodibility. It also depends on other factors including soil texture, past moisture content, void ratio, pH, and composition or ionic strength of the eroding water.

Other properties of soil include the storage capability of soil, which is actually caused by absorption. Because soil can supply trace metal nutrients for plants, it is considered as a support for the plant kingdom. Soil is classified as an ion exchanger. It is possible to be used as a waste-disposal method for treating radioactive metals. Soil can behave as a catalyst for the denitrification of many organic compounds. The silicate chemistry indeed exhibits a host of channeling and spacial sites in the many wonderful three-dimensional tessellations.

A suggested hierarchy of erodibility based on the unified soil classification system gray symbols is as follows:

most erodible → least erodible

ML > SM > SC > MH > OL >> CL > CH > GM > GP > GW

This erodibility hierarchy is simple, but based on graduation and plasticity indices of remolded or disturbed soils. It fails to take into account effects of soil structure, void ratio, and antecedent moisture content.

Erosion of soils is a function of climate, topography, vegetative cover, soil properties, and the activities of animals and humans. A so-called **universal soil loss equation** (USLE) is commonly used to estimate sediment loading from surface erosion. It can be written as follows:

$$Y = \sum_{i=1}^{n} A_i \left(R.K.L.S.C.P.Sd \right) \qquad [13\text{-}8]$$

where

Y = sediment loading from erosion (ton/yr)

n = number of subareas

A_i = acreage of subarea (acre)

R = rainfall factor

K = soil erodibility factor

L = slope-length factor

S = slope-gradient factor

C = cover factor

P = erosion control practice factor

Sd = fraction of total erosion which is delivered to stream

Table 13-13. Reductive Protection of Ground Cover Against Erosion: Values For *C* Factor

Land-User Groups	Examples	Range of "C" Values
Permanent Vegetation	Protected woodland	0.0001-0.45
	Prairie	
	Permanent pasture	
	Sodded orchard	
	Permanent meadow	
Established Meadows	Alfalfa	0.0004-0.3
	Clover	
	Fescue	
Small Grains	Rye	0.07-0.5
	Wheat	
	Barley	
	Oats	
Large-Seeded Legumes	Soybeans	0.1-0.65
	Cowpeas	
	Peanuts	
	Field peas	
Row Crops	Cotton	0.1-0.70
	Potatoes	
	Tobacco	
	Vegetables	
	Corn	
	Sorghum	
Fallow	Summer fallow	1.0
	Period between plowing and growth of crop	

Source: U.S. EPA Office of Research and Development (ORD): *Loading Functions for Assessment of Water Pollution from Nonpoint Sources*. National Technical Information Service, Springfield, VA (1976), p. 59.

Suitable values for these parameters for a specific condition and area are commonly found in monographs and tables. The *C* factor can be located in Table 13-13. For example, *R* for a certain location can be found from Figure 13-17. Wischmeier has published a convenient nomograph that can be used to determine erodibility *K*-values of soils due to water erosion. The nomograph is valid for exposed subsoils at construction sites and farmlands. Five soil parameters are required:

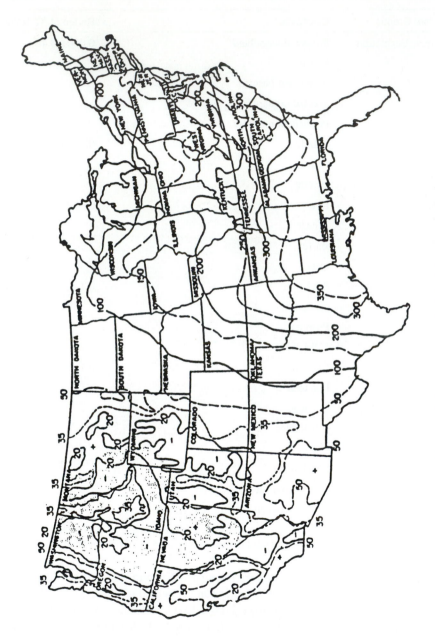

Figure 13-17. Average annual values of rainfall factor, *R*.

- percent silt and very fine sand (0.002-0.10mm),

- percent sand (0.10-2.0mm),

- percent organic matter,

- structure, and

- permeability.

The first three parameters will often suffice to provide a reasonable approximation of the erodibility. This approximation can be refined by including information on permeability and soil structure as indicated on the nomograph. The soil erodibility, K, can be found in Figure 13-18, with information on soil structure.

The topographic factor (LS) can be found in Figure 13-19. For example, for a plot of land east of the Mississippi River with a slope of 6% and a slope length of 250, the topographic value is 1.0%. The cover factor depends on the type of vegetation on the land. The P factor for a crop land with 6% slope and contour strip-cropping is 0.25 (see Table 13-14). The fraction of total erosion that is delivered to the sediment is available from the U.S. Department of Agriculture.

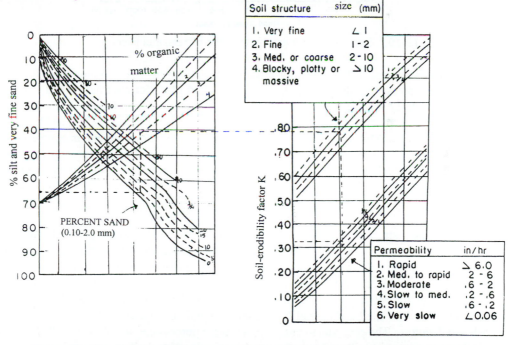

Figure 13-18.   Soil erodibility nomograph for calculating values of K. [For example, assume a lab analysis indicates soil with: 65% silt and very fine sand; 5% sand (.10-2.0 mm); 3% organic matter; fine granular soil (1-2 mm); slow to medium permeability (0.2-0.6 in/hr). The sample K value is 31.]

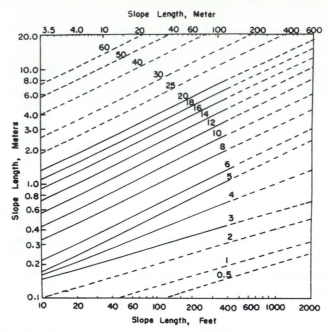

Figure 13-19.   Slope effect for area east of the Mississippi River.

Various control technologies for erosion are available. The common ones for agriculture are terracing and diversions. In siliculture, good plans for road design and transportation are crucial for erosion control. Biological methods for using biopolymer as cement-
ing agents are in the development stages.

According to **Mohr-Coulomb failure criteria**, rupture along a plane in a material occurs by a critical combination of normal and shear stresses and not by normal and shear
stress alone. The relation between normal and shear stress on failure plane can be given by

$$\tau = c + \sigma \tan\phi \qquad\qquad [13\text{-}9]$$

where τ is shear stress at failure and σ is the normal stress on the failure plane. Cohesion is
shown by c and ϕ is the angle of friction. Because granular soils have no cohesion ($c=0$),
chemical additives are used for increase of cohesion for improving the bonding space, as
shown in Figure 13-20. The biopolymers from bacteria maybe an alternative for this application in the future; for example, the application of slime-forming bacteria to the Earth
structures (such as shell and core of Earth dams and embankments) can be similar to lime or
ash stabilization. The procedure consists of adding a percentage of stabilizer to the soil layers during compaction. To enhance the strength of subsurface soil of structure's foundation,
pressure injection of slime-forming bacteria may be utilized. The same idea can be used for
mitigating liquefaction during earthquake, if the bacteria can be injected below the foundation.

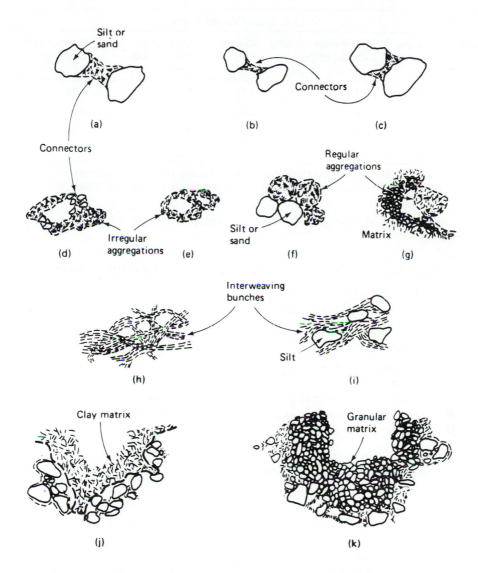

Figure 13-20. Schematic representations of particle assemblages; (a), (b), (c) connectors; (d) irregular aggregations linked by connector assemblages; (e) irregular aggregations forming a honeycomb arrangement; (f) regular aggregations interacting with silt or sand grains; (g) regular aggregation interacting with particle matrix; (h) interweaving bunches of clay; (i) interweaving bunches of clay with silt inclusions; (j) clay particle matrix; (k) granular particle matrix (after Collins and McGown, 1974,loc.cit.).

Table 13-14.   "P" Values for Erosion Control Practices on Cropland

Slope	Up and Downhill	Cross-slope Farming Without Strips	Contour Farming	Cross-slope Farming with Strips	Contour Strip Cropping
			Type of Control Practice		
2.0-7	1.0	0.75	0.50	0.37	0.25
7.1-12	1.0	0.80	0.60	0.45	0.30
12.1-18	1.0	0.90	0.80	0.60	0.40
18.1-24	1.0	0.95	0.90	0.67	0.45

Source: U.S. EPA Office of Research and Development (ORD): *Loading Functions for Assessment of Water Pollution from Nonpoint Sources*. National Technical Information Service, Springfield, VA (1976), p. 64.

Incidentally, coal mining, if not well designed, has multiple adverse impacts on the environment:

- disturbance of the land by strip mining with its attendant effect on streams,
- acid mine drainage problems,
- subsidence of the land resulting from less coal being left in place to support the overburden,
- mine fires, and
- refuse banks from mining and coal preparation.

Good examples of these effects of the improper exploitation of natural resources can be illustrated by the whole commonwealth of Pennsylvania, the strip mining of the Dakotas, and the heap mining of copper in Arizona.

13.2.5   Biodegradation in Soil

Many soil bacteria, fungi, and animals, along with catalytic surfaces provided by clay minerals are capable of removing or detoxifying a variety of harmful substances, as shown in Figure 13-21. Figure 13-22 illustrates the decomposition of the organic matter and the formation of humic substances in soil. In addition, the pathway of the microbial degradation of cotton fiber is given in Figure 13-23. The unique ability of soil to detoxify and adsorb substances that would be considered pollutants if released to the air and water environments has caused it to be used extensively as a treatment medium for such waste materials. Land filling and land treatment techniques have been used in environmental engineering practices. Details of the treatment will be discussed in Chapter 14. Also in Section 29.2.5 (volume 4B) we have a discussion on bioreclaimation and biorestoration. As a result of limitations on the population of soil microorganisms and their ability to biodegrade complex xenobiotics, there is usually a maximum rate at which a soil can carry out particular chemical transformations. Refer to Chapter 29 of the next volume for more details of biotransformations and biodegradations. Because the structure of synthetic compounds is getting more complex than the naturally occurring substances, the biodegradation rate of the xenobiotics is becoming much slower. The accumulation of these toxic materials in soils presents a great danger to us.

After soil is formed it can take compaction, consolidation, pore pressure, lateral pressure, and settlement. Most important is that soil is a host of a great variety of microorganisms. There are overall presence of enzymes in soil as detected by any enzyme tests. In ecological language, the organisms are as syntrophism (e.g., commensalism, predation, and competition); they are not neutralism or amensalism. (See Chapter 28 of the volume 4B for microbial interactions in detail.) The final bioproduct is humus, which is refectoric.

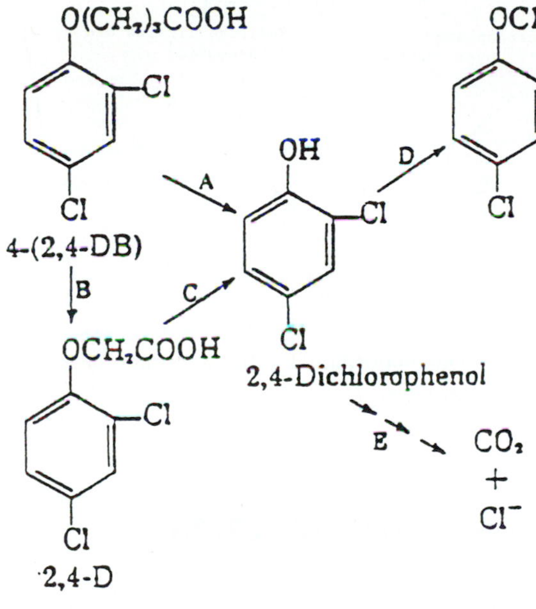

A: Defusing (*Flavobacterium*)
B: Activation (soil)
C: Detoxication (*Arthrobacter*, soil)
D: Addition reaction (*Arthrobacter*)
E: Degradation (*Pseudomonas*, soil)

Initial steps in the metabolism of several phenoxyalkanoate herbicides.

Figure 13-21. Degradation reactions in contrast to other processes.

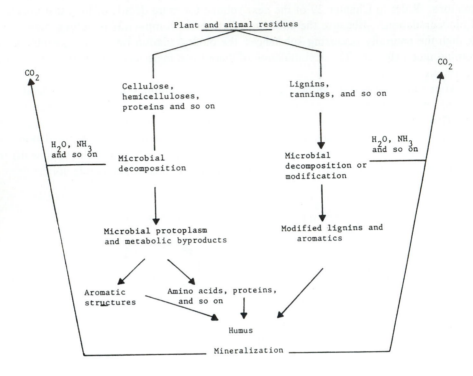

Figure 13-22.   Organic matter decomposition and the formation of humic substances in soil. (Source: Stevenson, 1964.)

13.3 UBIQUITOUS GLOBAL SOIL POLLUTION

Sodium cyanide has been known as a very poisonous material for a long time. But as shown in Table 13-15, it is not as toxic as some manmade organic materials. Dioxin (2,3,7,8-TCDD) has the lowest LD_{50} content based on mass. Humans also think that incineration is the safest way to destroy toxic materials. It is astonishing to find that there still are many toxic substances produced, among which dioxin is one, from the incineration of wastes at high temperature as shown in Table 13-16. PCBs have been widely used as plasticizers, transformer fluids, lubricants, and hydraulic fluids. Although their application is now restricted, large quantities have been widely spread in our environment. They are widely present in a wide variety of marine creatures (refer back to Figures 3-4, 3-5, and 3-6) and inextricably entwined in the food chain.

Table 13-15. Toxicities of Selected Poisons

Substance	Molecular Weight	Minimum Lethal Dose (mol/ kg)
Botulinum Toxin A	9.0×10^5	3.3×10^{-17}
Tetanus Toxin	1.0×10^5	1.0×10^{-17}
Diptheria Toxin	7.2×10^4	4.2×10^{-12}
2,3,7,8-TCDD[a]	322	3.1×10^{-9}
Saxitoxin	372	2.4×10^{-8}
Tetrodotoxin	319	2.5×10^{-8}
Bufotoxin[b]	757	5.2×10^{-7}
Curare	696	7.2×10^{-7}
Strychnine	334	1.5×10^{-6}
Muscarin[b]	210	5.2×10^{-6}
Dtisopropylfluorophosphate	184	1.6×10^{-5}
Sodium Cyanide	49	2.0×10^{-4}

Source: Pland and Kende. These data were compiled by Mosher et al. and the values indicate only relative toxicity. It should be noted that the values deal with different species, routes of administration, survival times and, in one case, mean lethal dose rather than minimum lethal dose. Except where noted, administration was by the intraperitoneal route in mice.

[a] LD_{50} on oral administration in a guinea pig.

[b] Intravenous injection in a cat.

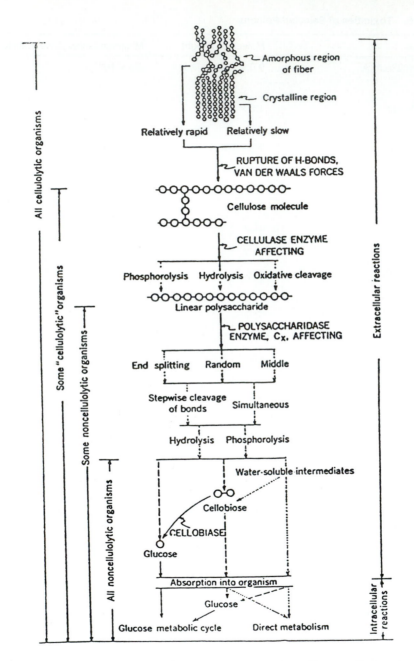

Figure 13-23.   The microbial degradation of cotton fiber (Source: R.G.H. Siu, "Micro-biological Decomposition of Cellulose," Reinhold Publishing Corporation, 1951).

Table 13-16. HRGC/LRMC Analytical Results for CDD/CDF in Ash Sample from Incineration of Waste Containing PCP

CDD/ CDF	Total Number of Apparent Isomers	Total Detected (ng/ g)	Minimum Detectable Concentrated (ng/ g)
MCDF	3	75	0.1
DCDF	8	25	0.3
TrCDF	8	15	0.6
TCDF	7	7	0.5
PCDF	5	8	1
HxCDF	5	5	1
HpCDF	2	6	1
OCDF	1	2	1
MCDD	1	1	0.1
DCDD	4	5	0.3
TrCDD	5	2	0.6
TCDD	4	4	0.2
PCDD	5	32	1
HxCDD	5	81	1
HpCDD	2	117	1
OCDD	1	198	1

Source: Recent analysis by Wright State University.

1. Extraction of CDD and CDF from the sample matrix using organic solvents.

2. Preliminary separation of CDD and CDF from other constituents of the matrix, which also have been extracted (including other chlorinated materials) using acid-base treatments and liquid chromatography with alumina, silica gel, and /or other suitable columns.

3. Further fractionation of the CDD and CDF using normal and reverse-phase high-performance liquid chromatography (HPLC); and

4. Analysis of the prepared abstracts containing CDD and CDF using capillary-column gas chromatography, mass spectrometry (GC-MS). Both low- and high-resolution mass spectrometry may be used in this analysis, depending on the sample.

A case study of dioxin contamination in the United States is present here. Dioxin (2,3,7,8-TCDD), is a byproduct of herbicides, some of them used during the Vietnam War as shown in Table 13-17. It was later found to be an extremely toxic material that causes death, birth defects, and so on. Many people have been exposed to it, as demonstrated by Table 13-18.

Table 13-17. Agent Orange Had Far Less Dioxin Than Earlier 2,4,5-T Herbicides Used in the Vietnam War

Code Name	Herbicide	Quantity, Gal	Period of Use	2,3,7,D-TCDD, ppm
Orange	2,4-D; 2,4,5-T	10,646,000	1965-1970	1.98
White	2,4-D; pilioram	5,633,000	1965-1971	—
Blue	Cacodylic acid	1,150,000	1962-1971	—
Purple	2,4-D; 2,4,5-T	145,000	1962-1965	32.8[a]
Pink	2,4,5-T	123,000	1962-1965	65.6
Green	2,4,5-T	8,200	1962-1965	65.6
Total:		17,705,200		

[a] Assumed level from one known and four probable samples of purple. Note: pink and green levels are twice that of purple because they were full-strength 2,4,5-T.

Sources: Proceedings from 2nd Continuing Education Conference on Herbicide Orange, May 1980; and Air Force OEHL Technical Report on Toxicology, Fate and Risk from Agent Orange and Dioxin, October 1978.

Table 13-18. Workers Exposed to Dioxin

Date	Exposed	Location of Accident	Remarks
1948	250	Monsanto's 2,4,5-trichlorophenol plant in Nitro, West Virginia	122 cases of chloracne being studied; so far, 32 deaths vs. 48.4 expected; no excess deaths from malignant neoplasms or circulatory disease.
1953	75	BASF's 2,4,5-trichlorophenol plant at Ludwigshafen, West Germany	55 cases of chloracne, 42 severe; 17 deaths so far vs. 11 to 25 expected (4 gastrointestinal cancers and 2 oatcell lung cancers); most common injuries were impaired senses and liver damage.
1956	?	Rhone-Poulenc's 2,4,5-trichlorophenol plant in Grenoble, France	17 cases of chloracne, also elevated lipid and cholesterol levels in blood.
1963	106	NV Philips' 2,4,5-T plant in Amsterdam, The Netherlands	44 chloracne cases (42 severe), of whom 21 also had internal disturbances; 8 deaths so far (6 possible myocardial infarctions); some symptoms of fatigue.
1964	61	Dow Chemical's 2,4,5-tricholorphenol plant at Midland, Michigan	49 cases of chloracne; deaths so far 4 vs. 7.8 expected, 3 cancer deaths vs. 1.5 expected, one a soft tissue sarcoma.

Data assembled in pamphlet from U.S. Occupational Safety and Health Administration (OSHA), 1982.

Table 13-19.   2,3,7,8-TCDD Is One Compound in a Family

All dibenzo- -dioxins have a three- ring
structure consisting of two benzene rings
connected by oxygen atoms:

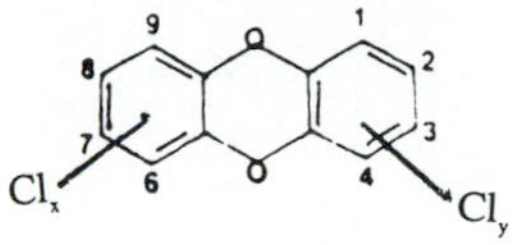

And 2,3,7,8-tetrachlorodibenzo- - dioxin
is one of the 75 possible chlorinated
dioxins:

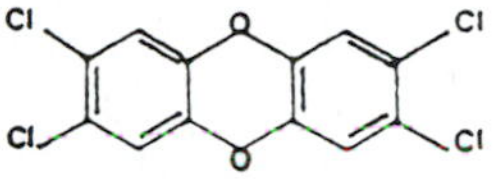

Related are chlorinated dibenzofurans:

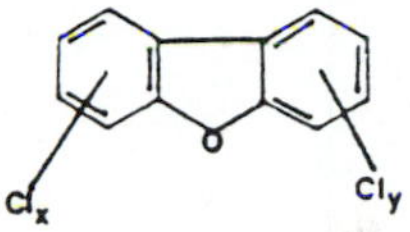

Dioxin precursors combine
to form dioxin in the
general reaction:

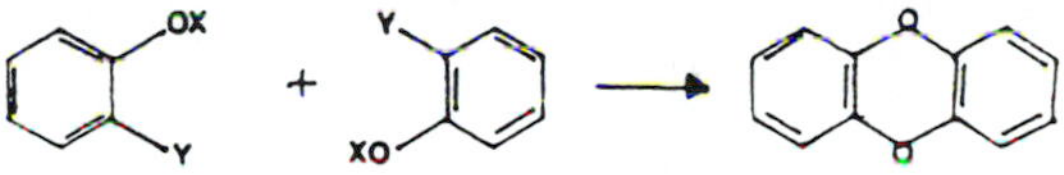

For example, 2,3,7,8-TCDD is the most
likely result from the reaction of
2,4,5-trichlorophenol:

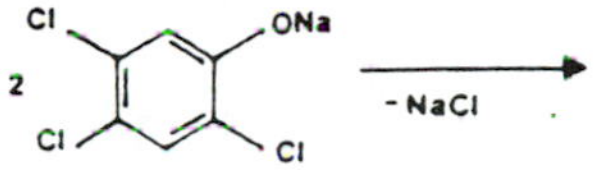

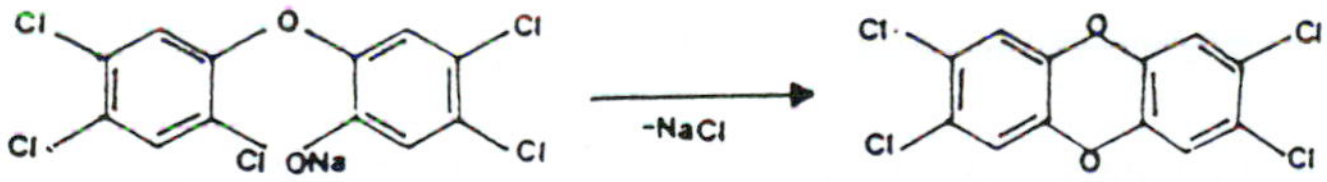

And chlorophenols can be formed from phenols (by combustion) and chloride oxidation to
chlorine.

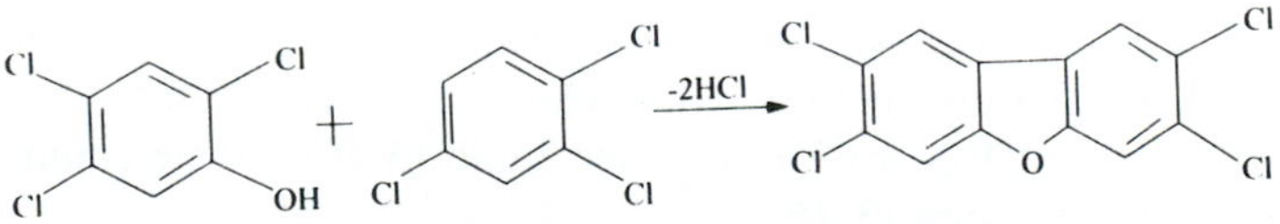

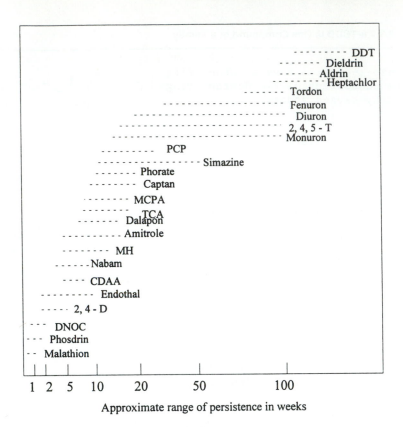

Figure 13-24.   Persistence of pesticides in soil.

Table 13-19 shows the pathway of dioxin production. Two major types of chlorinated compounds are formed: the chlorinated dibanzo dioxins (CDD) and the chlorinated dibenzo furans (CDF). Dioxin is very refractory and very resistant to biodegradation. Referring to Figure 13-24 for persistence of pesticides in soil, the half-life for dioxins in soil was thought to be less than a year, but in the case of dioxin concentration in Missouri, it was found that high residual dioxin concentration persists even after 15 years. The detailed mechanism of dioxin's effect on cellular biology is not yet fully understood, as shown in Figure 13-25.

The dioxin's precursor comes from chlorinated aromatics. Most of these are the remains from pesticides and insecticides. Most chlorinated insecticides left in the soil will yield these precursors for CDD or CDF (e.g., see Table 13-16). Some common chlorinated insecticides are shown in Figure 13-26.

An interesting study was made to determine the sperm density in the United States as a function of time, as shown in Table 13-20. The results are frightening, for the sperm density is decreasing sharply. The decrease may be a result of the exposure to the toxic substances shown in Table 13-21. Here we have another hint that if pollution cannot be properly controlled, the human species may be extinct in the near future.

Table 13-20. Sperm Density in United States Males As a Function of Time

Year	Number of Cases	Mean Sperm Density (10^6 cell/ ml)	Comments
1929	271	100[a]	
1938	200	120[a]	0.5% had < 20×10^6/ ml 25% had < 60×10^6/ ml
1949	49	145	Range = $50\text{-}321 \times 10^6$/ ml
1950	100	101	
1951	1,000	107	29% had < 60×10^6/ ml 44% had > 100×10^6/ ml
1974	386	48	
1975	1,300	79	Median = 65×10^6/ ml
1975	100	81	Median = 61×10^6/ ml
1977	4,122	70	Median = 50×10^6/ ml 23% had < 20×10^6/ ml
1979	22	62	
	24	22[b]	

[a] Wives were pregnant at the time.

[b] Occupational dibromochloropropane exposure for 60 days or more.

Table 13-21.   Statistical Parameters Relating Sperm Density to Toxic Substances

Precursor Structures	m/z	Number of Chlorines	Slope (SD/ Intensity)	R Square Change	Significance
	427	6	0.22	0.048	0.040
	241	3	-0.11	0.054	0.010
Heptachlorobiphenyl	373	6	-0.15	0.037	0.005
	343	4	-0.16	0.021	0.005
	230	5	-0.01	0.017	0.006
Trichlorophenol	231	4	0.08	0.012	0.007
Hexachloronaphthalene	313	5	0.01	0.011	0.009
Pentachlorophenol	263	5	0.00	0.013	0.010
Hexachlorobiphenyl	339	5	-0.10	0.005	0.015
	463	7	-0.04	0.008	0.020
	318	3	-0.09	0.015	0.021
Tetrachlorodiphenylether (?)	287	3	-0.09	0.008	0.026
Hexachlorobenzene	282	6	0.04	0.005	0.035
	212	3	0.20	0.003	0.049
	239	4	0.03	0.003	0.065
	241	3	0.02	0.002	0.087
	224	3	-0.14	0.002	0.115
	251	5	-0.12	0.001	0.152
Pentachlorobiphenyl	305	4	-0.09	0.001	0.198
Octachlorobiphenyl	407	7	-0.03	0.001	0.251

13.3.1   DDT and PCB

We have noticed the worldwide pollution of various organochloro-compounds even in pristine portions of land such as an isolated island without human activities, as shown in Table 13-22. Chemically **DDT** stands for 2,2-di-p-chlorodiphenyl-1,1,1-trichloroethane (see Figure 13-26 for structure). It is readily synthesized with high yield in the laboratory (used to be a standard organic chemistry preparation for students taking their first course in organic chemistry) by a Friedel-Crafts reaction of trichloroacetaldehyde and chlorobenzene.

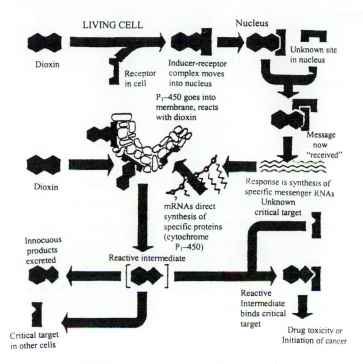

Figure 13-25. Dioxin's effects on cellular biology.

Table 13-22. DDT and PCB Residues in Oceanic Birds and Fishes

Species	Locality	DDT (Wet Wt., ppm)	PCB (Wet Wt., ppm)
Shearwater	Mexico	3.0	0.4
	California	11.3	1.1
	New Brunswick	40.9	52.6
	California	32.0	2.1
	New Brunswick	70.9	104.3
Petrel	Bermuda	6.4	—
	California	66.0	24.0
	Mexico	9.2	1.0
	Mexico	3.2	0.35
	Baja California	953	351
	New Brunswick	164	192
	New Brunswick	199	697

Table 13-22. (continued)

Species	Locality	DDT (Wet Wt., ppm)	PCB (Wet Wt., ppm)
Anchovy	San Francisco Bay	0.33-0.59	—
	Monterey	0.90	—
	Morro Bay	0.74	—
	Port Hueneme	3.04	—
	Los Angeles	14.0	1.0
English sole	San Francisco Bay	0.19-0.55	0.05-0.11
	Monterey	0.76	0.04
Shiner perch	San Francisco Bay	1-1.4	0.4-1.2
Jack Mackerel	Channel Islands	0.56	0.02
Hake	Puget Sound	0.18	0.16
	Channel Islands	1.8	0.12
Bluefin tuna	Mexico	0.22-0.56	0.04
Yellowfin tuna	Galapagos Islands	0.07	—
	Central America	0.62	0.04
Herring	Baltic Sea	0.68	0.27
Plaice	Baltic Sea	0.018	0.017
Cod	Baltic Sea	0.063	0.033
Salmon	Baltic Sea	3.4	0.30

Source: Robert M. Garrels et al., *Chemical Cycles and the Global Environment*, p. 139; adapted from Robert W. Risebrough, "Chlorinated Hydrocarbons," in D. H. Hood edition, ed., *Impingement of Man on the Oceans* (New York: Wiley-Interscience, 1971), pp. 259–286.

In World War II, massive amounts of DDT were used to combat insect-borne diseases such as malaria, typhus, and diarrhea. It is so effective toward mosquitos, lices, and flies that in a short time these insects were totally wiped out, saving many lives. Similar to the miracle sulfa drugs that were in vogue during World War I, the deaths due to infectious disease were greatly reduced.

The metabolic product of DDT is DDE, 2,2-di-p-chlorodiphenyl-1,1-dichloroethylene. This is a simple dehydrochlorination reaction. DDT can be transformed to DDE, which is nontoxic, by an insect enzyme called DDT-*ase*, and further into DDA, as demonstrated in Figure 13-26. For industry production of DDT, there are frequently isomers in which the o-positions, rather than the p-positions, are substituted by chlorine as by-products. These isomers can act as estrogen mimics and can interfere with normal sex hormones. Development of breast and ovarian cancers in females and demasculinization in males is the consequence.

Table 13-23. Estimated Daily Content of DDT and DDE in Complete Meals in the United States

Year Location	Source	Number	DDT	DDE[a] as DDT	Total[a] as DDT	DDE as DDT (% of total)
1953-1954						
Wenaichee, Washington	Restaurant	18	0.178	0.102	0.280	37
Tacoma, Washington	Prison	7	0.116	0.063	0.179	55
1954-1955						
Talahassee, Florida	Prison	12	0.202	0.056	0.258	21
1956-1957						
Walla Walla, Washington	College dining room for meat abstainers	11	0.041	0.027	0.068	39
1959-1960						
Anchorage, Alaska	Hospital	3	0.184	0.029	0.213	14
1961-1962						
Washington, D.C.						
Baltimore, Maryland						
Atlanta, Georgia	Market basket survey	36[b]	0.026[c]	0.017[c]	0.045[c]	40[c]
Minneapolis, Minnesota						
San Francisco, California						
1962-1964						
Wenaichee, Washington	Restaurant	12	0.038	0.049	0.087	56
Wenaichee, Washington	Household	17	0.514	0.193	0.507	40

Table 13-23. continued

Year Location	Source	Number	DDT	DDE[a] as DDT	Total[a] as DDT	DDE as DDT (% of total)
1962-1964						
Atlanta, Georgia						
Baltimore, Maryland						
Minneapolis, Minnesota	Market basket survey	25[b]	0.023[c]	0.013[c]	0.036[c]	36[c]
St. Louis, Missouri						
San Franciso, California						
1964						
Baltimore, Maryland	Market basket survey	1[b]	0.025[c]	0.017[c]	0.040[c]	43[c]

[a] Total daily content in milligrams

[b] This figure refers to the number of diet samples, each consisting of the total normal 14-day food intake for males 16 to 19 years old, which were tested. In some instances, additional diet samples were taken and aliquots were analyzed for pesticide content of various classes of foodstuffs, but no compensate value was given.

[c] The author did not calculate the daily DDT or DDE intake. However, using the author's mean dietary concentrations of DDT and DDE and the mean daily food intake of 3.78 kg from the market basket survey, the reviewer has calculated the values shown.

(Source: from R.A. Horne, *Chemistry of Our Environment*, Wiley-Interscience, 1978.)

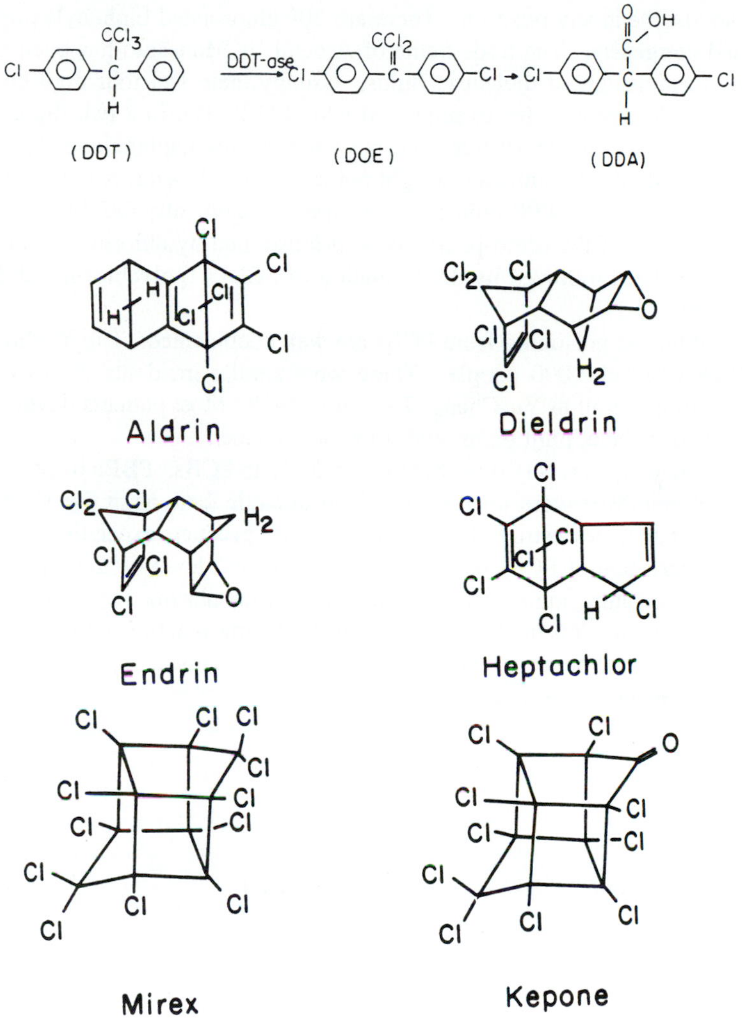

Figure 13-26. Organochlorine insectides. The top shows the transformation of DDT.

Although a total ban or severe restrictions have been imposed on DDT use for the past quarter of a century, the persistent nature is around. Almost daily we still have intake of DDT in some quantity without exceptions. Table 13-23 indicates the DDT exposure of an average meal, whether taken from restaurants or elsewhere.

PCBs in general are a mixture of the isomers of polychlorinated biphenyls originating from the chlorination of biphenyl under Lewis acid conditions. The number of chlorine atoms introduced into the biphenyl system can range from 1 to 10 (10 being perchlorobiphenyl) and can also be in any position. There are 209 chlorinated biphenyls possible, and these are termed **congeners**. The trade name of Aroclor by Monsanto has been commonly adopted for the formulations of dielectric fluids. Usually there is a four-digit code associated with each Aroclor product; for example, Aroclor 1242. The first two digits (12) indicate that 12 carbons are in the system (the system includes naphthalene, e.g., Aroclors 1016). The last two digits (42) indicate weight percentage of chlorine in the system. In the case of Aroclor 1242 there is 42% chlorine in sample. Analytically GC-MS can pin down most congeners. If one of the ortho-positions is unsubstituted by chlorine for PCBs, it can be consequently oxidized followed by the formation of PCDFs (polychlorinated dibenzofurans) (refer to Table 13-19).

Incidents of human poisoning from PCBs are well documented. The Yusho poisoning in Japan in 1968 affected 2,000 people. There were similar incidents involving cooking with PCB-containing rice oil in Yu-Cheng, Taiwan in 1978. Most patients develop an acne-like rash, feelings of fatigue, joint pains, and some liver cancer.

Polybrominated biphenyls (PBBs) behave similarly to PCBs. PBBs have been used as fire retardants. When PBBs were mistakenly added to cattle feed, as in the 1973 Michigan incident, the cattle had to be destroyed as well as the dairy products exceeding $100 million.

The total destruction of PCBs is often to the "six nines" level — that is, at 99.9999% level. A high temperature incineration method including plasma techniques is needed. Other chemical dechlorination methods, including the Wurtz reaction with sodium metals, are also possibilities, as shown in Figure 13-27. A photochemical method, ultrasound, as well as the use of anion radicals, is another way.

$$2R-Cl + 2Na \longrightarrow R-R + 2NaCl$$

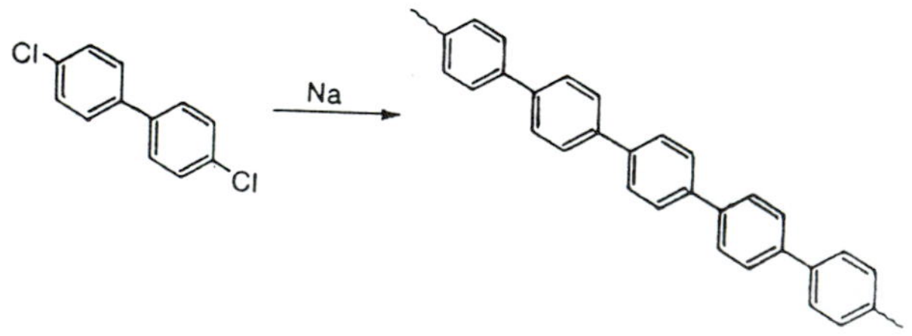

Figure 13-27.   Wurtz reaction.

$$ArCl \xrightarrow{\ hv\ } Ar + Cl$$

$$ArCl + amine \rightarrow amine^{+\cdot} + ArCl^{-\cdot}$$

$$ArCl^{-\cdot} \rightarrow Ar^- + Cl^-$$

$$ArCl^{-\cdot} + H^+ \rightarrow ArH + Cl$$

$$Na + ArH \rightarrow Na^+ + ArH^{-\cdot}$$

$$C_{10}H_8^{-\cdot} \ (naphthalenide, \ radical \ ion) + ArCl \rightarrow C_{10}H_8 + ArCl^{-\cdot} \rightarrow Ar + Cl^-$$

Electrochemically generated anion radicals in micellar form at alkaline conditions (isopropyl alcohol) also are used.

$$ArCl^{-\cdot} \rightarrow Ar + Cl^-$$

$$Ar + (CH_3)_2CHOH \rightarrow ArH + (CH_3)_2C(OH) \cdot$$

$$(CH_3)_2C(OH) \cdot + OH^- \rightarrow (CH_3)_2CO^{-\cdot} + H_2O$$

$$(CH_3)_2CO^{-\cdot} + ArCl \rightarrow (CH_3)_2{=}O + ArCl^{-\cdot}$$

Another type of dechlorination includes nucleophilic displacement; for example, using polyethylene glycol with KOH,

$$ArCl + 2KOH \rightarrow ArOK + KCl + H_2O$$

In this case, stabilization of OH$^-$ is done by placing the reaction as in a crown ether cavity in the aprotic medium. Nucleophilic displacement for aryl chloride dechlorination may involve a benzene intermediate with triple bonds in the aryl rings and the subsequent addition of water to form phenyls. In this regard $R_3Si - PR_2$ can also be used.

$$R_3Si - PR_2 + ArCl \rightarrow ArPR_2 + R_3SiCl$$

13.4 PESTICIDES AND STOCKPILE WASTES

Soil pollution could be typified as the malfunctioning of soil as an environmental component following its contamination with certain compounds, particularly as a result of human activities. Pesticides are a major source of soil pollution; hence, discussion in this section will be focused on them.

Insects share plant foods with us, but some of them are carriers of devastating diseases. Prior to 1940, the majority of pesticides were organic materials such as arsenate, lead, and mercury. They are often referred to as **first generation pesticides,** which are highly poisonous to insects. They are, however, highly poisonous to humans and animals as well. The discovery of DDT, which possesses insecticidal properties and relatively low human toxicity, marks the era of **second generation pesticides**. Tremendous efforts were made by large numbers of chemists to synthesize various organic pesticides. DDT was banned in the United States in 1973 because (1) it is highly **persistent**, meaning that it does not degrade in a reasonable period of time, and (2) it is oil soluble and hence accumulates in fat tissues, consequently building up in the food chain. A detailed discussion of this subject has been previously discussed.

TCDD (2,3,7,8- tetrachlorodibenzo-p-dioxin), a by-product from 2,4,5 trichlorophenol in the manufacture of the herbicide 2,4,5-trichlorophenoxyacetate (2,4,5T), causes birth defects, skin disorders, liver damage, and other adverse effects (refer to Table 13-19).

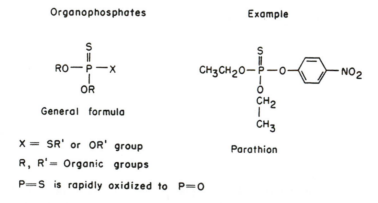

Figure 13-28.   Organophosphates; for example, parathion.

Table 13-24.   Lethal Dosage (LD$_{50}$ Oral) for Pesticides in Test Rats

Pesticides	LD$_{50}$ oral (mg/ kg)
Insecticides	
Aldrin	54-56
Arochlor (PCB)	250
Carbaryl	540
DDT	420-800 (60-75 dog)
Dichlorvos	56-80
Dieldrin	50-55
Endrin	5-43
Heptachlor	90
Lead arsenate	825 (192 sheep)
Lindane	125-200
Malathion	480-1500
Methoxychlor	5000-6000
Mirex	300-600
Nicotine	50-60
Parathion	4-30
Paris Green	22
Pyrethrins	820-1870
Herbicides	
2,4-D	666
Dioxin (impurity in 2,4,5-T)	0.03
Pentachlorophenol	27-80
Sodium arsenite	10-50
2,4,5-T	300 (100 dog)
Fungicides	
Copper sulfate	produces jaundice in sheep and chickens upon several months exposure
Mercurials (ethylmercury-p-toluenesulfonanilide)	100

Several nonpersistent classes of pesticides have been developed. Organophosphates and carbamates are the two major representative classes. The organophosphates all have a phosphorous atom connected by a double bond to either a sulfur or an oxygen atom and also by single bonds to oxygen or sulfur atoms with attached organic groups, as shown in Figure 13-28. The structure of carbamates is characterized by their having a carbon atom connected by a double bond to an oxygen atom and by single bonds to oxygen on one side and nitrogen on the other, each with attached organic groups. Both organophosphates and carbamates can react with water and oxygen to be decomposed within a few days once exposed in the environment. The LD_{50} and mode of action of these insecticides are listed in Table 13-24.

It is also interesting to note that the herbicide paraquat and its metabolite are related to 1-methyl-4-phenyl-1,2,3-tetrahydropyridine (MPTP), and MPTP can induce a kinsonian-like state in humans. Thus, pesticides may be causative agents for Parkinson's disease, as shown in Figure 13-29.

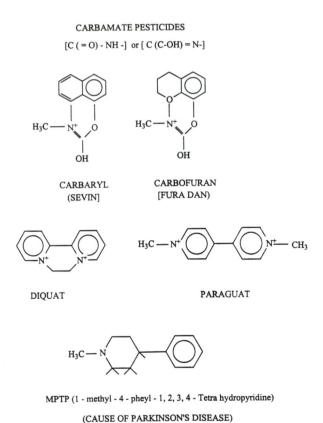

Figure 13-29.   Carbamate [-C(=O)-NH-] pesticides and MTTP.

13.4.1   The Third Generation Insecticides

In addition to the persistence of pesticides creating environmental problems, insect resistance has plagued producers of pesticides, resulting in the development of a new class of pesticides. The aims of **third generation pesticides** are to operate more selectively and to be composed of as natural compounds as possible. It was found that **juvenile hormones** can regulate growth and, if applied externally, prevent insects from developing. On the other hand, the **molting hormone** will hasten the insects' aging process, hence, shortening their life span. **Pheromones** are molecules that act as messengers between insects, guiding them to each other, to food supplies, or to avoidance of dangerous places. By applying sex pheromones, sex attractants, male insects can be excited to such a frenzy that they cannot find mates. Table 13-25 lists some insect sex pheromones and Table 13-26 tabulates some insect attractants.

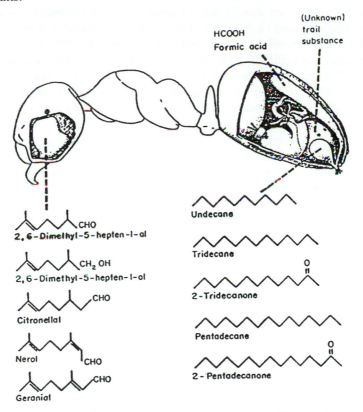

Figure 13-30.   The structural formulas of volatile substances found in various exocrine glands of *Acanthomyops claviger*. Terpenes are located in the mandibular gland in the head, and alkenes and keytones in Dufour's gland of the abdomen. All but pentadecane and 2-pentadecanone are efficient alarm substances. (Source: Wilson, 1970)

Another way to control the insect population is by sterilization. Male insects can be sterilized by **chemosterilants** or radioactivity. When these sterile insects are released to mate with females, they often displace potent ones, greatly reducing the population. Aziridine is one of the commonly used chemosterilants. Another group of chemicals that are useful in controlling insect damage to crops is the **antifeeding compounds**. The pests will die of starvation because they are prevented from eating the protected crops. Plants usually have some natural antifeeding compounds; for example, drismane was always found in the analysis of petroleum and coal compounds. Another pest control technology is the introduction of predators or diseases that may eliminate pests. Extensive care should be taken to ensure that they will not turn to other prey or hosts when the species to be controlled is gone. Another biological means is to introduce genetic defects into a species. In some cases, winter hibernation has been eliminated, insuring that the insects will perish during the cold winter.

Plants and animals are usually able to generate various chemicals for different purposes. For example, Figure 13-30 shows volatile substances found in *Acanthomyops Claviger*. **Interorganismic chemical effects** can be categorized into allelochemic effects (**interspecific** interactions or allelopathy) and **intraspecific** allomones (**intraspecific** interactions). Allelochemic effects (such as repellents, escape substances, venoms, and suppressants) have an adaptive advantage to the producing organism. Interspecific allomones include kairomones such as attractants, inductants, signals, and stimulants, and give an adaptive advantage to the receiving organism. Table 13-27 lists some allelopathic interactions. Pheromones, which are signals for reproductive behavior, social regulation, control of caste differentiation, alarm and defense, territory and trail marking, and food location, are examples of intraspecific chemical effects. A good hunting dog rolls itself in mud to disguise its scent before hunting. Understanding these interorganismic chemical effects is helpful when designing a well-integrated pest management plan.

A summary of the third-generation insecticides is listed here:

    (1) Attractants — sex pheromones; e.g., hexalure (for pink moth)
        (a) to trap male
        (b) for male confusion
        (c) for mating of sterilized female
    (2) Juvenile hormones
        dormancy for linden bug — keep it becoming mature
    (3) Molting hormone
        accelerate to become over-mature
        antijuvenile hormones; e.g., precocenes (for controlling the larva stage)
    (4) Insect predators
        bacteria and viruses
            Bacillus propillial against Japanese beetle
    (5) Antifeeding compounds
        drismane

Table 13-25.   Examples of Insect Sex Pheremones

Insect	Pheremone

Gypsy moth

$$\underset{\text{cis}}{CH_2CH(CH_2)_4CH-\!\!-CH(CH_2)_9CH_3}$$
with CH_3 branch and epoxide O

(disparture)

Fall armyworm moth

$$\underset{\text{cis}}{CH_3COCH_2(CH_2)_7CH=\!=CH(CH_2)_8CH_3}$$
(with O on the CO)

Cabbage looper moth

$$\underset{\text{cis}}{CH_3COCH_2(CH_2)_8CH=\!=CH(CH_2)_9CH_3}$$

European corn borer moth[a]
Red-handed leaf roller moth[b]
Smartweed borer[c]

$$\underset{\text{cis}}{CH_3COCH_2(CH_2)_9CH=\!=CHCH_2CH_3}$$

Oriental fruit moth[d]

$$\underset{\text{cis}}{CH_3COCH_2(CH_2)_4CH=\!=CH(CH_2)CH_3}$$

Pine beetle

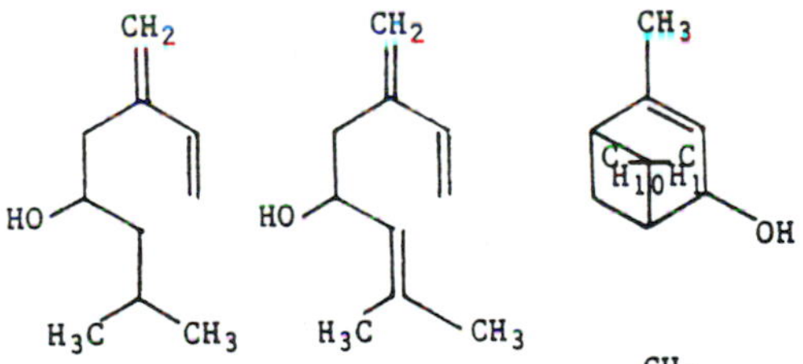

Western pine beetle

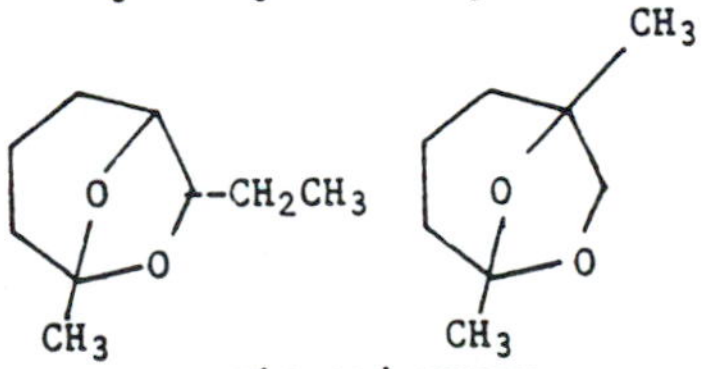

cis and trans

---

[a] The Iowa variety requires 4% trans-isomer while the New York variety requires 97% trans-isomer for maximal activity.

[b] 6-7% trans-isomer is required for maximal activity.

[c] 50% trans-isomer is required for activity.

[d] 8% trans-isomer is required for maximal activity.

Table 13-26. Insect Attractants

Insect attracted	Attractant
Mediterranean fruit fly	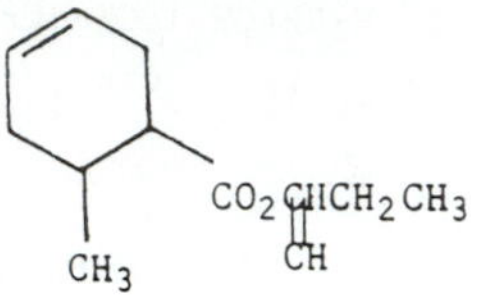 (Siglure)
Mediterranean fruit fly	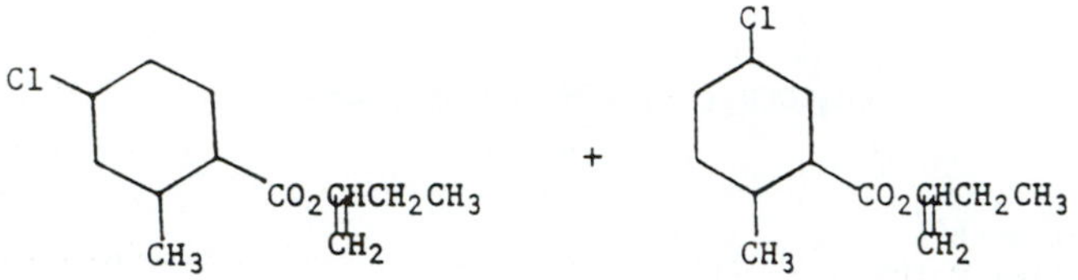 (Medlure)
Melon fly	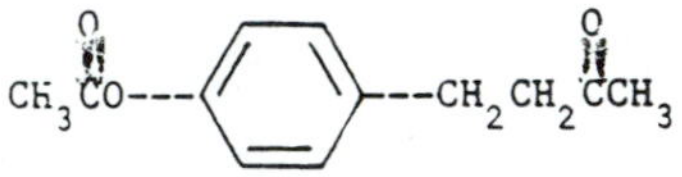
Ants	$CH_3C(=O)OCH_2CH_2CH_2CH_2CH_3$
Sugar beet wireworm	$CH_3CH_2CH_2CH_2CO_2H$
June beetle	$CH_3CH_2CH_2C(=CH_2)NH_2$

Table 13-27. Some Allelopathic Interactions

Source	Target	Chemical Nature
Plant versus Plant		
Hard chaparral	Competing herbs	Phenols
Soft chaparral	Competing herbs	Terpenes (camphor, cineole, etc.)
Walnut tree	Competing plants	Jugione
Grass (aristida eligantha)	N-fixing bacteria and green algae in soil; lack of N discourages other plants	Phenolic acids
Eucalyptus	An example of self-toxicity	
Plant versus Animal		
Buttercup	Grazing animals	Protoanemonia
Larkspur	Grazing animals	Neurotoxic alkaloids such as delphinine
Tobacco	Aphids	Nicotine
Foxglove	Vertebrates	Steriod cardiac glycomides
Oleander	One leaf can be fatal to humans	
Oak tree	Vertebrates, moth larvae and also fungi and viruses	Protein-binding tannins
Balsam fir	Insects	Hormones and hormone-analogue
Hypericum	Herbivores (some beetles [Crysolina] detoxify hypericia)	Hypericia (causes intense photo-sensitivity and blindness)
Cruciferae	Cabbage butterflies, moths, weevils, beetles and aphids	Mustard oils such as allyl iso-thiocyanane
Animal versus Animal		
Skunk	Anything	Butyl mercaptan
Bombardier beetle	Predators	Quinone spray
Monarch caterpillars	Birds	Cardiac glycomides obtained by feeding on milkweed
Grasshopper	Birds	
Animal versus Bacteria		
Man	Bacteria	Lynoxyme
Plant versus Fungus		
Orchid	Fungus	Orchinol
Potato	Fungus	Chlorogenic and caffeic acids

13.4.2   Neurotoxin and Stockpile Waste

The transmission of nerve impulses in the body between one nerve and another involves the release of acetylcholine (ACh) from the first nerve that diffuses across the interneuronal space to trigger a different nerve. To prevent continued stimulation, the ACh is hydrolyzed by the enzyme **acetylcholinesterase** (AChE) present in the space. A serine molecule in the active site of AChE is acetylated and the acetyl group is spontaneously hydrolyzed to regenerate the AChE. The organophosphorus compounds are potent inhibitors of AChE. In this case, we say that the organophosphate insecticides are acetylcholinesterase (AChE) inhibitors, as shown in Figure 13-31.

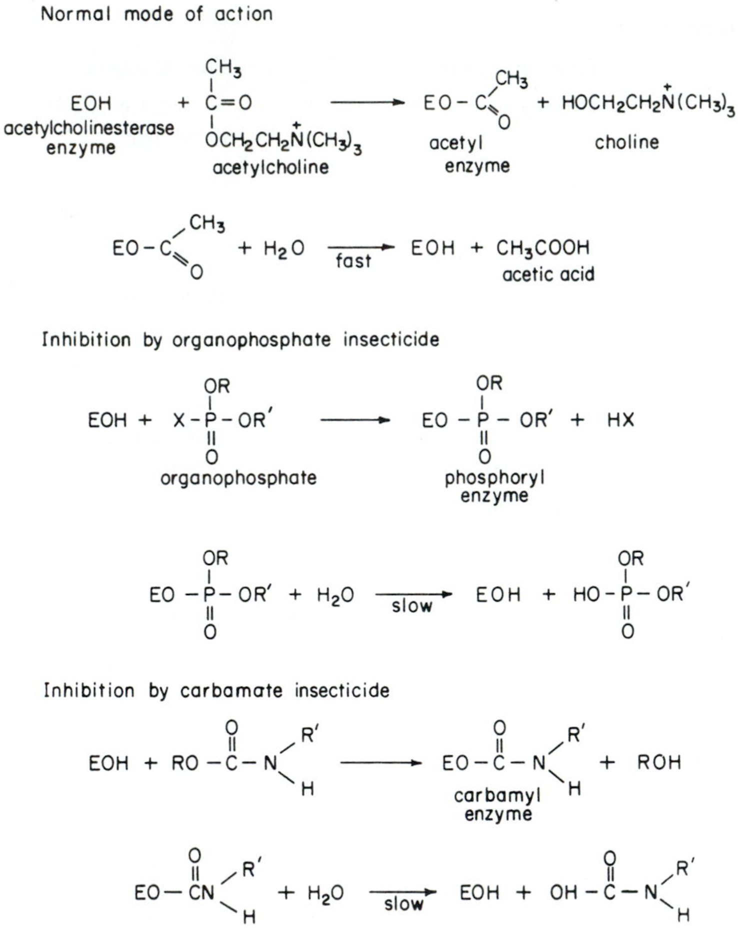

Normal mode of action

$$EOH + CH_3C(=O)OCH_2CH_2\overset{+}{N}(CH_3)_3 \longrightarrow EO-C(CH_3)(=O) + HOCH_2CH_2\overset{+}{N}(CH_3)_3$$

acetylcholinesterase enzyme + acetylcholine $\longrightarrow$ acetyl enzyme + choline

$$EO-C(CH_3)(=O) + H_2O \xrightarrow{fast} EOH + CH_3COOH$$

acetic acid

Inhibition by organophosphate insecticide

$$EOH + X-P(OR)(OR')(=O) \longrightarrow EO-P(OR)(OR')(=O) + HX$$

organophosphate $\longrightarrow$ phosphoryl enzyme

$$EO-P(OR)(OR')(=O) + H_2O \xrightarrow{slow} EOH + HO-P(OR)(OR')(=O)$$

Inhibition by carbamate insecticide

$$EOH + RO-C(=O)-N(R')(H) \longrightarrow EO-C(=O)-N(R')(H) + ROH$$

carbamyl enzyme

$$EO-CN(=O)(R')(H) + H_2O \xrightarrow{slow} EOH + OH-C(=O)-N(R')(H)$$

Figure 13-31.   Mechanism of acetylcholinesterase inhibition.

The same mechanism operates on humans when the body is confronted with a **chemical warfare** (CW) agent. For example, such nerve gases as G-agent or V-agent (please compare their structure with organophosphate; for example, parathion, shown in Figure 13-28).

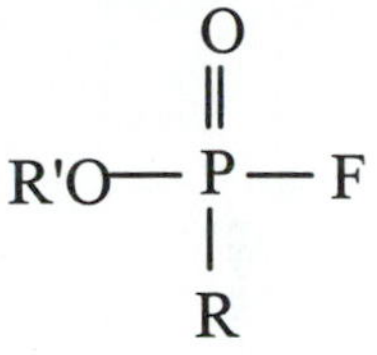

G-agent 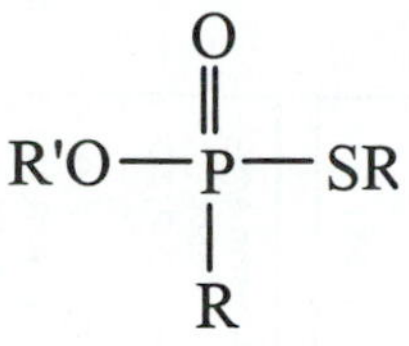 V-agent

In the case of sarin (G-agent), where R is C_3H_7 and R′ is CH_3, the $LСt_{50}$ is 50-100 mg-min m^{-3}. This lethal dosage is expressed both in amount and contact time. For example, the CS agent, shown in Figure 13-32, used for riot control by police, in most cities has LCt_{50} of 70,000 mg-min/m^3 for which 1-5 ng/m^3 is sufficient for control.

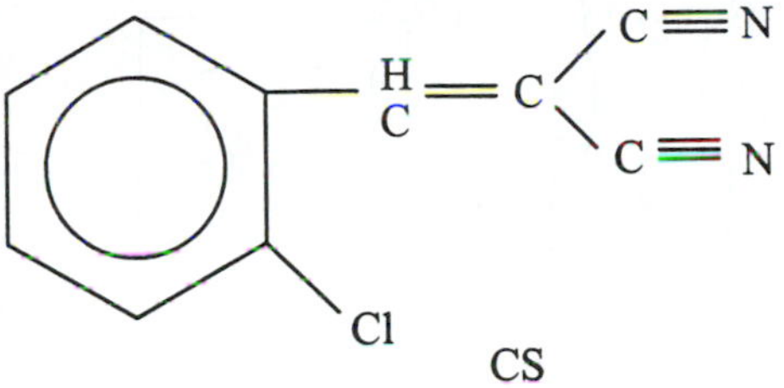

CS

LC_{t50}

70,000 mg-min m^{-3}

Figure 13-32.   Structure of CS agent and its lethal dosage.

Currently, some of these toxic chemical agents including GB, VX

$$(R = (iPr)_2 N(CH_2)_{2-}, R' = Et)$$

and the blister agents (e.g., mustard, 2, 2′-dichlorodiethyl sulfide) are stacked in eight contingenous United States sites, as shown in Figure 13-33, and also elsewhere in Russia. These must be destroyed by the end of 2004 due to the decomposition rate of the stabilizer of the munitions with explosives, including M55 rockets and M23 land mines. Destruction of these chemicals is done by incinerators, followed by pollution abatement. There are four types in general use: the hearth type, rotary kiln, conveyor, and the hopper type as shown in Figure 13-34. The efficiency is more than 99.99%. A full-scale facility is operational at Johnston Atoll, an island in the Pacific Ocean.

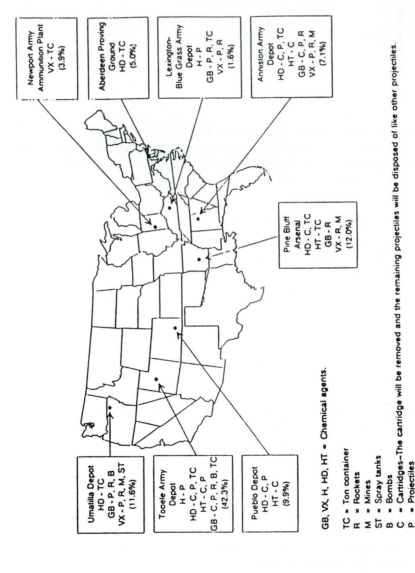

Newport Army
Ammunition Plant
VX - TC
(3.9%)

Aberdeen Proving
Ground
HD - TC
(5.0%);

Lexington-
Blue Grass Army
Depot
H - P
GB - P, R, TC
VX - P, R
(1.6%)

Anniston Army
Depot
HD - C, P, TC
HT - C
GB - C, P, R
VX - P, R, M
(7.1%)

Pine Bluff
Arsenal
HD - C, TC
HT - TC
GB - R
VX - R, M
(12.0%)

Umatilla Depot
HD - TC
GB - P, R, B
VX - P, R, M, ST
(11.6%)

Tooele Army
Depot
H - P
HD - C, P, TC
HT - C, P
GB - C, P, R, B, TC
(42.3%)

Pueblo Depot
HD - C, P
HT - C
(9.9%)

GB, VX, H, HD, HT = Chemical agents.

TC = Ton container
R = Rockets
M = Mines
ST = Spray tanks
B = Bombs
C = Cartridges—The cartridge will be removed and the remaining projectiles will be disposed of like other projectiles.
P = Projectiles

Figure 13-33.   United States stockpiles of nerve agents and munitions.

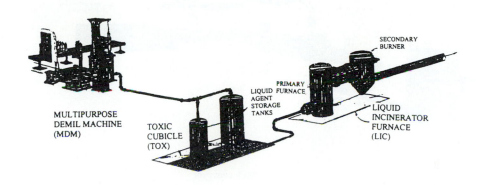

(A) LIC hearth type

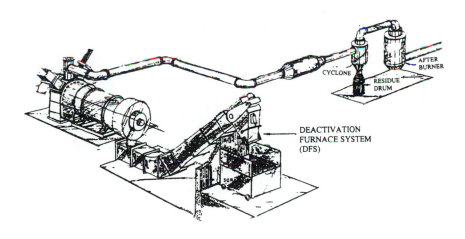

(B) DFS rotary kiln

Figure 13-34.   Incinerator types. (A)LIC hearth type, (B) DFS rotary kiln, (C) MPF conveyor, (D) DUN hopper type.

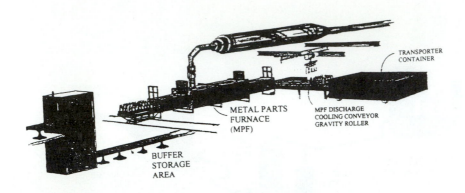

(C) MPF conveyor

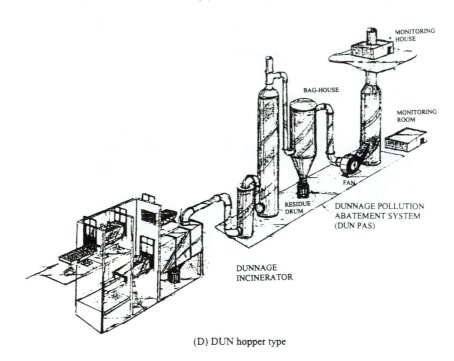

(D) DUN hopper type

Figure 13-34.   Incinerator types. (A)LIC hearth type, (B) DFS rotary kiln, (C) MPF conveyor, (D) DUN hopper type.

REFERENCES

13-1. D. J. Greenland and M. H. B. Hayes, *The Chemistry of Soil Constituents*, Wiley, New York, 1978.

13-2. G. H. Bolt and M. G. M. Bruggenwert, *Soil Chemistry*, Elsevier, New York, 1978.

13-3. K. W. Brown, G. B. Evans, Jr., and B. D. Frentrup, *Hazardous Waste Land Treatment*, Butterworth, Boston, 1983.

13-4. A. D. McLaren and G. H. Peterson, *Soil Biochemistry*, Marcel Dekker, New York, 1967.

13-5. R. D. Holtz and W. D. Kovacs, *An Introduction to Geotechnical Engineering*, Prentice-Hall, Englewood Cliffs, New Jersey, 1981.

13-6. R. Lal and B. A. Stewart, *Soil Degradation*, Springer-Verlag, New York, 1990.

13-7. F. J. Stevenson, *Humus Chemistry: Genesis, Composition, Reactions*, Wiley, New York, 1982.

13-8. G. Sposito, *The Chemistry of Soils*, Oxford University Press, New York, 1989.

13-9. T. F. Yen, *Chemistry of Marine Sediments*, Ann Arbor Science, Ann Arbor, Michigan, 1977.

13-10. N. F. Janes, *Recent Advances in the Chemistry of Insect Control*, Special Publication No. 53., Royal Society of Chemistry, London, 1985.

13-11. H.A. Horne, *The Chemistry of Our Environment*, Wiley, New York, 1978.

13-12. G.V. Chilingorian, E.C. Donaldson, and T.F. Yen, *Subsidence Due to Fluid Withdrawal*, Elsevier, Amsterdam, 1995.

13-13. M.D. Erickson, *Analytical Chemistry of PCBs*, 2nd ed., Lewis, Boca Raton, Florida, 1997.

13-14. R.W. Miller and R.L. Donahue, *Soils in Our Environment*, 7th ed., Prentice-Hall, Englewood Cliff, New Jersey, 1995.

13-15. R. A. Hites and S. J. Eisenreich, *Sources and Fates of Aquatic Pollutants*, American Chemical Society

13-16. W. Salomons, *Biogeodynamic of Pollutants in Soils and Sediments: Risk Assessment*, Springer-Verlag, Berlin, 1995.

13-17. R. A. Horne, *The Chemistry of Our Environment*, Wiley, New York, 1978.

PROBLEM SET

1. a) Assume that the industrial process for nitrogen fixation requires the breaking of the triple bond in N≡N by the reaction

$$N≡N + 3H_2 \rightarrow 2NH_3 \qquad\qquad [1]$$

Assume further that the natural process utilizing nitrogenase occurs by the sequential breaking of single bonds in N≡N by the reactions

$$N≡N + H_2 \rightarrow HN=NH \qquad\qquad [2a]$$

$$HN=NH + H_2 \rightarrow H_2N–NH_2 \qquad\qquad [2b]$$

$$H_2N–NH_2 + H_2 \rightarrow 2NH_3 \qquad\qquad [2c]$$

Reaction [1] requires an activation energy of 226 kcal to break the triple bond. The most energy-demanding step in process [2] is reaction [2a], which requires an activation energy of about 126 kcal to break N≡N to form HN≡NH. Calculate the ratio of the rate constants (k_{2a}/k_1) at 27°C for reaction [1] and reaction [2a] using the relationship

$$k \propto e^{\frac{-E_a}{RT}}$$

where E_a is the activation energy, $R = 1.99$ calories/°K/mol, and T is measured in degrees Kelvin.

b) From the value of (k_{2a}/k_1), is it surprising that microorganisms can fix nitrogen at ambient temperatures whereas the industrial process occurs between 400 and 600°C. Calculate the temperature at which k_1 equals the value of k_{2a} at 27°C.

2. An 830-acre watershed is located 5 miles south of Indianapolis in central Indiana. Given the information presented below, compute the projected sediment from sheet and rill erosion in terms of average daily loading.

180 acres of cropland

Corn; conventional tillage, average annual yield of 40 to 45 bushels/acre; cornstalks remain in fields after harvest; contour strip-cropped planting method; soil is Fayette silt loam; slope is 6%; slope length is 250 feet.

220 acres of pasture

No canopy of tree or brush; cover at surface is grass and grasslike plants; 80% ground cover; soil is Fayette silt loam; slope is 6%; slope length is 200 feet.

430 acres of woodland

50% of area covered with tree canopy; 80% of area covered with leaf and limb litter; under-growth is managed and therefore minimal; slope is 12%; slope length is 150 feet.

Ἡ θάλασσα· πῶς ἔγινε ἔτσι ἡ θάλασσα;
Ἄργησα χρόνια στὰ βουνά·

    •   •   •   •   •

Μὰ μπορεῖ νὰ κακοφορμίσει ἡ θάλασσα;
Ἕνα δελφίνι τὴν ἔσκισε μιὰ φορὰ
κι' ἀκόμη μιὰ φορὰ
ἡ ἄκρη τοῦ φτεροῦ ἑνὸς γλάρου.

"The sea: how did it become so, the sea?
For years I lingered in the mountains;

    •   •   •   •   •

Can it be, though, that the sea has become infected?
A dolphin lanced it once,
and another time
the tip of a gull's wing."

— ΓΙΩΡΓΟΣ ΣΕΦΕΡΗΣ
(George Seferis)
ΤΡΙΑ ΚΡΥΦΑ ΠΟΙΗΜΑΤΑ
(Three Secret Poems)

CHAPTER **14**

PEDOSPHERE — HAZARDOUS WASTE AND REMEDIATION

Soils are good media for receiving a great variety of wastes. Due to excessive loading, some specific soil sites are exceeding the saturation limit. In this chapter, solid wastes (including municipal and agricultural types) and their associated problems of disposal and leachate control are first evaluated. The concept of recycling and reuse is discussed especially with regards to plastic wastes. Current developments of degradable plastics are emphasized, and the problem concerning heavy metals that add a burden to the soil is addressed.

Basics related to hazardous wastes and their nature are presented. The widespread amounts of harmful toxic substances occurring in soil are mentioned, especially with reference to heavy metals. Finally, the remediation technology of soil is discussed, including the principles of bioaccumulation, soil vapor extraction, immobilization and encapsulation, and some approaches to in-situ and on-site remediation techniques.

14.1 Solid Waste Chemistry

Solid waste and **refuse** have the same meaning and are used synonymously. In highly populated areas, the magnitude of the problem resulting from the generation, collection, and disposal of solid waste is insurmountable. In the United States, it was estimated that the national average of solid waste generation amounts to 3.1 kg/capita-day, as shown in Table 14-1. Even in 1968, the United States collected and disposed of 1.27 Pg of solid waste in urban areas, and New York City alone used 60 hectares of Staten Island for disposal and incineration of solid waste. The cost is three times higher than that of the total coal mining of West Virginia and the subsequent delivery to New York City. To state how grave the problem is, one can simply say that each year the United States population throws out 48 billion cans, 28 billion bottles, 4 million tons of plastic, 30 million tons of paper and 100 million tires. Most of this debris has to be disposed by towns and cities at a cost that is only exceeded by local expenditures on education and highway construction.

Based on the waste classification of the Incineration Institute of America, solid wastes include trash, rubbish, garbage, refuse, animal and agriculture wastes, and even some forms of liquid wastes. Table 14-2 is sample municipal waste composition from the east coast of the United States. From the table, the majority of the organic portion of the wastes can be equivalent to cellulose except ca. 5% of leather, rubber, and plastics. In this manner the organic portion of solid waste can be treated as **cellulose**, especially if one wishes to convert it into useful products. Table 14-3 shows the chemical analyses of a great variety of municipal wastes. Variation of the energy content ranges from 2,000 –19,000 Btu/lb.

Table 14-1.   Annual and Daily Production of Solid Wastes in the United States

Type of waste	Total mass (10^{10} tonnes/ yr)	Per capita (kg/ day)
Household, commercial, municipal	226	3.1
Collected	172	2.4
Uncollected	54	0.7
Industrial	100	1.4
Mineral	1000	14
Agricultural	1860	25
Farm animal wastes	1360	19
Crop residues	500	7
Total (rounded)	3200	44

Source: R.J. Black et al., "The National Solid Wastes Survey: An Interim Report," U.S. Dept. of Health, Education and Welfare. Washington, D.C. 1968.

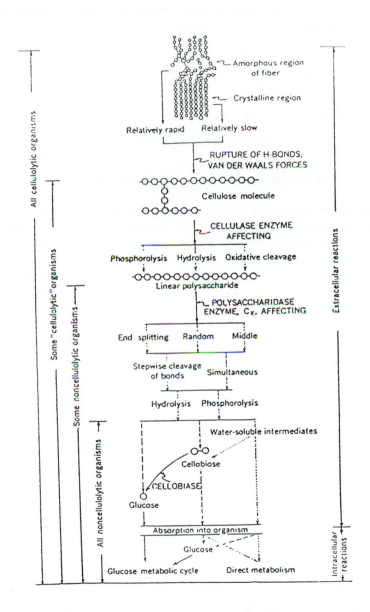

Figure 14-1. The microbial degradation of cotton fiber. (Source: R.G.H. Siu, "Micro-biological Decomposition of Cellulose," Reinhold Publishing Corporation, 1951.)

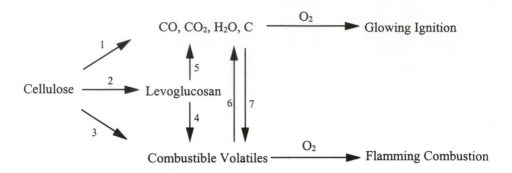

Figure 14-2.   The general reactions involved in pyrolysis and combustion of cellulose.

Chemistry and biochemistry of cellulose are essential to the understanding of thermal decomposition and enzyme hydrolysis related to conversion and landfill technology. For example, the biodegradation scheme of cellulose is illustrated in Figure 14-1, and the pyrolysis and combustion are given in Figure 14-2.

A great variety of unit process equipment and devices for material recovery in the solid waste processing plants are illustrated in Table 14-4. These common and simple devices are also illustrated for reference.

Table 14-2.   Sample Municipal Composition — East Coast U.S.

WEIGHT PERCENT			
Physical		Rough Chemical	
Cardboard	7%	Moisture	28.0%
Newspaper	14	Carbon	25.0
Miscellaneous paper	25	Hydrogen	3.3
Plastic film	2	Oxygen	21.1
Leather, molded plastics, rubber	2	Nitrogen	0.5
Garbage	12	Sulfur	0.1
Grass and dirt	10	Glass, ceramics, etc.	9.3
Textiles	3	Metals	7.2
Wood	7	Ash, other inserts	5.5
Glass, ceramics, stones	10	Total	100.0
Metallics	8		
Total	100		

Conversion of wastes by pyrolysis, yields of products.

Table 14-3. Ultimate Analysis of Typical Municipal Refuse Components

Refuse Component	C (%)	H (%)	O (%)	N (%)	S (%)	Inerts [a]	Btu/lb	% Moisture	% as delivered
Newspapers	49.14	6.10	43.03	0.05	0.16	1.43	7.974	5.97	10.33
Brown paper	44.90	6.08	47.84	0	0.11	1.01	7.256	5.83	6.12
Magazine paper	32.91	4.95	38.55	0.07	0.09	22.47	5.254	4.11	7.48
Corrugated boxes	43.73	5.70	44.93	0.09	0.21	5.06	7.043	5.20	25.68
Paper food cartons	44.74	6.10	41.92	0.15	0.16	6.50	7.258	6.11	2.27
Vegetable and food waste	49.06	6.62	37.55	1.68	0.20	1.06	1.795	78.29	2.52
Plastics (Average)	78.00	9.00	13.00				15.910		0.84
Evergreen trimmings	48.51	6.54	40.44	1.71	0.19	0.81	2.708	69.00	1.68
Lawn grass, green	46.18	5.96	36.43	4.46	0.42	1.62	2.058	75.24	1.68
Ripe tree leaves	52.15	6.11	30.34	6.99	0.16	3.82	7.984	9.97	2.52
Wood	49.00	6.00	42.00			2.28	6.840	24.00	2.52
Glass, ash, ceramics						100.00			8.50
Metals						100.00	2.66		7.53

[a] Inerts — ash, glass, metal, stone, ceramics.

Source: compiled from R.G. Bond and C.P. Straub, Handbook of Environmental Control, Vol. 2. Solid Waste, CRC, W. Palm Beach, Florida, 1973.

Table 14-4a.   Unit Process Equipment, Trommel, Shredder, Air Classifier, Magnet

TROMMEL—a perforated, rotating horizontal cylinder used to break open trash bags, remove glass in large enough pieces for easy recovery, and remove small abrasive items such as stones and dirt. Though trommels are used extensively in gravel and ore processing and for screening incinerator residue, there has been little experience in using a trommel before a shredder, and much must still be learned about its design and operation with raw refuse.

SHREDDER—a size-reduction machine which grinds mixed refuse to a more uniform particle size for further processing and breaks up composite items into their individual materials. Solid waste shredders are generally horizontal shafts with swinging hammers (as shown in the sketch) or vertical shaft ring grinders. The shredder must consistently produce the specified particle size range and must not permanently deform any of the materials in a way which interferes with subsequent processing steps.

AIR CLASSIFIER—a controlled air system used to separate light objects from the heavy fraction of waste. One form incorporates a column of air moving vertically upward as shredded refuse falls downward through it, as in the "zig-zag" type shown (A). Another type is a vibrating table with blowers arranged so that air is passed through the refuse and the light fraction is carried on. A third type employs a tilted, rotating drum (B). Each type must be investigated to determine performance relative to the others. For example, in preparing the light fraction of refuse as a fuel.

MAGNET—a standard industrial tool, used to remove iron and steel from the refuse stream. The magnet may be placed after the air classifier, where it recovers the steel (principally as a "cleaner" fraction than if it were located directly after the shredder). However, alternative locations should be investigated because the steel must be free of organic materials to be suitable for reuse. One possible location is following the rising current separator so that the metal is washed prior to removal.

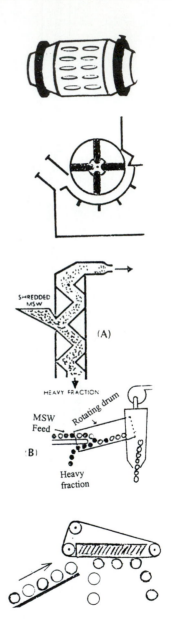

Table 14-4b.   Unit Process Equipment, Screens, Air Knife, Rising Current Separator, Heavy-Media Separator

SCREENS—devices used to separate materials by size and prepare fractions within the narrow size ranges required by some separation equipment. Although screening is a simple operation, in many instances the exact size of screen openings and the type of screens can be chosen only by experience.

AIR KNIFE—a jargon term for a blower device intended here to separate steel cans from more massive pieces of iron and steel, a necessary step because the two require different processes for reuse. Experimentation is required to discover the best design for this application as well as the best location in the flow chart. An air knife also may dry the metal if placed after the rising current separator.

RISING CURRENT SEPARATOR—a unit housing a flowing current of water used to carry off or wash away organic materials such as food wastes, heavy plastics, and wood from the air classified heavy fraction. Because the water is pumped upwards through the refuse, many material which normally would sink in water are able to float and be removed.

HEAVY-MEDIA SEPARATOR—a tank of dense fluid, actually a suspension of a mineral in water. When the mixture of glass, aluminum, and other non-ferrous metals is immersed in the liquid, the fluid density can be controlled so that the aluminum and glass float while the other metals sink. The NCRR ETEF is capable of producing appropriate fractions of municipal solid waste, otherwise unavailable for investigation of such factors as separating efficiency, throughout rates, particle size range, fluid density range, and ease of removal of the suspension from the product.

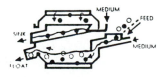

Table 14-4c.   Unit Process Equipment, Electrostatic Separator, Electrodynamic Separator, Electronic-Optical Sorter

ELECTROSTATIC SEPARATOR—a device utilizing the principle that electrical conductors lose an induced static charge faster than insulators. In this way, an electrostatic sorter can separate conducting materials (e.g. glass) after the particles are charged in a high voltage electrical field. This technique for sorting solid waste fractions is under investigation in several places; further investigation and refinement is necessary.

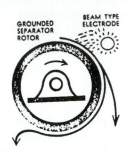

ELECTRODYNAMIC SEPARATOR—sometimes termed an "aluminum magnet" or eddy current separator, this separator uses the electrodynamic induction of a magnetic field as a method of sorting. If an alternating current is passed through a piece of metal, and properly applied, the metal temporarily becomes magnetic and can be deflected and separated; this principle has been used to separate aluminum and other non-ferrous metals. In pilot trials, aluminum can be separated clean enough for reuse, but much must still be learned about larger scale processing.

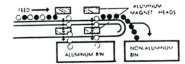

ELECTRONIC-OPTICAL SORTER—a unit which separates glass from stones and pieces of ceramics and sorts the glass according to color. A photo-electric detector determines the color of the pieces into the proper containers. This process is used in the food industry to separate good beans or rice from bad.

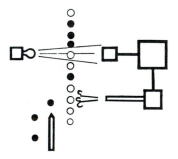

14.1.1   Recycling and Conversion

It should be mentioned that wastes and resources are related. For example, through biodegradation, biodecomposition, or biodisintegration, the wastes can be converted into useful energy, raw material, chemical feedstocks, and so on. Also, many wastes are the end products of biological deteriorations or breakdowns from past useful product or manufactured goods. This process can be illustrated as follows:

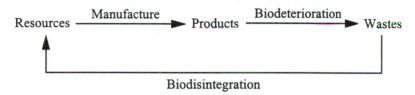

Of course, the conversion is not only limited through biological processes; a variety of physical-chemical methods, so-called recycling, are also available.

The buzzwords **waste minimization** and **waste reduction** have to do with the manufacturing of the products from the resources. Waste minimization involves the selection of alternative treatment processes that reduce the quantity or quality of the wastes requiring ultimate disposal. Waste reduction means the cutting down of the amount of wastes from their sources. The most efficient approach is source reduction and control of the manufacturing processes. Recent initiation of the many environmental-benign or environmental-friendly chemical processes is just a beginning of the effort.

The direct use of solid wastes to generate power is perhaps one of the most common traditional incineration methods. A discussion of this method will be found later in Chapter 23 of the accompanying volume. Other methods will include the partial oxidation or thermal treatment under limited air or inert atmosphere — that is, **pyrolysis** techniques. There are many versions of pyrolysis: flash pyrolysis, fluidized bed pyrolysis, hydropyrolysis, and so on; yet they are based on the same principle — thermal decomposition. Figure 14-3 illustrates cellulose molecules under thermal decomposition conditions. Actually, the thermal decomposition of cellulose as depicted by Figure 14-2 is quite complex. Most organic materials under pyrolysis conditions will yield the following fractions:

- gas
- char — solid phases
- tar and oil — liquid phases
- residue (could include some inorganics)

The chemical composition of these functions are illustrated in Table 14-5. Of course, the type of raw waste will greatly affect the distribution of the four fractions, shown in Table 14-6, as well as the energy distribution obtained, shown in Table 14-7. The presence of metals and glasses with organics during pyrolysis will also be possible. In this case, the glass, nonferrous and ferrous metals in waste will be recycled. Actually, Owen-Illinois has recorded a green glass as shown in Table 14-8. A common Garrett glass recovery process is shown in Figure 14-4.

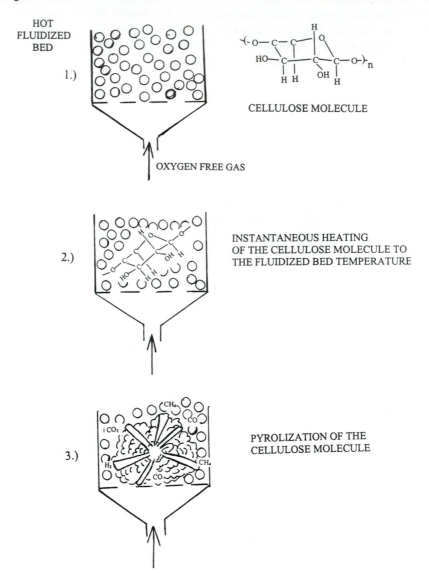

Figure 14-3.   Chemical reduction of the cellulose molecule. (1) and (2) Show the cellulose molecule being introduced into the hot fluidized bed. (3) Shows the cellulose molecule literally being rearranged by exploding into its pyrolysis gas products.

Table 14-5.   Typical Products of Pyrolysis

Char fraction, 20 wt.%; Heating value 9000 Btu/ lb	
48.8 wt.%	Carbon
3.9	Hydrogen
1.1	Nitrogen
0.3	Sulfur
31.8	Ash
0.2	Chlorine
13.9	Oxygen (by difference)

Oil fraction, 40 wt.%; Heating value 4.8 MM Btu/ bbl. (10,500 Btu/ lb)	
57.5 wt.%	Carbon
7.6	Hydrogen
0.9	Nitrogen
0.1	Sulfur
0.2	Ash
0.3	Chlorine
33.4	Oxygen (by difference)

Gas fraction, 27 wt.%; Heating value 550 Btu/ cu. ft.	
0.1 mol%	Water
42.0	Carbon monoxide
27.0	Carbon dioxide
10.5	Hydrogen
<0.1	Methyl chloride
5.9	Methane
4.5	Ethane
8.9	C_3 to C_7 hydrocarbons

Water fraction, 13 wt.%	
Contains:	Acetaldehyde, Acetone, Formic acid, Furfural, Methanol, Methylfurfural, Phenol, Etc.

Table 14-6.   Average Yields of Pyrolysis Products from Douglas Fir Bark, Rice Hulls, Grass Straw, and Cow Manure

	Weight Percentage of Dry Feed			
	Oil	Char	Gas	Water
Douglas Fir Bark	35-50	50-25	5-15	10
Rice Hulls	40	35	10	15
Grass Straw	50	20	15	5
Cow Manure	30	45	15	10

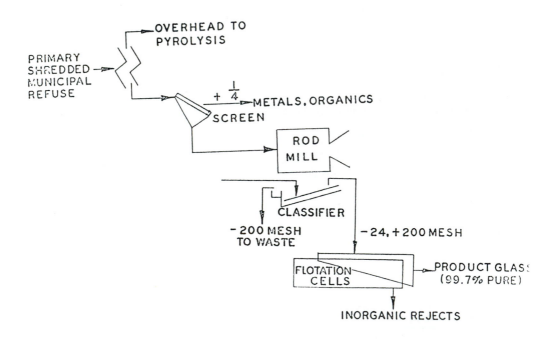

Figure 14-4.   Garrett glass recovery process.

Table 14-7. Energy Distribution - Pyrolysis of Wastes

Materials Pyrolyzed	Energy in Raw Refuse, Million Btu/ ton	Energy in Pyrolysis Products, Million Btu/ ton of Raw Refuse[a]			
		Gas	Char	Tar and Oil	Total[a]
Household Refuse	17.8	7.1	5.9	2.3	15.3
Industrial Refuse	9.1	6.1	1.7	0.6	8.4
Scrap Tires	33.5	8.7	15.9	6.8	31.4
Battery Cases — Hard Rubber	26.9	6.0	19.0	1.6	26.6
Waste Bark and Sulfite Liquor	13.6	6.6	4.7	1.7	13.0
Battery Cases — Plastic	37.7	8.3	0.3	30.4	39.0
Rice Hulls	13.2	3.6	7.0	1.6	12.2
Rice Straw	12.2	4.0	5.9	1.5	11.4
Cattle Manure	14.2	6.3	5.2	1.2	12.7
Paper Mill Sludge	10.7	4.6	4.4	0.2	9.2
Raw Sewage	14.2	8.3	3.2	2.3	13.8

[a] Does not account for energy required for pyrolysis nor for heat of drying wastes.

Table 14-8. Chemical Compositions of Green Glass

Oxide	Typical Production Green (%)	Recovered from San Francisco Refuse (%)
SiO_2	71.6	72.34
Al_2O_3	1.5	2.20
MnO_2	0.01	0.008
CaO	10.8	9.76
MgO	0.7	0.79
Na_2O	14.5	13.77
K_2O	0.3	0.84
Fe_2O_3	0.19	0.106
PbO	0.003	0.031
Cr_2O_3	0.23	0.048
TiO_2		0.048

Source: Data supplied by Owen, Illinois.

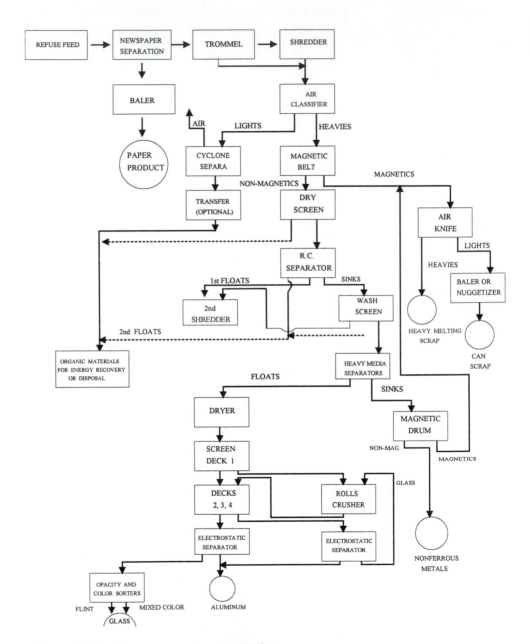

Figure 14-5.   Resource recovery processing.

Hydrogenation or hydropyrolysis is an important process to increase the liquid portion of the fractions. So-called waste-to-oil or **refuse derived fuel** (RDF) is based on the principle that cellulose or carbohydrate can be converted into hydrocarbons either under or upon the base catalyzed condition or hydrogen atmosphere.

The alkaline catalyzed mechanism is as follows:

1. at 160°C $Na_2CO_3 + 2\ CO + H_2O \rightarrow 2\ HCOONa + CO_2$

2.

3. at 250°C

4. $OH^- + CO \rightarrow HCOO^-$

5. $(2y + 2)HCOO^- + C_x(H_2O)y \rightarrow C_xH_{2y+2} + yH_2O + (2y + 2)CO_2$

Here, $C_x(H_2O)_y$ is a carbohydrate, C_xH_{2y+2} is a hydrocarbon, and $x = y$. If $x \neq y$, water molecules may be used for adjustment. For hydrogenation, more hydrogen has to be introduced to the system:

$$900°C,\quad C_x(H_2O)_y \rightarrow x\ CO + y\ H_2$$

$$< 300°C,\quad x\ CO + 2(x + 1)\ H_2 \rightarrow C_xH_{2x+2} + x\ H_2O$$

Here, $(x + 2)H_2$ mole hydrogen has to be introduced in order to have a liquid hydrocarbon (refer to Fischer-Tropsch synthesis in Chapter 5). For fuels, a rule of thumb is that the more the hydrogen atoms are accommodated to carbon atoms, the more the solid form (C or C_nH_m, $m \ll n$) will transform to a liquid form (C_nH_{2n+2}) and finally to a gas as methane (CH_4).

A typical flow chart of resources recovery from wastes is shown in Figure 14-5. An actual process working in San Diego is illustrated in Figure 14-6.

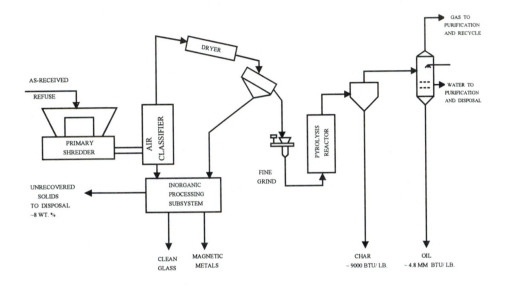

Figure 14-6.   Recycling of solid wastes via pyrolysis.

14.1.2   Disposal: Landfill and Leachate

Bioconversion of solid wastes is also a traditional method of resource recovery, as shown in Figure 14-7 by means of microorganisms.   During bioconversion, humus also will be formed.   A general scheme is

$$C_aH_bO_cN_dS_e + (a - b/4 - c/2 + 3d/4 + e/2)H_2O \rightarrow (a/2 + b/8 - c/4 - 3d/8 - e/4)CH_4$$

$$+ (a/2 - b/8 + c/4 + 3d/8 + e/4)CO_2$$

$$+ dNH_3 + e\,H_2S$$

Sometimes the equation can be written with the wastes expressed by $CH_aO_bN_c$, for example,

Cardboard	$CH_{1.604}$	$O_{0.734}$	$N_{0.003}$
Newspaper	$CH_{1.521}$	$O_{0.655}$	$N_{0.002}$
Garbage	$CH_{1.652}$	$O_{0.497}$	$N_{0.057}$

The products in this manner can be

	H_2O	CO_2	CH_4
Cardboard	0.234	0.484	0.561
Newspaper	0.294	0.474	0.526
Garbage	0.381	0.438	0.561

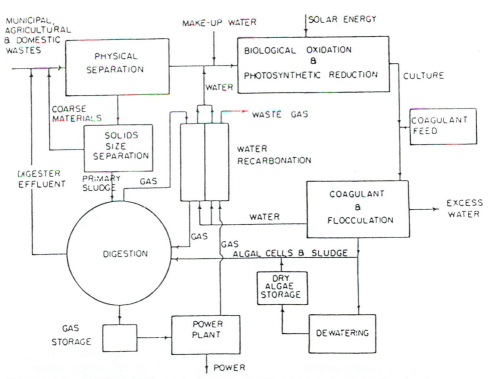

Figure 14-7. Schematic diagram of system for the biological conversion of solar energy to electrical power.

The gas obtained from these experiments often has a volume ratio of CO_2/CH_4 of 0.75, which is close to the value anticipated. To purify the bioproduced gas into useful fuel (such as even low-Btu gas), often the removal of water by absorption, adsorption, and scrubbing of impurities (such as H_2O, H_2S, and NH_3) is needed. The gas purification process is illustrated by Table 14-9.

A typical sanitary waste **landfill** with compact clay liners from the Michigan Department of Natural Resources is schetched in Figure 14-8. The importance is that the design has to be some distance away from residue and water table, and in the bottom there must be room for leachate collection. Usually the top is covered by an impermeable cover and may be equipped with gas producing wells. At the cap of the cover the soil is unstable; it is better to have its use as a recreation site—e.g., the Rose Bowl in Pasadena, CA is a landfill as designed by F.W. Bowerman of the University of Southern California.

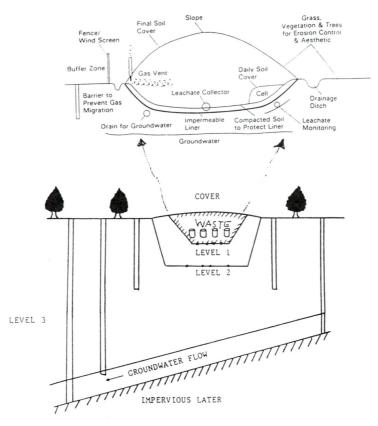

Figure 14-8. Cross-section through a sanitary landfill. Three levels of safeguard in hazardous waste landfills. Level 1: Linear plus leachate collection/treatment. Level 2: Back up liner plus leachate collection/treatment. Level 3: Wells to monitor end, if needed control leachate plume.

Table 14-9. Gas Purification Process

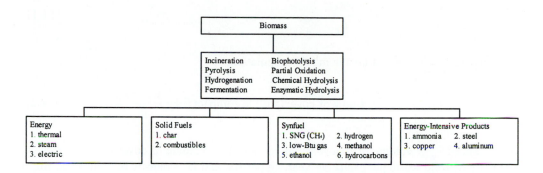

Gas Purification Processes

Objective	Processes
Removal of water vapor	Absorption by hydroscopic liquids diethylene or triethylene glycol salt brine
	Adsorption in activated solid dessicents
	Molecular sieve
	Activated carbon
	Silica gel
	Activated alumina
	Condensation by compression/cooling
Removal of sour gas	Molecular sieve method
	Scrubbing with alkaline solution
	Membrane separation

The volume of a landfill can be estimated from the following

$$V = \frac{PEC}{D_c}$$

[14-1]

where V = volume of land in m^3, P = population,

$$E = \text{ratio of cover (soil) to compact fill} = \frac{V_{sw} + V_c}{V_{sw}}$$

[14-2]

(where V_{sw} = volume of solid waste in m^3, and V_c = volume of cover in m^3), C = average mass of solid waste per capita per year, kg/person, and D_c = density of compacted fill in kg/m^3.

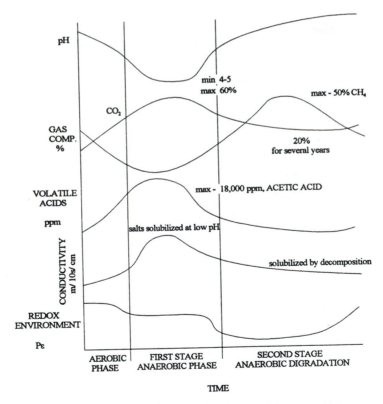

Figure 14-9.   The theoretical degradation of a landfill. (Replotted after Pojasek, R.B., Ed., *Toxic and hazardous waste disposal*, Volume 2, Ann Arbor Science, Ann Arbor, Michigan, 1977.)

There are three stages for the biological activities of a landfill as indicated by Figure 14-9:

1. Aerobic decomposition stage

- usually short since high BOD with little oxygen
- increase in landfill temperature
- dissolution of highly soluble salts
- few organics produced

2. Anaerobic decomposition stage (2 stages)

stage 1

- facultative anaerobes produce large amounts of low molecular weight aliphatic acids and carbon dioxide
- reduction in leachate pH and redox environment
- dissolution of sparingly soluble inorganic salts produce leachate of high conductivity

stage 2

- increase in leachate pH (decrease in conductivity) due to degradation of low molecular weight acids - methane produced from CO_2 and organic acids

3. Final aerobic stage

- incoming oxygenated water and cessation of biological activity

The preceding list is the basis for the production of landfill gas.

A serious concern about landfills is the generation of **leachate** as a result of infiltration of surface water passing through the waste disposal site. In modern landfills there are dual leachate collection systems, one is located between the two impermeable liners for the bottom and sides, and another above the top liner of the double-liner system. The flexible liner is made of geofabric or geomembrane material such as chlorosulfonated rubber or chlorinated polyethylene which is resistant to biodegradation. Leachate is collected in perforated pipes that are imbedded in granular material.

Usually the leachate contains constituents from the wastes which are water soluble and also the products of chemical and biochemical transformation of the wastes. A typical composition is shown in Table 14-10. The pH values vary but always are in the lower range, as shown in Table 14-11. One problem is that the lower volume state of Mn^{2+} and Fe^{2+} may become insoluble Mn^{4+} and Fe^{3+} hydrated oxides upon exposure to air and thus clog the leachate collection system.

Table 14-10. Characteristics of Leachate Sanitary Landfills (mg/L)

Constituent	Range*	Typical value
Organic strength, COD	1,000-30,000	10,000
BOD$_5$	200-20,000	6,000
Total solids	2,000-5,000	3,000
Total nitrogen	20-1,000	200
Alkalinity (as $CaCO_3$)	200-5,000	400
Soluble salts (Cl, SO_4)	200-3,000	500
Iron	50-800	100
Lead	1-10	2
Zinc	25-250	50
pH	5-8	6

Source: Adapted from Chian and DeWalle, 1977, Tchobanoglous et. al., 1977, and Vesilind and Rimer, 1981.

*
Except for pH

Other biochemical processes used for refuse conversion include anaerobic and aerobic decomposition. In the former method, solid waste is mixed with sewage sludge and the mixture is digested. Although operational problems made this process impractical on a massive scale, single-household units admixed with human excreta have been used. The aerobic decomposition is well known as **composting**, usually utilizing long rows of shredded refuse as windows and allowing sufficient oxygen to penetrate the compost pile. This is usually referred to as **static pile composting** and can produce excellent soil conditioners. (See Section 29.2.3 in the accompanying volume of *Environmental Chemistry*.)

14.2 PLASTIC WASTES

From domestic wastes, the value of waste plastics have been raised from 2–3% to 3–4% steadily since 1970. Most plastics found in solid wastes are the **thermoplastic** types. In contrast, the **thermosetting** ones only account for a small fraction, as shown in Figure 14-10. The thermoplastic types usually consist of the following:

- polyolefins, including high- and low-density polyethylene (HDPE and LDPE), and polypropylene (PP)
- styrenes, including polystyrene (PS) and acrylonitrile-butadiene-styrene (ABS)
- vinyls, primarily polyvinyl chloride (PVC) and polyvinylidene chloride (PVDC)

Table 14-11. The pH Ranges of Representative Leachates

Landfill Site	Age of refuse (yr)	pH
Hughes (1971)	17	7.0
Pohland (1975)	1	5.33
Pohland (1975)	2	5.3
Pohland (1975)	3	5.3
Merz (1954)	1.5	5.6-7.5
Emcon (1974)	2	4.7-5.4
Chain & Dewalle (1977)	0.25	5.63
Reinnart & Ham (1971)	0.33	5.97
Fungaroli (1971)	2	3.7-8.5
Qasim & Burchinal	0.33	5.88-6.48
Zenone (1974)	15	5.7-6.9
Zenone (1974)	13	7.1-7.6
Johansen & Carlson (1976)	3.5	5.9
Johansen & Carlson (1976)	2.5	5.2
Wigh (1979)	3	5.4
Wigh (1979)	5	5.5
Fungaroli & Steiner (1979)	2	5.53
Fungaroli & Steiner (1979)	4.5	5.36
Fuller (1978)	6 mo.	5.5-6.3
Rovers & Farquhar (1973)	1	5.3-11.5
SCS Engineers Site A (1976)	Active	5.37-6.11
SCS Engineers Site D (1976)	2	5.3-6.65
Apgar & Langmuir (1971)	<1	6.6
Apgar & Langmuir (1971)	5.3	6.46
Meichtry (1971)	>3	5.75
Meichtry (1971)	>6	7.4
Summary range values		3.7-11.5 (Norm = 5.3)

Furthermore, the majority of the thermoplastics found in wastes are related to packaging in one way or another; for example, adhesives, coatings, containers, films, sheets, and so on, as indicated by Table 14-12. Of course in waste streams (items such as hardware, toys, and furniture of the nonpackaging portion) are also found, but it is only a small portion.

Table 14-12.   Plastic Resins Consumed by Packaging Industries in 1971

| Products | Consumption by Plastic Types, Millions of Pounds | | | | | |
	Polyethylene	Vinyls	Styrenes	Polypropylene	Other	Total
Adhesives		43			11	54
Coatings	424	110		4	75	613
Closures	50	15	21	35	28	149
Containers and lids	1,030	145	810	65	80	2,130
Film and sheet	1,400	110	45	100	65	1,720
Total	2,904	423	876	204	259	4,666

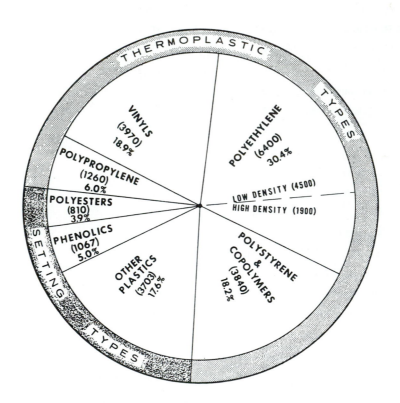

Figure 14-10.   Plastics production in the U.S.A. in 1971 was 21,050 millions pounds. Graph shows distribution by types, millions of pounds in parentheses, and percent of total production. (Source: J.W. Jensen, J.L. Holman and J.B. Stephenson in T.F. Yen, *Recycling and Disposal of Solid Wastes*, p. 220, Ann Arbor Science, 1974.)

Because plastics are resistant to biodegradation by nature, the alternative is thermal decomposition. We will attempt to explain some problems regarding this approach. In general, the bulk of a given type of plastic is from a given type of polymer. Polymers decompose into fragment molecules (radicals) or monomers depending on their structure, via heat, radiation, and mechanical means. Under pyrolysis or incineration, the polymer decomposition is equivalent to depolymerization. It is essential to know that depolymerization is different from polymerization, because it can rarely achieve 100% monomer recovery, especially for a polymer mixture. In many cases, the monomer formation is interrupted by the activity of the free radical as a result of cross-linking. Similar to the general free radical reactions, the presence of hydrogen atoms tends to stabilize the reactive radicals; whereas oxygen atoms enhance cross-linking. Table 14-13 represents the depolymerization mechanisms. In pyrolysis, saturated hydrocarbons (such as polyethylene or polypropylene) are expected to dehydrogenate to create either internal or vinyl unsaturation. Both sites can initiate polymerization or polycondensation reactions. As a result, this will lead to char formation, as shown in Figure 14-11. In case of heat treatment under deficient oxygen conditions, various active functional groups on the polymer intermediates will result, as shown in Table 14-14.

Table 14-13. Depolymerization (Source: G.A. Zerlant and A.M. Stake in T.F. Yen, *Recycling and Disposal of Solid Wastes*, Ann Arbor Science, 1974, p. 177.)

	Structure transformation		Monomer Yield
PMMA	$-CH_2-\underset{COCH_3}{\overset{CH_3}{C}}-$ $\longrightarrow$	$-\overset{CH_3}{\underset{COOCH_3}{CH-C}}-$ Stable Nonreactive $\longrightarrow$	100%
PMS	$-CH_2-\overset{CH_3}{C}-$ (phenyl) $\longrightarrow$	$-CH-C-$ (phenyl) $\longrightarrow$	100%
PS	$-CH_2-CH-$ (phenyl) $\longrightarrow$	$-CH_2-$ (phenyl) Unstable Reactive $\longrightarrow$	40% at 300-400°C. More monomer with higher nitrogen pressure ---------------------- Fragments at <500°C. More fragments with higher nitrogen pressure.
PE	$-CH_2-CH_2-$ $\longrightarrow$	$-CH_2-\overset{\cdot}{CH}-$ $\longrightarrow$	Fragments - 400°C
TFE	$-CF_2-CF_2-$ $\longrightarrow$	$-CF_2-\overset{\cdot}{CF}-$ $\longrightarrow$	>95% - 500°C, low pressure 16% - 600°C, atmospheric Fragments - 1200°C, low pressure

Table 14-14.   Pyrolysis and the Effect of Oxygen

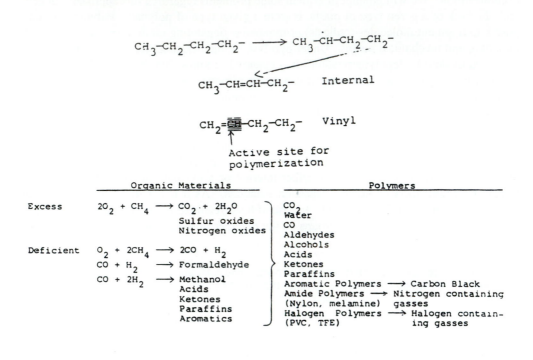

	Organic Materials	Polymers
Excess	$2O_2 + CH_4 \longrightarrow CO_2 + 2H_2O$ Sulfur oxides Nitrogen oxides	CO_2 Water CO Aldehydes Alcohols
Deficient	$O_2 + 2CH_4 \longrightarrow 2CO + H_2$ $CO + H_2 \longrightarrow$ Formaldehyde $CO + 2H_2 \longrightarrow$ Methanol Acids Ketones Paraffins Aromatics	Acids Ketones Paraffins Aromatic Polymers $\longrightarrow$ Carbon Black Amide Polymers $\longrightarrow$ Nitrogen containing (Nylon, melamine) gasses Halogen Polymers $\longrightarrow$ Halogen contain- (PVC, TFE) ing gasses

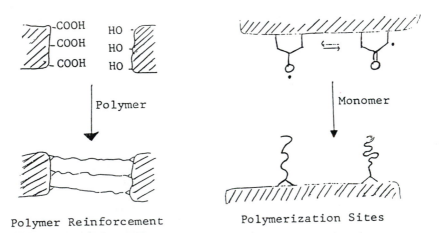

Polymer Reinforcement   Polymerization Sites

Figure 14-11.   Reactions involving charred residue. (Completely charred polymeric materials have chemically reactive groups that can be sited for covalent-bonding reactions).

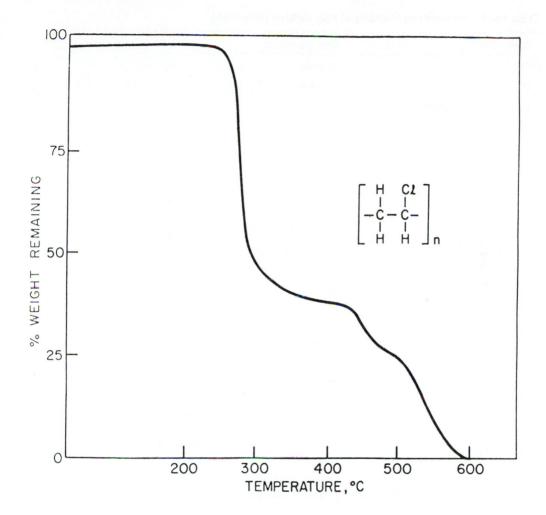

Figure 14-12. TGA of polyvinyl chloride.

Analytical tools such as **differential thermal analysis** (DTA), which gives the temperature at which heat is liberated or absorbed, and **thermogravimetric analysis** (TGA), which provides a record of weight changes as the temperature is increased, simulate the actual thermal decomposition of the polymers. In general, polymers containing carbon and hydrogen will yield carbon monoxide and aldehydes under recycling operations. Polymers containing nitrogen, halogens, and sulfur will yield toxic and corrosive gas such as hydrogen cyanide, hydrogen chloride, and sulfur dioxide. A typical TGA curve of polyvinyl chloride is shown in Figure 14-12. The combustion products based on TGA studies of polyurethane are listed in Table 14-15.

Table 14-15.   Combustion Products of Polyurethane (from TGA)

Compound	Quantity (mg/ g)
CO_2	425-800
CO	175-300
Cyanide ion (as HCN)	5-50
Methane	2-5
Ethylene	2-5
Ethane	1
Propylene	2-4
Propane	<1
Methanol	0.01-0.03
Acetaldehyde	0.03-0.05
1-Butene	<1
Butane	<1
Propionaldehyde	1-5
Acetone	1-5

For the finished plastic products a great variety of chemical additives have to be introduced. In some formulations the contents of these additives could exceed 20% by weight and many of them are highly toxic — for instance, fillers and fire retardants used for plastics, including antimony oxide, barium metaborate, talc, mica, zinc borate, titania, molybdenum disulfide, sulfur, and carbon. Reinforcements such as glass fibers, dusts, and pure metal powders of which the particles are small (ca. 1μm), are often used. Furthermore, many of the raw additives are not pure material; for example, zinc oxide contains 0.08% lead oxide and 0.05% cadmium oxide. In some plastic recycling (for example, spent propellant and projectile binders) the inorganics become the desirable recoverables (for example, aluminum or magnesium powder).

Antioxidants (such as stable free radicals) are introduced to stabilize the polymer from ozone and ultraviolet attack. In recent years, **photodegradation** for polymers has become important. Photosensitizers are added to aid polymer degradation by the transfer of electronic energy from a donor molecule to a polymer. Examples of these are nitroso compounds, quinones, benzophenones, and diketones, which can be photoexcited to triplet states, or can be formed as adduct biradicals. These biradicals are charge-transfer complexes that weaken the polymer backbone, causing chain scission. This principle is the basis of **biodegradable polymers**, as shown in Figure 14-13. The high altitude weather balloon is made in this manner to be able to self-destruct in a given period in the future

Separation schemes based on the differences in density of refractive indexes have been able to provide methods for sorting different classes of polymers if the feed stream is a mixture of plastics. Based on liquid media separation, it is possible to sort out five major types of plastics from a mix feed as follows:

	Density	Media
Polypropylene	0.90	water-alcohol 0.91
Low density polyethylene	0.92	water-alcohol 0.93
High density polyethylene	0.94-0.96	salt water 1.20
Polystyrene	1.05-1.06	
Polyvinyl chloride	1.22-1.38	

Finally, a potential application of recycling technology has been developed for waste plastics, as shown in Figure 14-14. We also would like to emphasize the importance of scrap tire recycling. More than two billion used tires have been stockpiled in the United States; and of the additional 285 M tires discarded each year, only 100 M are recycled, leaving the remaining 185 M for illegal dumps or heap piling across the country. In many tropical regions in the world, the abandoned tires may provide breeding for disease-carrying mosquitoes or rats. Stockpiling of tires often cause tire fires, just as coal piles; their self-ignition fire is difficult to extinguish. Burning will induce smoke that often is toxic. The popular method for tire recycling is the crumb rubber process, which is a mechanical size reduction of rubber into granular form for fillers of playgrounds and roads. A new process involving a multistage of solvent swelling and ultrasound assisted chemical degradation can remove a high level of the sulfur linkages (devulcanization). Virgin polymers as well as carbon blacks can be recovered.

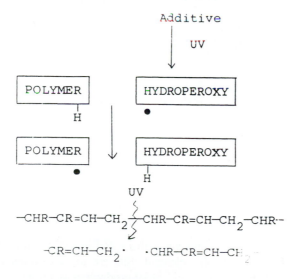

Figure 14-13.   Photodegradation.

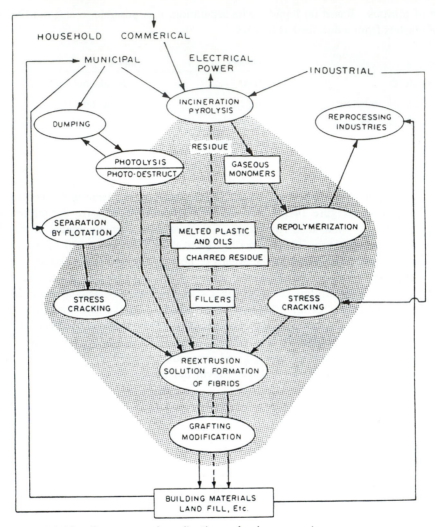

Figure 14-14.   Sources and applications of polymer waste.

14.3 HEAVY METALS

In addition to the organic carcinogenic chemicals as discussed in the previous chapter, another environmental concern is that metallic elements that are toxic to human beings are being spread around increasingly as a result of industrial production and use.

Table 14-16. Trace Metals That May Pose Health Hazards in the Environment

Element	Sources	Health Effects
Nickel	Diesel oil, residual oil, coal, tobacco smoke, chemicals and catalysts, steel and nonferrous alloys	Lung cancer
Beryllium	Coal industry (new uses proposed in nuclear power industry, as rocket fuel)	Acute and chronic system poison, cancer
Boron	Coal, cleaning agents, medicinals, glass making, other industrial	Nontoxic except as borane
Germanium	Coal	Little innate toxicity
Arsenic	Coal, petroleum, detergents, pesticides, mine tailings	Hazard disputed, may cause cancer
Selenium	Coal, sulfur	May cause dental caries, carcinogenic in rats, essential mammals in low doses
Yttrium	Coal, petroleum	Carcinogenic in mice over long-term exposure
Mercury	Coal, electric batteries, other industrial	Nerve damage and death
Vanadium	Petroleum (Venezuela, Iran), chemicals and catalysts, steel and nonferrous alloys	Probably no hazard at current levels
Cadmium	Coal, zinc mining, water mains and pipes, tobacco smoke	Cardiovascular disease, hypertension in humans suspected, interferes with zinc and copper metabolism
Antimony	Industry	Shortened life span in rats
Lead	Auto exhaust (from gasoline), paints (prior to about 1948)	Brain damage, convulsions, behavioral disorders, death

Source: Baltelle Memorial Institute, Dartmouth Medical School, 1971.

Table 14-16 lists **trace metals** that may pose health hazards in the environment. These elements occur naturally in the Earth's crust and human beings have been living with them throughout evolutionary history. However, the amounts of them that are being stirred up and spread around have been increasing greatly, to a toxic level, with the advance of industrialization. Many metallic elements are essential to life. But excess amounts will be very toxic to humans. It seems that our maximum amount of nutrient requirement is different for different metals. For example, there are only 5 g of iron, but 80 mg of copper in our body. Many metal elements do deposit in the lithosphere (as sulfide ores) and finally are stored in the pedosphere from the hydrosphere via biosphere cycle.

Heavy metals are, strictly, those beyond Rb (At. wt. is 37); yet commonly they refer to Cd, Cr, Co, Cu, Fe, Pb, Mn, Hg, Ni, Ag, and Zn (At. wt. is higher than 20, and their density is higher than water). The nonmetals, such as arsenic and selsnium, being quite toxic also are included in as trace metals. They, in particular, readily form arsenate and selenate, the forms belonging to the bulk of the first generation insecticides; for example, lead arsenate $Pb_3(AsO_3)_2$ and so on. A wealth of information regarding trace metals can be found in the annual conferences of "Trace Metals in the Environment", which have been held for the last two decades, and are currently held at the University of Missouri at Rolla. Their proceedings are excellent references.

There are two criteria for heavy metals appearing in the literature.

- **Interference Factor** (IF) $= \dfrac{\text{total anthropogenic emissions}}{\text{total natural emissions}}$

- **Technophility Index** (TP) $= \dfrac{\text{annual mining activity}}{\text{mean concentration of element in crust}}$ [14-3]

14.3.1 Mercury

Mercury has the potential to cause nerve and brain damage. Table 14-17 lists the industrial consumption of mercury in the United States. The largest consumption of mercury is in chlor-alkali production. Figure 14-15 gives a schematic diagram of a mercury cell for chlor-alkali production. For each ton of chlorine produced, there are about 0.1 to 0.2 kilograms of mercury lost to the atmosphere. It is estimated that 25,000 tons of chlorine are produced each year. Table 14-18 lists the major sources of mercury in the environment. It has been said that the production of chlorine is proportional to the release of mercury in the environment. The chlorination of water is for environmental protection. Yet we trade off with another evil. The Reed Paper Company controversy in 1970, where fish in the adjacent river were found to contain 0.5 ppm of mercury, is a good case to illustrate this point. In recent years, a new method for the chlor-alkali process that does not involve mercury has been developed.

Table 14-17. Industrial Consumption of Mercury in the United States (1969)

Industry	Consumption (tonne)
Chlor-alkali	1575
Electrical apparatus	1417
Paints	739
Scientific instruments	531
(thermometers, barometers, etc.)	
Dentistry	232
Catalysts	225
Agricultural	204
(seed dressings, etc.)	
Laboratory use	155
Pharmaceuticals	55
Pulp and paper	42
Other	736
Total	5911

Table 14-18. Sources of Mercury in the Environment

Source	Quantity of mercury (tonnes)	
	Production	Estimated release[a]
Total world production of Hg from ores (1900-1970)	361,000	120,000
World production of Hg from ores (1970)	10,000	3,300
Total world release from fossil fuels (1900-1970)	—	150,000
World release from fossil fuels (1970)	—	4,800
Total anthropogenic release (1900-1970)	—	270,000
Annual release by rock weathering	—	800
Total release by rock weathering (1900-1970)	—	5,700
Total quantity of Hg in oceans	—	45,000,000
(approximately 60,000 year half-life before sedimentation)		
Total Hg released by weathering during earth's lifetime	—	1,600,000,000

Source: J. Gavis and J.F. Ferguson, *Water Res.*, 6, 989–1008 (1972).

[a] Estimated on the basis of one-third of production since this fraction was unaccounted for in the United States from 1945-1958.

The mercury-containing effluents from various industries often leave substantial quantities of mercury in the sediment of nearby lakes and bays. The sediments often contain the methane-producing bacteria that slowly convert the mercury deposits into methyl mercury, which quickly enters the food chain, as shown in Figure 14-16. The methylation of Hg is done through vitamin B_{12} in fish.

$$L_5–Co–CH_3 + Hg^{2+} \rightarrow L_5Co^+ + CH_3Hg^+$$

$$2CH_3Hg^+ \rightarrow Hg(CH_3)_2 + Hg^{2+}$$

Through bioaccumulation (a detailed discussion regarding bioaccumulation will be given later in this chapter), or bioamplification, the mercury contaminants propagate in the food chain, as shown in Figure 14-17. Although new technology has been introduced to almost all mercury-using plants, and this has eliminated most of the mercury in their effluents, relatively large amounts of mercury have already been dumped in sediments and will continue to be a source of methyl mercury for many years to come.

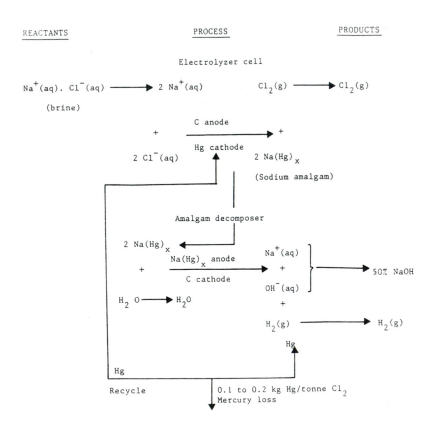

Figure 14-15.   Schematic diagram of mercury cell for chlor-alkali production.

(i)

Mechanism of Propagation

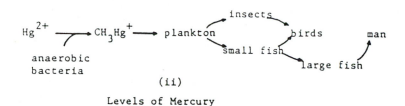

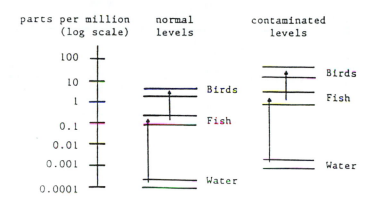

Figure 14-16.   Propagation of mercury in food chain.

Both aryl and alkyl mercurials are efficient fungicides; for example, phenyl mercuric dimethyldicthiocarbonate, PhHg Se (=S)—N(CH$_3$)$_2$, is used in papermills as a slimicide and a mold-retardant for paper. Ethylmercuric chloride, C$_2$H$_5$HgCl, is used as a seed fungicide. Often seed grains are coated with alkyl mercury halides for protection. This practice becomes a major source for mercury poisoning.

An infamous case of mercury poisoning occurred in Minamata, Japan, between 1953 and 1960. A total of 111 cases of poisoning and 43 deaths were reported in the fishing village. The so-called "Minamata diseases" gave symptoms such as numbness of lips and limbs; impaired vision, hearing, and speech; and difficulties in walking and coordination. Later on it was found that the mercury in fish averaged 5–20 ppm and was actually poisoned by CH$_3$Hg$^+$ in fish.

Consumption of mercury in food can range from no ill effect (0.1 mg/day) to a toxic or a lethal dose (20 mg/day), as shown in Figure 14-18. The expression "mad as a hatter" derives from exposure of hat-makers to mercury in the form of Hg(NO$_3$)$_2$, which was in the felt. Other occupations that have this potential hazard include gilding and mirror-making as well as thermometer manufacturing. They all involve neurological disorders. Even today we still practice mercury amalgam by dentists in a patient's mouth. The antidote for acute mercury poisoning is the British Anti-Lewiside (BAL). The complex BAL·Hg is not a simple monomeric chelate; instead, it forms a polymer of (BAL·Hg)$_n$ or, as shown in Figure 14-19.

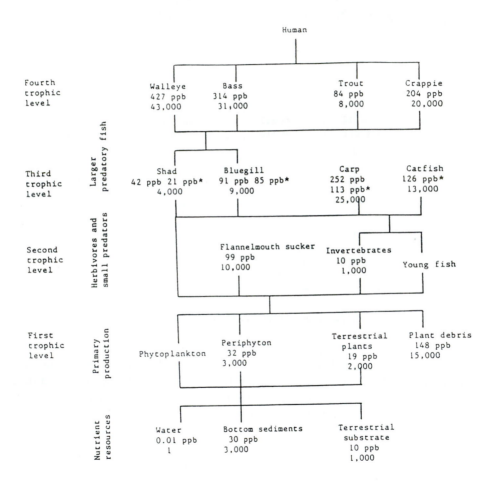

Figure 14-17.   Bioamplification of mercury in Lake Powell, Utah and Arizona. The mean level of mercury in parts per billion (ppb) and the amplification factor above the surrounding water are given for each species. Thus, the Walleye contains a concentration of mercury 43,000 times that of the water. (Source: L. Potter, D. Kidd, and D Standiford. *Environ. Sci. Technol.* 9 (1), 41–46, 1975.)

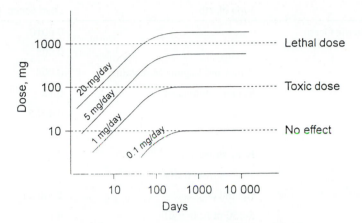

Figure 14-18.   Accumulation curves for different levels of mercury in the diet. (Source: N.J. Bunce, 1994)

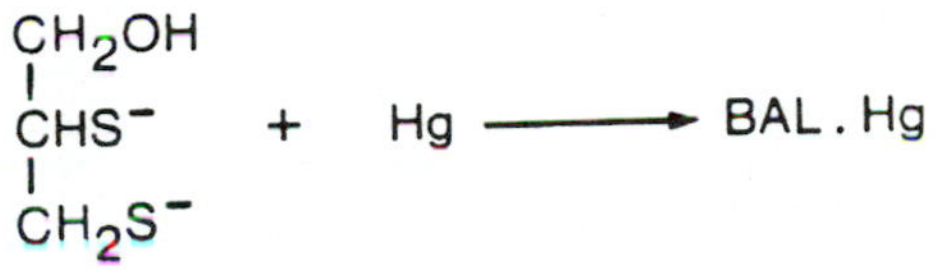

$$\begin{array}{c} CH_2OH \\ | \\ CHS^- \\ | \\ CH_2S^- \end{array} \quad + \quad Hg \quad \longrightarrow \quad BAL \cdot Hg \qquad \log K = 25.7$$

BAL

$$\cdots S-Hg-S \underset{CH_2CH}{\diagdown} \underset{|}{\diagup} \overset{S-Hg-S}{\diagdown} \underset{CH_2CH}{\diagdown} \underset{|}{\diagup} \overset{S-Hg-S}{\diagdown} \cdots$$
$$CH_2OH \qquad CH_2OH$$

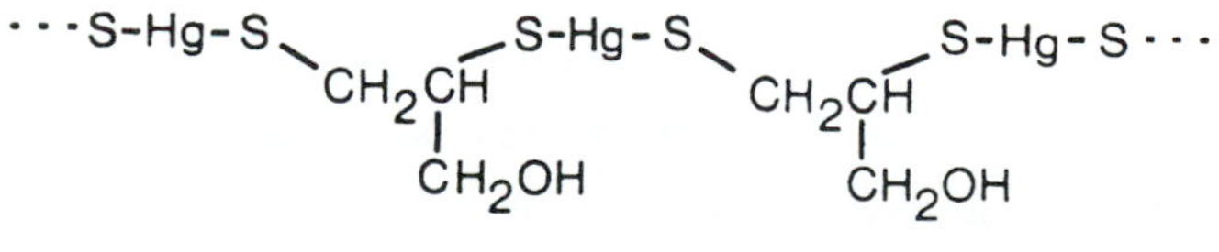

$(BAL \cdot Hg)_n$

Figure 14-19.   Polymer form of BAL. (See also Figure 2-4 for chelates.)

Table 14-19. Atmospheric Lead Concentrations at Different Sites

Location	Type of site	Lead concn. ($\mu g/m^3$)
North Central Pacific Ocean		0.0010
Greenland		0.005
California	White and Laguna Mountains	0.008
California	Remote mountains	0.12
Berlin	Quiet streets	0.4-0.5
Philadelphia		1.6
Berlin	Busy street	3.8
New York	2-75 m from traffic	4.1
Los Angeles	Central city	4.3-6.6
Detroit	5-150 m from traffic	4.8
Los Angeles	4-20 m from traffic	7.6

Source: H.A. Waldron and D. Stöfen, "Sub-clinical Lead Poisoning," Table 4, pp. 10–11. Academic Press, New York, 1974.

Table 14-20. Lead Content of Human Blood

Lead (ppm)	Significance
0.01	"Natural" blood lead level before man began using lead
0.10	Lower limit of "normal" blood level in the United States
0.25	Mean blood lead level in the United States
0.25	Suggested "danger" blood lead level for children
0.30	Mean blood lead level in Glasgow children
0.30	Lowest lead level found in industrially exposed adults having mild symptoms of lead poisoning
0.31	Mean blood lead level in Manchester children
0.40	Upper limit of "normal" blood lead level in the United States
0.40	Lower average blood lead level in children showing lead poisoning symptoms
0.40	Lowest approximate level found in industrially exposed adults having severe symptoms of lead poisoning
0.70	European "danger" threshold for occupational poisoning
0.80	United States "danger" threshold for occupational poisoning

Source: T.J. Chow, *Chem. Brit.* 9 (6), 260 (1973).

14.3.2 Lead

Due to tetraethyl lead as an important additive to gasoline, the roadway pollution of lead in highways is worldwide. It is not unusual to have 1000 ppm of lead concentration in the soil of an urban area. Some airborne lead concentrations are illustrated in Table 14-19. Auto exhaust includes $PbCl_2$, $PbBrCl$, and $PbBr_2$, because dichloroethane and dibromoethane are added for avoidance of valve-sticking problem of Pb deposit. Other sources of lead include the spent lead-acid battery. Physiological effects of lead poisoning for the most part include damage to heme synthesis or kidney function or permanent nerve dysfunction if the blood lead level reaches 0.33–0.8 ppm. The mean blood level for traffic police and automobile-tunnel employees is already 0.3 ppm, as shown in Table 14-20. It has been argued with some cogency that lead poisoning contributed to the decline of the Roman Empire. The ruling aristocracy had lead plumbing and drank wine from lead-lined casks. With the prohibition and decreased use of lead plumbing, lead-based paints, lead ceramic glazes, and leaded gasoline, it is hopeful that our pollution and consequently the poisoning will be diminished.

For children, the high body burden of Pb will cause mental retardation and hyperactivity. According to the United States Centers for Disease Control, the blood level of each child should be kept below $10\mu g/100mL$ ideally, and the avoidance of levels up to $25\mu g/100mL$ will save society approximately \$4,600 in health and special education costs per child. Data from the Greenland ice sheet shows that the lead increase was initiated by the Industrial Revolution. However, recent findings verify that there was an increase in 500 B.C. and 400 A.D. as well, as shown in Figures 14-20 and 14-21.

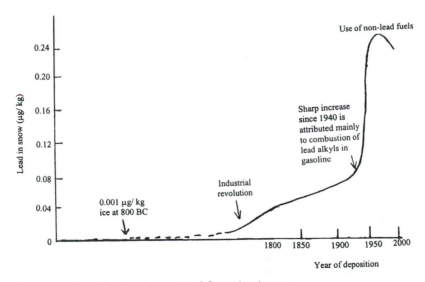

Figure 14-20.   The lead content of Greenland snow.

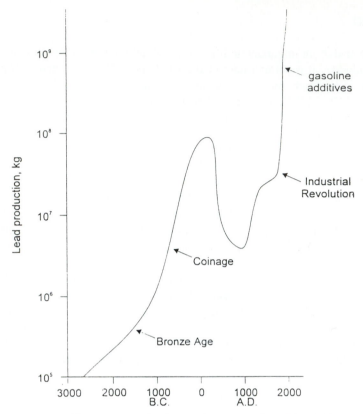

Figure 14-21.   Historical production and consumption of lead. (Source: J.O. Nriagu, *The Biochemistry of Lead*, Elsevier/North Holland Biomedical Press, Amsterdam, 1978, and from *Pathways, cycling and transformation of lead in the environment*, Ed. P.M. Stokes, Royal Society of Canada, 1986.)

14.3.3   Cadmium

The chemical nature of **cadmium** is similar to zinc.   They become insoluble in marine sediments as sulfides in the reducing condition especially when the sediment is anaerobic; they become soluble in aerobic condition; for example, the soluble ion pair of $CdCl^+$, due to the oxidative release of CdS.   In seawater, most Cd appears as chloride complexes, such as $CdCl^+$(29%), $CdCl_2$(37%), $CdCl_3^-$(31%), and Cd^{2+}(2%).

Cadmium is known to cause hypertension and kidney damage.   Studies have shown that there is correlation between the death of cronical uremia and the drinking water quality — especially that of well water.   Figure 14-22 is a schematic of the metabolism of cadmium.

Outbreaks of cadmium poisoning also have occurred in Japan in the Sasu River Basin. Many people developed a painful condition of their bones in which they were subjected to numerous fractures. This disease is called "itai itai" (ouch ouch). The cadmium content of paper is quite high due to the sizing additives. In this manner, a development of hypertension also can occur due to cigarette smoking.

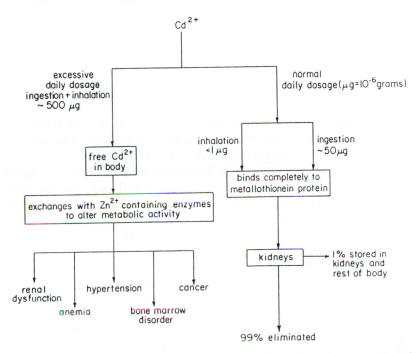

Figure 14-22.   Metabolism of cadmium. (Source: Dose date abstracted from L. Friberg, M. Piscator, and G. Nordberg, Cadmium in the Environment. Cleveland: CRC Press, 1971, pp. 25, 26.)

14.4 HAZARDOUS WASTE

The production and use of large quantities of organic and inorganic chemicals has resulted in the output of a great deal of by-products and waste material, much of which is hazardous. In addition, there are numerous solid wastes generated at the same time (see Table 14-1). It is important to classify the hazardous waste material. Some of the hazardous chemicals will be very persistent if no abatement method is imposed. For example, the half-life of vinylidene chloride is longer than one hundred thousand years by precipitation (Table 14-21).

Table 14-21.   Estimated Atmospheric Half-Lives of Five Hazardous Chemicals, Assuming Removal Only by Dissolution in Raindrops

Compound	P_{ia}, in torr	x_{ia}	α_i	$\tau_{\frac{1}{2}}$, in year
Acrylonitrile	1.14×10^2	1.0	9.05×10^3	0.8
Benzo(a)pyrene	5.46×10^{-9}	2.8×10^{-11}	5.4×10^3	1.4
Ethylene dichloride	8.4×10^1	1.6×10^{-3}	1.9×10^1	3.9×10^2
Tetrachloroethylene	1.85×10^1	1.1×10^{-5}	6.1×10^{-1}	1.2×10^4
Vinylidene chloride	6.17×10^2	3.9×10^{-5}	6.5×10^{-2}	1.1×10^5

Hazardous waste consists of individual waste materials or combinations of wastes that are presently or potentially dangerous to humans or other living organisms. For regulatory purposes, hazardous wastes are defined in terms of flammability (F), corrosivity (C), reactivity (R), and toxicity (T). **Flammable hazardous wastes** include: (1) liquids having a flash point below 60°C, (2) nonliquids liable to cause fires through friction, absorption of moisture, or spontaneous chemical change and liable, when ignited, to burn so vigorously or persistently as to create a hazard, (3) ignitable compressed gases, and (4) oxidizers. **Corrosive hazardous wastes** include: (1) aqueous wastes with a pH of less than or equal to 2.0 or greater than or equal to 12.5, and (2) liquid wastes capable of corroding steel at a rate greater than or equal to 0.250 inches per year.

Reactive hazardous wastes are those including explosiveness (E) that (1) readily undergo violent chemical changes, (2) react violently or form potentially explosive mixtures with water, (3) generate toxic fumes in a quantity sufficient to present a danger to human health, (4) explode when subjected to a strong initiating force, or (5) explode at normal temperatures and pressures. **Toxicity of hazardous wastes** is defined in terms of the level of contaminants in a leachate from hazardous wastes obtained by means of a specified extraction procedure. Basically, a waste is classified as toxic if leachate from it, extracted by an acidic medium with a pH of 5.0, contains 100 times or more the approved levels of any of the toxic contaminants identified in the National Interim Primary Drinking Water Standards.

	Type	Action
PE	Production of Evil	Plan for Emergency
R	Reactivity	Recognition
F	Flammability	Forecast
E	Explosiveness	Evaluation
C	Corrosiveness	Control
T	Toxicity	Training

Table 14-22. Ten Sites Ranked the Most Dangerous Abandoned Hazardous Waste Dumps in the Nation

Site Name	Hazard	Years of Disposal	Type of Waste	Contaminants
FMC Corp. Fridley, Minnesota	Contamination of drinking water source for cities of Fridley and Brooklyn Center; pollution of Mississippi River, the source of potable water for Minneapolis	Early 1930s to early 1970s	Solvents, paint sludges, painting waste	Trichloromethylene, methyl chloride, benzene, others
Tyboon Corner Landfill New Castle County, Delaware	Surface water and groundwater contamination	na	Sanitary, industrial waste	na
Brown Lagoon Brown Borough, Pennsylvania	Groundwater and surface water contamination. Lagoon lies adjacent to Bear Creek, which joins the Allegheny River, a water source for Pittsburgh	na	Wastes from coal mines, oil fields, and chemical firms	na
Industri-Plex 128 (Mark Phillip Trust) Woburn, Massachusetts	Surface water and groundwater contaminations	1953 to 1981	Wastes from manufacture of insecticides, explosives, acids, tanned hides, and residues	Arsenic, lead, chromium, others
Liport Landfill Gibbsoboro and Pittman Townships, New Jersey	Surfacewater, ground water and air pollution; site is located in area of fruit orchards	1958 to 1971	Domestic and industrial wastes	Benzene, toluene, bis(2-chloromethyl) ether, beryllium, mercury
Sinclair Refinery Wellsville, New York	Surface water and possibly ground water contamination	na	Refinery wastes, including oil sludges and fly ash	Mercury, polychlorinated biphenyls, oil components

Table 14-22.   (continued)

Site Name	Hazard	Years of Disposal	Type of Waste	Contaminants
Price Landfill Pleasantville, New Jersey	Groundwater contamination of potable water source of Pleasantville; plume of contamination threatens Atlantic City	1969 to 1976	Sanitary and industrial wastes	Benzene, chloroform, trichloroethylene
Pollution Abatement Services, Oswego New York	Surface water and groundwater pollution; polluted surface water discharges into Lake Ontario	1970 to 1976	Polymer gas, plating wastes, metal sludges, paint wastes, laboratory chemicals	Large quantities of polychlorinated biphenyls, others
Laboratory Site Charles City, Iowa	na	na	na	na
Helen Kramer Landfill Mantua Township, New Jersey	Surface water and groundwater contamination	1970 to 1980	Sanitary, construction and nonchemical industrial wastes	na

na= not available

Source: Data courtesy of the American Chemical Society.

Table 14-23. Hazardous Waste from Specific Sources

Hazardous Waste Number	Hazardous Waste	Hazard Code
Petroleum refining		
KD48	Dissolved air flotation (DAF) float from the petroleum-refining industry	(T)
KD49	Slop oil emulsion solids from the petroleum refining industry	(T)
Leather tanning and finishing		
KD53	Chrome (bloc) trimmings generated by the following subcategories of the leather tanning and finishing industry: hair pulp/chrome tan/retan/wet finish; hair save/chrome tan/retan/wet finish; retan/wet finish; no beam-house; through-the-bloc; and shearling	(T)
Iron and Steel		
KD60	Ammonia lime still sludge from coking operations	(T)
Primary zinc		
KD67	Electrolytic anode slimes/sludges from primary zinc production	(T)

Table 14-24. Discarded Commercial Chemical Products, Off-Specification Species, Containers, and Spilled Residium

Hazardous Waste Number	Hazardous Waste
PO23	Acroleum 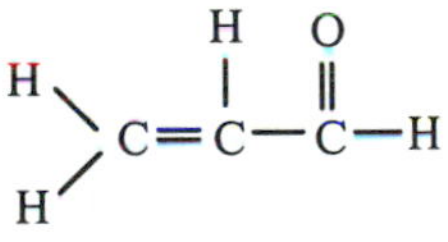 $H_2C=CH-CHO$ (structure shown)
PO13	Barium cyanide, Ba $(CN)_2$
PO24	P-Chloroaniline, 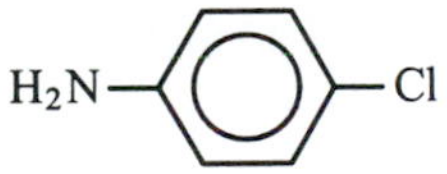 $H_2N-C_6H_4-Cl$ (structure shown)
PO50	Endosulfan. (6,7,8,9,10,10-hexachloro-1,5,5a,6,9,9a-hexahydro-6,9-methano-243-benzodioxathiapan 3-oxide)
PO63	Hydrocyanic acid, HCN
PO65	Mercury fulminate, $HgC_2N_2O_2$
PO61	Nitroglycerine, 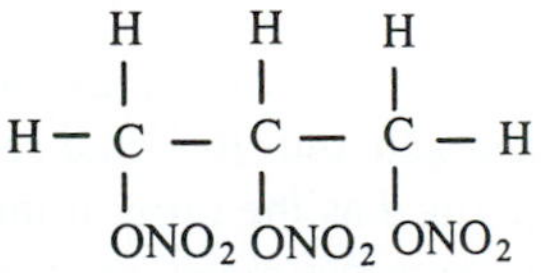 (structure shown)

The buzzword "**perfect**" helps us to remember the major types of hazardous materials. In the case of emergency response to a major accident, certain action also should be taken.

The Environmental Protection Agency (EPA) estimated, even as of 1976, that 35 billion kilograms of hazardous waste were being produced annually and that only 10% was disposed of in an environmentally acceptable manner. By August of 1983, the figure had jumped to 150 billion kilograms and by 2000 this figure is estimated to be about 260 billion kilograms. There are about 14,000 abandoned hazardous waste sites in the United States. The ten most dangerous dumps are listed in Table 14-22, and there are the Superfund sites ready for cleanup.

Table 14-23 lists examples of hazardous wastes from some specific sources, while Table 14-24 lists some wastes from discarded commercial chemical products, off-specification materials, containers, and spill residues.

14.5 REMEDIATION TECHNOLOGY

A number of processes are employed for the treatment of hazardous wastes. Generally there are (1) biological treatments, (2) chemical treatments, such as wet air oxidation, dechlorination, precipitation, complexation, electrolysis, oxidation, and reduction, (3) physical treatments, such as thermal treatment by microwave, photolysis, or electrokinetic treatment, (4) immobilization, such as microencapsulation, vitrification, adsorption, chemisorption, passivation, reprecipitation, (5) deep well injection, (6) land treatment, (7) solar evaporation, (8) incineration, and (9) resource recovery.

A **toxicity characteristic leaching procedure** (TCLP) has been developed by the U.S. EPA for measuring the likelihood of toxic material releasing into the environment and causing harm to organisms. If the material is solid, the appropriate surface-to-weight ratio is selected to cut the solid into a smaller size, and allowed to extract and buffer with several pHs; the extracts are then analyzed for a list of specified VOCs and metals to determine if the wastes exceed certain levels of contaminants.

14.5.1 Bioaccumulation

In Columbia River Valley, the ^{32}P pollution for plants is 7500 × of that of the soil; for adult swallows the value becomes 75,000 ×, and finally for young swallows, the value reaches 500,000 ×.

We would like to briefly review the bioaccumulation and the volatility of hazardous wastes in soil. Bioaccumulation can serve as an indicator of how a toxic substance propagates in the food chain and gets into the final receptor, the human being. The **bioconcentration factor** (BCF) is defined as the ratio of the concentration of chemicals at equilibrium in the organism (dry weight) to the mean concentration of chemicals in solution. There are several empirical formulae used to estimate the BCF. To estimate BCF from the octanol-water partition coefficient (K_{ow}), use

$$\log \text{BCF} = 0.76 \log K_{ow} - 0.23 \qquad [14\text{-}4]$$

To estimate BCF from the solubility in water (S), use

$$\log \text{BCF} = 2.791 - 0.564 \log S \qquad [14\text{-}5]$$

To estimate BCF from the soil adsorption coefficient (K_{oc}), use

$$\log \text{BCF} = 1.119 \log K_{oc} \qquad [14\text{-}6]$$

Table 14-25 gives the comparison of estimated values with laboratory measurements of BCF.

14.5.2 Soil Vapor Extraction

Hazardous wastes or chemicals often contaminate subsurfaces due to chemical spills, illegal dumping, corrosion-caused leaks, or other causes. It is instructive to know how to estimate the volatilization of chemicals from soil.

For the volatilization from soil, such as TCE, and ethylene dibromide using the one-dimensional equation

$$\frac{\partial^2 C}{\partial z^2} - \frac{1}{D} \frac{\partial C}{\partial t} = 0 \qquad [14\text{-}7]$$

where

C = concentration in soil (M/L^3)

z = distance measured normal to soil surface, surface is zero (L)

D = diffusion coefficient in soil (L^2/T)

t = time (T)

Boundary conditions
$C = C_0$ at $t = 0$, $0 \le z \le L$
$C = 0$ at $z = 0$, $t > 0$

$$\frac{\partial C}{\partial z} = 0 \text{ at } z = L \qquad [14\text{-}8]$$

The solution is

$$C(z,t) = \frac{4C_0}{\pi} \sum_{n=0}^{\infty} \frac{(-1)^n}{(2n+1)} \exp\left[-D(2n+1)\pi^2 \frac{t}{4L^2}\right]\left[\cos(2n+1)\pi \frac{(L-z)}{2L}\right] \qquad [14\text{-}9]$$

where

L = soil layer length (L)
f = flux of compound (M/L^2T)

$$f = \frac{DC_0}{(\pi Dt)^{\frac{1}{2}}}\left[1 + 2\sum_{n=1}^{\infty}(-1)^n e^{\frac{-n^2L^2}{Dt}}\right] \qquad [14\text{-}10]$$

Increasing L or decreasing t or D and if the summation is small, then

$$f = \frac{DC_0}{(\pi DT)^{\frac{1}{2}}} = C_0\left(\frac{D}{\pi t}\right)^{\frac{1}{2}} \qquad [14\text{-}11]$$

To obtain the concentration of volatiles in the soil column, we will list the following: Solving the one-dimensional diffusion equation,

$$C(z,t) = C_0 \operatorname{erf}\left[\frac{z}{2(DT)^{\frac{1}{2}}}\right] \qquad [14\text{-}12]$$

Solving the error function,
(a) for values of x ≥ 2

$$\operatorname{erf}(x) \approx 1 - \left[\frac{e^{-x^2}}{x\pi^{\frac{1}{2}}}\right] \qquad [14\text{-}13]$$

(b) for values of x → 1, set x = 1 + v (v << 1)

$$\operatorname{erf}(x) \approx \operatorname{erf}(1) + \frac{2v}{e\pi^{\frac{1}{2}}} \qquad [14\text{-}14]$$

Table 14-25. Comparison of Estimated Values with Laboratory Measurements of BCF

Compound	Physical/Chemical Parameter for Estimate			Estimated BCF			Laboratory measurement $\overline{BCF}$
	K_{over}	S(ppm)	K_{oc}	From K_{over}	From S	From K_{oc}	
Nitrobenzene	851	1,700	---	99	9.1	---	15.1
Carbon tetrachloride	437	800	---	17	14	---	30
p-Dichlorobenzene	2,400	79	---	220	53	---	215
Atrazine	427	33	149	59	86	---	7.94
1,2,4-Trichlorobenzene	17,000	30	---	970	91	---	2,800
Methoxychlor	20,000	0.003	80,000	1,100	16,000	8,100	8,300
Naphthelene	50,100	31.0	1,300	2,200	88	80	427
Pentachlorophenol	126,000	14	900	4,400	140	53	770
Hexachlorobenzene	170,000	0.035	3,910	5,600	4,100	280	18,500
Heptachlor	275,000	0.030	---	8,000	4,500	---	9,500
Biphenyl	5,750	7.5	---	420	71	---	437
DDT	562,000	0.0017	23,800	14,000	23,000	27,000	29,400
Aroclor 1254	2,950,000	0.01	42,500	49,000	8,300	4,000	100,000
Chlordane	1,000,000	0.056	---	21,000	120	---	37,800

$$\text{erf}(1) = .8427$$

(c) for values of $x \leq 0.1$

$$\text{erf}(x) \approx \frac{2x}{\pi^{\frac{1}{2}}}$$
[14-15]

Volatilization of toxic chemicals from soil is different from that of from water. The basis is the analysis of the heat balance between the evaporating chemicals (or water) and air. Computation of the flux of volatile pollutants can be made if the diffusion coefficient, D_v, of the particular chemical in air is known. If not, one can evaluate from two other chemicals as long as the diffusion coefficients are known; for example,

$$\frac{D_1}{D_2} = \left(\frac{M_1}{M_2}\right)^{\frac{1}{2}}$$
[14-16]

The flux is expressed as follows:

$$f = \frac{\dfrac{\rho_{max}(1-h)}{\delta}}{\left[\dfrac{1}{D_v} + \dfrac{\lambda_v^2 \rho_{max} M}{kRT^2}\right]}$$
[14-17]

where

$f =$ flux of compound (M/L^2T)

$\rho_{max} =$ saturated vapor concentration at the temperature of the outer air (M/L^3)

$h =$ humidity of the outer air $(0 \leq h \leq 1)$

$\delta =$ thickness of stagnant layer through which the chemical must pass (L)

$D_v =$ diffusion coefficient of vapor in the air (L^2/T)

$\lambda_v =$ latent heat of vaporization (cal/M)

$M =$ molecular weight (M/mol)

$k =$ thermal conductivity of air (cal/LK)

$R =$ gas constant (cal/mol)

$T =$ temperature (K)

Table 14-26. Chemical and Environmental Data for Estimation of Trichloroethylene Volatilization

Parameter	Symbol	Value
Characteristics of TCE at T=293°K		
Saturated vapor concentration	ρ_{max}	4.3×10^{-4} g/cm^3
Diffusion coefficient in air	D_v	0.072 cm^2/s
Heat of vaporization	λ_v	63.2 cal/g
Thermal conductivity of air	k	61×10^{-6} cal/s-cm-K
Gas constant	R	1.987 cal/mole-K
Diffusion coefficient of vapor through soil	D	0.039 cm^2/s
Vapor pressure of TCE	P_{vp}	60 mm Hg
Vapor pressure of water	P_{H_2O}	17.54 mm Hg
Diffusion coefficient of water vapor through air	D_{H_2O}	0.239 cm^2/s
Initial concentration in soil (assumed)	C_0	0.05 g/cm^3
Adsorption coefficients (assumed)	$\begin{cases} \alpha \\ \beta \\ K_{oc} \end{cases}$	1 0 360
Solubility	S	1100 mg/L
Molecular weight	M	131.5 g/mole
Ratio C_l/C_g (=S/ρ_{max})	K_H	2.56 cm^3 air/cm^3 water
Environmental Characteristics (assumed)		
Humidity	h	0.5 (=50%)
Stagnant air layer thickness	δ	0.3 cm
Temperature	T	293°K
Wind speed	V	100 cm/s
Soil solid density	ρ_{solid}	2.65 g/cm^3
Soil bulk density =$(1-\eta-\theta)\rho_{solid}$	ρ_b	1.32 g/cm^3
Volumetric soil water content	θ	0.2 cm^3/cm^3
Soil air content	η	0.3 cm^3/cm^3
Depth of soil column	L	20 cm
Water vapor flux per unit area	f_w	6.7×10^{-2} g/cm^2/day

Values for certain input parameters may be found in various chemistry and physics handbooks or in the published literature. This chapter and other chapters also provide estimation methods for some of the parameters.

In case of trichloroethylene (TCE) the properties are summarized in Table 14-26. An example is illustrated here to show how the volalitization of some common pollutants can be evaluated.

[Example 14-1]   Find the flux of TCE at 20°C.

From Equation [14-17] and Table 14-26

$$f = \frac{\dfrac{(4.3\times10^{-4}\,\text{g/ cm}^3)\,(0.5)}{0.3\,\text{cm}}}{\dfrac{1}{0.072\,\text{cm}^2/\text{s}} + \dfrac{(63.2\,\text{cal/g})^2\,(4.3\times10^{-4}\,\text{g/ cm}^3)\,(131.5\,\text{g/mole})}{(61\times10^{-6}\,\text{cal/s}\cdot\text{cm}\cdot\text{k})\,(1.987\,\text{cal/mol}\cdot\text{K})\,(293\text{K})^2}}$$

$$= 5.04\times10^{-5}\,\text{g/ cm}^2\,\text{s}$$

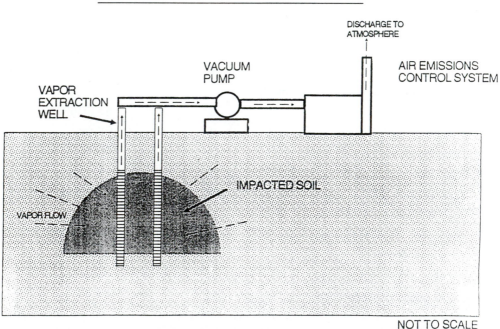

NOT TO SCALE

Figure 14-23.   Gasoline impacted soil vapor extraction system. (Source: T.J. Dolan, Environmental Applicartions, Inc.)

The soil vapor extraction system is established quite well now, as shown in Figure 14-23. The modeling is based on both Darcy's law as well as continuity equations, assuming homogenous soil properties and vapor composition. The formulation for computation can be summarized as the following steps:

Dalton's law

$$q = \frac{-k\nabla p}{\mu} \qquad [14\text{-}18]$$

Continuity

$$\frac{\partial(\eta, \rho)}{\partial t} = -\nabla(\rho q) \qquad [14\text{-}19]$$

State

$$\rho = \frac{MP}{RT} \qquad [14\text{-}20]$$

Governing equation

$$S \cdot \frac{\partial P}{\partial t} = \nabla(\rho \nabla p)$$

where

$$S = \frac{nM\mu}{RTk} \qquad [14\text{-}21]$$

14.5.3   Encapsulation and Vitrification

Usually the waste block can be coated with polyethylene as a jacket around the waste block. Often low molecular weight polybutadiene can be added to the block during heat under pressure as a binder as well as a cross-linking agent. To ensure that immobilization is permanent, the concept of **microencapsulation** has been adopted. The waste particles are admixed with a binding agent; for example, asphalt water emulsion. After the water is evaporated, the particles are coated with a layer of asphalt. The use of asphalt to encapsulate radioactive waste is worthy to mention because asphalt, especially the asphaltene portion, can tolerate the high energy radiation. No observable decomposition was found for a sample of asphaltene indicated under van der Graff generator for one week.

At a higher temperature range of ca. 1300°C, inorganic wastes for example the radio-active types can be encased in a medium of glass; this process is termed **vitrification**. Common glass composition involves different amounts of B_2O_3, Al_2O_3, CaO, MgO, and Na_2O in SiO_2 by fusion under high temperatures. Other vitrification methods include concrete, a mixture of asphalt and concrete, or titanate ceramics.

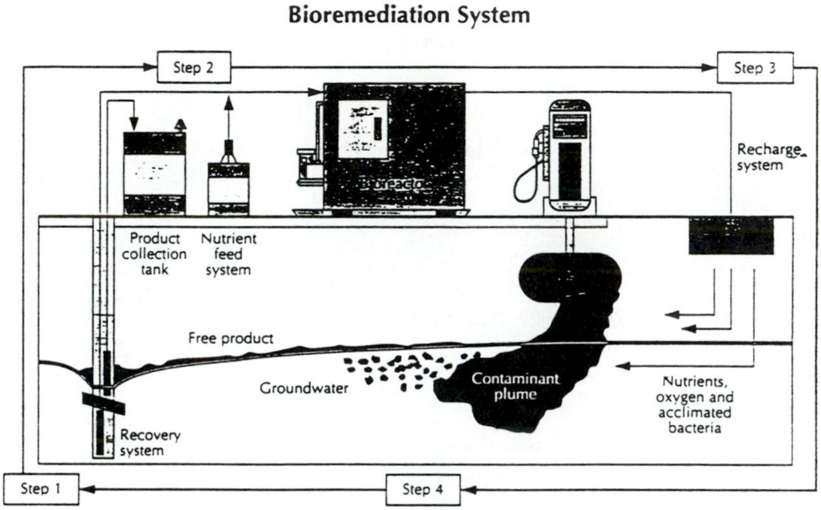

Bioremediation System

Figure 14-24.   A typical in-situ bioremediation system. (Source: B.N. Hicks and J.A. Caplan, *Pollution Eng.*, Jan 15, pp 30-33, 1993.)

14.5.4   In-Situ and On-Site Soil Remediation Methods

Soils have a great capacity for trapping and storage of a great variety of contaminants. Some of the common practices are listed as follows:

- **Soil Washing** — The contaminated soil is subject to high pressure jets of water to break down the soil structure. The drawback is that the contaminants seem to concentrate in the "fines," and are difficult to treat subsequently.

- **Soil Extraction** — Conventional organic solvents are used even under ultra-sound or supercritical fluid extraction conditions.

- **Thermal Desorption** — By heating the contaminated soils in a dry kiln at 200–500°C, the volatile off-gas is further treated. Sometimes other chemicals are added to the soil to enhance the release of contaminants.

- **Soil Incineration** — A method of treating at even higher temperatures for releasing all contaminants.

- **Soil Vitrification** — Electrodes are placed vertically in soil and the soil can be melted at 1600–2000°C in the zone that grows downwards from the electrode.

- **Electrokinetic Treatment** — Low-level DC current (mA/cm^2) of which a few volts are sent through the soil. Cations are transported toward the cathode and anions to the anode.

- **In-Situ Bioremediation** — Actually this is referred to as biostimulation, a process designed to degrade contaminants in soil with minimal disturbances, usually aerobically.

Applications are directed towards such hazards as petroleum hydrocarbons from **leaking underground tanks** (UGT). A typical layout scheme of in-situ bioremediation is shown in Figure 14-24. Figure 14-25 depicts applications for liquid and gaseous phase bioremediation. Usually an oxygen release compound is pumped in with the additional nutrients and bacterial seedings. As a parameter for monitoring the concentration of petroleum hydrocarbons, it is preferable to conduct all measurements of BTEX (benzene, toluene, ethyl benzene, and xylenes). In addition, the total chlorinated compound concentrations are also measured, as shown in Figure 14-26. In-situ stimulation is a process whereby a chemical is added. Besides the oxygen release agent such as urea-oxygen adducts, hydrogen peroxide or nitrate solution is quite common. Also, the addition of naturally isolated or indigeneous microorganisms for a particular type of contaminate can be conducted, as shown in Table 14-27. For a detailed biotreatment, refer to Chapter 29 of the accompanied volume.

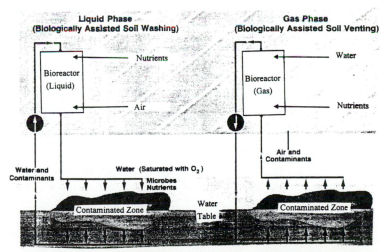

Figure 14-25. Liquid and gaseous phase bioremediation technologies. (Source: US DOE, Environmental Restoration of Waste and Management Program DOE/ EM - 0013P, 1991.)

Table 14-27.   Microorganism Known to Degrade Toxic Organic Pollutants

Organic pollutants	Organism
Phenolic compounds	*Achromobacter, Alcalegenes, Acenitobacter, Arthrobacter, Azotobacter, Bacillus cereus, Flavobacterium, Pseudomonas putida, P. aeruginosa and Nocardia Candida tropicalis, Debaromyces subglobosus, and Trichosporon cutaneoum, Aspergillus, Penicillium, and Neurospora*
Benzoates and related compounds	*Arthrobacter, Bacillus sp., Micrococcus, Moraxella, Mycobacterium, P. putida and P. fluorescence*
Hydrocarbons	*Escherichia coli, P. putida, P. aeruginosa, and Candida*
Surfactants	*Alcaligenes, Achromobacter, Aerobacter aeruginosa, Bacillus, Citrobacter, Clostridium resinae, Corynebacterium, Flavobacterium, Nocardia, Pseudomonas, Candida, and Cladosporium*
Pesticides	
DDT	*P. aeruginosa,* 640X
Linurin	*B. sphaericus*
2,4-D	*Arthrobacter and P. cepacia*
2,4,5-T	*P. cepacia*
Parathion	*Pseumodonas sp. and E.coli; P. stutzeri and P. aeruginosa*

Source: D.L. Wise, Biotreatment Systems, Vol 1, CRC Press, 1988.

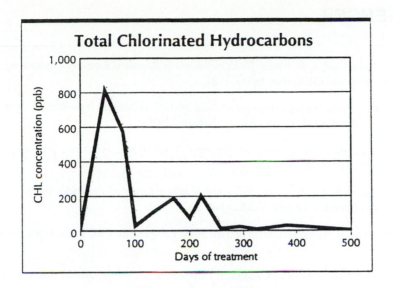

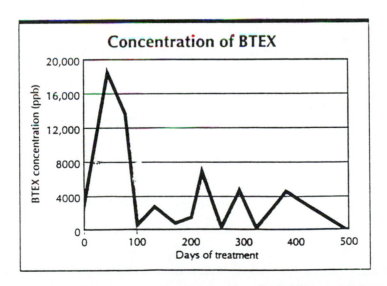

Figure 14-26. Total chlorinated hydrocarbons and BTEX concentrations from one worst-case monitoring well. (Source: B.N. Hicks and J.A. Caplan, loc. cit.)

REFERENCES

14-1.   P. A. Veslind and A. E. Rimer, *Unit Operations in Resource Recovery Engineering*, Prentice-Hall, Englewood Cliffs, New Jersey, 1981.

14-2.   T. F. Yen, *Recycling and Disposal of Solid Wastes, Industrial, Agricultural, Domestic*, Ann Arbor Science Publishers, Ann Arbor, Michigan, 1975.

14-3.   P. J. Knox, *Resource Recovery of Municipal Solid Wastes*, American Institute of Chemical Engineers, New York, New York, 1988.

14-4.   K. D. Racke and J. R. Coats, *Enhanced Biodegradation of Pesticides in the Environment*, American Chemical Society, Washington, D.C., 1990.

14-5.   D. W. Connell, *Bioaccumulation of Xenobiotic Compounds*, CRC Press, Boca Raton, Florida, 1989.

14-6.   E. A. McBean, F. A. Rovers and G. J. Farquhar, *Solid Waste Landfill Engineering and Design*, Prentice-Hall, Englewood Cliffs, New Jersey, 1995.

14-7.   C. A. Wentz, *Hazardous Waste Management*, McGraw-Hill, New York, New York, 1989.

14-8.   J. T. Pfeffer, *Solid Waste Management Engineering*, Prentice-Hall, Englewood Cliffs, New Jersey, 1992.

14-9.   N. J. Bunce, *Environmental Chemistry*, 2nd ed., Wuerz Pub., 1994.

14-10. C. Polprasert, *Organic Waste Recycling*, 2nd ed., Wiley, New York, 1996.

14-11. J.T. Cookson, Jr., *Biremediation: Engineering Design and Application*, McGraw-Hill, New York, 1995.

14-12. E.L. Appleton, "A Nickel-Iron Wall Against Contaminated Groundwater," Env. Sci. Technol. *30* 536A (1996).

14-13. G. D. Andrews and P. M. Subramanian, *Emerging Technolgies in Plastics Recycling*, American Chemical Society, Washington DC, 1992.

14-14. B. Varon, *Soil Pollution: Processes and Dynamics*, Springer-Verlag, Berlin, 1996.

14-15. C. J. Watras and J. W. Huckabee, *Mercury Pollution: Integration and Synthesis*, CRC Press, Boca Raton, Florida, 1994.

14-16. S. Willetts, "Mercury and Arsenic Wastes: Removal, Recovery, Treatment and Disposal," Chemical Ind., *17* 689 (1994).

14-17. C. G. Down and J. Stocks, *Environmental Impact of Mining*, Applied Science, Barking, England, 1977.

14-18. J. Douglas, "Cleaning up Mercury with Genetic Ecology," EPRI Journal, *10*, 20 (1994).

PROBLEM SET

1. A municipal solid waste has the following chemical composition

Component	Wet mass, kg	Dry mass, kg	Composition, kg					
			C	H	O	N	S	Ash
Food	15	4.5	2.16	0.29	1.69	0.12	0.02	0.23
Paper	45	42.3	18.40	2.54	18.61	0.13	0.08	2.54
Cardboard	10	9.5	4.18	0.56	4.24	0.03	0.02	0.48
Plastics	10	9.8	5.88	0.71	2.23	—	—	0.98
Garden trimmings	10	4.0	1.91	0.24	1.52	0.14	0.01	0.18
Wood	5	4.0	1.98	0.24	1.71	0.01	—	0.06
Totals	95	74.1	34.51	4.58	30.00	0.43	0.13	4.47

Derive an approximate chemical formula for the organic portion of the waste. You have to normalize the composition on a moisture-free and ash-free basis. Estimate its energy content by the modified Dulong formula

$$kJ/kg = 337\%C + 1428[\%H - (\%O/8)] + 9\%S$$

2. If a sanitary landfill were set in clay having 50% porosity and if the coefficient of hydraulic conductivity is 1×10^{-7} cm/s, calculate how long it would take the leachate to percolate from the bottom of the landfill through the underlying soil to the groundwater table 1.5 m below, using Darcy's law (assuming that the leachate is not allowed to build up in the landfill and the underlying soil is saturated).

3. What is bioconcentration factor (BCF)? Veith measured the BCF for DDT in fish as 2.94×10^4. Suppose BCF can be estimated from (a) water solubility, S; (b) octanol-water partition coefficient, K_{ow} and (c) soil adsorption coefficient, K_{oc}. When BCF values are plotted vs. those parameter in a log-log paper, straight-line relationships with intercepts, b, and slopes, m, are formed. From the value of the parameters, which BCF is close to the experimental laboratory value of 29,400?

		b	m
K_{ow}	5.62×10^5	−0.23	0.76
S	1.7×10^{-3}	2.791	−0.564
K_{oc}	2.3×10^4	−1.579	1.119

CHAPTER 15

BIOSPHERE — GEOCHEMICAL ASPECTS

*T*his and the next chapter are devoted to the **biosphere**, the realm of living organisms and their interactions with the lithosphere, the hydrosphere, and the atmosphere. In this chapter, we will discuss the geochemical aspects of the biosphere, and the next chapter will cover health and risk aspects. The chapter will begin with an introduction to the exosphere, followed by an explanation of the radioactive dating method, which can determine the age of the Earth. The third section will describe some important principles in biochemistry. In the realm of biopolymers, we will address the question of what life is and how it evolves, especially the problem of chemical evolution and autopoiesis. The last part concentrates on environmental geochemistry. The exploration and significance of geochemical biomarkers (or the molecular fossils) will be explained. Especially the global geochemical cycles of carbon from long-range past to the future will be examined by the kinetic model.

The theme of the chapter is addressed to the general introduction of geochemistry, one of the oldest disciplines in the advancement of modern science. Unfortunately, it has been neglected in the realm of environmental engineering and science except the geotechnical aspect of it. Only until recently, with the emphasis on soil and groundwater remediation, have people begun to pay attention to the geochemical aspect of the minerals and soils. Again, this is a fragmented end-piece of knowledge. We feel the overall underlying principles in geochemistry will have a broad impact to investigators practicing environmental engineering.

Geology sometimes is referred to as earth science and planetary science. Accordingly, geochemistry deals with space chemistry; chemical evolution; transformation and occurrence of minerals and fossilized organic resources; the global geochemical cycles and reservoirs; the origin and diagenesis of organic deposits; the geochemical biomarkers, and so on. To understand the development of evolution, the concept of biochemistry and biopolymer are introduced here.

15.1 EXOSPHERE

As seen in Figure 15-1, the environment beyond the atmosphere is often called the **exosphere**. It includes the solar system, the galaxy, and the whole universe. It is now believed, according to the "big bang" theory, that the universe originated between 13 and 20 billion years ago from a giant fireball which emerged from an infinitely dense collection of neutrons. The "big bang" resulted in the formation of hydrogen and some helium nuclei from which the galaxies and stars evolved. The "big bang" initiated a process of evolution that continues now and seems to extend into the future. Figure 15-2 shows the lifecycle of a star.

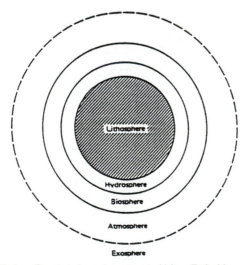

Figure 15-1.   Our total environment. (After R.A. Horne, 1978.)

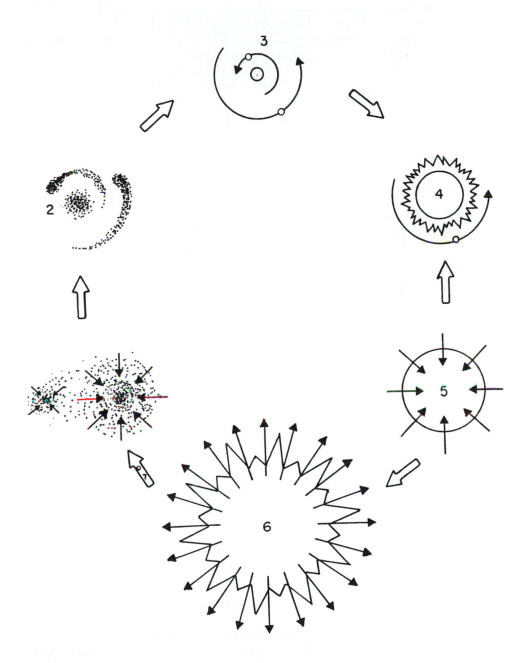

Figure 15-2.   Lifecycle of a star. (After R.A. Horne, 1978.)

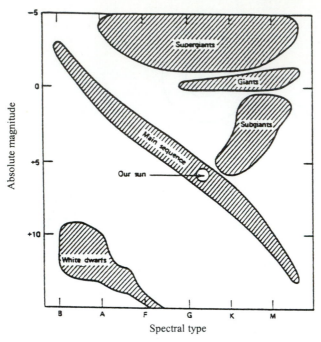

Figure 15-3.   Hertzprung-Russell diagram. (After R.A. Horne, 1978.)

In astrophysics, the color indexes of galaxies are commonly used as age indicators, old galaxies being redder and brighter than young ones. The spectral type is related to the temperature of the galaxy as follows. When stars evolve, they become redder and brighter as they leave the main sequence for the red giant branch, as shown in Figure 15-3, the **Hertzsprung-Russel diagram**. The location of a star in the diagram can give some information about its age.

Now, while the universe is almost entirely made up of hydrogen and helium, it does include a significant amount of heavier elements such as O, C, N, P, S, Fe, and Mg. All these elements are believed to have been produced in the early history of the galaxy, prior to the formation of the solar system. It is also believed that the planets and the sun in the solar system were formed from the same material; that is, they started with the same initial chemical composition. Cosmochemistry mainly deals with the formation and concentration of these major elements and their compounds. Carbon has been found to be a universal element; for example, meteorites contain organic carbon in the range of 0.15% (1.99% by wt.) and this is called **retigen**. Figure 15-4 gives the relative abundance of elements in the universe.

It is now a widely accepted theory that elements heavier than hydrogen and helium are synthesized from these remnants of the "big bang" by nuclear reactions in stars. At high temperatures, the activation barrier to fusion of hydrogen is overcome and a nuclear reaction called "**hydrogen burning**" occurs. As a result, helium is produced, accompanied by a release of energy. If there is a small amount of ^{12}C present, the following catalytic nuclear reaction may be the major pathway for hydrogen burning:

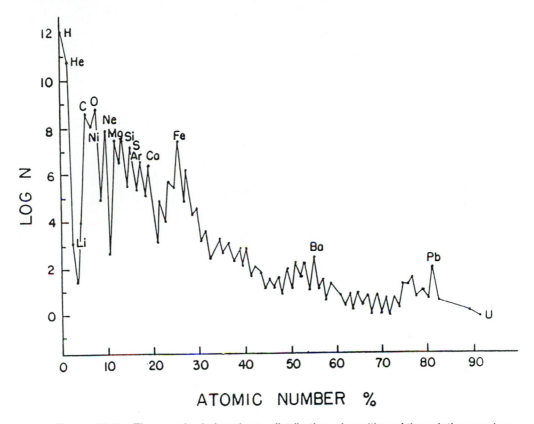

Figure 15-4. The standard abundance distribution—logarithm of the relative number of nuclei as a function of Z. (After Cameron)

$$^{12}_{6}C + ^{1}_{1}H \rightarrow ^{13}_{7}N + \gamma \rightarrow ^{13}_{6}C + _{1}\beta$$

$$^{13}_{6}C + ^{1}_{1}H \rightarrow ^{14}_{7}N + \gamma$$

$$^{14}_{7}N + ^{1}_{1}H \rightarrow ^{15}_{8}O + \gamma \rightarrow ^{15}_{7}N + _{1}\beta$$

$$^{15}_{7}N + ^{1}_{1}H \rightarrow ^{12}_{6}C + ^{4}_{2}He$$

$$\overline{}$$

$$4^{1}_{1}H \rightarrow ^{4}_{2}He + 3\gamma + 2_{1}\beta$$

Similar to this hydrogen burning is the process of nuclear fusion mentioned in Chapter 7. The sun and other stars give off their energy by a similar process: $4 \, ^1H \rightarrow \, ^4He + energy$ as 3.78×10^{23} erg/sec consuming in 10^{11} years.

G- and Cooler star may have the following process:

$$^1H + \, ^1H \rightarrow \, ^2H + \, _1\beta$$

$$^1H + \, ^2H \rightarrow \, ^3He + \gamma$$

$$^3He + \, ^4He \rightarrow \, ^7Be + \gamma$$

$$^7Be \rightarrow \, ^7Li + \, _1\beta$$

$$^1H + \, ^7Li \rightarrow \, ^4_2He$$

With the energy from the hydrogen burning, the temperature of the star rises to a level where the activation barrier for hydrogen burning is exceeded. Then helium can be converted to carbon and oxygen as follows:

$$^3_2He + \, ^4_2He \rightarrow \, ^7_4Be + \gamma$$

$$^7_4Be + \, ^1_1H \rightarrow \, ^8_5B + \gamma$$

$$^8_5B \rightarrow \, ^8_4Be + \, _1\beta$$

$$^8_4Be + \, ^4_2He \rightarrow \, ^{12}_6C$$

$$^{12}_6C + \, ^4_2He \rightarrow \, ^{16}_8O$$

If the temperature becomes even higher, carbon and oxygen atoms can proceed to generate other heavier nuclei such as Ne, Na, Si, P, and S as follows:

$$^{12}_{6}C + ^{12}_{6}C \rightarrow ^{20}_{10}Ne + ^{4}_{2}He$$

$$^{12}_{6}C + ^{12}_{6}C \rightarrow ^{23}_{11}Na + ^{1}_{1}H$$

$$^{16}_{8}O + ^{16}_{8}O \rightarrow ^{28}_{14}Si + ^{4}_{2}He$$

$$^{16}_{8}O + ^{16}_{8}O \rightarrow ^{15}_{15}P + ^{1}_{1}H$$

$$^{16}_{8}O + ^{16}_{8}O \rightarrow ^{31}_{16}S + ^{1}_{0}n$$

Should the temperature reach 3×10^9 K, the nuclei would have enough energy to overcome the activation barrier of all nuclear reactions. The Ni atom can be generated from the α-**process**, in which the intermediate nuclei photodisintegrate with the emission of α-particles, which in turn can be captured by the surviving nuclei to build higher mass elements.

$$^{28}Si \rightarrow 7\,^{4}He$$

$$^{28}Si + 7\,^{4}He \rightarrow ^{56}Ni$$

$$2\,^{28}Si \rightarrow ^{56}Ni$$

The ^{56}Ni formed from the α-process is not stable and will convert to ^{56}Fe through an **e-process** (β-decay).

$$^{56}_{28}Ni \rightarrow ^{56}_{27}Co \rightarrow ^{56}_{26}Fe$$

A summary of the exosphere and the origin of chemical elements are as follows:

- **Exosphere** 1 light year = 10 T km
- **Solar System** $\rightarrow$ Galaxy $\rightarrow$ Universe
  (10 G km)   (0.1 M light year) (10 G light year)

- **Cosmochemistry** He, H_2, OH, CO, CN, CS, SiO, etc.
  (from microwave resonance)

- **Stellar Chemistry**

Hertzsprung-Russell diagram

$$R \rightarrow N$$
$$O \rightarrow B \rightarrow A \rightarrow F \rightarrow G \rightarrow K \rightarrow M$$

(Bluish white) (white) (yellow)   (orange)   (red)

$$S \rightarrow Se$$
(red)

increase in temperature $\leftarrow$

The main sequence of the color scheme and the examples of some common stars in Hertzsprung-Russell diagram are illustrated as follows:

Sequence type	Color	Examples
O	Blue	Alnitak
B	Blue	Rigel, Regulus, Spica
A	White	Sirius, Vega, Altair, Denub
F	Yellow-white	Procyon, Canopus
G	Yellow	Sun, Capella, α- Centaurus A
K	Orange	Arcturus, Aldeburan, 61 Cygni
M	Red	Belilgeuse, Antures, Wolf 539

- **M-Red Giant**

3-particle collision

Nucleosynthesis $3\ ^4He \rightarrow\ ^{12}C$

$4\ ^4He \rightarrow\ ^{16}O$

$(^{12}C + {}^4He \rightarrow\ ^{16}O)$

Thus, n ^4He can produce stable atoms such as ^{20}Ne, ^{24}Mg, ^{28}Si, ^{32}S, and so on.

- **α-Process (α-Recombination)**

photodisintegration at 3×10^9 K and recombination

$$^{28}Si \rightarrow 7\ ^4He$$

$$^{28}Si + 7\ ^4He \rightarrow\ ^{56}Ni$$

- **e-Process (β-Decay)**

$$^{56}_{28}Ni \xrightarrow{\beta}\ ^{56}_{27}Co \xrightarrow{\beta}\ ^{56}_{26}Fe$$

- **s- and r-Process (Neutron Capture)**

$$^{56}_{28}\text{Ni} \xrightarrow{\ ^1_0 n\ } {}^{57}_{28}\text{Ni} \xrightarrow{\ ^1_0 n\ } {}^{58}_{28}\text{Ni}$$

s (slow process) — red giant
r (rapid process) — supernova explosion

The preceding processes describe how all the elements in the periodic table are formed.

15.2 RADIOACTIVE DATING

The age of the earth and the solar system can be estimated by the radioactive dating method, based on an accurate determination of the ratio of radioactive isotopes to their stable daughter products. For example, one of the isotopes of potassium is continuously trans-formed into the elements argon and calcium.

$$^{40}\text{K} \rightarrow {}^{40}\text{Ca}$$

$$^{40}\text{K} \rightarrow {}^{40}\text{Ar}$$

Let us consider the granitic black mica biotite, a mineral rich in potassium. The pre-dominant potassium isotope is ^{39}K, which is stable, while a small fraction of potassium sites are occupied by the radioactive ^{40}K. Assuming that 12% of the decay results in the formation of ^{40}Ar, there is an accumulation of ^{40}Ar at the expense of ^{40}K with increasing time. Hence, the older a given crystal of biotite, the more ^{40}Ar it should contain. The age of the sample would then be readily estimated by measuring the relative amount of ^{40}K and ^{40}Ar. For a radioactive isotope,

$$P(t) = P(0)e^{-kt} \qquad\qquad [15\text{-}1]$$

where

$P(t)$ = the number of atoms at the geological age, t,
$P(0)$ = the number of atoms at $t = 0$
k = the decay constant (refer to Section 7.1.3)

Assuming a closed system, the mass is conserved, thus

$$P(0) = P(t) + \Delta D \qquad\qquad [15\text{-}2]$$

where D denotes the total number of daughter atoms produced before time, t. For this special case, 12% of total decays of ^{40}K becomes ^{40}Ar, thus

$$D_A = 0.12[P(0) - P(t)] \qquad\qquad [15\text{-}3]$$

Combining the preceding equations, we obtain

$$\frac{D_A}{P(t)} = 0.12\left(e^{kt} - 1\right) \qquad\qquad [15\text{-}4]$$

If there are no argon atoms present in the rock at $t = 0$, then $D_A = \Delta D_A$. The equation can be rewritten and solved for t

$$t = \frac{1}{k}\ln\left(\frac{D_A(t)}{0.12\,P(t)}\right) \qquad\qquad [15\text{-}5]$$

An isotope of rubidium, which may substitute for potassium in mineral lattice, decays into a single daughter compound, an isotope of strontium as follows

$$^{87}\text{Rb} \rightarrow {}^{87}\text{Sr}$$

The preceding process is also used as a geological clock. To determine the age of the sample, it is necessary to estimate the total amount of ^{87}Rb and ^{87}Sr in the sample and the amount of ^{87}Sr at $t = 0$, ^{87}Sr$_o$. Because ^{87}Rb decays only to ^{87}Sr, Equation [15-5] becomes

$$t = \frac{1}{k}\ln\left(\frac{{}^{87}\text{Sr}^*}{{}^{87}\text{Rb}} + 1\right) \qquad\qquad [15\text{-}6]$$

where $^{87}\text{Sr}^* = {}^{87}\text{Sr} - {}^{87}\text{Sr}_o$.

Estimation of $^{87}\text{Sr}^*$ poses a great experimental difficulty, while ^{87}Sr and ^{87}Rb are readily measurable quantities. To solve the problem, $\left[\dfrac{{}^{87}\text{Sr}^*}{{}^{87}\text{Rb}}\right]$ was determined graphically from isotopic data on a series of rocks from some formations exhibiting different ratios of ^{87}Sr/^{87}Rb. The following relationship could be easily derived:

$$\frac{{}^{87}\text{Sr}}{{}^{86}\text{Sr}} = \left(\frac{{}^{87}\text{Sr}^*}{{}^{87}\text{Rb}}\right)\frac{{}^{87}\text{Rb}}{{}^{86}\text{Sr}} + \frac{{}^{87}\text{Sr}_0}{{}^{86}\text{Sr}} \qquad\qquad [15\text{-}7]$$

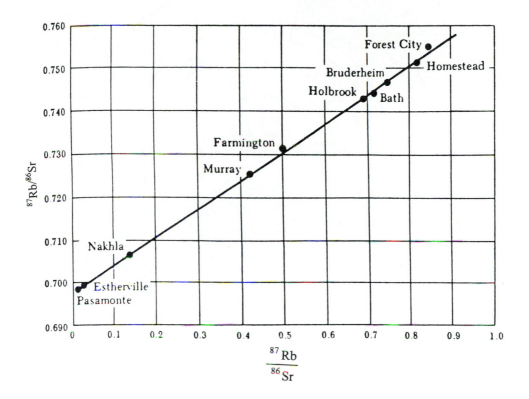

Figure 15-5. Rb-Sr isochron diagram for stony meteorites. The slope of the line gives an age of about 4.3 billion years.

By plotting $^{87}Sr/^{86}Sr$ against $^{87}Rb/^{86}Sr$, the slope will be $^{87}Sr^*/^{87}Rb$. For stony meteorites, the slope was found to be 0.0615 , as shown in Figure 15-5. Inserting this value back into Equation [15-6], and using $k = 1.39 \times 10^{-11}$ years^{-1}, we obtain the age of the stony meteorites

$$t = \frac{1}{1.39 \times 10^{-11}} \ln(0.0615 + 1) = 4.3 \text{ billion years}$$

Using this method on various samples, the age of earth was determined to be in the range of 3.2 and 5.7 billion years. Figure 15-6 gives a common classification of geological age.

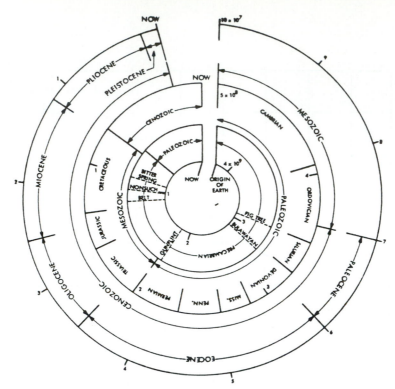

Figure 15-6.   Geological ages from the origin of the earth to present. (Source: T.F. Yen.)

15.3 BIOCHEMISTRY

The three most important chemical components in organisms are proteins, cellulose (or polysaccharides), and fats. The individual compounds from which these components are made are amino acids, simple sugars (such as glucose), and carboxylic acids. The twenty-some amino acids are the most important compounds found in proteins. Their structures are shown in Table 15-1 and their three-letter and one-letter abbreviations are also listed in Table 15-2. There are five purine and pyrimidine bases generally found in nucleic acids, shown in Table 15-3.

We will now address some of the important characteristics of the amino acids and the derived compounds that make them so significant to our life: (1) They have amphoteric behavior by which they can adjust themselves to any pH condition.

$$R - \underset{\underset{NH_2}{|}}{CH} - COOH \leftrightarrow R - \underset{\underset{NH_3^+}{|}}{CH} - COO^-$$

(2) The amino acid can be either hydrophobic or hydrophilic, depending on the chain length of the R-group. Thus, it can form a biological membrane that can control the solute and solvent transport between the organism and its surroundings. (3) The amino acid can form polyamino acid (polypeptide) in various molecular weights, as shown in Table 15-4. There are further unique properties, (4) to (6), of the polypeptides (proteins) ,which will be discussed in the next section.

Table 15-1. Some Important Building Blocks of Biochemistry

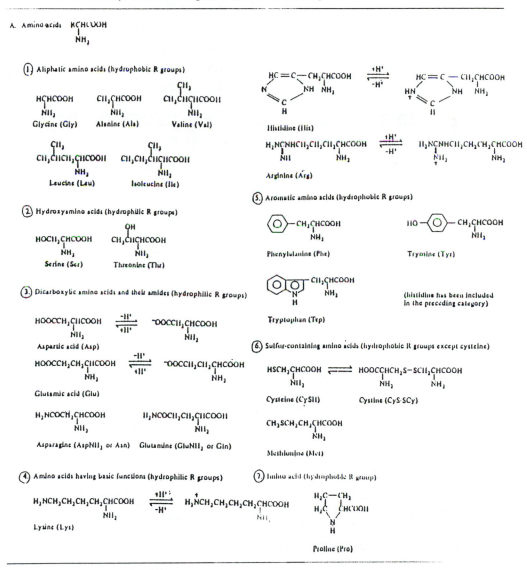

Table 15-2.   One- and Three-Letter Symbols for the Amino Acids

A	Ala	Alanine	M	Met	Methionine
B	Asx	Asparagine or aspartic acid	N	Asn	Asparagine
C	Cys	Cysteine	P	Pro	Proline
D	Asp	Aspartic acid	Q	Gln	Glutamine
E	Glu	Glutamic acid	R	Arg	Arginine
F	Phe	Phenylalanine	S	Ser	Serine
G	Gly	Glycine	T	Thr	Threonine
H	His	Histidine	V	Val	Valine
I	Ile	Isoleucine	W	Trp	Tryptophan
K	Lys	Lysine	Y[*]	Tyr	Tyrosine
L	Leu	Leucine	Z	Glx	Glutamine or glutamic acid

[*] The one-letter symbol for an undetermined or nonstandard amino acid is X.

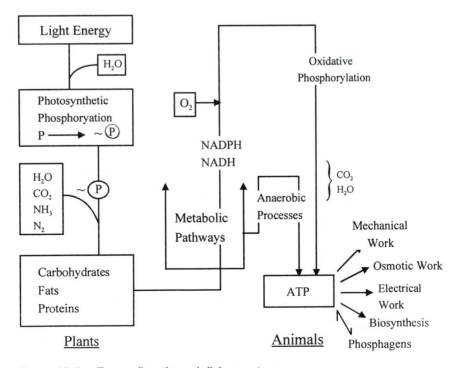

Figure 15-7.   Energy flow through living systems.

The metabolic process common in life is biogenesis or **anabolism**, which is referred to as the building process of macromolecules from simple molecules; and the so-called **ergbolism** is a light conversion process involving ATP (adenosine triphosphate); lastly, the metabolic breakdown is termed **catabolism**. The energy flow through living systems is essential for both plants and animals, as shown in Figure 15-7. As basic information, the autotrophic metabolism has a feedback to heterotrophic metabolism, as shown in Figure 15-8. Detailed accounts of metabolism and microbial biochemistry will be given in Chapter 27. The biomolecules universally involved in energy conversion are as follows:

Name	Symbol
Adenosine triphosphate	ATP
Nicotinamide adenine dinucleotide	NAD^+
Nicotinamide adenine dinucleotide phosphate	$NADP^+$
Flavin mononucleotide	FMN
Flavin adenine dinucleotide	FAD
Quinones	CoQ
Heme containing molecules, cytochromes	Cyt
Ferredoxin, iron containing, nonheme molecules	Fd

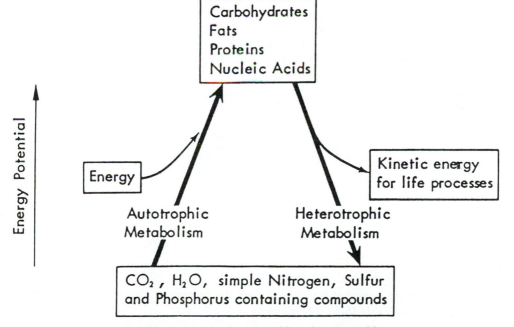

Figure 15-8.   Feedback system of autotrophic to heterotrophic.

Table 15-3. Pyrimidine and Purine Bases

Pyrimidine Bases

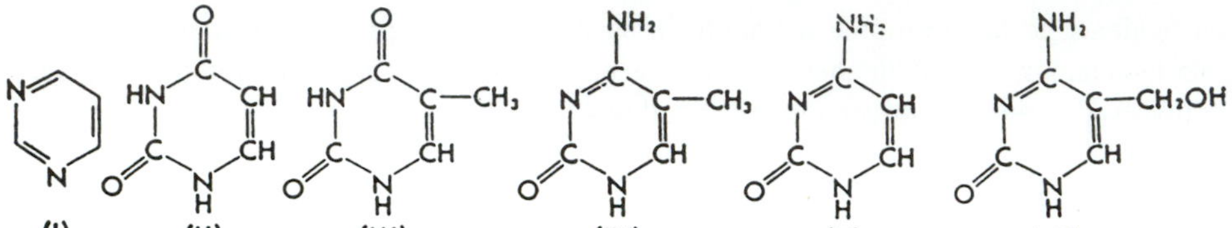

(I) (II) (III) (IV) (V) (VI)

Pyrimidine (I) Uracil (II) Thymine (III) 5-Methylcytosine (IV) Cytosine (V)

5-Hydroxymethylcytosine (VI)

Purine Bases

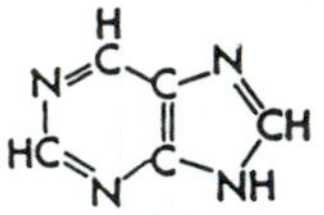

(I)

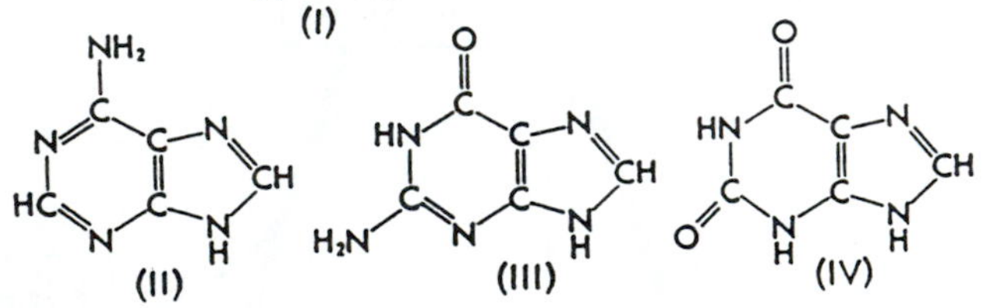

(II) (III) (IV)

Purine (I)

Adenine 6-Aminopurine (II) Guanine 2-Amino-6-Oxypurine (III) Xanthine 2,6-Dioxypurine (IV)

The high energy compounds always contain the energy-rich phosphate bonds that can easily be cleaved (see Table 15-5). For example,

$$ADP + \text{phosphate} + \text{energy} \leftrightarrow ATP + H_2O$$

Table 15-4. Linking of Biomonomers To Form Active Biomolecules

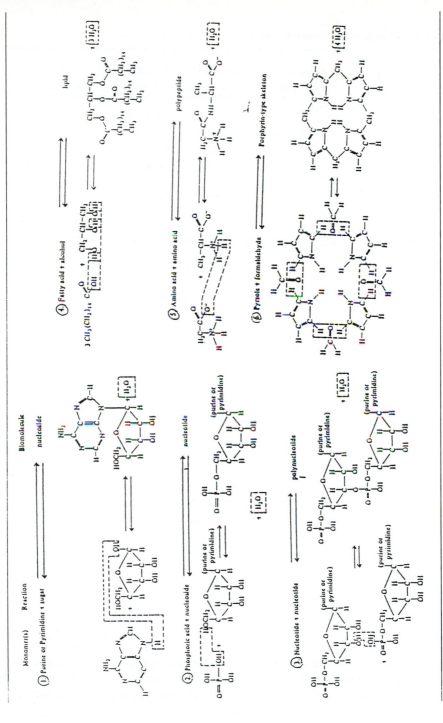

Source: J.W. Moore and E.A. Moore, 1976.

Table 15-5.   Energy Rich Phosphate Bonds

Characteristic Linkage	General Formula	General Designation	Biochemical Example	ΔG° (kcal/mole)
$-\overset{\text{O}}{\overset{\|}{\text{C}}}-\overset{\text{H}}{\text{N}}\sim$	$R\overset{\text{NH}}{\overset{\|}{\text{C}}}-\overset{\text{H}}{\text{N}}\sim\text{(P)}$	Guanidinium phosphate	Creatine phosphate	-10.5
			Arginine phosphate	-9.0
$-\overset{\text{O}}{\overset{\|}{\text{C}}}-\text{O}\sim$	$R\overset{\text{CH}_2}{\overset{\|}{\text{C}}}-\text{O}\sim\text{(P)}$	Enolphosphate	Phosphoenol pyruvate	-12.8
$-\overset{\text{O}}{\overset{\|}{\text{C}}}-\text{O}\sim$	$R\overset{\text{O}}{\overset{\|}{\text{C}}}-\text{O}\sim\text{(P)}$	Acylphosphate	Acetyl phosphate	-10.5
$-\underset{\text{HO}}{\overset{\text{O}}{\overset{\|}{\text{P}}}}-\text{O}\sim$	$RO\underset{\text{HO}}{\overset{\text{O}}{\overset{\|}{\text{P}}}}-\text{O}\sim\text{(P)}$	Pyrophosphates	Adenosine diphosphate	-7.6
$-\overset{\text{O}}{\overset{\|}{\text{C}}}\sim$	$R\overset{\text{O}}{\overset{\|}{\text{C}}}\sim SR'$	Acyl thioester	Acetyl CoA	-10.5

15.3.1   Biopolymer

Polymer usually indicates a high molecular weight of multiple sequences of repeating units. These repeating units are derived from the **monomer** from which the polymer is synthesized. Many monomers do have specially functional groups or unsaturation through which the polymer linkages can be formed either through condensation or addition. Polyester is a condensation polymer where the bonds are formed from difunctional alcohol (diol) and acids (dicarboxylic acid) as monomers. Polyvinyl chloride is an additional polymer that is made from the monomer vinyl chloride through the unsaturated double bonds of the vinyl functions (α-olefins).

Polymer chain entanglement in the solid state is the key characteristic to show that the mechanical properties of high molecular-weight large molecules are different from those of small molecules. The traditional use of polymers as flexible or high strength materials is based on the interactions of large molecules to assume certain configurations and conformations with backbone chain atoms as well as side groups. Other uses of polymers, such as electrical conductors or semiconductors (e.g., polyacetylenes), are still in the developing stages. The potential use for polymer-bond catalysts which combines the advantages of both homogeneous and heterogeneous catalysts at fixed sites are the better mediators now. Furthermore, the use of polymers which bear antigens, whole cells, and enzymes can separate reactive sites, prevent denaturation of proteins and allow sequenced reactions such as controlled releasing of chemotherapeutic agents. Of course the most important value of polymers of biological origin is their function as coding systems and templates of replications, as shown in Figure 15-9.

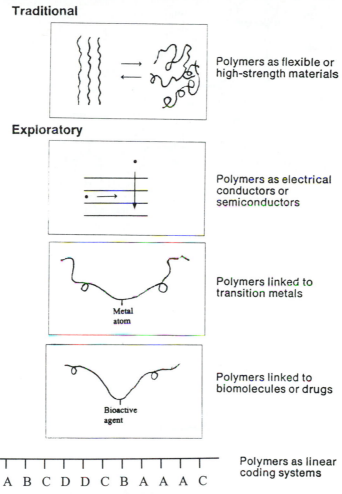

Traditional — Polymers as flexible or high-strength materials

Exploratory — Polymers as electrical conductors or semiconductors

Polymers linked to transition metals (Metal atom)

Polymers linked to biomolecules or drugs (Bioactive agent)

A B C D D C B A A C — Polymers as linear coding systems

Figure 15-9.   New uses of polymers.

Polymers can be classified as **homopolymers** with one type of repeating unit. If there are more than one type of repeating units (two, for example), they are called **copolymers**; three, **terpolymers**; and so on until the repeating units reach n, for which the word is **multipolymer**. For giant bioactive molecules the biopolymers, such as proteins, are made from a combination of different amino acids. It is possible to prepare a polypeptide of the 22 different acids.

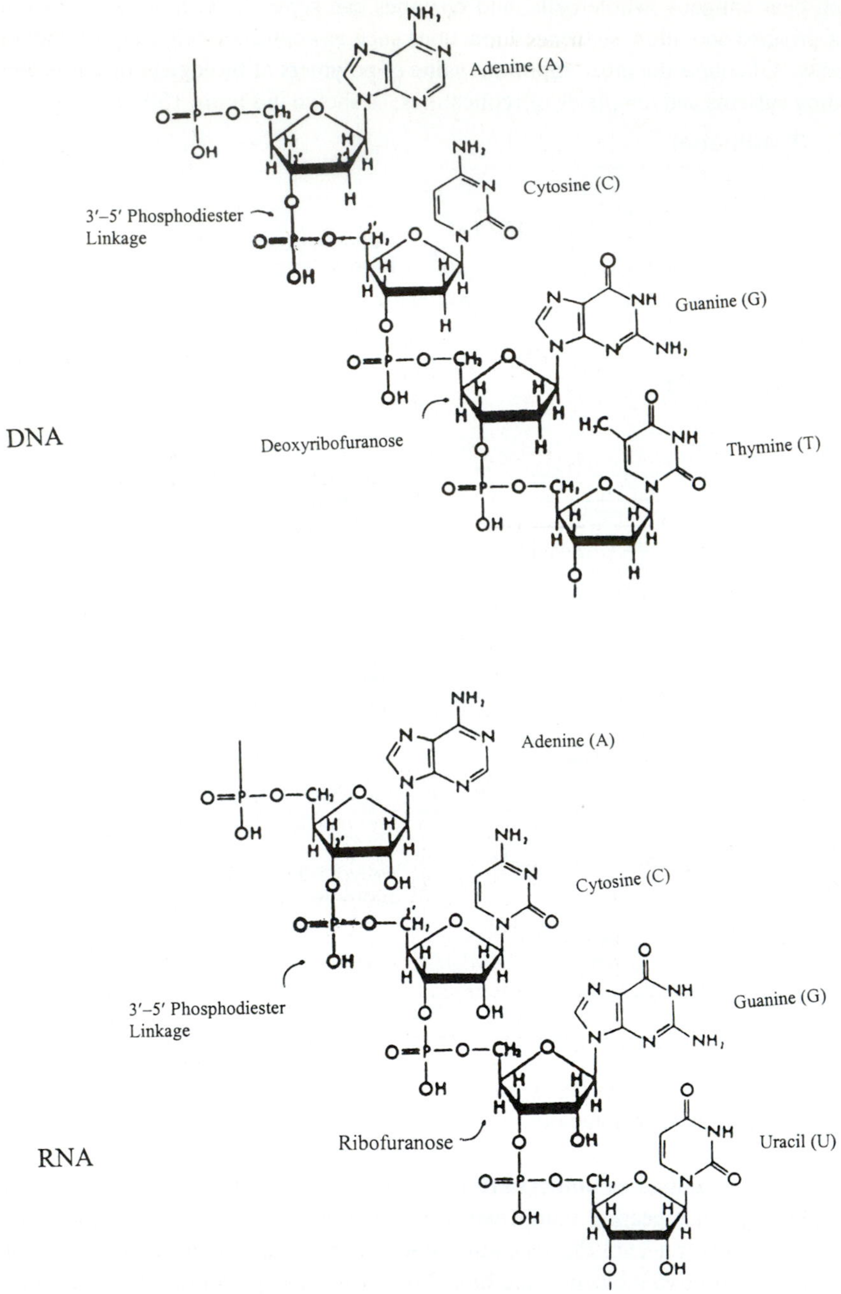

Figure 15-10.   Structures of DNA and RNA.

Linking of biomonomers to form low molecular-weight polymers (**oligomers**) is also important in biology. Table 15-4 illustrates such oligomer formation; for example, **nucleoside** is formed by purine or pyrimidine and a simple sugar (scheme 1). The **nucleotide** is formed through nucleoside and phosphoric acid (scheme 2). Nucleotide can be further condensed into polynucleotide (scheme 3). A trinucleotide is generally referred to as nucleic acid (oligonucleotide), which can form with three different bases. Both RNA and DNA are tetranucleotides. The former is with ribose (sugar) and four bases, ACGT (A, adenine; C, cytosine; G, guanine; T, thymine), which is called **ribonucleic acid** (RNA). The latter is with deoxyribose and four bases, ACGU (the ACG is same as above; U stands for uracil), and is called **deoxyribonucleic acid** (DNA). Both chemical structures of RNA and DNA are depicted in Figure 15-10. DNA exists in cells of all organisms; its sequences in every species can map the life phylogeny. DNA profiling can identify each individual human, and it has become a powerful tool in forensics. RNA is the messenger for replication and is essential for genetic information.

Table 15-6. Approximate Torsion Angles for Some Regular Peptide Structures

Structure	ϕ	ψ
Hypothetical fully extended polyglycine chain	−180	+180
β-poly(L-alanine) in antiparallel-chain pleated sheet	−139	+135
Parallel-chain pleated sheet	−119	+113
Polyglycine II	−80	+150
Poly(L-proline) II	−78	+149
Collagen	−50, −76, −45	+153, +127, +148
Right-handed α helix	−57	−47

Let us proceed further on to the unique properties of polypeptides or proteins, that are derived from amino acids which have discussed in the last section (Section 15.3) on the properties of amino acids and their derivatives. Figure 15-11 shows two peptides in the completely extended β-conformation, and Figure 15-12 gives a conformational map for allowed values of the torsional angles. These conformation maps will help us to understand why proteins possess the following unique properties of as listed in (4), (5), and (6) below. For an explanation of the torsional angle and bonding, refer to Chapter 2. Table 15-6 lists approximate torsion angles for some regular peptide structures. More unique properties are: (4) Hydrogen in the structure that can perform both intra- and inter-molecular hydrogen bonding. The hydrogen bonding also exists between side-group bases of DNA. (5) There are certain allosteric enzymes that help the protein fit the substrate, as shown in Figure 15-13. (6) The combination of DNA and protein constitutes the basic design feature of all present terrestrial organisms. Replicable DNA messages are translated into functional protein sequences, as shown in Figure 15-14, where R, T, and C stand for different kinds of activity: replication, translation, and control. Figure 15-14 also summarizes all the unique properties of amino acid and polypeptides.

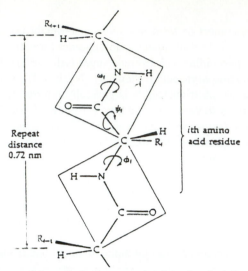

Figure 15-11. The peptide units in the completely extended β conformation. The torsion angles ϕ_i, ψ_i, and ω_i, are defined as 0° when the main chain atoms assume the cis or eclipsed conformation. The angles in the completely extended chain are all 180°.

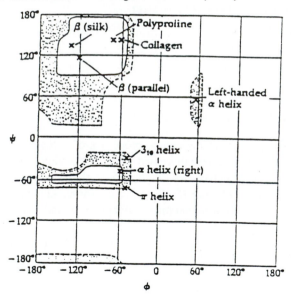

Figure 15-12. Calculated Ramachandran diagram or conformational map showing allowed values of ϕ and ψ. The two irregularly shaped boxes on the left side of the figure represent the regions in which no steric hindrance exists. Note that the β pleated sheet, collagen, and α helix structures fall within these regions. The stippled regions are those in which some hindrance exists, but for which real molecular structure are possible.

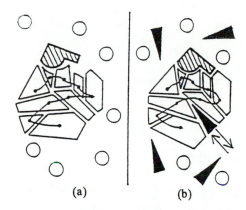

Figure 15-13. (a) Protein does not fit substrate. (b) In the presence of a third molecule, the protein may assume an alternative tertiary structure that does fit the substrate.

$$\underset{\underset{NH_2}{|}}{R\text{-}CH} - COOH \quad \rightleftarrows \quad \underset{\underset{NH_3^{\oplus}}{|}}{R\text{-}CH} - COO^{\ominus}$$

(1) Amphoteric — be in any pH environment

Zwiter ion

(2) hydrophobic — hydrophilic

— adjust the unit of R

(3) polymeric — polyamino acids

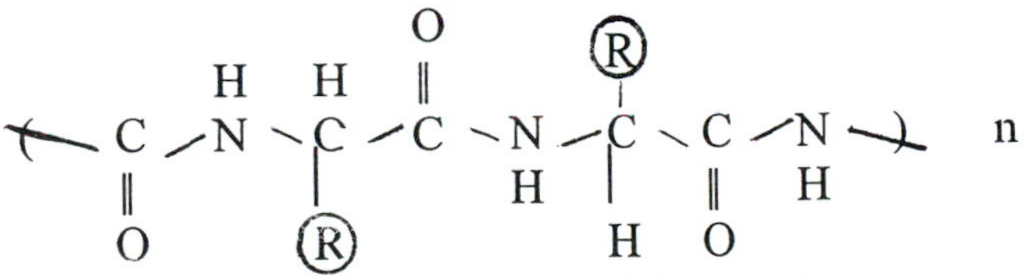

$$\left\{ \underset{\underset{O}{\parallel}}{C} \diagdown N \diagdown \underset{\underset{\textcircled{R}}{|}}{\overset{H}{C}} \diagdown \underset{\underset{H}{\parallel}}{\overset{\overset{O}{\parallel}}{C}} \diagdown N \diagdown \underset{\underset{H \quad O}{\parallel}}{\overset{\textcircled{R}}{C}} \diagdown \underset{\underset{H}{}}{C} \diagdown N \right\}_n$$

Polypeptides

α-helix, Φ, Ψ torsional angles

Figure 15-14. Summary of the properties of amino acids.

(4) H-bonding

$$- \; \overset{\diagdown}{N}-H \; \ldots .O = \overset{\diagup}{\underset{\diagdown}{C}}$$

intramolecular vs intermolecular

(5) Protein synthesis

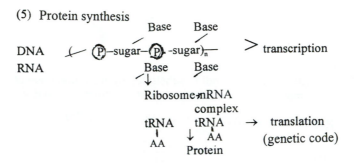

(6) Secondary Structure

Watson-Crick double chain

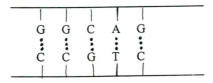

(7) Allosteric

Enzyme — tertiary bonding
quarternary structure (control)

Figure 15-14.   Summary of the properties of amino acids. *continued*

15.3.2 Chemical Evolution

Other planets in the solar system also have a core, a mantle, a crust and an atmosphere. However, only on Earth are there structures that can replicate themselves, change into different forms by mutation and genetic recombination, and transmit such changes to their descendants. The mineral analysis of the lunar samples from Apollo 11 and 12 showed that the soils of the moon are similar to those of the earth. However, no porphyrin, an indicator of living matter, was detected. In this section, we will discuss the formation of the biosphere.

Prior to the emergence of the first life forms, the biomonomers and polymers necessary for building a living structure may have been synthesized through processes that were not mediated by any living system. That is to say, there may be a period of chemical evolution preceding the biological evolution in the development of the biosphere.

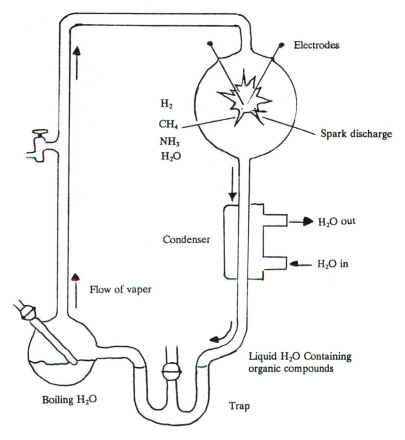

Figure 15-15.   Apparatus used by Miller for simulation of primitive earth atmosphere. (Source: J.W. Moore and E.A. Moore, 1976)

In 1957, Miller performed the first successful primitive earth simulation. The apparatus he used is shown in Figure 15-15. The chromatographic analysis indicates that many organic compounds essential to life were formed by the electrical charge of an inorganic mixture in a reducing primitive atmosphere, as shown in Table 15-7. Since then, many other investigators have also carried out primitive earth simulations. In addition to amino acids, purines, pyridines, sugars, nucleosides, nucleotides, and porphyrins have been synthesized (Table 15-8). Therefore, we may assume that all that is necessary for synthesis of the building blocks in biochemistry is the interaction of compounds containing the appropriate element with a source of energy (One of the examples is the amino acids with different functional groups that provde specialty proteins as shown in Table 15-1.).

Table 15-7. Structures and Yields of Some Compounds Formed by Electrical Discharge in a Reducing Primitive Atmosphere

Name	Yield (mol)	% Yield	Structure
Formic acid	233	3.9	$HCOOH$
Glycine	630	2.1	H_2NCH_2COOH
Glycolic acid	560	1.9	$HOCH_2COOH$
Lactic acid	390	1.8	$CH_3CH(OH)COOH$
Alanine	340	1.7	$CH_3CH(NH_2)COOH$
Propionic acid	126	0.6	CH_3CH_2COOH
Acetic acid	152	0.5	CH_3COOH
Glutamic acid	6	—	$HOOCCH_2CH_2CH(NH_2)COOH$
Aspartic acid	4	—	$HOOCCH_2CH(NH_2)COOH$

Based on initial carbon.

Source: S.L. Miller, J. Amer. Chem. Soc., 77, 2351 (1955); Biochim. Biophys. Acta, 23, 480 (1957).

Table 15-8. Representative Abiotic Synthesis Experiments

Compound Class	Reactants	Energy	Products
Amino Acids	CH_4, NH_3, H_2, H_2O	Electric discharge	Amino acids, hydroxy acids, HCN, urea
	Ammonium fumarate	Heat	Aspartic acid
	CO_2, NH_3, H_2, H_2O	Electric discharge	Amino acids
	CH_4, NH_3, H_2O, H_2, CO_2, N_2	x-ray	Amino acids
	Ammonium acetate	γ-ray	Glycine, aspartic acid, diaminosuccinic acid
	Ammonium carbonate	β-ray	Glycine
	CH_4, NH_3, H_2O	UV	Glycine, alanine
	NH_3, HCN, H_2	Heat (343 K)	Amino acids
	CH_4, NH_3, H_2O	Accelerated electron	Glycine, alanine

Table 15-8. continued

Compound Class	Reactants	Energy	Products
	CH_4, NH_3, H_2O	Heat (>1123 K)	Amino acids
	CO, H_2, NH_3 (Ni-Fe, Fe_3O_4, Al_2O_3, SiO_2 catalysts)	Heat (750-1000 K)	Amino acids
	HC-CN, HCN, NH_3, H_2O	Heat (373 K)	Aspartic acid
Purine, pyrimidines	HCN, NH_3, H_2O	Heat (373 K)	Adenine
	Malic acid, urea, polyphosphoric acid	Heat (403 K)	Uracil
	CH_3, NH_3, H_2O	Accelerated electron	Adenine
	CO, H_2, NH_3, catalysts	Heat (700-1000 K)	Adenine, guanine
Sugars	HCHO, CH_3CHO; glyceraldehyde, acetaldehyde, $Ca(OH)_2$	Heat (323 K)	2-deoxyribose 2-deoxyxylose
	HCHO	UV	Ribose, deoxyribose
Nucleotides	Adenosine, polyphosphate ester	UV	AMP, ADP, ATP
	Nucleoside, phosphate	Heat (433 K)	Nucleotides
	Nucleosides, polyphosphoric acid	Heat (295 K)	Nucleotides
Hydrocarbons	Methane	Electric discharge	Higher hydrocarbons
	Methane	Heat (1273 K; silica gel)	Higher hydrocarbons
	CO, H_2, catalysts	Heat (750-1000 K)	Linear alkanes
Porphyrins	Pyrrole, benzaldehyde	γ-ray	Tetraphenylporphyrin
	Pyrrole, formaldehyde Ni^{2+}, Cu^{2+}		Porphyrin
	CH_4, NH_3, H_2O	Electric discharge	Porphyrin
	CO, H_2, NH_3, catalysts	Heat (750-1000 K)	Cyclic or linear pyrrole polymers

Source: S.W. Fox, K. Harada, G. Krampitz, and G. Mueller, Chemical origin of cells. *Chem. Eng. News*, June 22, p. 86 (1970).

Formaldehyde and hydrogen cyanide are the two most important reactive compounds in the initial synthesis of biomonomers. Carbohydrates may be regarded as polymers of formaldehyde. In organic compounds, the $-C\equiv N$ group can undergo hydrolysis to produce carboxylic acids and consequently the amino acids. The highly unsaturated triple bonds allow many molecules to have additional reactions with HCN to produce high molecular weight compounds.

After the chemical evolution, the next step in the development of the biosphere is the initiation of the biological evolution, as shown in Figure 15-16. In addition, Figure 15-17 illustrates a diagrammatic representation of a possible scheme of primordial biogenesis. The first living organisms probably grew in shallow bodies of water under anaerobic condition. The stages in evolution of the atmosphere and hydrosphere with evolution of organisms are shown in Figure 15-18.

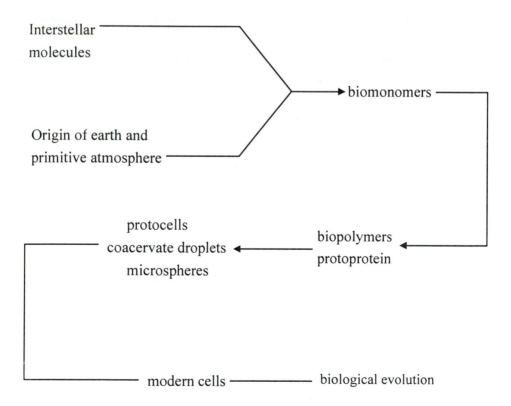

Figure 15-16.   Flow sheet for one view of chemical evolution.

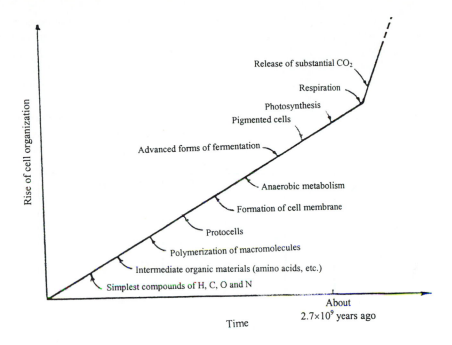

Figure 15-17. Diagrammatic representation of a possible scheme of primordial bio-genesis. This figure is highly over-simplified and is intended only as a convenient means of visualizing the probable sequence of phases in the overall process.

15.3.3   Chemical Autopoiesis

The word **autopoiesis** is derived from the Greek "auto" (self) and "poiesis" (formation) in attempt to define the minimal life. An autopoietic unity is a unity that is self-generating and self-perpetuating as a consequence of its own activities within a boundary of its own making. Both self-replicating reverse micelles and self-replicating vesicles have been studied. It is possible through the studies of membrane-mimetic chemistry to mimic cellular systems under prebiotic conditions.

A hypothetical model of the origin of life is depicted in Figure 15-19. Using clay as an example in a stream, there are four particular distinct patterns that have printed themselves many times to create four regions in which the physical consistency of the clays is different. The so-called sloppy, sticky, lumpy, and tough characteristics will represent the disorder to be ordered gradually as the water flows. Recently biomolecules can be synthesized, which indicates definitely their self-replicating capabilities and mutant properties.

The pattern of molecular association and assemblage will yield specific functions in a number of geometric arrangements (tessellation), as seen in Figure 15-19.

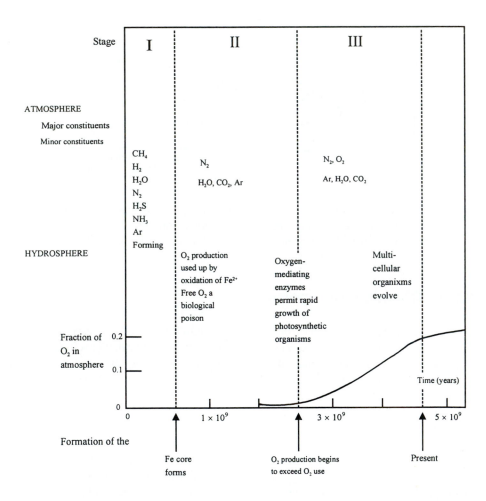

Figure 15-18.   Stages in the evolution of the atmosphere and hydrosphere. (Source: J.W. Moore and E.A. Moore, 1976.)

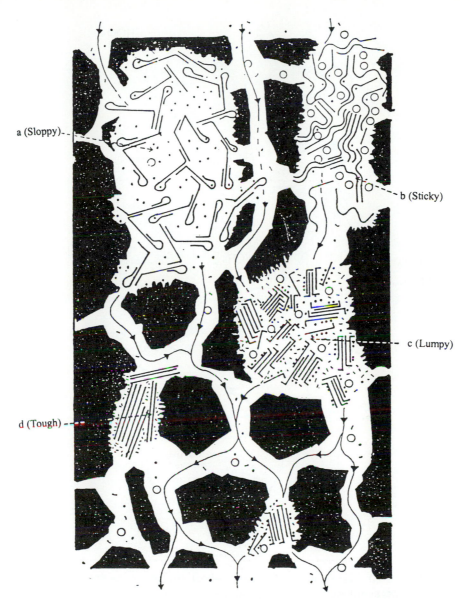

a (Sloppy)

b (Sticky)

c (Lumpy)

d (Tough)

Figure 15-19. A hypothetical 'origin of life.' We imagine clay platelets forming replicatively from solutions flowing through porous rock and sand. Different substitution patterns give clays that have different folding habits and which stick to each other in different ways: They also adsorb and entrain different proportions of molecules in the environment. Thus, some patterns survive and replicate more effectively than others. (Redrawn after A.G. Cairns-Smith, the life puzzle, University of Toronto press, 1971.)

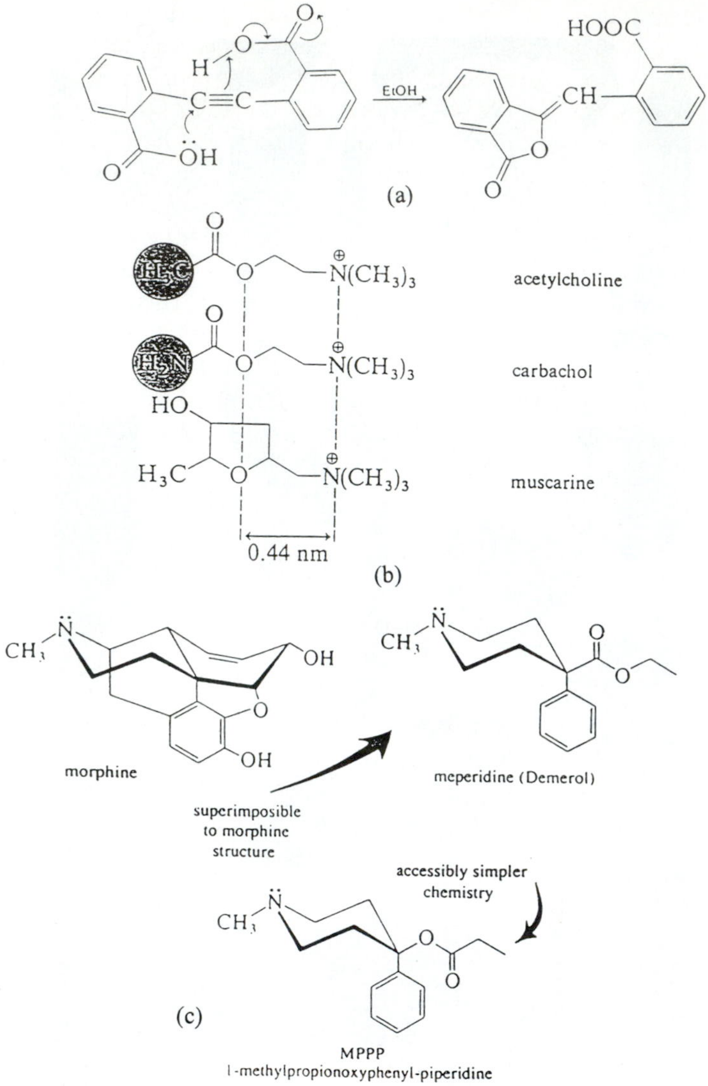

(a)

acetylcholine

carbachol

muscarine

0.44 nm

(b)

morphine

meperidine (Demerol)

superimposible
to morphine
structure

accessibly simpler
chemistry

(c)

MPPP
1-methylpropionoxyphenyl-piperidine

Figure 15-20.   (a) Example of proximity effect; (b) Difference between two neurotransmitters and muscarine; and (c) MPPP.

A few simple principles of bioorganic chemistry should be reviewed here as the molecular basis of autopoiesis: (1) proximity effect, (2) molecular adaptation, and (3) molecular
recognition at a super molecular level. An example of the proximity effect is that 2,2'-tolane-
carboxylic acid in ethanol is converted with ease to 3-(2-carboxy-benzilidene)phthalate, as
shown in Figure 15-20. In contrast the corresponding reaction of 2-tolanecarboxylic or 2,4'-

tolanecarboxylic is 10^4 slower. Therefore, the 2,2'-position must participate in the transition state. This type of complementary bifunctional catalysis is a simple model for enzyme activity. Molecular adaptation can be illustrated with pharmacological activities. For example, the difference between two neurotransmitters and the mushroom poison, muscarine (in *Amanita muscaria*), is such that the biostatic equivalence is clear (unblocked) or blocked by competition, as shown in Figure 15-20. Another example of molecular adaptation is the analgesic properties of morphine, demerol, and MPPP (Figure 13-27). Actually, MPPP can be hydrolyzed to MPTP (similar to herbicide; see Figure 15-20), which can become MPPT, a neurotoxic pyridine metabolite that can cause Parkinson's disease. Molecular recognition in the sensory response can be illustrated by the optical isomerism. For example, the L-L isomer, aspartame, is 200x sweeter than sugar, and the corresponding L-D isomer is bitter. Another example is P-4000, in that a slight change from NH_2- to NO_2- groups will switch the quality from extremely sweet to extremely bitter, as shown in Figure 15-21. To summarize, no matter whether the formations involved are recognition (receptor), or release and transport (transporter), or molecular catalysis (catalyst), these functional approaches to the formation of supermolecular devices that can aid the organized assemblies are most helpful, as shown in Figure 15-22.

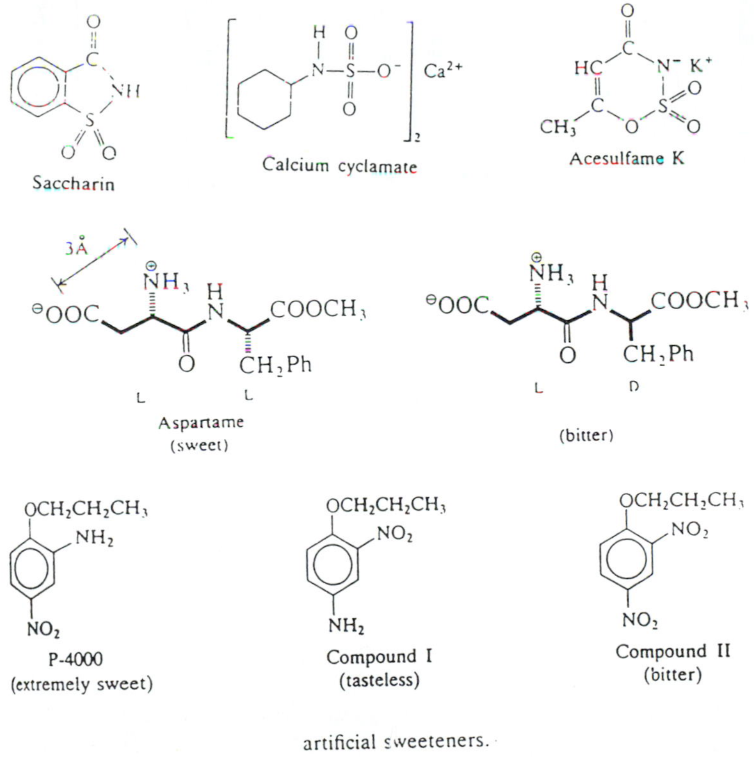

Figure 15-21. Artificial sweeteners.

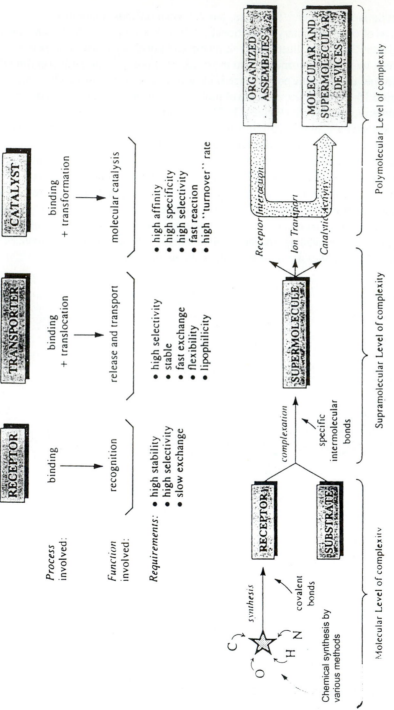

Figure 15-22.   From atoms to molecules to supramolecules. (Adapted from Dugas.)

15.4 ENVIRONMENTAL GEOCHEMISTRY

As mentioned, the planets and the sun in the solar system started with the same initial chemical composition. However, the current composition of the earth's crust varies considerably from that estimated for the universe as a whole. The deficiency factor, the logarithm of the ratio of cosmic abundance/terrestrial abundance, commonly serves as an indicator. The values of the deficiency factor for H and He are 6.6 and 14.2, respectively, meaning that the universe has a much higher concentration of these two elements than the earth. Similarly, many volatile, inert elements such as N_2 and the noble gases have escaped from the earth. From the kinetic theory of gases, the average molecular speed at a given temperature T is $(3RT/M)^{1/2}$, where M = molecular weight. To escape the gravitational field of the earth, a particle's vertical velocity must exceed

$$V_{escape} = (2GM_b/r)^{1/2}$$

where
G (= 6.672×10^{-11} $m^3s^{-2}kg^{-1}$) is the gravitational constant
M_b = mass of the earth (6.0×10^{24} Kg)
r = radius of the earth (6.4×10^6 m).

It was found from detailed calculations that only those gases with an average molecular speed less than one-fifth of the escape velocity are expected to remain on the earth over the billions of years.

During the formation of the earth, most of the oxygen was present as oxides and sulfur was in the form of sulfides. Of the dozen or so compounds, metals including iron were present in an excess over oxygen and sulfur, and they remained in a molten, metallic phase. Because of its greater density, iron associated with other metals and migrated toward the center of the earth, while the less denser silicates, oxides, and sulfides floated to the surface. As a result, the three main structural components of the earth — core, mantle, and crust, — were formed.

The formation of the earth and the loss of gaseous elements are essential and a brief outline is listed here:

- Formation of Earth

α-β-γ theory, this theory is named after the 3 physicists, Alpher, Bethe, and Gamow. Actually, the theory represents α-recombination and β-emission accompanied by γ-emission (isomerization). Thus, successively through neutron capture to build up heavy elements, planets, asteroids, and meteorites originated from an interstellar cloud.

- Loss of Gaseous Elements

deficiency factor of elements = log(cosmic abundance)/(territorial abundance) e.g., $H = 6.6$

$He = 14.2$

Average Molecular Speed $= (3RT/M)^{1/2}$

$V_{escape} = (2GM_b/r)^{1/2}$

G = gravitational constant = 6.67×10^{-11} m^3/s^2/kg

M_b = mass of body where gravitational field is to escape = 6.0×10^{24} kg

$r = 6.4 \times 10^6$ M (surface to center of body)

$$A.M.S. < 1/5 \ V_{escape}$$

- <u>Remaining Elements</u>

Ne, He — most deficient

H, N — next deficient

C in CH$_4$, CO, CO$_2$ — intermediate

Mg, Al, Si, Fe close to cosmos

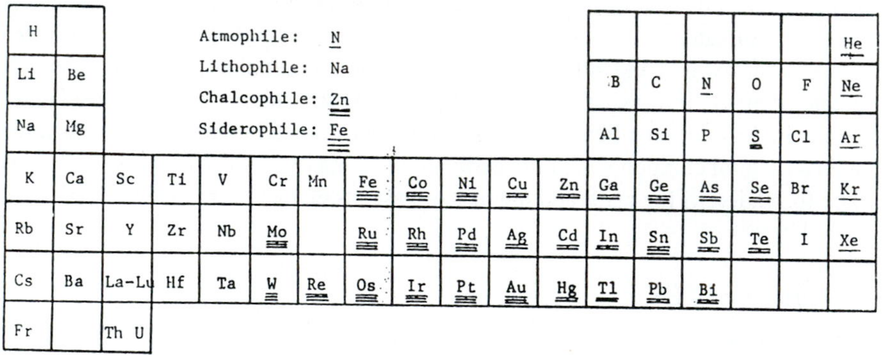

Figure 15-23.   The geochemical classification of elements in relation to the periodic system. (Source: B. Mason. *Principles of Geochemistry*. 3rd ed. Wiley, New York, 1966.) Only the most characteristic geochemical property is indicated in the case of elements that display more than one type of behavior.

Goldschmidt classified the metal elements according to their preference to (1) Sidero-phile — dissolve in the core of the iron, (2) Charcophile — be in the crustal phases with sulfide as major anionic constituents, (3) Lithophile — be in the oxide and silicate lattices of the mantle and crust, and (4) Atmophile — gaseous component, shown in Table 15-9. The relationship between Goldschmidt's geochemical classification and periodic table is shown in Figure 15-23. In general, the metallic lithophiles are more readily oxidized; that is, they have more negative reduction potentials than iron, as shown in Table 15-10. Their presence in the oxide phase resulted from the inability of metallic iron to replace them from their compounds.

Table 15-9. Goldschmidt's Geochemical Classification of the Elements

Term	Characteristic Property	Elements Included [*]
Siderophile	Association with metallic iron	Fe, Co, Ni, Ru, Rh, Pd, Os, Ir, Pt, Mo, W, Re, Au, Ge, Sn, C, P, (Pb, As, S)
Chalcophile	Tendency to form sulfide minerals	Cu, Ag, Zn, Cd, Hg, Ga, In, Tl, (Ge, Sn,), Pb, As, Sb, Bi, S, Se, Te, (Fe, Mo, Cr)
Lithophile	Tendency to be bound to oxide ions	Li, Na, K, Rb, Cs, Be, Mg, Ca, Sr, Ba, B, Al, Sc, Y, Rare Earths, (C), Si, Ti, Zr, Hf, Th, (P), V, Nb, Ta, Cr, (W), U, F, Cl, Br, I, Mn, (H, Tl, Ga, Ge, Fe)
Atmophile	Tendency to occur as a gaseous component of the atmosphere	N, He, Ne, Ar, Kr, Xe

[*] Elements in parentheses show the indicated characteristic to a lessen extent.

Source: B. Mason. *Principles of Geochemistry*, 3rd Ed. Wiley, New York, 1966; L.H. Ahrens, *Distribution of the Elements in Our Planet*. McGraw-Hill, New York, 1965

The lithophiles tend to be bound to oxide ions and form three-dimensional arrays. Four basic rules govern the formation of stable ionic lattices:

- The principle of hard and soft acids and bases applies; that is, hard acids prefer to bond to hard bases, and soft acids prefer soft bases. Hard acids and bases are small and not polarizable, while soft acids and bases have large radii and are easily polarized. Because O^- is a hard base, hard cations (such as $Ca^+ +$ and Rb^+) will be preferred and soft cations (such as $Cu^+ +$ and Ag^+) will scarcely be found.

- The smaller ions will form stronger bonds.

- If the two cations have nearly the same radius, the one with the greater charge will form a more stable lattice.

- When substitutions of ions having different charges (isomorphous substitution) are made, electroneutrality must be maintained.

After the earth's core, mantle, and crust differentiated themselves, a variety of processes acted to transform the igneous rock. In some cases, these processes have served to concentrate compounds to favorable deposits; thus, the ores. The processes of metamorphosis, weathering, hydrothermal transport, and sedimentation have all contributed to ore formation. **Metamorphosis** refers to changes induced in crustal rock adjacent to a molten magma. For example, iron (II) oxide can be oxidized in the presence of carbonate minerals to form magnetite, an important iron ore. Most ores of chalcophiles (such as Zn, Cu, Pb, Hg, and Ag) are formed through the hydrothermal transport process, using ZnS as an example,

$$ZnS + 2\ HCl = ZnCl_2 + H_2S$$

Because $ZnCl_2$ is volatile and water soluble, the hydrothermal transport process allows it to be transported for some distance before the gas is cooled or the acid is neutralized by some relatively basic rock, where ZnS is precipitated. Weathering can wash off soluble minerals and leave insoluble ones. Bauxite, the main source of aluminum, is commonly found in tropical regions where high rainfall prevails. In the oceans, sedimentation of low solubility minerals is also a concentration process.

Table 15-10.   Electrode Potential and Solubilities of Selected Elements Related to Geochemical Classification

Element	Reduction Potential	Solubility of Sulfide in H_2O (M)
		Lithophiles
Li/Li$^+$	−3.045	Soluble
Ca/Ca^{2+}	−2.866	—
Al/Al^{3+}	−1.662	Hydroxide precipitates more readily than sulfide
Cr/Cr^{3+}	−0.774	Hydroxide precipitates more readily than sulfide
		Chalcophiles
Zn/Zn^{2+}	−0.7628	1.58×10^{-11}
Ga/Ga^{3+} (borderline lithophile)	−0.529	—
Cu/Cu^{2+}	+0.337	8.94×10^{-19}
Ag/Ag$^+$	+0.7991	1.76×10^{-17}
		Siderophiles
Fe/Fe^{2+}	−0.429	6.32×10^{-10}
Ni/Ni^{2+}	−0.250	5.48×10^{-11}
Sn/Sn^{2+}	−0.136	1.00×10^{-13}
Rh/Rh^{3+}	+0.80	—
Pd/Pd^{2+}	+0.987	—
Au/Au$^+$	+1.691	—

The outline that follows summarizes this section.

- Primary Differentiation of Elements

3-layer cake   crust - mantle - core
Fe has a greater density - sinks
less dense metal Ni, Au, Pt - along the way
less dense - float on surface
metal carbides, oxides, sulfides

- Secondary Differentiation of Elements

Isomorphous substitutes - close pack lattice
Silicates and oxides
1) hard acid or base (small radius) as stable
2) if same, greater charge is more stable

- Concentration of Elements

1) segregation of molten magma
2) metamorphosis $CO_2 + 3FeO \rightarrow Fe_3O_4(ore) + CO$
3) weathering
4) hydrothermal transport

$$ZnS + 2HCl = ZnCl_2 + H_2S \text{ (more soluble in water)}$$

5) sedimentation

$$PO_4^{-3} + Ca^{2+} \rightarrow Ca_5(PO_4)_3OH\downarrow$$

15.4.1 Geochemical Biomarkers

There are molecules originating from the biosphere that are relatively stable toward biodegradation (refractoric) and can survive in geological time spans. These molecules can behave as tracers or indicators of a given geological age. Another term is **molecular fossils** because they can be relatively isolated or determined in a complex environment. We will discuss two types of biomarkers: the **porphyrins**, and the **terpenoids**. The first type is the pigments used widely by organisms for energy transport; for example, chlorophyll a or heme (cytochrome). The second type includes isoprenoids (C_5), monoterpenes (C_{10}), sesquiterpenes (C_{15}), diterpenes (C_{20}), sesterterpenes (C_{25}), triterpenes (C_{30}), and tetraterpenes (C_{40}). For the first type, the metalloporphyrins are extremely stable; for example, vanadyl porphyrin can be found in the Nonesuch formation of the PreCambrian era. The geochemical transformation from chlorophyll a to such geoporphyrins is illustrated by Figure 15-24. For the second type, the isoprene units are originated from energy storage; for example, the isopentenyl pyrophosphate and dimethylallyl pyrophosphate can be easily compiled or aggregated through either head-to-head or head-to-tail orientation in straight chains or in a cyclic fashion.

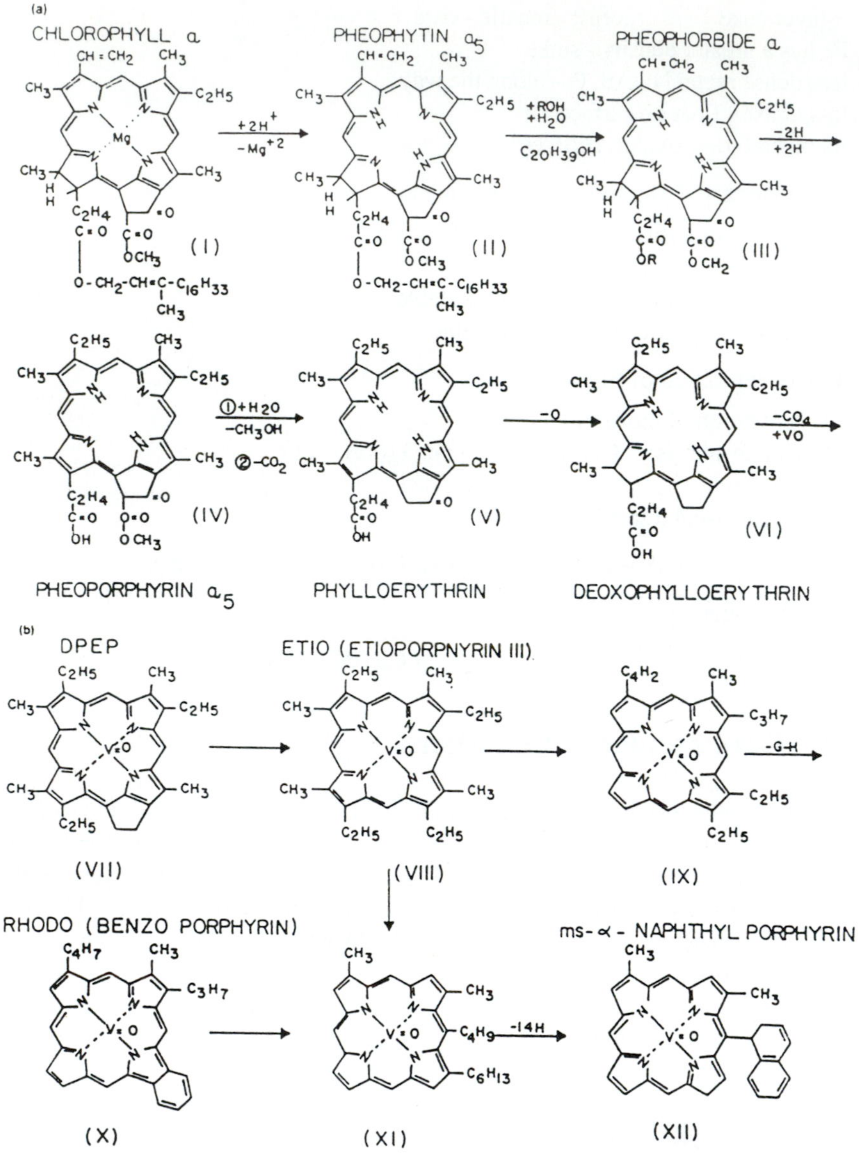

Figure 15-24.   Proposed geochemical transformation of chlorophyll to vanadyl DPEP and other stable vanadyl chelates. (a) Chlorophyll to dexophylloerythin. (b) DPEP to ms-α-naphthyl porphyrin. (Source: T. F. Yen and G.V. Chilingarian, 1994.)

Terpenes, I_i (j),

$$I_i = A, B \ldots$$
$$j = 1, 2 \ldots 5$$

(i=2, AB; i=3, ABC; i=8, A ... H)

(1 and 5 are equivalent)

i = 1, isoprene

$$\overset{5}{\underset{1\ 2\ 3\ 4}{C}}\!-\!C\!-\!C\!-\!C$$

i = 2, monoterpene

(i) $A(1-4)B$ myrcene

(ii) $A\binom{4-3}{1-4}B$ menthol

(iii) $A\binom{2-4}{4-3}B$ thujone
       $\binom{1-4}{}$

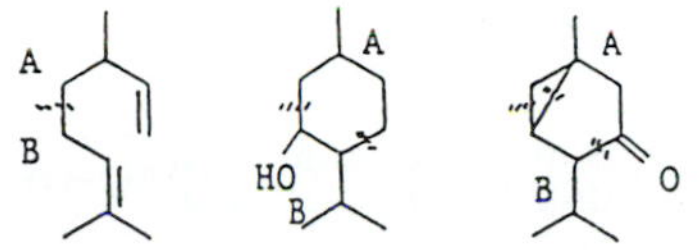

i = 3, sesquiterpene

$A\binom{3-4}{4-1}B\binom{3-4}{4-1}C$ Bulgarene

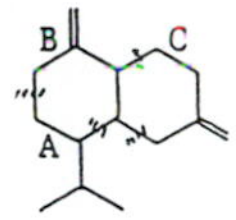

i = 4, diterpenes

(i) $A(4-1)B(4-1)C(4-1)D$ phytane

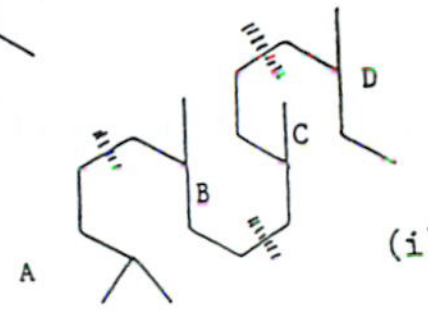

(ii) $A\binom{2-3}{4-1}B\binom{2-3}{4-1}C\binom{5-3}{4-4}D$ Abietane

(iii) $A\binom{1-3}{4-1}B\binom{2-3}{4-1}C\binom{2-1}{4-4}D$ Kawane
      $\binom{}{5-3}$

i = 5, sesterterpene

$A(4-1)B\binom{4-4}{3-2}C\binom{3-3}{1-1}D(4-1)E(4-3)C$

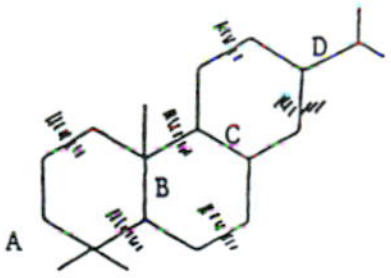

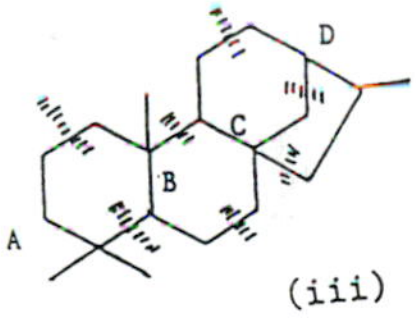

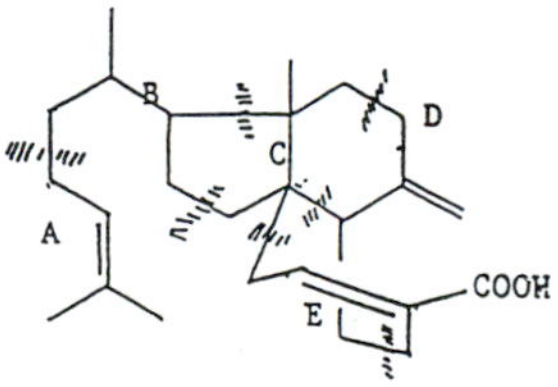

Gascardic acid

Figure 15-25.   Generalized terpenoid structure. (Source: T. F. Yen, Y. Li, and M. C. Liu, Geochem. Div., ACS, 1990.)

i = 6, triterpenes

A(4-1)B(4-1)C(4-4)D(1-4)E(1-4)F   squalene

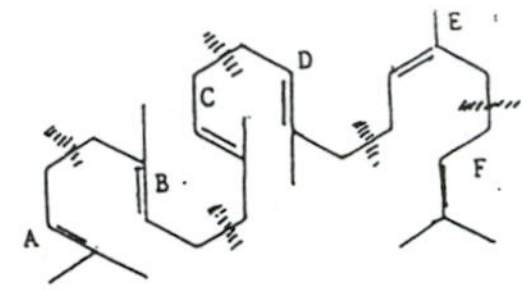

$A\binom{4-1}{2-3} B\binom{4-1}{2-3} C\binom{4-1}{2-3} D\binom{4-4}{2-3} E(1-4)F - A(1) - A(5) - C(5)$

cholesterol

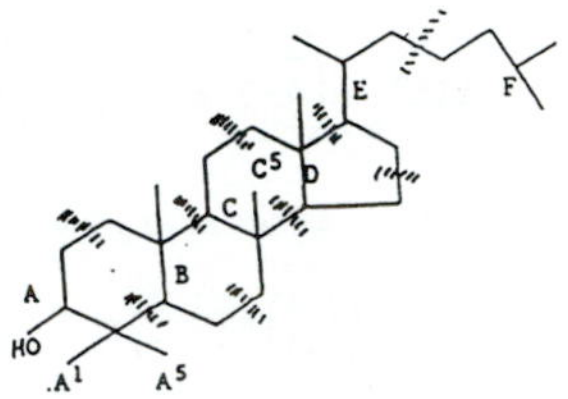

$A\binom{4-1}{2-3} B\binom{4-1}{2-3} C\binom{4-4}{2-2} D\binom{3-2}{1-4} E\binom{3-3}{1-4} F$ hopane

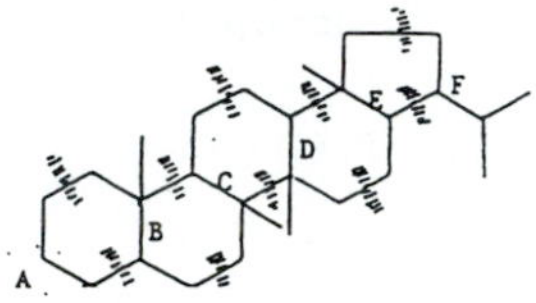

i = 8, tetraterpene

A(4-1)B(4-1)C(4-1)D(4-4)E(1-4)F(1-4)G(1-4)H

lycopene

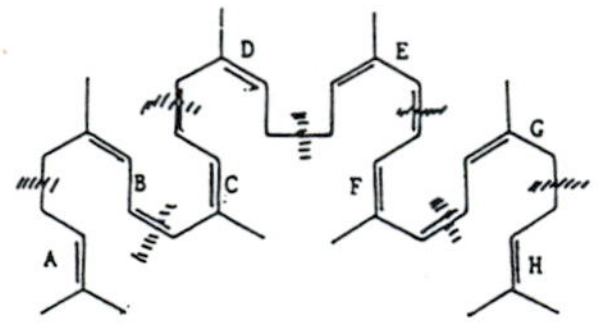

$A\binom{4-1}{2-3} B(4-1)C(4-1)D(4-4)E(1-4)F(1-4)G\binom{3-2}{1-4}H$

β-carotene

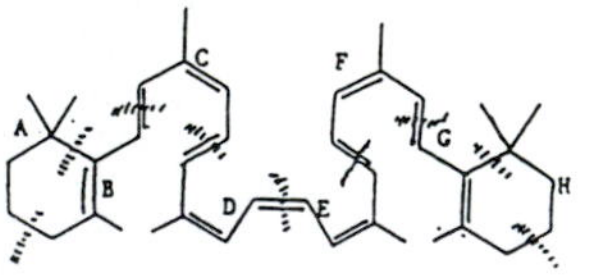

Figure 15-25.   Generalized terpenoid structure. (*continued*)

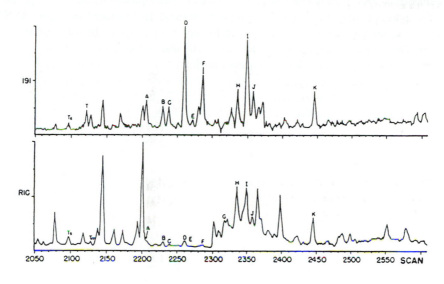

Compound	Name	M.W.	Identification
$C_{27}H_{46}$	18α(H)-22,29,30-trisnorhopane	370	Ts
$C_{27}H_{46}$	17α(H)-22,29,30-trisnormeohopane	370	Tm
$C_{29}H_{50}$	17α(H),21β(H)-30-norhopane	398	A
$C_{30}H_{50}$	hop-17(21)-ene	410	B
$C_{29}H_{50}$	17β(H),21α(H)-normoretane	398	C
$C_{30}H_{52}$	17α(H),21β(H)-hopane	412	D
$C_{30}H_{52}$	unknown C_{30} triterpane	412	E
$C_{30}H_{52}$	17β(H),21α(H)-moretane	412	F
$C_{31}H_{54}$	22S-17α(H),21ε(H)-30 homohopane	426	G
$C_{31}H_{54}$	22R -17α(H),21β(H)-30 homohopane	426	H
$C_{30}H_{52}$	gammacerane	412	I
$C_{30}H_{52}$	17β(H),21β(H)-hopane	412	J
$C_{30}H_{54}$	17β(H),21α(H)-homomoretane	426	J
$C_{31}H_{54}$	17β(H),21β(H)-30 homohopane	426	K

Figure 15-26.   Spectral records of the triterpanes identified in black trona water. (Source: T.F. Yen and J.M. Moldowan. *Geochemical Biomarkers*, Harwood Academic Pub., 1988, p. 442.)

A system for treating terpene systems has been developed. Using the symbol I (J) for the number of isoprene units (e.g., if I = 2, monoterpenes), I is A, B, C,... indicating the sequence of isoprene units and (J) in which J = 1, 2, ...5 (1 and 5 are equivalent) shows the positions of where the isoprene units are coupled. A detailed method is illustrated in Figure 15-25. In practice, the diterpenes and the triterpenes are frequently employed. In many cases, the nor-series (meaning one carbon less) or derivatives of –OH and –COOH are involved.

Geochemical biomarkers have been used in characterization of nature waters, e.g., black trona water in the northern Green River Basin. Both pentacyclic triterpenoids and steranes have been isolated, as shown in Figures 15-26 and 15-27. In this case, the tri- and tetracyclic terpanes have also been identified, as shown in Figure 15-28.

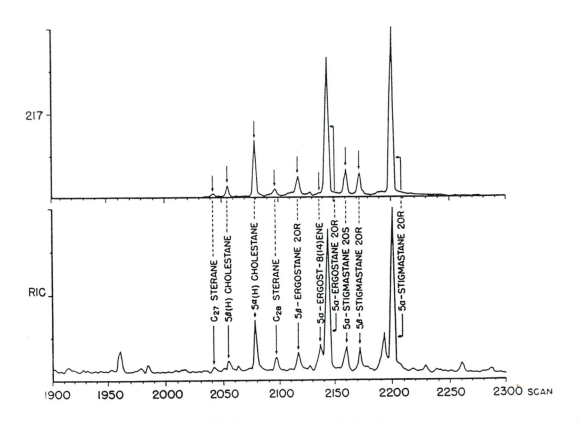

Figure 15-27.   Distribution pattern of steranes (m/z at 217) with the compounds identified (Source: T. F. Yen and J.M. Moldowan, 1988).

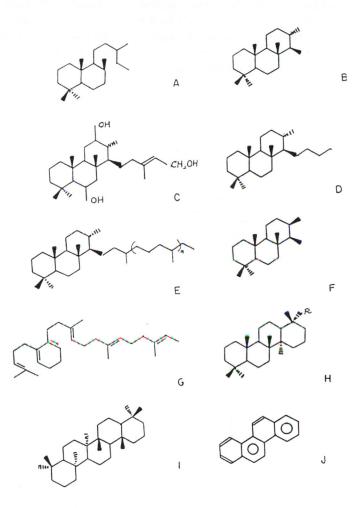

Figure 15-28. Tri- and Tetracyclic terpanes and related compounds. (a) labden C_{20}; (b) C_{20} Tricyclic diterpane, (b) can be found through (a); (c) cheilanthatriol; (d) cheilanthane found as 18, 19-bisnor 13 β (H). 14α(H) cheilanthane; (e) C_{30} tricyclic triterpane (n=1), C_{40} tricyclic tetraterpane (n=3), when n=4 a C_{45} tricyclic terpane is obtained; (f) isocopa-lane; (g) an hexaisoprenoid; (h) tetracyclic terpanes, R = H, C_{24} 17, 21-secohopane; (i) gamacerane; (j) chrysene. (Source: Wang, Y., Wang, L.S. and Yen, T. F., 1988.)

15.4.2   Long-Range Geochemical Cycles

The dynamic nature of the common geochemical processes is universally important in dealing with global kinetics. The long-range carbon cycle based on Holland, as shown in Figure 15-29 is illustrated here. There are a total of nine reservoirs whose contents and fluxes are in units of PgC and PgC/yr, respectively. For simplicity of the kinetic treatment of multiple reservoirs, we will limit our calculation to two, A_1 and A_2, as shown in the scheme that follows the treatment formulated by Lasaga.

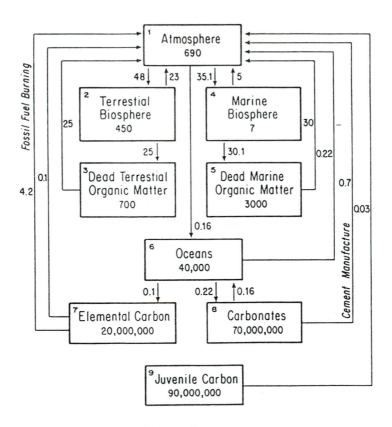

Figure 15-29.   The long-term carbon cycle. (Modified from Holland, 1978.) The reservoir contents of PgC and the fluxes in units of PgC/yr.

where A_i is reservoir contents (a particular element in reservoir i) and k_{ij} is the rate constants of first order. Flow can be expressed as $K_{ij}A_i$. We can write the simple rate equations

$$\frac{dA_1}{dt} = -k_{12}\,A_1 + k_{21}\,A_2 \qquad\qquad [15\text{-}8]$$

$$\frac{dA_2}{dt} = k_{12}\,A_1 - k_{21}\,A_2 \qquad\qquad [15\text{-}9]$$

or in matrix form

$$\frac{d}{dt}\begin{pmatrix} A_1 \\ A_2 \end{pmatrix} = \begin{vmatrix} -k_{12} & k_{21} \\ k_{12} & -k_{21} \end{vmatrix}\begin{pmatrix} A_1 \\ A_2 \end{pmatrix} \qquad\qquad [15\text{-}10]$$

The solution of Equation [15-10] takes the form

$$A(t) = a_1 e^{E_1 t}\psi_1 + a_2 e^{E_2 t}\psi_2 \qquad\qquad [15\text{-}11]$$

where E_1 and E_2 are the eigenvalues and ψ_1, ψ_2 are the eigenvectors of the matrix K defined by

$$K = \begin{vmatrix} -k_{12} & k_{21} \\ k_{12} & -k_{21} \end{vmatrix} \qquad\qquad [15\text{-}12a]$$

To obtain the eigenvalues of K, we solve the determinantal equation

$$\begin{vmatrix} -k_{12}-E & k_{21} \\ k_{12} & -k_{21}-E \end{vmatrix} = 0 \quad\text{or}\quad (k_{12}+E)(k_{21}+E) - k_{12}\,k_{21} = 0 \qquad\qquad [15\text{-}12b]$$

The solution to this quadratic in E is

$$E_1 = 0 \qquad\qquad E_2 = -(k_{12} + k_{21}) \qquad\qquad [15\text{-}13]$$

To obtain the eigenvectors, we must solve the equation

$$K\,\psi_i = E_i\,\psi_i \qquad\qquad [15\text{-}13a]$$

or

$$\begin{vmatrix} -k12 & k21 \\ k12 & -k21 \end{vmatrix} \begin{pmatrix} a \\ b \end{pmatrix} = E \begin{pmatrix} a \\ b \end{pmatrix}$$

[15-13B]

If $E = 0$, then

$$\begin{vmatrix} -k_{12} & k_{21} \\ k_{12} & -k_{21} \end{vmatrix} \begin{pmatrix} a \\ b \end{pmatrix} = 0$$

[5-13c]

or

$$-k_{12}a + k_{21}b = 0; \ k_{12}a - k_{21}b = 0$$

[15-13d]

Either equation yields

$$b = \frac{k_{12}}{k_{21}} a$$

[15-13e]

because a can be arbitrary, we can set $a = 1$, as follows:

$$\psi_1 = \begin{pmatrix} 1 \\ \dfrac{k_{12}}{k_{21}} \end{pmatrix}$$

[15-13f]

Likewise, to find ψ_2, we must solve for $K \ \psi_2 = E_2 \ \psi_2$

$$\begin{vmatrix} -k_{12} & k_{21} \\ k_{12} & -k_{21} \end{vmatrix} \begin{pmatrix} a \\ b \end{pmatrix} = -(k_{12} + k_{21}) \begin{pmatrix} a \\ b \end{pmatrix}$$

[15-13g]

or

$$-k_{12}a + k_{21}b = -(k_{12} + k_{21})a; \ k_{12}a - k_{21}b = -(k_{12} + k_{21})b$$

[15-13h]

These equations reduce to $a = -b$. Hence, setting $a = 1$ once more

$$\psi_2 = \begin{pmatrix} 1 \\ -1 \end{pmatrix}$$

[15-13i]

Having obtained the eigenvalues and eigenvectors of K, the general solution, Equation [15-11] becomes

$$A(t) = \begin{pmatrix} A_1(t) \\ A_2(t) \end{pmatrix} = a_1 \exp(0 \cdot t) \begin{pmatrix} 1 \\ \dfrac{k_{12}}{k_{21}} \end{pmatrix} + a_2\, e^{-(k_{12}+k_{21})t} \begin{pmatrix} 1 \\ -1 \end{pmatrix} \qquad [15\text{-}14]$$

To obtain the coefficients a_1 and a_2, we need the initial condition of our cycle; that is, A_1^0 and A_2^0. From Equation [15-14] it follows that, setting $t = 0$,

$$A_1^0 = a_1 + a_2 \; ; \; A_2^0 = \frac{k_{12}}{k_{21}} a_1 - a_2 \qquad [15\text{-}15a]$$

Equation [15-14] also can be expressed as

$$A^0 = \psi a \qquad [15\text{-}15b]$$

where the ψ matrix is comprised of the eigenvectors ψ_1 and ψ_2

$$\psi = \begin{vmatrix} 1 & 1 \\ \dfrac{k_{12}}{k_{21}} & -1 \end{vmatrix} \qquad [15\text{-}15c]$$

The solution to Equation [15-15A] is

$$a_1 = \frac{k_{21}\left(A_1^0 + A_2^0\right)}{k_{12} + k_{21}} \; ; \; a_2 = \frac{k_{12}\,A_1^0 - k_{21}\,A_2^0}{k_{12} + k_{21}} \qquad [15\text{-}16a]$$

or

$$a = \psi^{-1} A^0 \qquad [15\text{-}16b]$$

where the inverse of the matrix in Equation [15-15c] is

$$\psi^{-1} = \frac{1}{k_{12} + k_{21}} \begin{vmatrix} k_{21} & k_{21} \\ k_{12} & -k_{21} \end{vmatrix} \qquad [15\text{-}16c]$$

Combining Equations [15-14] and [15-16a], we have the final equations

$$A_1(t) = \frac{k_{21}(A_1^0 + A_2^0)}{k_{12} + k_{21}} + \frac{k_{12}(A_1^0 - k_{21} A_2^0)}{k_{12} + k_{21}} \exp[-(k_{12} + k_{21})t] \qquad [15\text{-}17A]$$

$$A_2(t) = \frac{k_{12}(A_1^0 + A_2^0)}{k_{12} + k_{21}} - \frac{k_{12}(A_1^0 - k_{21} A_2^0)}{k_{12} + k_{21}} \exp[-(k_{12} + k_{21})t] \qquad [15\text{-}17B]$$

Notice there is only one zero eigenvalue signifying that the cycles will return to a unique steady state. Also, the none-zero eigenvalue of the #2 reservoir cycle is $-(k_{12} + k_{21})$, a negative eigenvalue is required for the cycle to be stable. Furthermore, the response time of the cycle can be obtained from the exponential term of Equation [15-17].

$$\tau_{response} = \frac{1}{k_{12} + k_{21}} \qquad [15\text{-}18]$$

The residence time of our element (at steady state) in reservoirs one (1) and two (2) are given by

$$\tau_{residence}^{(1)} = \frac{A_1^{steady}}{(dA/dt)_{input}} = \frac{A_1^{steady}}{(dA/dt)_{output}} = \frac{A_1^{steady}}{k_{12} A_1^{steady}} \qquad [15\text{-}19]$$

Thus

$$\tau_{residence}^{(1)} = \frac{1}{k_{12}} \qquad [15\text{-}20A]$$

$$\tau_{residence}^{(1)} = \frac{1}{k_{21}} \qquad [15\text{-}20B]$$

Now we will turn our attention to the #9 reservoir of the Holland's model in Figure 15-29. Reservoirs 1–5 represent the interactions between the atmosphere and the biosphere; because carbon cycles are much faster in these reservoirs, they comprise the short-term carbon cycle. The long-term cycle involves important additional processes. These processes include the burial of a small fraction (<0.01%) of the dead marine organic matter, which escapes oxidation to CO_2 in the water column and is incorporated into sediments. It is this small fraction that is responsible for the net supply of oxygen to the atmosphere. The other major geochemical process in the long-term cycle is the weathering of carbonates and silicates in ancient sediments and the deposition of authigenic carbonates and silicates in new sediments. CO_2 is the weathering agent in the crust. For example, carbonates weather according to the reaction

$$CaCO_3(s) + CO_2(g) + H_2O \leftrightarrow Ca^{2+} + 2HCO_3^-$$
(calcite)

For each mole of calcite dissolved, one mole of CO_2 is consumed from the atmosphere. The reverse holds during the deposition of carbonates. Likewise, the dissolution and deposition of Mg-, Na-, and K-silicates follow reactions similar to

$$MgSiO_3 + H_2O + 2CO_2 \leftrightarrow Mg^{2+} + H_4SiO_4 + 2HCO_3^-$$

The carbonate reactions are more important than the silicate reactions in the long-term carbon cycle.

Figure 15-29 also includes the oxidation of elemental carbon (7→1 flux) in ancient sediments. It also gives the anthropogenic contributions from fossil fuel combustion and cement manufacturing. The juvenile carbon reservoirs are planned for balancing the fluxes only.

Table 15-11.   Long-Term Carbon Cycle. Nonzero Rate Constants (in yr⁻¹)

$k_{12}= 6.9565 \times 10^{-2}$	$k_{14}= 5.0870 \times 10^{-2}$	$k_{16}= 2.3188 \times 10^{-4}$
$k_{21}= 5.1111 \times 10^{-2}$	$k_{23}= 5.5556 \times 10^{-2}$	$k_{31}= 3.5714 \times 10^{-2}$
$k_{41}= 7.1429 \times 10^{-1}$	$k_{45}= 4.300$	
$k_{51}= 1.0 \times 10^{-2}$	$k_{56}= 3.3333 \times 10^{-5}$	
$k_{61}= 5.50 \times 10^{-6}$	$k_{67}= 2.500 \times 10^{-6}$	$k_{68}= 5.50 \times 10^{-6}$
$k_{71}= 5.000 \times 10^{-9}$	$k_{86}= 2.2857 \times 10^{-9}$	$k_{91}= 3.333 \times 10^{-10}$

Source: Lasaga, 1981, with the permission from Mineralogical Society of America.

Using linear approximation and ignoring the anthropogenic sources, the rate constants, as listed in Table 15-11 for the carbon cycle in Figure 15-29, are obtained. Next, we diagonalize the resulting k matrix as Equation [15-12a] for the first eight reservoirs (the 9→1 flux is ignored), and the resulting eigenvalues of E are listed in Table 15-12. The resulting eigenvectors are also listed in Table 15-12. Assuming A0 vector are the initial reservoir contents, then a vector can be obtained by Equation [15-16b] or

$$A(t) = -1.5780 \times 10^{-4} \psi_1 e^{E_1 t} - 0.3848 \psi_2 e^{E_2 t} + 0.6637 \psi_3 e^{E_3 t} + 1.2437 \psi_4 e^{E_4 t}$$
$$+ 1452.04 \psi_5 e^{E_5 t} - 8181.80 \psi_6 e^{E_6 t} + 6.3893 \times 10^6 \psi_7 e^{E_7 t} - 7.61157 \times 10^7 \psi_0 e^{E_0 t}$$

[15-20]

Table 15-12.   Long-Term Carbon Cycle

Eigenvalues (yr^{-1})

$E_1 = -5.022$ $E_2 = -1.612 \times 10^{-1}$ $E_3 = -8.488 \times 10^{-2}$

$E_4 = -1.963 \times 10^{-2}$ $E_5 = -5.989 \times 10^{-5}$ $E_6 = -7.157 \times 10^{-6}$

$E_7 = -4.152 \times 10^{-9}$ $E_0 = 0$

Eigenvectors

$$\psi_1 = \begin{bmatrix} 0.10865 \\ -0.15378 \times 10^{-2} \\ 0.17135 \times 10^{-4} \\ -0.75444 \\ 0.64732 \\ -0.93140 \times 10^{-5} \\ 0.46370 \times 10^{-11} \\ 0.10201 \times 10^{-10} \end{bmatrix} \quad \psi_2 = \begin{bmatrix} 0.57395 \\ -0.73223 \\ 0.32419 \\ 0.60161 \times 10^{-2} \\ -0.17114 \\ -0.79032 \times 10^{-3} \\ 0.12257 \times 10^{-7} \\ 0.26966 \times 10^{-7} \end{bmatrix} \quad \psi_3 = \begin{bmatrix} -0.20176 \\ -0.64424 \\ 0.72796 \\ -0.20821 \times 10^{-2} \\ 0.11962 \\ 0.50429 \times 10^{-3} \\ -0.14853 \times 10^{-7} \\ -0.32676 \times 10^{-7} \end{bmatrix}$$

$$\psi_4 = \begin{bmatrix} -0.18228 \\ -0.14568 \\ -0.50307 \\ -0.18565 \times 10^{-2} \\ 0.83215 \\ 0.74080 \times 10^{-3} \\ -0.94364 \times 10^{-7} \\ -0.20760 \times 10^{-6} \end{bmatrix} \quad \psi_5 = \begin{bmatrix} -0.10627 \\ -0.69349 \times 10^{-1} \\ -0.10806 \\ -0.10782 \times 10^{-2} \\ -0.46485 \\ 0.86517 \\ -0.36116 \times 10^{-1} \\ -0.79451 \times 10^{-1} \end{bmatrix} \quad \psi_6 = \begin{bmatrix} -0.1839 \times 10^{-1} \\ -0.83736 \times 10^{-2} \\ -0.13028 \times 10^{-1} \\ -0.13025 \times 10^{-3} \\ -0.55860 \times 10^{-1} \\ -0.76266 \\ 0.26660 \\ 0.58630 \end{bmatrix}$$

$$\psi_7 = \begin{bmatrix} 0.12884 \times 10^{-4} \\ 0.84024 \times 10^{-5} \\ 0.13070 \times 10^{-4} \\ 0.13070 \times 10^{-6} \\ 0.56016 \times 10^{-4} \\ 0.23993 \times 10^{-3} \\ 0.70694 \\ -0.70727 \end{bmatrix} \quad \psi_0 = \begin{bmatrix} -0.86386 \times 10^{-5} \\ -0.56339 \times 10^{-5} \\ -0.87638 \times 10^{-5} \\ -0.87638 \times 10^{-7} \\ -0.37559 \times 10^{-4} \\ -0.40689 \times 10^{-3} \\ -0.20344 \\ -0.97909 \end{bmatrix}$$

From Reviews in Mineralogy, Volume 8, 1981 with the permission of Mineralogical Society of America.

To find the steady state of the carbon cycle, we only need to allow $t \to \infty$ in Equation [15-20], thus

$$A_{\text{steady}} = -7.61157 \times 10^7 \psi_0 \qquad [15\text{-}21]$$

By multiplying the ψ_0 eigenvector as listed in Table 15-12 by -7.61157×10^7, we obtain the steady state of the reservoir content as follows:

A_i^{steady}	in Pg C
A_1	657.5
A_2	428.8
A_3	667.1
A_4	6.67
A_5	2858.9
A_6	30971
A_7	1.5485×10^7
A_8	7.4524×10^7

This type of calculation can be used to assess each reservoir; for example, the atmospheric carbon computed by Lasaga for the connection of anthropogenic influence. Assuming

$$k_{71} = 2.15 \times 10^{-7} \text{ yr}^{-1}$$

$$k_{81} = 1.0 \times 10^{-8} \text{ yr}^{-1} \qquad [15\text{-}22]$$

The new k matrix, E_1 to E_4 remain the same, other eigenvalues are changed $E_5 = -5.988 \times 10^{-5}$ /yr, $E_6 = -7.241 \times 10^{-6}$ /yr, and $E_7 = -1.503 \times 10^{-7}$ /yr. Also assuming that fossil burning is around 500 years, then evalution of CO_2 gas is as follows

$$A_1(t) = -0.0015 \ e^{-5.02t} - 18.253 \ e^{-.0612t} - 11.074 \ e^{9.08488t} - 18.748 \ e^{-001963t}$$
$$- 10377.96 \ e^{5.988 \times 10^{-5}t} - 11508.78 \ e^{-7.241 \times 10^{-6}t} + 16150.79 \ e^{-1.503 \times 10^{-7}t} + 6474.029 \qquad [15\text{-}23]$$

The preceding Equation [15-23] is already corrected with fossil fuel combustion and cement manufacturing.

A plot for atmospheric CO_2 with long-term global cycle is indicated in the upper graph of Figure 15-30 with years expressed in log scale using Equation [15-20]. Notice in this instance that the near term of 100 years does not show any increase of temperature. If the fossil fuel and other chemicals are input, the near-term picture will be changed dramatically. For example there is a constant increase if anthropogenic influence is modified. In the lower graph of Figure 15-30, the Equation [15-23] is used for calculation.

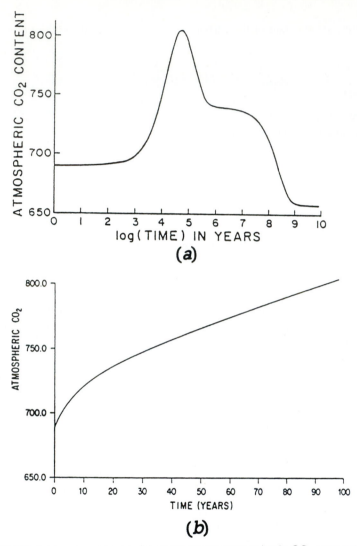

Figure 15-30. (a) Long-range vs. (b) short-range atmospheric CO_2 concentration. (After Lasaga with the permission from Mineralogical Society of America.)

As global warming is a problem for the future, can we, as human ingenuity extends, find another pathway for reduction of the atmospheric carbon? Many versions of carbon cycles illustrate the distribution of carbon in the biosphere with similar features as the Holland version, as shown in Figures 15-31 and 15-32 from Bolin. Because the dominant carbon reservoir is in the sediment, a tremendous amount of which is locked in and is not being circulated, can we explore this resource as a food to relieve the world's hunger problem?

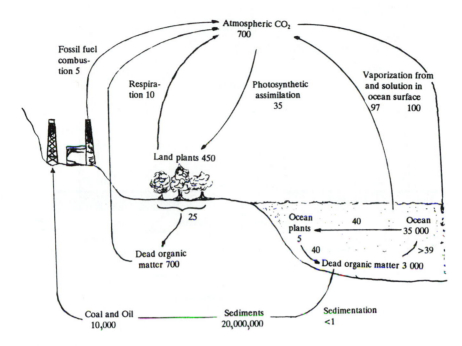

Figure 15-31.   The carbon cycle. Numbers represent quantities of C in various reservoirs or annual flows from one reservoir to another. All are in units of 10 tonne.
Source: B. Bolin, *Sci. Amer.* 223(3), 125–132 (1970)

At the end of this section, let us go back to take a look at the whole biosphere. Actually the biosphere is stratified and is only limited to certain depths in the atmosphere, lithosphere, and hydrosphere, as shown in Figure 15-33. Through biological activity, the plants enrich certain elements such as O, K, and P. The following shows the sequence of abundance of elements in the cosmos in plants:

$$\text{cosmos: } H > He > O > C > K > N > Si > Fe > S > Al > Ca > Na > P > K$$

$$\text{plants: } O > H > C > K > N > Si = Ca > Mg > P > Na > Fe > S$$

In Figure 15-34, the elemental distribution in our blood is very close to that from the granite in the earth. The biosphere is an integral part of the universe and cannot be separated. The lithosphere, hydrosphere, atmosphere, pedosphere, and biosphere are interconnected and unified.

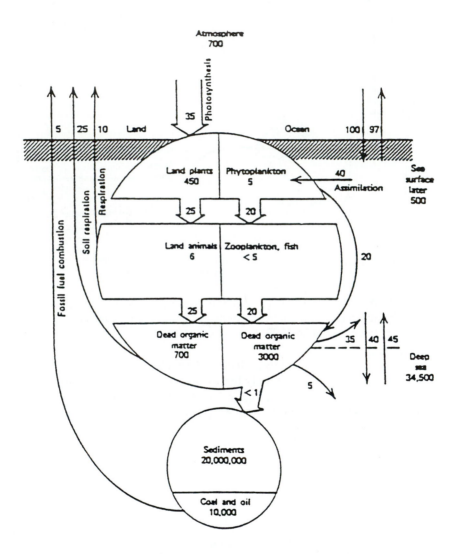

Figure 15-32.   Distribution of carbon. Reservoir numbers are in billions of tons (metric) and flux numbers are in billions of tons per year (values, except for land animals, are from Bolin, 1970).

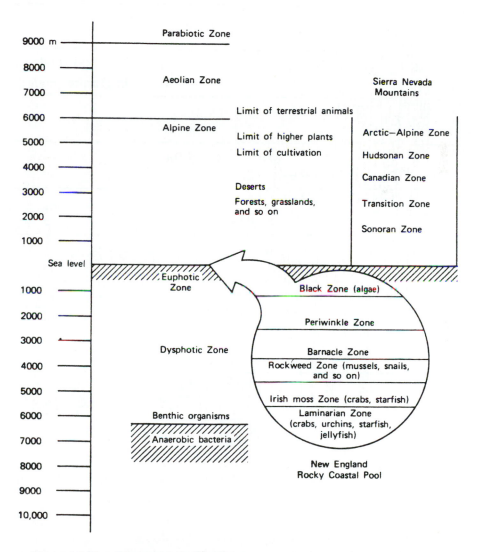

Figure 15-33.   Biosphere stratification.

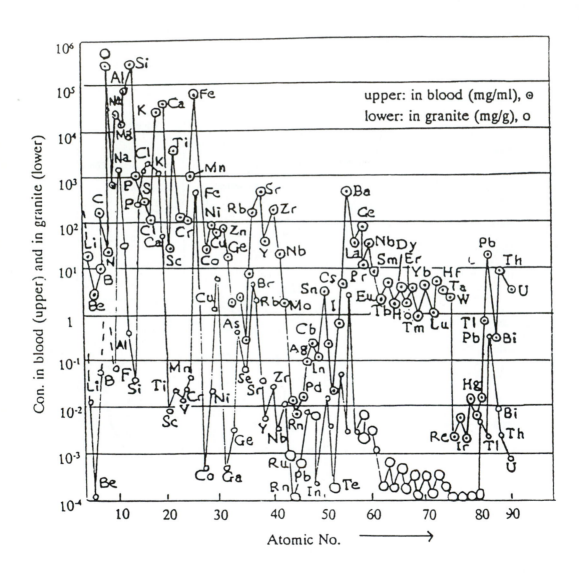

Figure 15-34.   Elemental distribution in biosphere and lithosphere. (Source: T.F. Yen.)

REFERENCES

15-1. A. G. Cairns-Smith, *The Life Puzzle*, University of Toronto Press, Toronto, 1971.

15-2. T. F. Yen, "Terrestrial and Extraterrestrial Stable Organic Molecules," in *Chemistry in Space Research*, (R. F. Landel & A. Rembaum, eds.), American Elsevier, New York, 1972.

15-3. I. Thornton (ed.), *Applied Environmental Geochemistry*, Academic Press, New York, 1983.

15-4. R. Balian, J. Aadouze, and D. N. Schramm (eds.), *Physical Cosmology*, North-Holland, New York, 1980.

15-5. D. H. Kenyon and G. Steinman, *Biochemical Predestination*, McGraw-Hill, New York, 1969.

15-6. R. S. Kandel, *Earth and Cosmos*, Pergamon, New York, 1980.

15-7. A. H. Brownlow, *Geochemistry*, Prentice-Hall, Englewood Cliffs, New Jersey, 1979.

15-8. A. C. Lasaga and R. J. Kirpatrick, *Kinetics of Geochemical Processes*, Mineralogical Society of America, Washington, DC, 1981.

15-9. T. F. Yen and J. M. Moldowan, *Geochemical Biomarkers*, Harwood Academic, Chur, Switzerland, 1988.

15-10. R.A. Horne, *The Chemistry of Our Environment*, Wiley-Interscience, New York, 1978.

15-11. J.J. W. Rogers, *A History of the Earth*, Cambridge University Press, Cambridge, England, 1994.

15-12. A. Braibanti, *Bioenergetics and Thermodynamics: Model Systems*, Reidel, Dordrecht, Holland, 1980.

15-13. B. Mason, *Principle of Geochemistry*, Wiley, New York, 1960.

15-14. D. W. Waples, *Geochemistry in Petroleum Exploration*, International Human Resource Development Corp., Boston, Massachusetts, 1985.

15-15. S. S. Bucher, R. J. Charlson, G. H. Orians, and G. V. Wolfe, *Global Biogeochemical Cycles*, Academic Press, London, 1992.

15-16. R. M. Garrels, F. T. Mackenzie, and C. Hunt, *Chemical Cycles and Global Environment, Assessing Human Influences*, William Kaufmann, California, 1973.

15-17. D. Arnett, *Supernovae and Nucleosynthesis*, Princeton University Press, Princeton, New Jersey, 1996.

15-18. K. S. Thorne, *Black Holes and Time Warps*, W. W. Norton, New York, 1994.

PROBLEM SET

1. Use a handbook to compare the densities of the following substances: Fe, Ca, Al, Ca_2SiO_4, and Mg_2SiO_4. How do these densitite affect the use of slugs in metal recovery?

2. Calculate the number of kilograms of potential HF air pollution which could be avoided by spreading manure at the rate of 2.5 tons/hectare on a 100-hectare farm instead of a quantity of superphosphate fertilizer which could yield equivalent phosphorous.

$$CaF_2 \cdot 3Ca_3(PO_4)_2 + 7H_2SO_4 + 3H_2O \rightarrow 3Ca(H_2PO_4)_2 \cdot H_2O + 2HF + 7CaSO_4$$

3. Write the following chemical equations:

a.) Hydrogen burning to form α-particles.

b.) α-process of $_{14}Si^{28}$.

c.) e-process of $_{27}Co^{59}$.

d.) β-decay of $_{28}Ni^{56}$.

e.) β-process of $_{14}Si^{28}$.

f.) $_{13}Al^{27}(\alpha,n)_{15}P^{30}$.

g.) The formation of $_6C^{14}$ in the upper atmosphere.

4. As the velocity of fluid flow over a bed of sediments wherein the applied force is causing sediment to move from bed to flow, the critical stage of erosion entrainment or the threshold of movement is defined as boundary shear stress. Write an expression for the critical stress assuming that the effective weight of the particle is given by Stoke's Law; the force acting downward will be $Fg \sin \alpha$, where α is the angel between Fg and the particle; and a tangential drag force per unit area of J_0 on the bed. (Courtesy of J.R.L. Allen).

C H A P T E R **1 6**

BIOSPHERE — TOXICOLOGY AND RISKS

This chapter continues the subject of the biosphere, focusing on health and life aspects. The chapter starts with a discussion on the quality of human life and the factors that may affect it. Following, we will briefly review some environmental aspects of food, and we will examine the nature of cancer, one of the most dreaded diseases. We will also discuss radon and the general problems and risks associated with it. Finally, we will discuss the effects of exposure to sound, microwaves, and other electromagnetic forces.

  We will illustrate some simple calculations of exposures to chemicals in relation with occupational toxicology. Throughout the text the internal pollution both voluntary and involuntary, are exemplified. Many of the exposures result to severe hazards.

16.1 THE QUALITY OF LIFE

As the world becomes more industrialized in an attempt to maximize the **quality of life** (QOL) for society, many adverse environmental problems (which tend to worsen the quality of life) arise as well. There is actually a trade-off between a new public policy and a new invention, which is designed to bring up the living standard, and its association with environmental problems. Coping with the total environment requires individual and group activity. In addition, various technologies and ideologies for coping with the material and spiritual environments have been developed. Taking these into consideration, we can see the quality of life as an operational concept as shown here:

The **Quality of Life** (QOL) can be expressed as material and spiritual aspects.

	Individual	Societal
Material	P, Provision of materials	E, Environment Quality
Spiritual	F, Fulfillment in psychic realm	J, Justice in righting wrongs

$$R = E + P \text{ if F, J fixed } (R = \text{resource})$$

If S is a satisfactory index, then

$$QOL = f(S_P, S_E, S_F, S_J) \qquad\qquad [16\text{-}1]$$

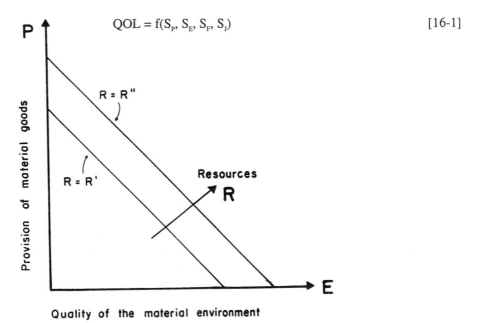

Figure 16-1.   Resource in material aspects of quality of life.

Resources, R, are often limited at a given moment, and when R decreases, at least one other goal variable (P, E, F, or J) must decrease. On the other hand, when R increases, it is possible to increase one or more of the goal variables without an accompanying decrease in any of them. Figure 16-1 illustrates an example of this analysis. For this special case, F and J are fixed, while P is plotted as the y-axis and E as the x-axis. At any given time, P and E cannot be chosen independently, but are constrained by a fixed amount of resources; for example, R''. If, for any reason, E increases, P will have to decrease. For instance, money spent for air pollution control devices will not be available for food or clothing. Only new technology that increases R would allow both P and E to increase. It is often the case that resources are decreasing, say from R'' to R', and sacrifices must be made in E or P or both. A decision has to be made to determine the trade-off point.

If factors affect societal decisions when there occurs a change in resources, a first step might be to suggest alternatives. For example, the following is a list of the consequences of possible strategies to meet a decrease in the availability of gasoline.

	ΔP	ΔE	ΔF	ΔJ
Price rationing	(+)	(-)	+	-
Coupon rationing	(-)	(+)	-	+
Travel restriction	0	+	-	-
Relax environmental constraints	+	-	+	-

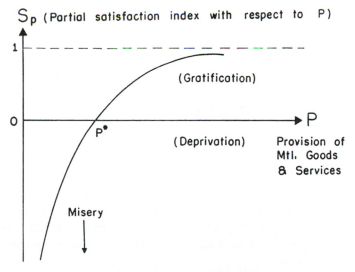

Figure 16-2.   Properties of satisfactory parameters.

However, there is no basis for decision; the preceding table does not show that a decrease in E, say, is to be weighted against an increase in P. It is instructive to find a function of P, E, F, and J that could sense the signal of the quality of life. We assume that the quality of life can be positively correlated with a satisfaction index, S: The greater the quality of life is, the greater S will be. As a first approximation, the overall satisfaction, S, can be taken as the sum of the four partial satisfaction indices, S_P, S_E, S_F, and S_J, each index corresponding to the satisfaction with respect to the degree of attainment of the respective goal variable when the other three goal variables are held constant. Figure 16-2, as an example, shows the general feature of the function S_P. In the figure, as P increases, S_P increases, but at a decreasing rate. At a very low P value, satisfaction tends to reach negative infinity. The overall satisfaction index should be maximized by choosing a balance among P, E, F, and J, making each partial satisfaction function not too small and above all positive, so that the sum of the partial satisfaction indices is as favorable as practicable.

Usually the **parameter impringed unit** (PIU), which has to do with human interest, aesthetics, biology, and environmental pollution, is an important factor to evaluate the environmental impact — so-called the **environmental impact unit** (EIU). It can be shown as follows:

$$\text{Environmental Impact Unit (EIU)} = (\text{EQI})(\text{PIU}) \qquad [16\text{-}2]$$

$$\text{EQI (Environmental Quality Index)} = (\text{expected quality})/(\text{ideal quality}) \qquad [16\text{-}3]$$

PIU (Parameter Impringed Unit) consists of:
   Ecology (species, habitats, ecosystems)

   Aesthetics (biota, wetlands, forestry)

   Environmental Pollution (water, air, soil)

   Human Interest (education, culture, life patterns)

16.1.1   Oplimization for the Infrastructure

As population increases, many of the estimated services projects (such as wastewater treatment plants) should have constructed to handle additional demand (such as interceptor sewers). In theory, the capacity expansion should stay ahead of the growth of wastewater flow or demand in MGD. The question is, what is the optimal expansion size, and what should the timing be. Considering the facility cost; there is strong argument for building large size. Counteracting this approach is that expenditures are committed to the future, **the present worth cost** is decreased. In general, both wastewater plants and interceptor sewers are controlled by economics as follows:

$$C(x) = ax^b \qquad [16\text{-}4]$$

where $0 < b < 1$

a = constant

b = economy of scale factor

x = hydraulic design capacity (e.g., MGD)

$C(x)$ = present worth cost of capital plus operation and maintenance ($M)

The trade-off is between economic of scale (building large now) and discounting (building small now). A method approach to this problem is using unconstrained optimization by nonlinear programming. To optimize any unconstrained function; for example,

$$z = f(x_1, x_2, ... x_n) \qquad [16\text{-}5]$$

The condition is for

$$\nabla f = \left(\frac{\partial f}{\partial x}, \frac{\partial f}{\partial x_2} ... \frac{\partial f}{\partial x_n} \right) = 0 \qquad [16\text{-}6]$$

Thus, the function has a critical point, crystallizing point, at x_0 if $\nabla f = 0$. If $f^{n+1}(x_0) \neq 0$, then $f(x)$ has a maximum of $f^{n+1}(x) < 0$ (n is odd), and $f(x)$ has a minimum of $f^{n+1}(x) > 0$ (n is odd).

Solving the trade-off problem, we designate:

D = rate of linear demand increase (MGD per year)

t = time in years

r = rate of discount selected by Congress for use in water resource project (in %)

and also now the point of capacity expansion is $t_0, t_1, t_3, ... n$ with the corresponding expansion capacity identical, then

$$x_1^* = x_2^* = x_3^* ... = x_n^* \qquad [16\text{-}7]$$

and

$$(t_1 - t_0) = (t_2 - t_1) = (t_3 - t_2) = t' \qquad [16\text{-}8]$$

therefore

$$x_i^* = Dt' \qquad\qquad [16\text{-}9]$$

and $\exp(-rt')$ is part of the present worth cost.

Thus, for all expansions over n periods of the length of t' years

$$C(x) = ax^b\, e^{-rt_0} + ax^b\, e^{-rt'} + ax^b\, e^{-2rt'} + \ldots + ax^b\, e^{-nrt'}$$

If $t_0 = t$

$$C(x) = ax^b\, (1 + e^{-rt'} + e^{-2rt'} + \ldots + e^{-nrt'}) + ax^b\, [1 + e^{-rt'} + (e^{-rt'})2 + \ldots + (e^{-rt'})n] \qquad [16\text{-}10]$$

and

$$0 < \frac{1}{e^{rt'}} < 1 \ \text{ for } \ r > 0,\ t' > 0 \qquad\qquad [16\text{-}11]$$

as $n \to \infty$, the geometric series converges to $1/(1 - e^{-rt'})$

Thus Equation [16-4] becomes

$$C(x) = \frac{ax^b}{\left(1 - e^{-rt'}\right)} \qquad\qquad [16\text{-}12]$$

substitute $x = Dt'$ and express Equation [16-12] in log scale

$$\ln C(x) = \ln a + b \ln(Dt') - \ln\left(1 - e^{-rt'}\right) \qquad\qquad [16\text{-}13]$$

or after differentiation,

$$\frac{\partial}{\partial t'}[\ln C(x)] = \frac{b}{t_0'} - \frac{re^{-rt_0'}}{1 - e^{-rt_0'}} = 0$$

Employing this equation, t_0' can be solved for fixed values of b, economy of scale factor and r, discount rate. Table 16-1 lists the results for such a calculation. Considering the federal discount rate, low interest rates (2–4%) prevailing in the 60s, peaked in the late 80s as 8.875% and even in fiscal 1996 this was 7.625%. In comparison, funds for general obligation bonds and revenue bonds are lighter. The traditional design periods for waste-water treatment plants and interceptor sewers have been 20 and 50 years respectively.

Table 16-1. Optimal Expansion Time for (a) Treatment Plants (years; USEPA, 1975); (b) Interceptor Sewers (years; USPEA, 1975)

Treatment Plants

Discount	Economy of Scale Factor		
Rate (%)	0.6	0.7	0.8
5	19	13	9
7	13	10	6
10	9	7	4
12	8	6	4

Interceptor Sewers

Discount	Economy of Scale Factor		
Rate (%)	0.3	0.4	0.5
5	40	31	24
7	28	22	17
10	20	16	12
12	18	14	10

16.2 CHEMICAL TOXICOLOGY

This section deals largely on the chemical toxicity originated from **internal pollution**. This term defines that the harmful materials used by man, that enter the body through ingestion, inhalation, and application as cosmetics to the body. For example, esophageal cancer formed in Casping region is correleable to the high salinity of the lithoral soils. Food additives as well as the nutrition supplements are involuntary intakes for necessary food and medicine. At this time, we should include a large number of toxic substances which are subjected to voluntary intake. Both involuntary and voluntary introduction to the body are the causes of internal pollution. This list will include socially acceptable use of alcohol, tobacco, and even many hallucinating drugs from psychotomimetic plants, such as marijuana. A great number of hallucinogens and neurohumors are known to be used in religious ceremonies, such as peyote rites of the American Indians. The active component is mescaline derived from peyote cactus. Chemical structures of narcotics, such as morphine, also can be comparable to many of the hallucinating drugs such as psilocybin, harmine, muscimole, PCP, etc., that contain two nitrogens with four carbons apart. Activity is enhanced by placing an aromatic ring α to the nitrogen to form an indole ringlike system. With exception to this rule is morphine, the N-containing ring is a six carbon caged structure, yet the dibenzofuran-like base is similar to that of Δ'-tetrahedrocannabinol, the active component of marijuana. A potent synthetic substance called LSD conforms with the rule that four carbons between two nitrogens with one nitrogen in an indole ring are required to give hallucinogenic properties. This physiological property may be due to the interference or competition of serotonin in human brains.

Food additives and the above mentioned drugs cause internal pollution via oral route. One should not forget the intakes from the lung and skin. For example, hexachlorophene have been legitimately used as hygienic spray or vaginal deodorant for years. Even hospitals wash human babies with a diluted solution of hexachlorophene to ensure against infections and diaper rash. As developed in this section, most of the internal pollutants cause genetic changes which become mutagenic and may even lead to carcinogenic.

The chemical structures of most internal pollutants so far discussed can be found in Figure 16-3.

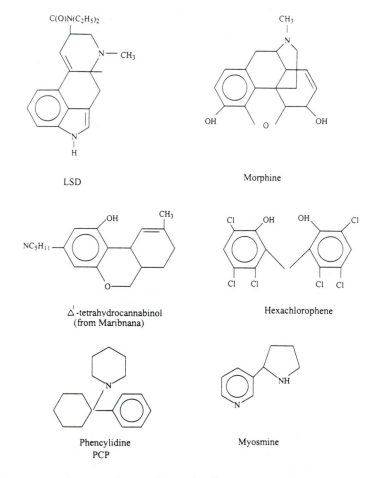

Figure 16-3.   Structure of some internal pollutants.

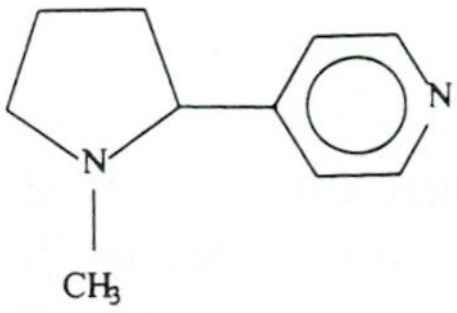

Nicotine

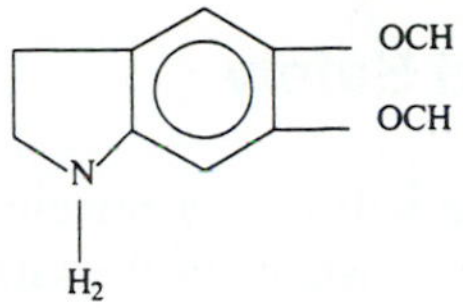

Mescaline
(peyote cactus)

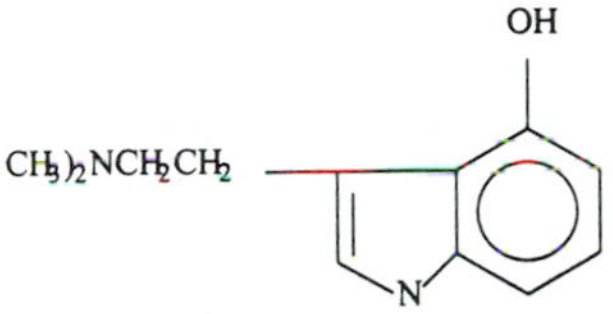

Psilocin

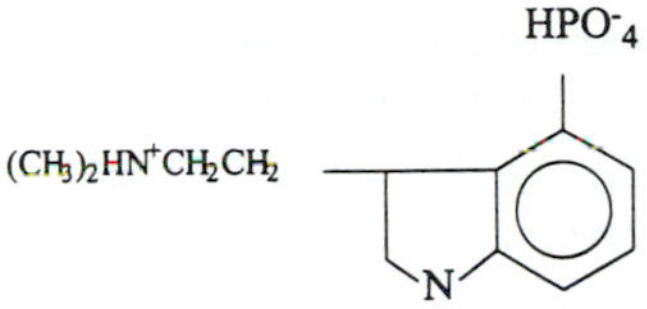

Psilocybin
(mushrooms)

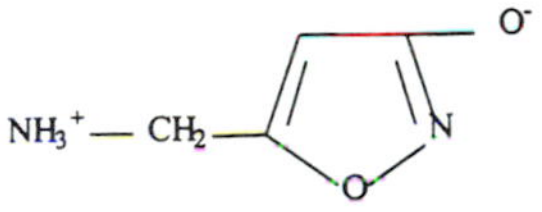

Muscimole
(Amanita)

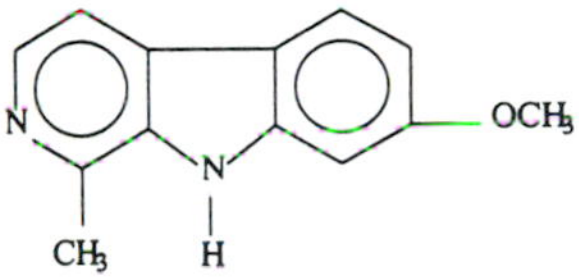

Harmine
(Banisteriopsis)

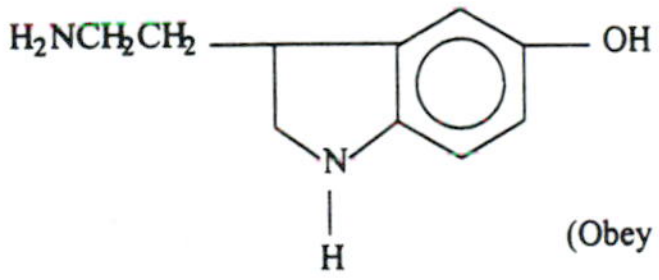

Serotonin

(Obey the 4 carbon and indole rule between 2 nitrogens.
(Imbalance may cause schizopherenia.)

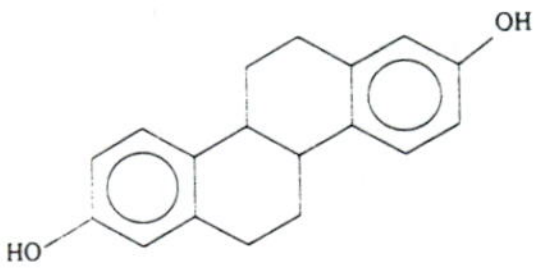

Diethylstibesterol   (DES)

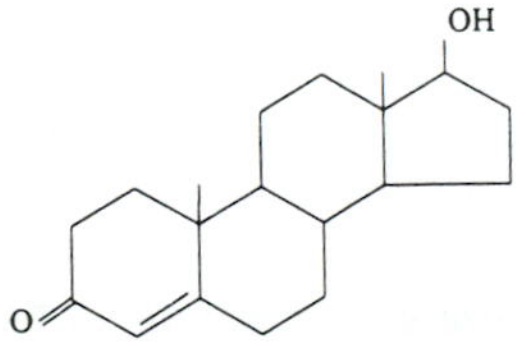

Testosterone (male)

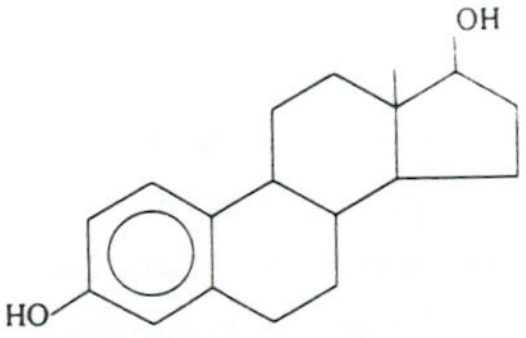

Esterone (female)

Figure 16-3.   Structure of some internal pollutants. (continued)

16.2.1   Food Safety

In this section we will briefly review some environmental aspects of food. The public is confused and concerned about the safety of the food it consumes because it receives mixed views from presumably reputable people on the safety of food. Some experts claim that one element or another of our diet is unsafe; others say this is untrue. The following are some collected facts for your own judgment.

Table 16-2.   Confirmed Foodborne Diseases, 1979

Microbial Agents	Outbreaks	Cases
Clostricium botulinum	7	9
Clostridium perfringens	20	1110
Salmonella sp.	44	2794
Shegella sp.	7	356
Staphylococcus aureus	34	2391
Vibrio parahaemolyticus	2	14
Other bacteria	5	133
Viruses	6	229
Trichinella spiralis	11	93
Chemical Agents		
Naturally occurring seafood toxins	30	217
Toxic mushrooms	1	2
Heavy metal	1	18
Other chemicals	4	13
Total	172	7379

Table 16-2 gives the data for foodborne diseases in 1979. There are 172 incidents involving almost 7,400 cases in which the cause of illness could be established. From time to time we discover microbial hazards that we did not know of before. Potentially one of the most serious biological agents of all are the fungal poisons called **mycotoxins**. The best known and probably the most important of these is **aflatoxin**, which was discovered over 25 years ago in moldy peanut meal. It is a potent liver carcinogen in a broad range of animal species. Epidemiological studies in several tropical areas support the assumption that aflatoxin can cause liver cancer in humans.

Food additives perform a variety of functions in foods. The principal benefits of the use of food additives are cost reduction, user convenience, nutrition, food quality and attractiveness, prevention of microbial contamination, and an increase in the variety of foods available to the consumers. A sampling of additives according to function includes anti-caking agents, antioxidants, colors, curing and pickling agents, emulsifiers, enzymes, flavoring agents, leavening agents, nutrient supplements, thickeners, and texturizers. Table 16-3 lists all the chemical additives in a loaf of bread. An important factor in evaluating the possible hazard of a food ingredient is the quantity ingested.

Table 16-3. Additives in a Loaf of Bread

Preservatives	Calcium propionate, sodium diacetate, sodium propionate, acetic acid, lactic acid
Leavening Agents	Potassium acid tartrate, monocalcium phosphate, sodium acid pyrophosphate
Bleaching Agents	Benzoyl peroxide, chlorine dioxide, nitrosyl chloride, oxides of nitrogen
Bread "Improvers"	Potassium bromate, potassium iodate, calcium peroxide
Antioxidants	Butylated hydroxytoluene, butylated hydroxyanisole, propyl gallate, nordihydroquaiaretic acid
Emulsifiers	Lecithin, monohlycerides, diglycerides, sorbitan, and polyoxethylene fatty acids

In addition,

The Wheat is grown contaminated with fertilizers, herbicides, and pesticides

The Grain on storage is treated with rodenticides, fungicides (some of them have mercury compounds), and insecticides

The Water added to the flour may have been purified with alum, chlorine, copper sulfate, and serta ash, and fluoride compounds may have been added (recently epidemics of acute hemolytic anemia in uremic patients have been traced to chlorination of urban drinking water by chloramine bacteriacides

The Sugar (or dextrose) added to the flour may have been refined with lime, sulfur dioxide, phosphates, and charcoal

The Salt may contain added iodide and carbonates of calcium and magnesium

The Yeast has been fed on ammonia salts

The Shortening is refined, bleached, and decolorized and has been exposed to traces of nickel; antioxidants; citric, ascorbic, and phosphoric acids; and has been glycerinated

Source: R.M. Linton, *Terricide*, Little Brown & Co., Boston, 1970

Table 16-4 lists the 15 **GRAS** (generally recognized as safe) food ingredients used in the food industry annually. Use of sucrose appears to have been under-reported. Including use in beverages, the total use was 70 lb. per capita in 1971 and probably about the same in the 1980s. Table 16-5 lists the natural flavoring substances used in the largest amounts in the six years following 1976. Table 16-6 lists the 15 synthetic substances used in the greatest amounts in flavoring by the processed food industry. To emphasize the modern-day diet, the beverages and the foods we take contain many chemical additives, as well as DDT and its derivatives (referring back to Section 13.3). The latter insecticides have been banned years ago, but the residue survives in the soil environment for a long duration.

Table 16-4.   Annual GRAS Food Ingredients Used by Food Industry

Substance	Annual Use	
	Million lb	lb/Capita
Sucrose	5000	23
Corn syrup	1530	7.2
Sodium chloride	1420	6.7
Dextrose	266	1.3
Mono- and diglycerides	86	0.40
Hydrochloric acid	82	0.38
Caramel	74	0.35
Sodium bicarbonate	60	0.28
Yeasts	57	0.27
Citric acid	57	0.27
Calcium phosphate, monobasic	48	0.23
Monosodium glutamate	28	0.13
Carbon dioxide	27	0.13
Hydrolyzed vegetable proteins	23	0.11
Sodium aluminum phosphate	15	0.07

Meat eaters do have to worry about the artificial **estrogens**, such as stibesterol and diethystibesterol (DES), because capsules or pellets of DES are implanted in chicken's necks or in the ears of cattle to produce tender meat. These artificial estrogens are similar in structure to human sex hormones. The chemical structure of DES and sex hormones are also shown in Figure 16-3. They have the potential to alter secondary sex characteristics and are also strongly carcinogenic. Many natural toxicants are found in plant foods. **Coniine** is present in berries, and a toxic incident can account for what is written in the Bible. The chemical structures of a number of nitrogen bases that are toxic are presented in Figure 16-4. Mycotoxins, such as the aflatoxins in groundnut meal, which are the secondary metabolic products of certain fungi that are toxic to man and domestic animals, are the cause of the acute haemolytic symptoms of some individuals after eating foods containing fava beans which may contain **vicine** and **convicine**. Many naturally occurring antioxidants, such as the active components in rosemary leaves, or **sinigrin** (for chemical strutures please refer to Figure 16-4) in mustard, radish, and brassica vegetables, are flavoring agents acquainted by

man. Lima beans, cassava, and sweet potatoes are food plants contain cyanogentic glycosides which release HCN upon hydrolysis. The cyanide content of lima beans varies from
10 mg to 300 mg per 100 g of seed. The movement of agriculture toward the use of lower
levels of agrochemicals and the exploration of integrated systems of pest management will
be accompanied by the search for new crop varieties possessing enhanced natural resistance
that may be termed as natural pesticides. These natural pesticides will include tannins, lec-
tins, alkaloids, antioxidants, and glycosides. The current fashion of increasing one's intake
of green vegetables and dietary fiber will also result in an increased intake of biologically
active food constituents whose long-term effects on human health has not yet been determined. It is certain that the intake of such compounds by vegetarians may be 10–100 fold
greater than that for an equivalent omnivore population.

Mutagens do associate with food. The relationship between cancer and food will be
discussed in the following section.

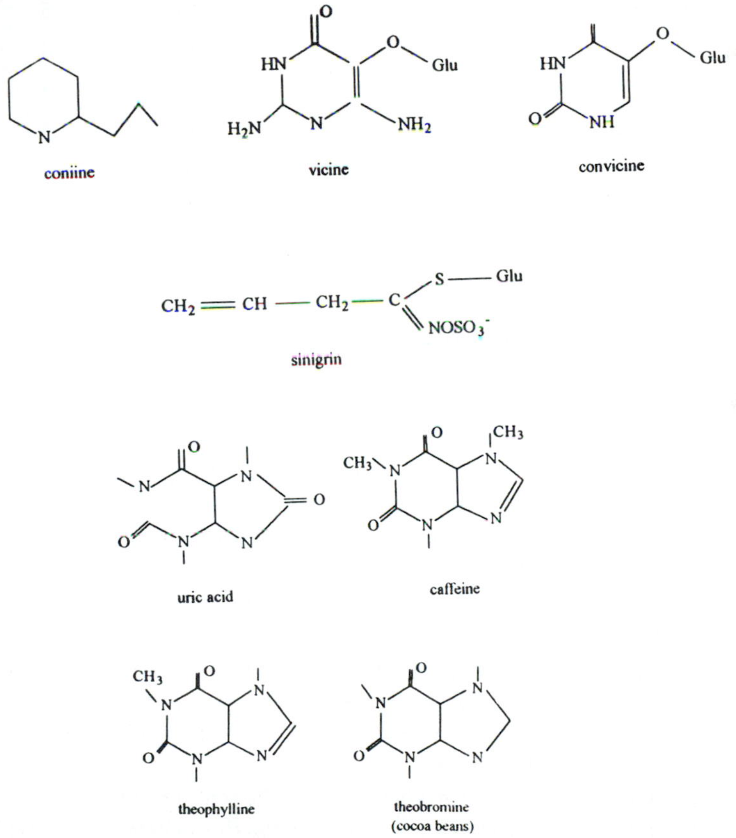

Figure 16-4. Structure of toxic nitrogen bases including caffeine and related compounds.

Table 16-5.   Natural Flavoring Substances Reported Used by Food Industry in Largest Amounts in Six Years Period after 1970

Substance	1000 lb/year	mg/(capita day)
Mustard, yellow	31,000	170
Pepper, black	19,051	108
Malt extract	7,050	40
Pepper, red	2,334	14
Caffeine	2,000	11
Lemon oil	1,547	9
Cassia	1,147	7
Oregano	920	5
Peppermint oil	870	5
Nutmeg	770	4
Caraway seed	634	4
Cocoa extract	536	3
Cloves	519	3
Allspice	495	3

NAS/NRC Surveys

16.2.2   Carcinogenesis and Mutagenesis

Although there are numerous toxic effects, either acute or long-term, associated with chemicals, one of the most dreaded is cancer. Cancer was responsible for almost 20% of all deaths in the United States in the 1980s. Above all, there is a strong likelihood that most cancers have environmental causes. One of the most striking pieces of evidence for this comes from the pattern of the incidences of cancer in different parts of the body in different countries. Japanese people have much higher death rates from stomach and liver cancer and lower rates from colon and prostate cancer than do white residents of California. However, these differences are much less pronounced in Japanese immigrants to California. In addition, there is a marked correlation between the increase in cigarette smoking among men early in the century and the incidence of lung cancer some 20 years later. Many chemicals are capable of causing problems. Table 16-7 gives a list of chemical **carcinogens** along with the types of cancer they produce.

We do not know exactly how chemical carcinogens produce cancer, but it is likely that they attack the DNA molecules. The following summarizes some types of chemical carcinogenesis that chemically alter the base pair duplications in DNA. Some of the alteration mechanisms are listed here:

Table 16-6. Synthetic Flavoring Substances, Adjuncts and Adjuvents, Reported Used in Largest Amounts

	Usage	
Substance	1000 lb/year	mg/(capita day)
Monosodium glutamate	18,000	104
Isopropyl alcohol	4,000	
Malic acid	3,000	17
Acetone	570	3.6
Ethyl acetate	560	3.2
Methyl salicylate	280	1.6
Ethyl acetoacetate	68	0.36
4-(methylthio)-2-butanone	59	0.34
Thiamine hydrochloride	57	0.33
Isobutyl acetate	44	0.25
Ethyl maltol	38	0.22
Isoamyl butyrate	36	0.21
Butyric acid	27	0.15
Triacetin	20	0.16
Acetaldehyde	19	0.11

1977 NRC survey

Chemical Carcinogenesis

- change of base by nitrous acid — conversion of NH_2- to OH-

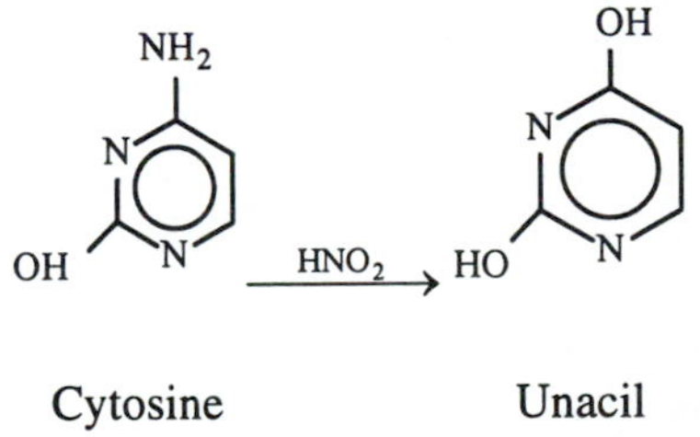
NH2
N
OH
N
HNO2
OH
N
HO
N
Cytosine
Unacil

- alkylation by alkylating agent to the base — e.g., by N-nitrosoamine or ethylene oxide

$$RNH - H = 0 \rightarrow RN = N - OH \rightarrow R - N+ \equiv N$$

N-nitrosoamine

$$CH_2 — CH_2$$
$$\diagdown \diagup$$
$$O \qquad \rightarrow OCH_2CH_2^+$$

ethylene oxide

- intercalation by agents such as heterocyclics or PAH; e.g., acridine

Any damage to DNA can result in mistakes in the genetic code. Often this results in the death of the cell, but if the cell survives, the mistake can be passed on to the daughter cells when the DNA is copied. This is called **mutation** and might cause an alteration in some function of the organism. Cancer is a condition in which a cell grows and divides uncontrollably, invading normal body tissues. Most cancer-producing chemicals have to be activated in the organisms to express their carcinogenic properties.

There are about 500 new chemicals that are marketed each year; therefore, singling out the potentially carcinogenic ones is a primary concern in cancer control. Studying the effects of chemicals on rats has proven to be the most valuable screening method to date, but it is time-consuming and the results are often inconclusive. The most widely known of the new tests is one developed by Ames at University of California, Berkeley. The **Ames test** is based on the fact that, with a few exceptions, carcinogens are also mutagens. The test is inexpensive, takes only a few days to complete, and only needs microgram amounts of the chemical. It is performed in a petri dish on various strains of *Salmonella typhimurium*, bacteria that are developed for detecting and classifying mutagens. Each tester strain has a specific mutation in one of the genes of the operon for histidine synthesis, which makes it require added histidine for growth. A chemical with mutagenic activity can cause a back-mutation in the operon, which restores the capacity for histidine synthesis. The indication of a positive result is the growth of the revertant bacteria around the spot where the chemical was applied.

Table 16-7. Chemicals Recognized as Human Carcinogens

Chemical Mixtures	Site of Cancers
Soots, tars, oils	skin, lungs
Cigarette smoke	lungs
Industrial chemical	
2-Naphthylamine	urinary bladder
Benzidine	urinary bladder
4-Aminobiphenyl	urinary bladder
Chloromethyl methyl ether	lungs
Nickel compounds	lungs, nasal sinuses
Chromium compounds	lungs
Asbestos	lungs
Arsenic compounds	Skin, lungs
Vinyl chloride	liver
Drugs	
N, N-bis(2-chloroethyl)-2-naphthylamine	urinary bladder
Bis(2-chloroethyl)sulfide (mustard gas)	lungs
Diethylstilbestrol	vagina
Phenacetin	renal pelvis
Naturally occurring compounds	
Betel nuts	buccal mucosa
Aflatoxins	liver
Potent carcinogens in animals to which human populations are exposed	
Cyclamates	bladder
Sterigmatocystis	liver
Cycasin	liver
Safrole	liver
Pyrrolizidine alkaloids	liver
Nitroso compounds	esophagus, liver, kidney, stomach

Source: C. Heidelberge, "Chemical Carcinogenesis," *Annu. Rev. Biochem.*, 44 (1975).

The detection of carcinogens or mutagens in foods was not studied extensively until the development of the Ames test. Using the Ames test, mutagens were found in coffee, tea, alcoholic spirits, wines, and spices, as shown in Table 16-8. Mutagens are found to be formed during cooking, because pyrolysis of protein has been shown to cause the formation of mutagens (Figure 16-5 shows the increase of mutagens with the cooking time).

Table 16-8.   Mutagenic Activities Induced by One Cup of Coffee or One Glass of Whisky or Brandy

	Number of Revertants [a]
Coffee [b]	135,000
Whisky [c]	3,600
Brandy [c]	8,000

[a] *C. typhimurium* TA 100 without 69 mix was used.

[b] one cup contained 150 mL coffee

[c] one glass contained 30 mL whisky or brandy

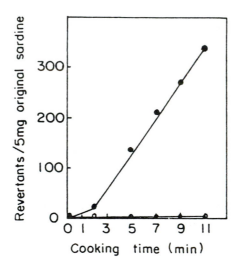

Figure 16-5.   Mutagenicity of sun-dried sardines broiled at various times. *S. typhimurium* TA98 with (•) and without (o) S9 mix was used for the assay.

For a large number of toxic compounds, the correlation between the mutagenic potential and carcinogenic potential is not linear, as shown in Figure 16-6. For example, some heterocyclic amines are mutagenic, but their carcinogenic potentials are not very high. It is clear from Figure 16-6 that these mutagens deviate greatly from those obtained for some typical carcinogens.

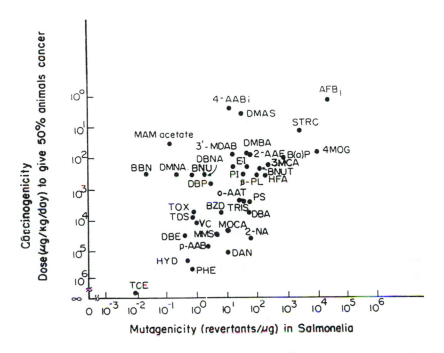

Figure 16-6. Relationship between mutagenicity in *S. typhimurium* and carcinogenicity. Abbreviations used: p-AAB, p-aminoazobenzene; 4-AABi, 4-acetylaminobiphenyl; 2-AAf, 2-acetylaminofluorene; o-AAT, o-aminoazotoluene; AFB, aflatoxin B; BBN, N-butyl-N-butanolnitrosamine; BNU, N-n-butyl-N-nitrosourea; BNUT, N-n-butyl-N-nitrosourethane; B(a)P, beno[a]pyrene; BZD, benzidine, DAN, 2,4-diaminoanisole; DBA, dibenz[a,h]anthracene; DBE, 1,2-dibromoethane; DBNA, N, N-di-n-butylnitrosamine; DBP, 1,2-dibromochloropropane; DMAS, 4-dimethylaminostrilbene; DMBA, 7,12-dimethylbenz[a]anthracene; DMNA, N, N-dimethylnitrosamine; EI, ethyleneimine; HFA, N-hydroxy-2-acetylaminofluorene; HYD, hydralarine; MAM acetate, methylazoxymethanol acetate; 3MCA, 3-methylcholanthrene; 3'-MDAB, 3-methyl-4 dimethylaminoazbenzene; MMS, methyl methanesulfonate; MOCA 4, 4'methylene-bis (2-chloroaniline); 2NA, 2-naphthylamine; PHE, phenacetin; PI, prophyleneimine; β-PL, β-propholactone; PS, propane sultone; STRC, sterigmatocystin; TCE, trichloroethylene; TDS, toluenediamino sulfate; TOX, toxaphene; TRIS, tris (2,3-dibromopropylphosphate); VC, vinylchoride.

It is also important to note here that **teratogens** are different from either mutagens or carcinogens. Table 16-9 depicts the complex sequence of events in teratogenesis. Although some parts in the table may be held in common with carcinogenesis (e.g., certain causes) and mutagenesis (e.g., somatic mutations and chromosomal aberrations), many aspects are unique to teratogenesis, thus further emphasizing the basic differences existing among these processes. Table 16-10 shows conditions of exposures that determine the response in carcinogenesis, mutagenesis, and teratogenesis.

Table 16-9.   Summary of Teratogenesis

Causes	→ Mechanisms	→ Manifestations
Action of an agent from the environment on the embryo or the germ cells, e.g.,		
Radiations	→ Reaction within the embryo or germ cells, such as one or more of the following:	
Chemicals		
Dietary deficiency		→ Pathogenesis, initiated by one or more of the follow-ing:
Infection	Mutation	
Hypoxia, etc.	Chromosomal nondusjunction	Cell death
Temperature	Mitotic interference	Mitotic rate change
Endocrine imbalance	Altered nucleic acid integrity or function	Reduced biosynthesis
Physical trauma	Lack of precursors, aubstrats, etc.	Altered differentiation schedules
Placental failure	Altered energy sources	Impeded morphogenetic movement
	Changed membrane character-istics	Etc.
	Water-electrolyte imbalance	
	Enzyme inhibition	
		And leading to abnormal tissue and organ develop-ment which determine the nature and incidence of final defect

Table 16-10.   Conditions of Exposure That Determine the Response in Carcinogenesis, Muta-genesis, and Teratogenesis

	Susceptible Tissues	Optimal Time of Exposure	Duration and Level of Dosage
Carcinogen	Proliferating tissues	Uncertain, probably all states capable of mitosis	Usually chronic, possibly all doses
Mutagen	Germinal tissues	All stages of remetogenesis	Either acute or chronic, possibly all doses
Teratogen	Possibly all immature tissues	Highest during early differentiation	Acute only, above usual no effect level

16.2.3 Radon

As discussed previously in Section 7.1.5 (on nuclear power), naturally occurring radioactivity may originate from the decay series of uranium (4n + 2), thorium (4n), and actinium (4n + 3) as shown in Table 16-11. Because mass lost in the decay series is due almost exclusively to α emission (mass of 4), the mass numbers of the members of a given series may be represented by 4n, of which n is an integer. The sources of radon and other isotopes are also listed in Table 16-11 (e.g., ^{222}Rn is radon, ^{220}Rn is thoron and ^{219}Rn is actinon). Each of the series begins with a very long half-life time (~4.5 billion years) equivalent to the age of the earth. The 4n + 1 series is not found in nature in any significant amount, but laboratory tests indicate that ^{237}Np (also long-lived) can also produce it. Whatever amount was present would have decayed by now. All these led to the end product of lead. Radon also can give daughters; for example, ^{218}Po (α-emitter), ^{214}Pb (β- and γ-emitter), and so on.

Table 16-11. Some Characteristics of the Natural Radioactive Decay Series

Series	Uranium	Thorium	Actinium
Mass number code	4n+2	4n	4n+3
Long-lived parent and half-life	^{238}U 4.51×10⁹ y	^{232}Th 1.39×10¹⁰ y	^{235}U 7.13×10⁸ y
Radium parent and half-life	^{226}Ra 1,600 y	^{223}Ra 11.4 d	^{224}Ra 3.66 d
Radon isotope and half-life	^{222}Rn (radon)	^{220}Rn (thoron)	^{219}Rn (actinon)
	3.82 d	55.6 s	4.0 s
Potential alpha energy in shorg-lived	19.2 Mev	20.9 Mev	20.8 Mev
radon decay chain (OECD-1983)	per atom	per atom	per atom
Stable end product	^{206}Pb	^{208}Pb	^{207}Pb

* The potential alpha energy is the total alpha energy emitted during the decay of an atom along its decay chain.

Source: M. Wilkening

Radon and its decay products can be delivered to sensitive tissue in the lung respiratory system. Usually an adult can be expected to breathe at a rate of 0.75 m³/min. Typical aerosol concentrations are ca. 10^{10}/m³ with radii ca. 0.5 μm. Assuming that the average amount of indoor air contaminants is 50 Bq/m³ of radon, 40 Bq of radon are taken in lung per minute. This activity will reach the bronchial tube and damage the basal cells underneath. In many locations, especially underground tunnels and mines, the radioactivity can exceed up to 10,000 times this amount (Table 16-12). Even the radon level in a popular spa, Badgastein, in the Austrian Alps is 1.1×10^5 Bq/m³. Lung cancer is a common illness in underground mining because many of the mines have radon levels up to 100,000 Bq/m³, or 2900 pC$_i$/L.

Table 16-12.   Radon Released from Mines and Mills

Metal	Type of Mine/Mill	Number of Sources	Radon Release Per Source (Bq y^{-1}×10^{10})
Uranium	Underground	305	25,000
Uranium	Open pit	63	7,250
Uranium	Mill	20	10,400
Iron	Underground	11	560
	Open pit	57	70
Copper	Underground	15	20
	Open pit	46	1,500
Zinc	Underground	36	850

Source: R.H. Johnson Jr., et al., in *Natural Radiation Environment* (Bombay), Wiley Eastern Limited (1982) pp. 182–183.

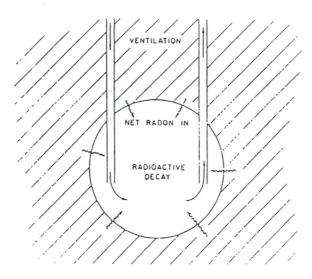

Figure 16-7.   Factors governing the radon balance in an underground cavity. (After M.H. Wilkening and D.E. Watking, *Health Phys.* 31, 139 (1976))

Radon concentration in an underground cavity can be evaluated so that ventilation processes can be utilized. As shown in Figure 16-7, radon-rich air within the cavity is replaced by outside air from the outside having a low radon content. For a cavity of interior surface S and volume V,

$$SE = \lambda VC + Q(C - C_{od}) \qquad\qquad [16\text{-}14]$$

where E is the net inward flux of atoms/sec/m^2, λ is the decay constant for ^{222}Rn, C and C_{od} are the radon concentrations within the cavity and outdoors respectively in atoms of ^{222}Rn/m^3, and Q is airflow m^3/sec. If one brings the outdoor air ($C_{od} \sim 0.2$ pC$_i$/L) relative to that within the cave ($C \sim 40$ p C$_i$/L), and allows C_{od} to be negligible,

$$C = \frac{SE}{\lambda V + Q}$$
[16-15]

In this manner, for the Carlsbad Caverns in New Mexico, the radon-rich air in the cave is displaced by cooler air from the surface through natural ventilation, which is caused by the temperature differences between the cave and outside air. Some methods used for measuring **radon flux** are explained by Figure 16-8 (the accumulator, flow, and adsorption methods). The flux density or exhalation rate can be expressed in the transfer rate as Bq/m^2/sec. To reduce the hazard of radon in domestic homes, use either the drain-tile suction or sub-slab suction, and gas-proofs liners should be installed.

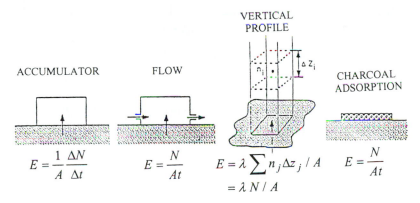

Figure 16-8. Methods used in measuring radon flux. E is the flux, A is the area covered by the device or system, t is the accumulation time, N is the quantity of radon, and λ is the decay constant for radon. (M. Wilkening, Ref.16-1)

16.3 RISK ASSESSMENT AND OCCUPATIONAL TOXICOLOGY

The risk can be simply expressed in **standard mortality ratio** (SMR)

$$SMR = \frac{\text{observed death}}{\text{expected death}}$$
[16-16]

For example, the ratio of lung cancer death in a population of smokers to the lung cancer death in a nonsmoking population of the same size is 11. Consequently the SMR is 11, meaning that the risk of death from lung cancer is 11 times as high for a heavy smoker as for a nonsmoker.

Actually the lifetime risk can be obtained from the dose-response curve shown in Figure 16-9.

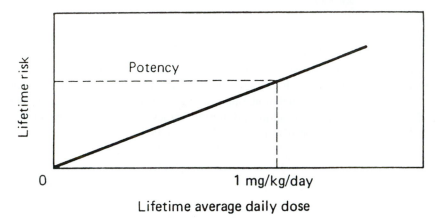

* The potency factor is the slope of the dose-response curve at low doses.

Figure 16-9.   Dose-response curve (G.M. Masters, 1991, Ref.16-2).

Lifetime risk is a probability function of dose, d, such that (from multistage model)

$$\text{Risk} = P(d) = 1 - \exp[-(q_0 + q_1 d + q_2 d_2 + ...q_n d_n)] \qquad [16\text{-}17]$$

$q_0, q_1, q_2,...$ are parameters to fit the data.

The background rate for cancer incidence is when $d = 0$, or

$$P(0) = 1 - e^{-q_0} \approx \left\{ 1 - \left[1 + (-q_0) \right] \right\} = q_0 \qquad [16\text{-}18]$$

because

$$e^x = 1 + x + \frac{x^2}{2!} + ... + \frac{x^n}{n!} \approx 1 + x$$

if only two terms in the exponential function are used.

Therefore,

$$P(d) = 1 - [1 - (q_0 + q_1 d)] = q_0 + q_1 d = P(0) + q_1 d \qquad [16\text{-}19]$$

or

$$\text{additional risk} = P(d) - P(0) = q_1 d \qquad [16\text{-}20]$$

Therefore, lifetime probability is linearly related to dose.
The slope of risk versus dose curve at low dosage is called the **potential factor** (PF)
and

$$PF = -q_1 \qquad \text{in } (mg/kg/day)^{-1} \qquad [16\text{-}21]$$

d is in mg/kg/day

Lifetime risk= (PF)(chemical daily intake) = (PF)(CDI) for 70 yrs.

Some PF values are as follows:

Chemical	PF (oral route) (mg/kg/day)$^{-1}$
chloroform	6.1×10^{-3}
benzene	2.9×10^{-2}
dioxin	1.56×10^{-5}
PCB	7.7
TCE	1.1×10^{-2}

[Example 16-1]   THM in drinking water is 70 $\mu g/L$ for an adult of 70 kg who drinks 2
L/day. What is the risk? (After G. Masters)

$$CDI = \frac{(70 \times 10^{-6}\, g/L)(10^3\, mg/g)(2\, L/day)}{70\, kg}$$

$$= .002\ mg/kg/day$$

Using the RF values of chloroform listed in preceding tables for the RF values of THM. We obtain

$$\text{Risk} = (PF)(CDI) = (6.1 \times 10^{-3})(2 \times 10^{-3}) = 12.2 \times 10^{-6}$$

Probability is 12.2 per million people for 70 yr
For population of 0.5 million

$$\text{Cancer/yr} = (500,000)(12.2/10^6)(1/70)$$

$$= .09 \approx 0.1 \text{ cancer/yr}$$

Table 16-13.   Threshold Limit Values (TLV) of Fossil Fuel Contaminants

Substance	ppm	mg/M^3
Coal dust (bituminous)	—	2
Coal tar pitch volatiles (benzene soluble fraction)	—	0.2
Anthracene	NC [a]	
Benzo(a)pyrene	C [b]	
Phenanthrene	NC [a]	
Acridine	NC [a]	
Chrysene	C [b]	
Pyrene	NC [a]	
Naphtha (coal tar)	100	400
Asphalt fumes	—	5
Phenol – skin	5	19
Cresol – skin	5	22
Naphthalene	10	50
Oil mist, particulate	—	5
Organic solvent		
Acetone	1,000	2,400
Allyl alcohol – skin	2	3
Butyl alcohol	100	300
Benzene – skin	25	80
Carbon tetrachloride – skin	10	65

Table 16-13.   continued

Substance	ppm	mg/M³
Carbon disulfide – skin	20	60
Chloroform	25	120
Cyclohexane	300	1,050
Dichloromethane	100	210
Heptane	500	2,000
Hexane	500	1,800
Methyl alcohol	200	260
Petane	500	1,500
Pyridine	5	15
Toluene	100	375
Xylene	100	435
Trace metals, gas, and inorganics		
Antimony (Sb)	—	0.5
Arsenic (As)	—	0.5
Cadmium (Cd)	—	0.2
Lead (Pb)	—	0.15
Chromium (Cr)	—	0.5
Mercury (Hg)	—	0.05
Tin (Sn)	—	0.1
Vanadium (V_2O_5) – dust	—	0.5
Ammonia	25	18
Carbon dioxide	5,000	9,000
Carbon monoxide	50	55
Chlorine	1	3
Hydrogen chloride	5	7
Hydrogen sulfide	0.05	0.2
Nitrogen dioxide	5	9
Sulfur dioxide	5	13

[a] NC: negative carcinogenicity

[b] C: positive carcinogenicity

The Occupational Safety and Health Act (OSHA) has set the **threshold limit values** (TLV) of many inorganic and organic contaminants that have been determined for the occupational worker being exposed to a certain chemical as illustrated in Table 16-13. The lifetime exposure of a worker is considered as 40 hours/week for 50 years. The **time-weighted average** exposure (T.W.A.) can be obtained as follows:

$$\frac{(\text{Exposure Time})\,(\text{Conc. "A"}) + (\text{Exposure Time})\,(\text{Conc. "B"}) + ...}{(\text{Total Work Time per Shift})} = \text{T.W.A.} \qquad [16\text{-}22]$$

Or

$$\frac{\sum_{i=1}^{n} (T_i)\cdot(C_i)}{T_{total}\,(\text{work time})}$$

= Time – weighted average concentration (T.W.A.) for this particular material

where

T_i = Duration of exposure period

C_i = Level of a specific contaminant during time period T_i,

T_{total} = Total work time per shift (7- to 8-hour workday)

A number of internal pollutants, for example, asbestos in the lead paints on walls, and the lead remains on highways have been reduced.

16.4 SOUND, MICROWAVE, AND OTHER ELECTROMAGNETIC EXPOSURE

Humans live surrounded by low-level electric and magnetic fields from electric powerlines and appliances and electronic devices. The frequencies exposed range is from 1–1022 Hz as indicated by Figure 16-10. The biological effects from low-level nonionizing fields are well established; for example, there are reports of cancer clusters in electromagnetic fields (EMFs) which are in-house near a 500 kV line, testicular cancer caused by police radar guns, spontaneous abortions by computer video display terminals (VDTs), alleged brain cancers caused by cellular phones, ill effects due to electric blankets of 30–300 mG, and so on. However, the health effects of electromagnetic fields still remain unresolved.

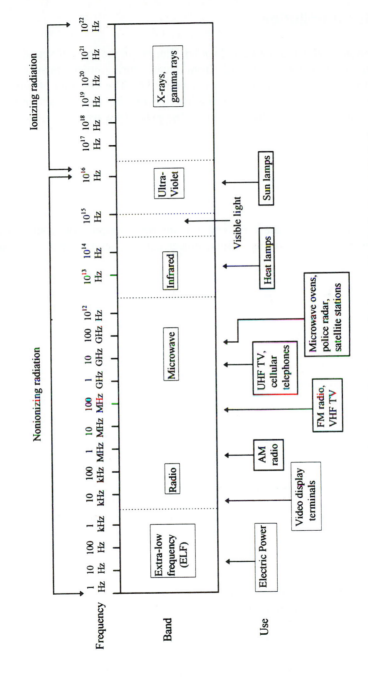

Figure 16-10.   Broad range of electromagnetic frequencies for human exposure.

16.4.1   Noise Pollution

Noise is commonly defined as unwanted sound. Energy in the form of sound waves may be produced in the form of energy residuals from manufacturing processes such as waste heat; fortunately, it is short-lived and relatively nonextensive. The vibration of solid objects will cause the surrounding air to undergo alternating compression and rarefaction in such a way as to effect changes in density and pressure. The pressure wave is obtained as **root mean square** (rms) sound pressure.

$$P_{rms} = \left(\overline{p^2} \right)^{\frac{1}{2}} = \left[\frac{1}{T} \int_0^T p^2(t)dt \right]^{\frac{1}{2}} \qquad [16\text{-}23]$$

where p is the amplitude of the wave and T is the time period. The sound intensity, I, is defined as the time-weight average sound power per unit area normal to the direction of sound propagation and

$$I = \frac{(P_{rms})^2}{\rho c} \qquad [16\text{-}24]$$

where

I = intensity in W/m^2

P_{rms} = root mean square sound pressure in Pa

ρ = density of medium in kg/m^3

c = speed of sound in medium in m/s

     usually $c = 20.05 \; T^{1/2}$

     where T is absolute temperature in K.

The scale of sound pressure ranging from the faintest sound to a loud sound of a rocket takeoff can be best expressed on the logarithm of the ratios of the measured quantities. Measurements on this scale are termed levels, and the unit is **bel** (named after Alexander Graham Bell).

$$L' = \log \frac{Q}{Q_0} \qquad [16\text{-}25]$$

where

L' is level in bels

Q is measured in quantity

Q_0 is reference quantity

Normally, for convenience of usage, a **bel** is divided into 10 subunits called **decibels** (dB) as

$$L = 10 \log \frac{Q}{Q_0}$$ [16-26]

Now, if $Q_0 = 10^{-12} \text{W}$

$\quad L = L_w$ (sound power level)

if $Q_0 = 10^{-12} \text{W/m}^2$

$\quad L = L_I$ (sound intensity level)

if $Q_0 = (P_{rms})_0^{\,2}$

$\quad L = L_P$ (sound pressure level)

Usually,

$$L_P = 10 \log \frac{(P_{rms})^2}{(P_{rms})_0^{\,2}} = 20 \log \frac{P_{rms}}{(P_{rms})_0}$$ [16-27]

In general, the reference pressure is 20 micropascals, 20 μPa. The scale established is in Figure 16-11. The average value of a collection of sound pressure level measurements is

$$\overline{L_P} = 20 \log \frac{1}{N} \sum_{j=1}^{N} 10^{\frac{L_j}{20}}$$ [16-28]

where

$\overline{L_P}$ = average sound pressure level in dB re: 20 μPa

N = number of measurements

L_j = the jth sound pressure level in dB re: 20 μPa where $j = 1,2,...,N$

The mathematical addition of decibels is quite complicated. A simplified procedure is the use of a graph as shown in Figure 16-12. As a rule of thumb, the equal sounds are added in terms of the L_p by 3 dB, and if one sound is more than 10 dB louder than a second sound, the contribution of the latter is negligible.

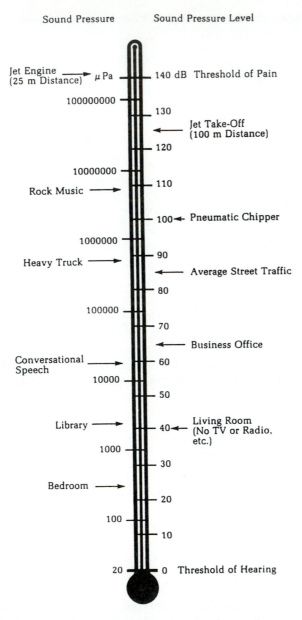

Figure 16-11.   Relative scale of sound pressure levels.

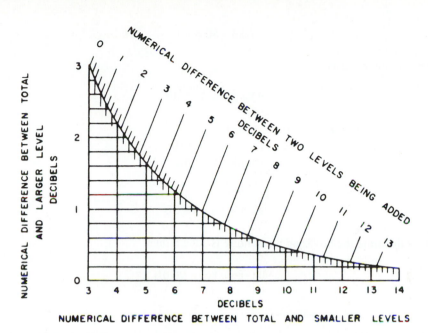

Figure 16-12.   Chart for combining different sound pressure levels. For example: Combine 80 and 75 dB. The difference is 5 dB. The 5 dB line intersects the curved line at 1.2 dB, thus the total value is 81.2 dB (from General Radio).

[**Example 16-2**]   A ground crew standing 50 ft. away from a four-engine jet when the first engine is turned on, will hear a sound intensity level of 80 dB. What L_p does the crew hear when the second, the third, and the fourth engines are turned on? Also, after the fourth engine is turned on, an arrival plane hovers over the crews head given 90 dB. What does the crew hear?

Assume each engine has a sound intensity level of 80 dB. From the chart of Figure 16-12, the difference between the two engine intensity levels is

$$80 - 80 = 0$$

A numerical difference of 0 is equivalent to adding 3 dB, thus

$$80 + 3 = 83 \text{ dB}$$

When the third engine is on

$$83 - 80 = 3$$

and simultaneously

$$83 + 1.8 = 84.8 \text{ dB}$$

So, for all four engines that are turned on

$$84.8 - 80 = 4.8$$

$$84.8 + 1.2 = 86 \text{ dB}$$

If at this time the hovering plane noise is added, then

$$90 \ (+86 - 86) = 90 \text{ dB}$$

American National Standard Institute (ANSI) prescribes three basic weighing networks (A, B, and C) when a sound level meter is used, the resulting level being dBA, dBB, etc. For a noise rating system, a statistical analysis indicates how frequently a particular sound level is exceeded; for example, if $L_{40} = 72$ dBA, then we know that 72 dBA is exceeded for 40% of the measured time. Thus we can write L_N, and a cumulative distribution curve can be constructed when L_N is plotted against N and $N = 1\%, 2\%, ...,$ and so on. (see Figure 16-13). A probability distribution curve also can be made (Figure 16-14). The equivalent continuous equal energy level, L_{eq}, can be applied to any fluctuating noise level. It assumes a constant noise level that, over a given time, expends the same amount of energy as fluctuating levels over the same time period.

$$L_{eq} = 10 \log \frac{1}{t} \int_{0}^{t} 10^{\frac{L(t)}{10}} \, dt \qquad\qquad [16\text{-}29]$$

where

t = time over which L_{eq} is determined

$L(t)$ = the time varying noise level in dBA

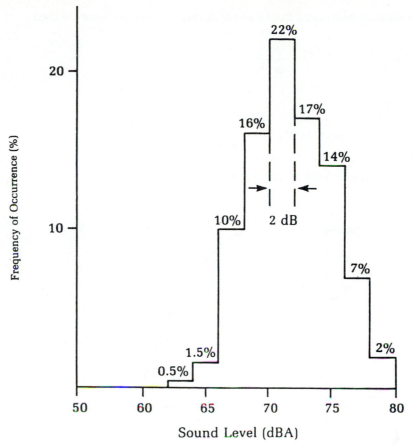

Figure 16-13.   Probability distribution plot. (After B & K Instruments, Inc., Cleveland.)

In practice,

$$L_{eq} = 10 \log \sum_{i=1}^{N} 10^{\frac{L_i}{10}} t_i$$ [16-30]

where

n = total number of samples taken

L_i = noise level in dBA of the ith sample

t_i = fruition of total sample time

If sound is transmitted from a source outward, an inverse square is used

$$I = \frac{W}{4\pi\, r^2}$$ [16-31]

where

I = sound intensity in W/m^2

W = sound power of source in W

r = distance between source and receiver in m

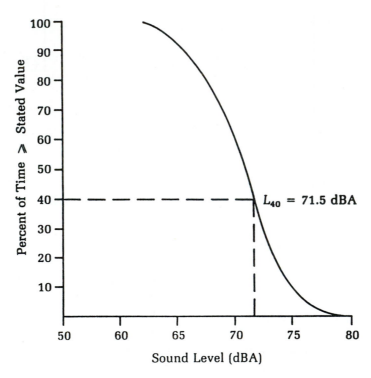

Figure 16-14.   Cumulative distribution curve. (After B & K Instruments, Inc., Cleveland.)

This measures L_w rather than L_p. For L_p one can derive

$$L_P \approx L_W - 20\log r - 11$$ [16-32]

where

L_p = sound pressure level in dB re: $20\mu Pa$

L_w = sound power level in dB re: $10^{-12}W$

$20 \log r$ = decibel transform = $10 \log r^2$

11 = decibel transform $\approx 10 \log (4\pi) = 10.99$

The directivity factor is a measure of the directivity of a spherical sound source by polar coordinates, or

$$DI_0 = L_{p\theta} - L_{P_s} \qquad [16\text{-}33]$$

where $L_{p\theta}$ is sound pressure level measured at distance r' and angle θ from a directive source radiating power W into anechoic space in dB, and L_{P_s} is sound pressure. The level is measured at distance r' from a nondirective source radiating power W into anchoric space in dB. For a source located on or nearby a hard and flat surface, the directivity index is

$$DI_\theta = L_{P\theta} - L_{PH} + 3 \qquad [16\text{-}34]$$

where L_{PH} is unique to the hard surface and the 3 dB addition is that measurement made over a hemisphere instead of a sphere. The intensity at a radius r is twice as large if a source radiates into a hemisphere rather than a sphere. Assuming the directivity pattern does not change its shape regardless of distance, then the directive index may be added to the inverse square law.

$$L_{P\theta} \approx L_N + DI_\theta - 20 \log r - 11 - A_e \qquad [16\text{-}35]$$

The last term A_e is the excess attenuation beyond wave divergence; for example, the attenuation may be by absorption in the air, or by rain, sleet, snow, fog, or by barriers, grass, shrubbery, trees, or by atmospheric turbulence, characteristics of the ground, and so on.

For **noise control** there are three different approaches for the abatement. The first is the control modification and reduction of the source or the noise output. There are various ways for reduction of impact forces—the reduction of speeds and processes and frictional resistance, or the noise breakages. The isolation and dampening of the vibrating elements as in the provision of mufflers and silencers would involve material science and the proper mechanical design. The next way is to alter or to control the transmission path and environment. Here the nullification of the amplitudes by another source signal out of phase in the noise path or by the use of barriers, screens, or deflectors becomes important. The sound-absorbing materials (such as acoustic tile, carpets, drapes, and asphalt or other polymeric foams) can be very useful. The **Sabin absorption coefficients**, α_{SAB}, at 125, 250, 500,

1000, 2000 and 4000 Hz, are in general use. Finally, the protection of the receiver by ear-plugs and muffs can actually reduce the noise by 15 to 25 dB as shown in Figure 16-15.

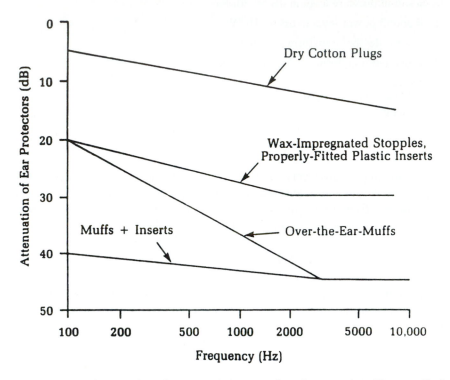

Figure 16-15.   Attenuation of ear protectors at various frequencies. (Source: National Bureau of Standards Handbook 119, 1976.)

The readers are asked to look at Figure 3-2, the generalized electromagnetic series. As the frequency increases from 1 to 10^{22} Hz, the energy of radiation or effect to human exposures also increases. In the audible range, sound and noise directly impact on the hearing. In this instance, discordant sound resulting from nonperiodic vibrations in air is defined as **noise**. Temporary or permanent damages leading to hearing loss is resulted from noise exposure of sufficient energy. The secondary effect is that the **acoustic pollution** (or noise pollution) draws emotional responses on conscious and subconscious levels and annoys, awakens, angers, distracts, frustrates, and creates stresses that result in psychological problems.

Even working with ultrasound region, for example, in the 25 to 40 kHz range, the overtones associated with the sonication still fall in the audible region of hearing. In working places, control and protection measures are made, such as sound isolation, absorption and damping. Biological and physiological effects in radio frequency and microwave regions are not clear. With the exception of selective frequencies in the x-band region,, the microwave will cause the thermal vibration of water molecules present in cells with the consequence of fatal destruction. Although the health effects of the low-level of the nonionizing field remains an issue, damages due to high dosages in a prolonged exposure remain a risk. Molecular vibration and rotation resulting to bond scission of weak linkages will cause cell disfunctions. Following the electromagnetic scale in Figure 3-2, the bombardment of outer electron will harm the eye and skin, such as the well-known ionizing radiation from ultraviolet beam. The incursion of biosphere system with electron, neutron, helium, gamma and other particles through x-ray, γ-ray and cosmic radiation causes irreversible injury as often referring to the **ionizing radiation**. A good example is that the wrinkles in the face of farmers are caused by the crosslinking of the keratin under UV radiation from the sun.

Humans as a part of the entire biosphere are adapted to the natural environment; however, when anthropogenic factors are imposed on, imbalance will occur with the consequence of mutagenicity as well as carcinogenicity. Internal pollutants discussed in this chapter included radon, noise, and unwanted nutritional supplements. At the end of the present volume, the reader should be able to use chemical principles discussed in various chapters for answering many of the present-day issues. For example, to answer the question why active or passive tobacco smoking is harmful, the reader can at least state:

- Smokes contain millions of Aitken particles. These particles have the right sizes to wedge into the pulmonary region to impair the exchange of oxygen from inhalation. (See Section 9.1)

- Tars consist of a number of PHA that will be in the smoke. Many of the PHA are carcinogenous such as benz (3,4) pyrene. (See Section 2.3.1)

- Tobacco contains nicotine, which contains two nitrogens, one in pyrrole, the other in pyridine, having four carbons apart. The original intention is for the tobacco plant to fight against aphids. Instead, humans who inhale it will have the equivalence of hallucinating properties of other psychrotomimetic plants. (See Section 16.2)

- Tobacco contains large amounts of CO, HCN acetaldehyde, and acrolein. The toxicity of CO is well known. (See Section 9.3.1) Both hydrogen cyanide and acrolein have metal-binding powers.

- Tobacco leaves have the concentration power to enrich the daughter neuclide of radon in such a way that the aerosol in the smoke may be radioactive. (See Sections 7.1.5, 7.4.2 and 16.2.3)

- Cigarette paper contains cadmium as sizing material. Cadmium will cause hypertension if diffused into the blood stream through smoking. (See Section 14.3.3)

- As a cigarette is lighted, the burning of tobacco will yield the thermal decomposition product, myosmine, from nicotine. Myosmine induces a strong, musty odor on clothing, furnishings, carpets and draperies in hotel rooms. So far, its toxicity is unknown. (See Figure 16-3)

REFERENCES

16-1.   M. Wilkening, Radon in the Environment, Elsevier, Amsterdam, 1990.

16-2.   G. M. Masters, Introduction to Environmental Engineering and Science, Prentice-Hall, Englewood Cliffs, New Jersey, 1991.

16-3.   C.S. ReVelle, E.E. Whitlatch, Jr., and J.R. Wrigeet, Civil and Environmental Systems Engineering, Prentice-Hall, Upper Saddle River, New Jersey, 1997.

16-4.   D.J. Montgomery, "Making the Quality of Life an Operational Concept," p. 46, Phi Kappa Phi Journal, Winter (1975).

16-5.   R. Fenwick and M. Morgan, "Natural Toxicants in Plant Food," Chem. Gt. Brit. 27, 1027-1029 (1991).

16-6.   B. Hideman, "Health Effects of Electromagnetic Fields Remain Unresolved," C & ZN, Nov. 8, 15-29 (1993).

16-7.   D.T. Allen and K.S. Rosselot, Pollution Prevention for Chemical Processes, Wiley, New York, 1997.

16-8.   National Academy of Sciences, Engineering with Ecological Constraints, National Academy of Engineering, Washington D.C., 1996.

16-9.   L. L. Beranek, Noise and Vibration Control, McGraw-Hill, New York, 1971.

16-10.   P. N. Cheremisinoff and F. Ellerbusch, Guide for Industrial Noise Control, Ann Arbor Science, Ann Arbor, Michigan, 1982.

16-11.   E. Miles, R. Pealy, and R. Stokes, Natural Resources Economics and Policy Applications, University of Washington Press, Seattle, 1986.

16-12.   S. E. Manahan, Environmental Chemistry, Lewis Publishers, Chelsea, Michigan, 5th ed., 1991.

16-13.   J. W. Moore and E. A. Moore, Environmental Chemistry, Academic Press, New York, 1976.

16-14.   D.G. Crosby, Environmental Toxicology and Chemistry, Oxford University Press, New York, 1998.

PROBLEM SET

1. A 70-Kg man is exposed to 5×10^{-5} mg/L of TCE in the air at his workplace. If he works for 8 hours per day, 5 days per week, 40 weeks per year in 10 year period and inhales 2 m^3/hr of air, what would be his lifetime risk (assuming the lifetime is 70 years)? What would the risk be to a 30-Kg child similarly exposed?

2. What is the concentration of VOC in drinking water that would result in a 10^{-5} risk for a 50-Kg person who drinks 2 L/day throughout his lifetime? Assuming the slope of a carcinogenic VOC with the dose-risk curve is 0.01 (mg/Kg/day)$^{-1}$.

3. A researcher is operating two sets of ultrasounds with different frequency. He hears a sound intensity level of 70 dB when the first ultrasound with lower frequency is turned on. The L_p that he hears when the second ultrasound is turned on is 72 dB. What is the intensity level of second ultrasound?

"And there went up a wind from the Lord and brought quails from the sea and let them fall by the camp . . . And the people stood up all that day and all that night and all the next day and they gathered the quails . . . And they spread them all abroad for themselves round about the camp. And while the flesh was yet between their teeth, ere it was chewed the wrath of the Lord was kindled against the people and the Lord smote the people with a very great plague."

Numbers 11:31-33

Apparently, the desert pigeons ate much of the ripe berries. These berries contain coniine, a 3-carbon substituted piperidine base (for structure see Table 16-4), which causes severe toxicity. After consuming many berries, the pigeons became intoxicated and fell on the campground. When the humans consumed the pigeons, they also became poisoned.

APPENDIX A

Link to Environmental Education and Awareness

The following is a list of commonly used web sites for Environmental education and awareness. Often, information regarding to the key words for environmental chemistry can be located. I thank Iris Yang for providing this information.

U.S. Environmental Protection Agency
http://www.epa.gov/

Florida Center for Environmental Studies
http://www.ces.fau.edu

Environmental Working Group
http://www.ewg.org/

Society of Environmental Journalists
http://www.sej.org/

EDF – Environmental Defense Fund WorldWide
http://www.edf.org/

Environmental News Network
http://www.enn.com/

Environmental Research Laboratories
http://www.erl.noaa.gov/

National Institute of Environmental Health Sciences
http://www.niehs.nih.gov/

EnviroLink
http://envirolink.org/start_web.html

Greenpeace
http://www.greenpeace.org/

The Chemical Scorecard
http://www.scorecard.org/

EE-Link: Environmental Education on the Internet
http://www.nceet.snre.umich.edu/

E – The Environmental Magazine
http://www.emagazine.com/

PMEL – Pacific Marine Environmental Laboratory
http://www.pmel.noaa.gov/

Environmental Technology Education
http://nvc.cc.ca.us/et/

Environmental Industry Web Site
http://www.enviroindustry.com/

Earth's 911: The Environmental Hotline
http://www.1800cleanup.org/

The Environment in Asia
http://www.asianenviro.com/

Directory of Environmental Resources on the Internet
http://www.envirosw.com/

American Academy of Environmental Engineers
http://www.enviro-engrs.org/

Environmental Professional's Homepage
http://www.clay.net/

U.S. Geological Survey
http://www.usgs.gov/

The Common Purpose Institute for Energy and Environmental Solutions
http://www.serve.com/commonpurpose/

The National Institute for Environmental Renewal
http://www.nier.org/

Internet Resources for the Environmental Scientist
http://www.imt.net/~dcouncil/env.html

GNET: The Global Network of Environment & Technology
http://www.gnet.org/

National Association of Environmental Professionals
http://www.enfo.com/NAEP/naepinfo.html

Environmental Modeling Center
http://nic.fb4.noaa.gov:8000/

Society of Environmental Toxicology and Chemistry (SETAC)
http://www.setac.org/

Environmental Law around the World
http://www.igc.org/igc/issues/el/

Environmental and Engineering Geophysical Society
http://www.esd.ornl.gov/societies/EEGS/

Air Pollution Related Web Sites
http://web.epa.ohio.gov/dapc/page/other.html

South Coast Air Quality Management District
http://www.aqmd.gov/

Environmental Organization WebDirectory
http://webdirectory.com/

National Resources Defense Council
http://mail.igc.apc.org/nrdc/worldview/intrworl.html#air

The Terrene Institute
http://www.terrene.org/index.htm

European Recycling and the Environment
http://www.tecweb.com/recycle/eurorec.htm

Global Recycling Network
http://grn.com/grn/

The Internet Consumer Recycling Guide
http://www.obviously.com/recycle/

Water Environment Federation
http://www.wef.org/

The Journal of Solid Waste Technology and Management
http://www.widener.edu/solid.waste/

U.S. Department of Energy
http://www.doe.gov/

Environmental Science and Technology News and Research Notes
http://www.pubs.acs.org (viewing for the recent issues)

American Lung Association
http://www.chesheire-med.com:80/programs/

APPENDIX B

PERIODIC TABLE OF THE ELEMENTS

IA																	INERT GASES VIIIA
1 1.00794 *H* Hydrogen	IIA											IIIA	IVA	VA	VIA	VIIA	2 4.002602 *He* Helium
3 6.941 *Li* Lithium	4 9.012182 *Be* Beryllium											5 10.811 *B* Boron	6 12.011 *C* Carbon	7 14.00674 *N* Nitrogen	8 15.9994 *O* Oxygen	9 18.9984032 *F* Fluorine	10 20.1797 *Ne* Neon
11 22.989768 *Na* Sodium	12 24.3050 *Mg* Magnesium	IIIB	IVB	VB	VIB	VIIB	VIIIB	VIII		IB	IIB	13 26.981539 *Al* Aluminum	14 28.0855 *Si* Silicon	15 30.973762 *P* Phosphorus	16 32.066 *S* Sulfur	17 35.4527 *Cl* Chlorine	18 39.948 *Ar* Argon
19 39.0983 *K* Potassium	20 40.078 *Ca* Calcium	21 44.955910 *Sc* Scandium	22 47.88 *Ti* Titanium	23 50.9415 *V* Vanadium	24 51.9961 *Cr* Chromium	25 54.93805 *Mn* Manganese	26 55.847 *Fe* Iron	27 58.93320 *Co* Cobalt	28 58.69 *Ni* Nickel	29 63.546 *Cu* Copper	30 65.39 *Zn* Zinc	31 69.723 *Ga* Gallium	32 72.61 *Ge* Germanium	33 74.92159 *As* Arsenic	34 78.96 *Se* Selenium	35 79.904 *Br* Bromine	36 83.80 *Kr* Krypton
37 85.4678 *Rb* Rubidium	38 87.62 *Sr* Strontium	39 88.90585 *Y* Yttrium	40 91.224 *Zr* Zirconium	41 92.90638 *Nb* Niobium	42 95.94 *Mo* Molybdenum	43 98.9063 *Tc* Technetium	44 101.07 *Ru* Ruthenium	45 102.90550 *Rh* Rhodium	46 106.42 *Pd* Palladium	47 107.8682 *Ag* Silver	48 112.411 *Cd* Cadmium	49 114.82 *In* Indium	50 118.710 *Sn* Tin	51 121.75 *Sb* Antimony	52 127.60 *Te* Tellurium	53 126.90447 *I* Iodine	54 131.29 *Xe* Xenon
55 132.90543 *Cs* Cesium	56 137.327 *Ba* Barium	57-71 *La-Lu*	72 178.49 *Hf* Hafnium	73 180.9479 *Ta* Tantalum	74 183.85 *W* Tungsten	75 186.207 *Re* Rhenium	76 190.2 *Os* Osmium	77 192.22 *Ir* Iridium	78 195.08 *Pt* Platinum	79 196.96654 *Au* Gold	80 200.59 *Hg* Mercury	81 204.3833 *Tl* Thallium	82 207.2 *Pb* Lead	83 208.98037 *Bi* Bismuth	84 208.9824 *Po* Polonium	85 209.9871 *At* Astatine	86 222.0176 *Rn* Radon
87 223.0197 *Fr* Francium	88 226.0254 *Ra* Radium	89-103 *Ac-Lr*	104 261.1087 *Rf*	105 262.1138 *Db*	106 263.1182 *Sg*	107 262.1229 *Bh*	108 *Hs*	109 *Mt*									

57 138.9055 *La* Lanthanum	58 140.115 *Ce* Cerium	59 140.90765 *Pr* Praseodymium	60 144.24 *Nd* Neodymium	61 146.9151 *Pm* Promethium	62 150.36 *Sm* Samarium	63 151.965 *Eu* Europium	64 157.25 *Gd* Gadolinium	65 158.92534 *Tb* Terbium	66 162.50 *Dy* Dysprosium	67 164.93032 *Ho* Holmium	68 167.26 *Er* Erbium	69 168.93421 *Tm* Thulium	70 173.04 *Yb* Ytterbium	71 174.967 *Lu* Lutetium
89 227.0278 *Ac* Actinium	90 232.0381 *Th* Thorium	91 231.0359 *Pa* Protactinium	92 238.0289 *U* Uranium	93 237.0482 *Np* Neptunium	94 244.0642 *Pu* Plutonium	95 243.0614 *Am* Americium	96 247.0703 *Cm* Curium	97 247.0703 *Bk* Berkelium	98 251.0796 *Cf* Californium	99 252.0829 *Es* Einsteinium	100 257.0951 *Fm* Fermium	101 258.0986 *Md* Mendelevium	102 259.1009 *No* Nobelium	103 260.1053 *Lr* Lawrencium

743

APPENDIX C

Some useful constants for lithosphere, hydrosphere, atmosphere and biosphere.

Quantity	Unit of Measurement	Symbol	Numerical Value
Area of continents	km^2	S_c	149×10^4
Area of world oceans	km^2	S_o	361×10^4
Mean height of continents above sea level	m	h_c	875
Mean depth of world oceans	m	h_o	= 3794
Mean position of earth's surface with respect to sea level	m	h_m	= 2430
Mean thickness of lithosphere within the limits of the continents	m	$h_{c.l.}$	35
Mean thickness of lithosphere within the limits of the ocean	km	$h_{o.l.}$	4.7
Mean rate of thickening of continental lithosphere	km	$\dfrac{\Delta h}{\Delta t}$	10 – 40
Mean rate of horizontal extension of continental lithosphere	m/ 10^6hr	$\dfrac{\Delta l}{\Delta t}$	0.75 – 20
Mass of lithosphere	km/ 10^6yr	m_t	2.267×10^{25}
Mass of water released from mantle and core in course of geological time	gr		3.400×10^{24}
Total reserve of water in the mantle	gr		2×10^{26}
Present day content of free and bound water in the earth's lithosphere	gr		$2.2 - 2.6 \times 10^{24}$ $1.8 - 2.7 \cdot 10^{24}$
Mass of hydrosphere	gr	m_h	1.664×10^{24}
Amount of oxygen bound in the earth's crust	gr		1.300×10^{24}
Amount of free oxygen	gr		1.5×10^{21}
Mass of atmosphere	gr	m_a	5.136×10^{21}
Mass of biosphere	gr	m_b	1.148×10^{19}
Mass of living matter in the biosphere	gr		3.6×10^{17}
Density of living matter on dry land	gr/ cm^3		0.1
Density of living matter in ocean	gr/ cm^3		15×10^{-8}

APPENDIX D

Some components of cigarette smoke.

Component	Emission (mg/ cigarette)	
	Mainstream Smoke	SidestreamSmoke
Tar	10.2 – 20.8*	34.5 – 44.1
Nicotine	0.46 – 0.92*	1.27 – 1.69
Carbon monoxide	18.3	86.3
Ammonia	0.16	7.4
Hydrogen cyanide	0.24	0.16
Acetone	0.58	1.45
Phenols	0.23	0.60
Formaldehyde	—	1.44
Toluene	0.11	0.60
Acrolein	0.084	0.825
NO_x	0.014	0.051
Opolonium–210 (pCi)	0.07	0.13
Fluoranthenes	7.7×10^{-4}	1.6×10^{-3}
Benzofluorenes	2.5×10^{-4}	1.0×10^{-3}
Pyrenes	2.7×10^{-4}	1.5×10^{-3}
Chrysene	1.9×10^{-4}	1.2×10^{-3}
Cadmium	1.3×10^{-4}	4.5×10^{-4}
Perylenes	4.8×10^{-5}	1.4×10^{-4}
Dibenzanthracenes	4.2×10^{-5}	1.4×10^{-4}
Anthanthrene	2.2×10^{-5}	3.9×10^{-4}

*Range is for filtered to unfiltered cigarettes.

Source: Data from S.A. Glantz, "Health Effects of Ambient Tobacco Smoke," in Indoor Air Quality, ed. P.J. Walsh, C.S. Dudney, and E.D. Copenhaver (Boca Raton, Fla.: CRC Press, 1984), Table 1, p.160.

APPENDIX E

Critical Values of *t*

	Level of significance for one-tailed test					
	0.10	0.05	0.025	0.01	0.005	0.0005
	Level of significance for two-tailed test					
	0.20	0.10	0.05	0.02	0.01	0.001
1	3.078	6.314	12.706	31.821	63.657	636.619
2	1.886	2.920	4.303	6.965	9.925	31.598
3	1.638	2.353	3.182	4.541	5.841	12.941
4	1.533	2.132	2.776	3.747	4.604	8.610
5	1.476	2.015	2.571	3.365	4.032	6.859
6	1.440	1.943	2.447	3.143	3.707	5.959
7	1.415	1.895	2.365	2.998	3.499	5.405
8	1.397	1.860	2.306	2.896	3.355	5.041
9	1.383	1.833	2.262	2.821	3.250	4.781
10	1.372	1.812	2.228	2.764	3.169	4.587
11	1.363	1.796	2.201	2.718	3.106	4.437
12	1.356	1.782	2.179	2.681	3.055	4.318
13	1.350	1.771	2.160	2.650	3.012	4.221
14	1.345	1.761	2.145	2.624	2.977	4.140
15	1.341	1.753	2.131	2.602	2.947	4.073
16	1.337	1.746	2.120	2.583	2.921	4.015
17	1.333	1.740	2.110	2.567	2.898	3.965
18	1.330	1.734	2.101	2.552	2.878	3.922
19	1.328	1.729	2.093	2.539	2.861	3.883
20	1.325	1.725	2.086	2.528	2.845	3.850
21	1.323	1.721	2.080	2.518	2.831	3.819
22	1.321	1.717	2.074	2.508	2.819	3.792
23	1.319	1.714	2.069	2.500	2.807	3.767
24	1.318	1.711	2.064	2.492	2.797	3.745
25	1.316	1.708	2.060	2.485	2.787	3.725
26	1.315	1.706	2.056	2.479	2.779	3.707
27	1.314	1.703	2.052	2.473	2.771	3.690
28	1.313	1.701	2.048	2.467	2.763	3.674
29	1.311	1.699	2.045	2.462	2.756	3.659
30	1.310	1.697	2.042	2.457	2.750	3.646
35	1.306	1.690	2.030	2.438	2.724	3.591
40	1.303	1.684	2.021	2.423	2.704	3.551
50	1.299	1.676	2.009	2.403	2.678	3.496
60	1.296	1.671	2.000	2.390	2.660	3.460
70	1.294	1.667	1.994	2.381	2.648	3.435
80	1.292	1.664	1.990	2.374	2.639	3.416
90	1.291	1.662	1.987	2.368	2.632	3.402
100	1.290	1.660	1.984	2.364	2.626	3.390
120	1.289	1.658	1.980	2.358	2.617	3.373
∞	1.282	1.645	1.960	2.326	2.576	3.291

EPILOGUE

Having reviewed chemistry and having examined the chemical characteristics of the major segments of our environment – lithosphere, atmosphere, hydrosphere, pedosphere and biosphere, it is crucial to learn the chemical interactions among those segments or cycles. About 400 years ago, a Chinese philosopher named Zhu-Tze noted: "Yin and Yang and the five major cycles are rotating correctly at first, later collision or friction of these cycles caused severe problems in nature." This is still true for our ecosystem today. Environmental deterioration and degradation are due to the incompatible and improper interaction of the major cycles. Between and among major cycles, there are many interactions: hydrosphere-lithosphere, atmosphere– hydrosphere, biosphere–lithosphere, biosphere–atmosphere, biosphere–hydrosphere, lithosphere –pedosphere, lithosphere-hydrosphere–biosphere, etc. that end up with the interaction among all five cycles.

A human being is chemical mote swimming in a chemical soup, which falls into the biosphere just as other living creatures. All the change within him and exposures outside him are chemical. The xenobiotics can be transported to him by the major cycles, and the major cycles can determine the effects of contact which result to a mechanism with consequence of fate. In general, the interactions of the five major cycles can cause environmental degradations as well as environmental health risks.

A few examples are illustrated here for the interactions of those cycles. In lithosphere-hydrosphere, for example, the immense water in the oceans may be a result of the squeezing of the material of the planet (lithosphere). Estimation has been made that during Earth's geological history, hot springs on continents and the ocean floor release 6.6×10^{16} g of water per year which will be 2×10^{26} of water. Another estimate revealed that the total gravity of water in the atmosphere, hydrosphere, biosphere, and buried in ancient sedimentary to be 1.7×10^{24}, which only accounts for 0.8% of the total discharge from the lithosphere. If only a fraction of the total was derived from magmatic source, hot springs can account for the total mass of world oceans.

A case of lithosphere-hydrosphere-biosphere interaction can be exemplified by the metals industry. Primary metals industry utilizes nearly 1 trillion gal. of process water per year; of this, iron and steelmaking require 80%, whereas the copper and aluminum industries consume the remainder. Hence, water pollution in an integrated steel mill represents a serious problem. For example, different types of wastewater are produced by individual stages, i.e., coke production, blast furnace, open hearth, hot mills, rolling mills, finishing mills, sanitary, boiler, and other uses.

Mankind's aspect of the biosphere still remains a central target for various pollutants to attack, whether they are transported through atmosphere, hydrosphere, pedosphere, lithosphere, or a combination of major spheres. For the coming millenium, as population increases with limited space, similar to xenobiotics, different pathogens, virus and even prions (special proteins) will become fatal to humans. Especially, the occurrence of methicillin-resistant *staphylococcus aureus* (MRSA), which consumes massive amounts of antibioticas and is persistent in the patient's body, is bad. In addition to the AIDS virus, the human immunodeficient virus (HIV), the hepatitis C virus (HCV), the herpes simplex virus (HSV), the adult T-cell leukemia virus (ATLV), the influenza virus type A-Hong Kong, etc. constitute serious hazards. Recent Hong Kong avian flu of H_xN_1 type has affect human and 1.4 m. of chicken have been slaughtered. (The letters stand for hemagglutinin, e.g., H_1, H_2, etc. and neuraminidase, e.g., N_1, N_2, etc. Both elicit an immune response.) Also, more than one million cows were destroyed due to the mad cow disease in England. Both the Creutzfeldt-Jakob disease (CJD) in which people lose coordination and the bovine spongiform encephalopathy (BSE) from mad cows are transmissible spongiform eucephalopathies (TSEs) which cause fatalities. The prion protein cellular (PrP^c) usually transmit the disease.

For the final few words after you finish with the book is that perhaps you will attain some chemical reasoning on many environmental problems as follows:

- Assess the consequences of smoking a whole cigarette. If smoking is done in an $8' \times 10'$ average room with little fresh air circulation, what is the consequence?
- Compute the output of the essential gaseous pollutants from 10 gallons of ordinary gasoline for an automobile without California Emission control.
- List the environmental damages of enhanced oil recovery. Propose also solutions.
- What is man's contribution by burning fossil fuels to obtain power absorbed and reflected? In order to increase 1 K of the ambient temperature, what is the duration of time if the rate of fossil burning is at the present rate?
- What is the limit of wind power based on power density consideration?
- For releasing of 1000 tonne of heavy oil into San Pedro Harbor near Los Angeles, list the environmental problems and the method for abatement.
- If diseases are related to the geological environments, outline the methodology to overcome this problem.
- Evaluate the fertilizer usages, the detergent usages and the water treatment usages of phosphorous and the effect to eutrophication.
- Review the chemical disposal methods of radioactive wastes.
- Tabulate a dozen of consumer goods and list all possible additives from the commercial labels. Discuss the physiological properties of these additives.
- Comment on the reformulated gasoline additives and their fate and mechanisms human health.
- What is the effect on children for lead in paint, on chinaware or in soil close to freeways.
- List the impacts of earthquakes on the environmental problem in Southern California.
- Compare and evaluate the impact of a leaf blower, a lawn mower and a garbage collection vehicle in an urban area.
- Investigate the possibility of replacing chloro organics with another chemical in refrigeration.
- What is the overall absorption in your body if you drink one liter of water containing 5 ppb of chloroform for 70 years of your life? How about other THMs?

- Assess the recent forest fires neighboring a metropolitan city and compare with the damage of El Niño near a major city.
- Evaluate the impact on air pollution for an outdoor barbecue and restaurant kitchen without control.
- Cite at least five reasons why tobacco smoking is not good.
- Propose a substitute of halone for forest fire fighting.